D0699108

The Yearbook of Agriculture 1969

FOOD FOR US ALL

The Yearbook of Agriculture 1969

UNITED STATES
GOVERNMENT PRINTING OFFICE

For Sale by the Superintendent of Documents
Washington, D.C. 20402 - Price $3.50

641.3
U58f

Food for us all starts with 3 million farmers who produce the beef and other foods we Americans consume at the rate of nearly 6,000 pounds a year for a family of four. About half of the total land area in the 50 States is devoted to farming.

Mechanization—as in wheat harvesting, above—plus other modern methods from farm to market help bring us our food for a smaller proportion of take-home pay than in any other country. Our highly efficient farming results in one farm worker being able to supply products for some 43 people.

Potatoes are harvested mechanically in Michigan, above. A Florida factory in the field or "mule train," below, spans 24 rows of celery at one time and harvests more than three acres a day. The celery is also cleaned and crated, and can be shipped direct from the field.

More than 23 million people, like this cannery worker, are employed in agribusiness—30 percent of our work force. Food processing often calls for complex machinery. The overhead system pictured here automatically feeds cans into filling machines.

Our country is the world's biggest exporter of farm products, with American hot dogs even becoming a popular new food in Japan, above, where they are often sold by street vendors from small motorized stands. U.S. wheat grower groups, working with USDA, introduced the hot dog to Japan. The photos below show grain inspection in Oregon, at left, and processing of bing cherries.

School milk, right, and school lunch as in Georgia, below, are two of many programs by which our nation improves nutrition among children and the poor.

Providing food for the millions of us who eat away from home each day is a major undertaking. At top, a chef for a contract food management firm prepares ham steaks garnished with pineapple slice and red cherry. Above, desserts for vending machines are evaluated by a taste panel for appearance, flavor, and consistency.

A homemaker could prepare a different meat dish every day, so many kinds and cuts of meat are available. Meat and poultry prepared in plants that ship into other States must be Federally inspected, and inspection is being extended to plants operating wholly within a State.

Ready-to-eat chickens, on left, are cooked for sale in supermarkets. Infrared cabinets are used to keep the chicken warm for the customer. Below, sugar 'n' spice glazed ham. USDA offers a voluntary meat and poultry grading service which aids the housewife in her food shopping.

Eggs are a remarkable storehouse of needed nutrients. They can play a main-dish role in breakfast or brunch, as in top photo. Candling, above, determines an egg's interior quality without breaking the shell. USDA grades eggs under a voluntary program. There are three consumer grades.

BUTTERMILK

Most of us enjoy milk or dairy products every day. Cheese, above, has countless forms—there are over 400 varieties of natural cheeses alone. Milk goes well with snacks, left, and other meals. Butter, right, is one of the oldest of our foods.

More than 240 species of fish and shellfish are sold. They make tasty soups from the sea, at right, and countless other dishes. The U.S. Department of the Interior provides voluntary inspection of seafood, and it grades 15 processed products.

Vegetables, top, come in many colors and textures, and shopping for them can be a delight if you know what to look for. Above, a model serves tossed salad.

getable display at the left includes a
llet readied for cooking Ratatouille—
cchini, eggplant, tomatoes, onions,
d green pepper. Above, vegetables are
rved with cream sauce, egg garnish.

uit is another major food class. Below,
sconsin cranberry beds are flooded
help in machine picking. Newly picked
nberries are floated to edge of beds
"boats." Right, cranberries get bath.

One of the biggest bonuses of fruit is that it is ready to serve in any of its forms with little or no preparation—as in completing the Ring-A-Round Strawberry Dessert above. At upper right, apples are tested in a USDA laboratory. At right, fruit and other food products are inspected after seizure at a New York international airport to prevent any foreign food pests from hitchhiking into the United States.

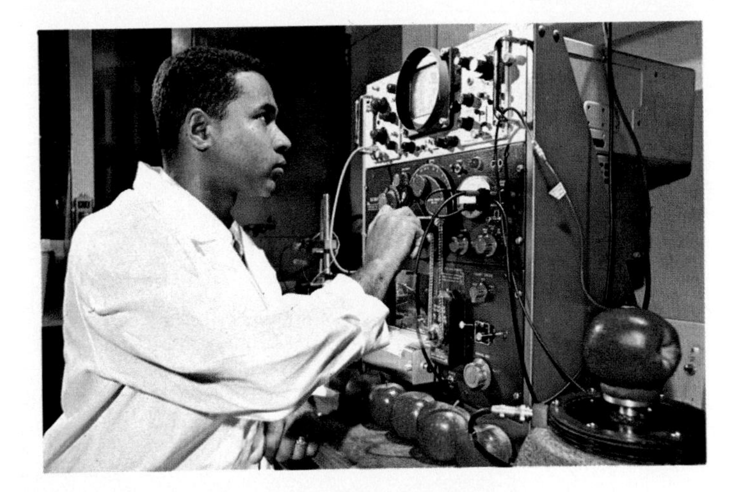

Cereal grains have been one of man's most important food plants since history began. Wheat, lower left, growing in Washington State, is most widely cultivated of these grains. Baked delicacies, upper left, include cranberry-orange bread, muffins, a coffeecake with broiled coconut topping, Florida tea ring. Ready-to-eat cereal, above, is longtime breakfast favorite with millions of Americans.

Desserts—from cakes to crepes—are some of the sweetest things in life. Citrus desserts are featured at far left. Peaches are another dessert favorite. Peach packing is pictured at the left.

Nuts give rich flavor, contrast in texture, and a pleasing garnish to other foods. Above, peanut products are used with salad, barbecue sauce, dip, soup, and dessert.

Pickles, olives, and relishes are good by themselves, but they also make almost any food taste better. Temptingly arrayed at top, they join deviled eggs, chicken salad and other sandwiches—good for a meal or snack—in the photo just above.

Milk and a fruit- or chocolate-flavored mix are the base for these four refreshing "instant" beverages surrounding a strawberry mint drink.

A basic meal can be a thing of beauty to eye and palate, as in the photo above. The choice of fruits and vegetables spells the difference in color, texture, and variety in the household menu. Note how shapes of the foods complement each other.

Patio cooking is fun time for teens, above, with steak on the grill. Outdoor cookery has become a way of life for most Americans, in fact. A flavorsome California shish kabob sizzles at upper right. Chicken over the coals, lower right, tempts the taste buds. One secret of successful barbecuing is a solid bed of glowing coals.

Foreword

CLIFFORD M. HARDIN

Secretary of Agriculture

FOOD FOR US ALL, the title of this Yearbook, means enough food—and the right food—for every American.

In a nation with the greatest food production capacity ever achieved—an ability in fact to produce considerably more than domestic and foreign markets can absorb—one might assume that the goal of food for us all would long since have been realized. Yet, it has not.

• There is still hunger in the midst of national plenty. Poverty-caused malnutrition is far more widespread than we previously had thought.

• Undernutrition, caused by ignorance or neglect, is a common fact of American life. There are still great gaps to be filled in the science of nutrition. The campaign to educate people about what makes a good diet and the relationship between diet and vigor, health, and longevity is only in its beginnings.

• We pride ourselves on having the world's cleanest and most wholesome food. Yet constant vigilance is needed to prevent careless or inadvertent contamination.

For years, the Nation has had ample physical and scientific resources to remedy all these conditions. What has been lacking is sufficient public awareness and concern. But now the conscience of America is aroused.

As President Nixon said early in 1969, "the moment is at hand to put an end to hunger in America . . . for all time."

Why do hunger and undernutrition persist in America?

Is it because of the farmer? Hardly.

He wants to produce enough to meet the nutritional needs of every man, woman, and child in this country. He does, and more.

As consumers, we have a stake in a productive and prosperous agriculture. In 1969, for example, we got a reliable, stable, and high-quality food supply for 17 percent of our after-taxes income—a far lower proportion than in any other country of the world. But to assure us a continued supply of good food, the economic position of our agricultural producers needs to be improved. Farm people are not sharing adequately in the Nation's abundance. They have less than three-fourths as much income per person as nonfarm people.

So remarkable has been the annual increase in farm output per man-hour—an increase roughly double that of industry—that one hour of U.S. farm labor in 1969 produced 2½ times as much as it did only 15 years earlier.

There is no shortage of food in America. Yet malnutrition and undernutrition continue because of two major factors.

The first and most obvious factor is lack of income. Many of the 25 million Americans with poverty level incomes are simply too poor to buy an adequate diet from the abundance available in the commercial market place.

The second factor, and one perhaps even more difficult to overcome, is a lack of knowledge of simple basic dietary rules, coupled with a lack of understanding of the importance of good nutrition.

This factor applies to every sector of American society. Even in the middle and upper income groups, we find nutritionally inadequate diets among a large proportion of adolescent girls, women, and elderly men.

Both poverty and lack of knowledge, however, hit particularly hard at low-income people.

When inadequate buying power is combined over a long period of time with inadequate knowledge of how to select and prepare food for good nutrition, poor nutrition becomes almost inevitable.

And from poor nutrition, in turn, there often stems debility and listlessness, with inability to get and keep a responsible job, or to profit sufficiently by education and training, or to strive in a meaningful way for self-improvement.

This is a vicious circle. It is vital that this circle be decisively broken.

But how? How do we assure improvements in the diets of our low-income families, and beyond them in the diets of the undernourished in more well-to-do groups?

As the reader will see, the Nation has, in being, delivery systems with a capability of reaching everyone in the U.S. who needs improved nutrition.

We have a food stamp program to increase the food purchasing power of millions of low-income people, and a food donation program through which the needy can receive substantial packages of basic and nutritious foods.

We have a supplemental foods program, available to every community, through which we provide enriched foods to meet the needs of new and expectant mothers, infants, and young children.

We have a child-feeding program, also available to every community, that can provide one, two, or three meals a day, plus nutritious snacks to children in day-care centers, settlement houses, and summer recreational activities.

We have the school lunch and school breakfast programs through which children may have at least one or two good meals a day through the school year.

We have a food and nutrition education program operating in all 50 States, the District of Columbia, Puerto Rico, and the Virgin Islands through which trained program aides show homemakers how to buy food and how to prepare nutritionally complete meals from purchased and donated foods.

We need to bring to maximum effectiveness all of these varied efforts to improve nutrition in America.

This Yearbook has valuable information for everyone interested in good nutrition. It will help us choose food for health and vigor. It gives shoppers hints on how to get more for food dollars. It describes how food wholesomeness, quality, and purity are safeguarded. It outlines the farmer's role. It tells the importance of our national role in helping feed hungry nations and aiding them to develop their agricultures as a major stride toward economic development. It describes the contribution of the food industry which brings food to our shopping baskets in a myriad of convenient forms.

In short, it provides basic, solid nutrition information needed by every consumer. What's more, I hope and believe it will be a useful gadfly to the American conscience. May it whet the appetite of every reader for action in achieving the goal of FOOD FOR US ALL.

Preface

JACK HAYES
Yearbook Editor

Food is in everyone's mind at least three times each day. This Yearbook tells agriculture's story in terms of food—how it's produced by the farmer, how it's marketed, and how the consumer can use it to best advantage in the home.

In effect, here is the national food story in some 400 pages, a popular encyclopedia of food for the consumer in country or city.

Food From Farm to You, first section of the Yearbook, describes the economics of food, from the farmer's field to the supermarket.

The second section, *Buying and Cooking Food*, is divided into the major food classes, from meat and poultry on to dairy products, fruits, vegetables, and—ultimately—pickles, spices, and herbs. Housewives may find the tips on buying and the recipes especially helpful.

Nutrition and planning meals are major components of the third section of the Yearbook, *Food and Your Life*. Some of the chapter subjects emphasize basic food needs, creating good food habits, and money-stretching ideas to make your food dollar go further.

A wide variety of authors wrote this book, and so it represents a diversity of views. Authors for the most part are from the U.S. Department of Agriculture, other Federal agencies, and State land-grant universities.

William S. Hoofnagle of the Economic Research Service was chairman of the Yearbook Committee that planned this volume. Others on the Committee were:

Agricultural Research Service—Marguarette M. Hedge, Irwin Hornstein, Ruth M. Leverton, and Irene H. Wolgamot.

Consumer and Marketing Service—Eleanor A. Ferris and Hyman M. Steinmetz.

Economic Research Service—Stephen J. Hiemstra and Rosalind C. Lifquist.

Federal Extension Service—Margaret C. Browne (ret.).

Food and Nutrition Service—Elizabeth S. Hight.

Foreign Agricultural Service—Kenneth W. Olson.

Forest Service—Clifford D. Owsley.

Department of Health, Education, and Welfare—Theresa A. Demus.

Department of the Interior—Rose G. Kerr.

Contents

FOOD FROM FARM TO YOU

BUYING AND COOKING FOOD

FOOD AND YOUR LIFE

Food from Farm to You

Wendell Clement
Kenneth R. Farrell

The Nation's Food Industry and You, the Consumer

Perhaps no industry is taken more for granted than the food industry.

As consumers, we have come to expect the supermarket shelves to be plentifully stocked with a wide choice of wholesome food, in the form and at the time we want it, day in and day out. But at the same time, how many of us ever stop to think about how the six to ten thousand items on these supermarket shelves got there? About the millions of individuals and billions of dollars required to produce and market food? About the fact that, as a Nation, we spend a smaller proportion of our take-home pay for food than in any other country in today's world?

If you lived in almost any other country, or if we in this country still had a food industry like that of the 1930's, most of us would have quite an adjustment to make in the way we shop for foods. We might be less inclined to take the industry for granted.

Imagine, if you will, that when you buy your week's groceries you would have to go to one store for dry groceries—canned foods, flour, sugar, cereal, coffee, and the like. Then move on to another for bread, rolls, cake, and cookies; find a produce store to get your fresh vegetables and fruit; a meat market, and maybe a still different place for fish.

Next add to this a drug store for toothpaste, soap, and aspirin; a department store for hose, furniture polish, cleaning fluids, and everyday cups and saucers. And, before you even started this trek, you might have to go to a bank to cash a check.

Today, we take for granted that all these foods, and many others not even produced in the 1930's, as well as everyday household needs—and check-cashing facilities too—will be available in our nearby supermarket so that we need make only one stop and be on our way home in about 30 minutes.

It is difficult for most of us to realize that in many countries people cannot take for granted even an adequate supply of basic foods, let alone having them in the form and at the time desired and available at convenient locations. Even today, hunger strikes two out of three of the world's population.

While pockets of poverty still remain in the United States, the food stamp and direct distribution programs offer us the promise that one day soon all of our people will have adequate food supplies.

Although we may take our food system for granted, the fact is that we depend highly upon it as consumers. So do millions of farmers who rely upon it to assemble, transport, process, package, and merchandise their commodities and return to them incomes that will afford them a satisfactory living. In addition, several million persons employed in processing and distributing food depend upon this industry as a source of income. Considering all components—farmers, processors, retailers, and so on—the food industry is the largest in the

Wendell Clement is Leader, Market Performance Research Group, Marketing Economics Division, Economic Research Service.

Kenneth R. Farrell is Acting Assistant Administrator, Economic Research Service.

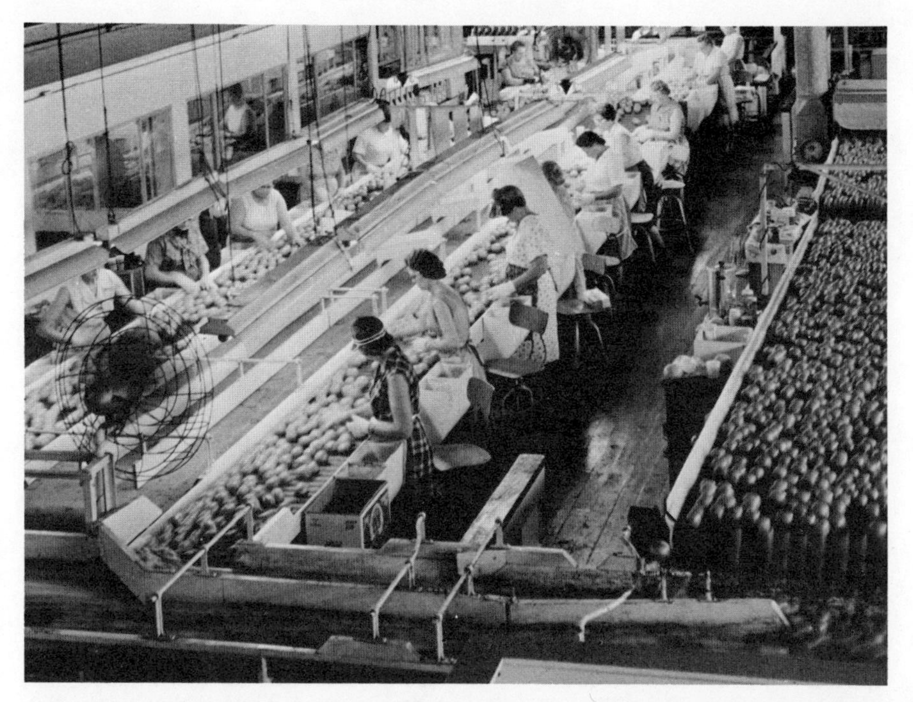

Sorting Florida oranges, before they are packed for fresh shipment. Oranges move from conveyor at right onto conveyors at left, where women remove offcolor and other defective fruit.

United States in terms of numbers of persons employed. So, in one way or another, we are all highly dependent upon it.

Few of us realize the magnitude of the task faced by the food industry in fulfilling our requirements for food and the many services we have come to expect. Consider the task faced by this industry in meeting all our expectations that the food will be available where and when we want it; in a form that we want; and at a price that will allow us to spend a large part of our income on other goods and services which we consider necessary for the good life.

To get food where we want it, the marketing system must assemble products from farms across the country. These must be sorted for uniformity and combined into units suitable for ease of handling and shipping. On the way from the farm to our grocery stores, food travels through a host of middlemen—packers, processors, warehouse operators, and wholesalers. During this roundabout trip, we expect the quality and wholesomeness to be preserved—particularly in fresh foods which, today, often travel long distances. All this must be a continuous process. New supplies must arrive at local warehouses and wholesalers almost daily. Getting foods where we want them requires a well-coordinated and dependable transportation system.

Making supplies available when we want them requires a lot of storage space. If foods were not stored during seasonal surpluses, we might be faced with periods of feast and famine. Each year at the end of the growing season, when supplies are plentiful, fresh products are stored in specially equipped warehouses. Processed foods are stockpiled. In addition to insuring a regular flow of food throughout the year, this also helps to stabilize prices.

Perhaps the greatest demands placed on the food industry result from the form in which we want our food. Due to our different social, cultural, and economic backgrounds, we possess a

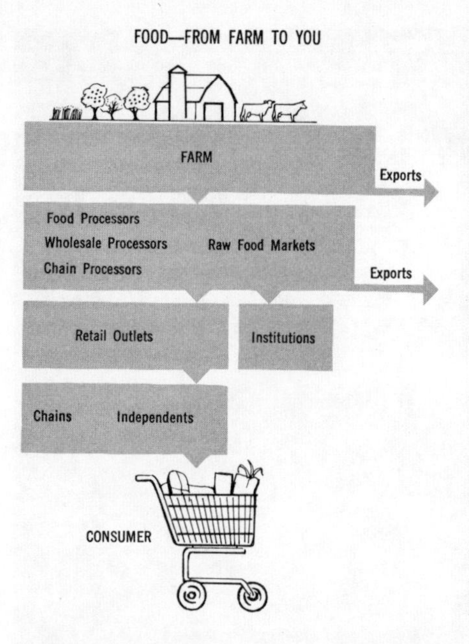

wide variety of tastes. And each of us expects to find what we like. Multiplying this by 60 million families results in a myriad of different wants and expectations. For example, one shopper may want a 2-inch cut of prime tenderloin steak; another may want thin-sliced pork chops. Some may want only fresh fruits and vegetables and cake flour, shortening, sugar, and eggs for a cake. An employed homemaker, pushed for time, may want all the convenience she can buy so meals at home can be quickly and easily prepared. A gourmet may hunt for the unusual food or one he had on his last trip abroad.

As we have become more affluent, we have not only demanded higher quality foods but foods with built-in chef services and convenience features. More foods are processed than ever before; frozen foods, high in quality and uniformity, are commonplace; so are dehydrated and precooked foods. Foods are packaged in containers of various size, shape, and composition to meet family needs and to provide maximum convenience in handling and storage in the home. As a result, retailers must stock a wide variety of foods in many forms to meet our diverse needs as consumers. Each year, large sums of money are spent by the industry developing new product forms or improving old ones. Many are accepted by consumers but are soon followed by a newer, more convenient or improved product. And so, the industry is constantly changing, each change designed to improve the firm's position in the marketplace and to gain the favor of the quality-minded, convenience-seeking consumer.

All along the way, our food industry has done much to maintain quality and sanitation standards. Starting at the farm, foods are sorted so that they can be sold on the basis of grades and other quality indications. More than 350 Federal grade standards and specifications have been set for foods, including meat, poultry, dairy products, fruits, and vegetables.

Many laws and regulations are designed to assure us wholesome, safe food. Most cities have ordinances that specify standards for the production and marketing of milk. The Federal Food, Drug, and Cosmetic Act prohibits the movement of adulterated and misbranded foods from one State to another.

The Meat Inspection and Poultry Products Inspection Acts have been important in regulating wholesomeness of these products. The laws provide for Federal inspection of red meat and all poultry products sold across State borders. The laws were strengthened recently to require that products sold within the State must be State-inspected under standards which are equal to Federal inspection.

In addition to providing us with food where, when, and in the form we want it, our food industry has kept its prices reasonable, relative to the prices of many other goods and services important in our economy and to the rising incomes of most Americans. In recent years, food prices have been rising—largely as the result of more built-in services and higher costs of labor and materials. But the fact is that, today, we spend a smaller share of our take-home pay for food than at any point in the history of our Nation. And for this smaller share, we are buying a wider assortment of foods—foods of higher quality with more services, and larger quantities of higher priced ones as well, like meat. Although we spend more dollars for our food, we have added many more dollars to our paychecks.

These achievements are even more impressive when we realize that there have been inflationary tendencies in most parts of the American economy since the end of World War II. The achievements would not have been possible without a greatly increased efficiency to offset the constantly rising costs of labor, materials, and other things that the food industry uses.

In the past two decades, improvements in efficiency have been made at all levels of the food system. Output per manhour has increased at an annual rate of 4 percent in food processing and 3 percent in food distribution. These productivity increases were made possible by large investments in plants and equipment, by adoption of new and improved techniques of handling, processing, and selling food, and by better management.

But the most spectacular gains in efficiency have come at the farm level. Increases in output per manhour have averaged about 6 percent per year. The importance of these gains is more apparent when we realize that in 1950, one farmworker supplied enough farm products for about 15 people, and today he supplies enough for nearly three times as many. These gains in productivity have been important in holding food costs in line and allowing us more money to buy other goods and services.

How is the vast food industry coordinated? How are the requirements of more than 200 million consumers of food matched with the actions of thousands of retailers, processors, transporters, and about 3 million farmers? What guides the industry in producing the foods and services when, where, and in the form wanted by consumers?

The guiding hand in such decisions is a highly developed and decentralized exchange system. When a homemaker purchases food at the supermarket, she transmits, in effect, a signal to the industry expressing her preferences and ability to buy. When she purchases one food instead of another, or one with more built-in services instead of an unprocessed or unpackaged food, the industry has a basis for planning its production and marketing activities.

These signals are transmitted from one part of the industry to another by means of a system of markets and prices, or other arrangements, such as contracts. For example, if a retailer finds that customers at his store are willing to purchase more of a food at a certain price, he may instruct his wholesale buyer or his buyer in the area where the product is produced to increase his purchases at a specified price. At each market there will be sellers anxious to get as much for this product as possible. So, bargaining between buyer and seller takes place, and ultimately the product changes ownership and becomes available to us, the consumers.

Although the markets for food are much more complicated than this simple illustration indicates, farmers, processors, retailers, and others in the industry depend upon them to provide guidance in their decisions of what, when, and where to produce and sell. This market mechanism is not perfect and it cannot instantaneously match consumer desires with supplies at each segment of the industry, but it does operate well over long periods of time.

Though we sometimes overlook this exchange system and the part it plays in guiding decisions in the food industry, its role is a vital one. Farmers and marketers depend upon the exchange system to yield prices that will reward them fairly and equitably, as well as to provide reliable guidance in their production decisions. As consumers, we are interested in having our preferences expressed at various levels of the industry as clearly and efficiently as is possible. For these reasons, various laws and regulations have been adopted to prevent unfair or inequitable practices in buying and in selling.

Putting all this together, we can see why a large and complex industrial network has emerged to meet our needs. This network is called "agribusiness." It begins with firms which supply products—such as seeds, fertilizers, petroleum products, and farm machinery—used by farmers in the production process. It includes the millions of farmworkers who till the land and harvest the crops. Added to these are the countless marketing firms involved in processing and moving the product from farmer to consumer.

The economic importance of this agribusiness complex is indicated by the amount of capital invested. The total assets now invested amount to more than $350 billion, two-thirds of which are invested at the farm level. Processing and distributing firms account for another fourth, and the suppliers of agricultural products for the remainder.

More than 23 million people, or about 30 percent of the total U.S. work force, are employed in this agribusiness complex. Of these, the farm firms and farm supply firms together

Livestock auction in Colorado. Electric scoreboard gives gross and average weight of stock lots.

Chicago Board of Trade, one of Nation's major food exchanges. The "pits" where buying and selling take place are enclosed by steps.

employ about 11 million; processing and distribution firms employ some 12 million.

By almost any measure, our food industry is large and of considerable economic and social significance. How well it operates is of concern to each of us, for we as consumers are the energizers which make the wheels of this big industrial complex turn. As such, we have our responsibilities to the food industry as well as the food industry to us. But perhaps our most important responsibility is to exercise intelligent choices in selecting products and in patronizing stores. Intelligent choice on our part drives the competitive wheels of industry to provide quality services and products. It also motivates firms to improve efficiency and search for better ways of getting things done.

We need to be informed about the food industry and the way it operates, to foster a healthy and enlightened attitude towards this industry and the public policies relating to it. We should understand, for example, that without profits the current investment of more than $350 billion would not have been made. Reasonable profits are necessary to attract capital to build stores in our communities, construct processing plants, and purchase farmlands. The costs of the many built-in food services are also incorporated into the price of the product. And, overall, the cost of doing business in the food industry is rising as it is in other industries.

As citizens, we should understand and support public policies which are aimed at maintaining and fostering an efficient, progressive, and responsive food industry. Public policies are needed which promote fair competition among participants in the food industry so that efficient firms can survive and grow. Then too, if we demand that the food industry be honest with us, we should deal fairly with it. Bad checks, pilferage, and destruction of property are examples of acts which add to marketing costs and to our food bill.

All of this implies that we as consumers ought to be knowledgeable about the food industry. Consumer education programs are important in providing this information. Workshops and study groups might be usefully employed. Homemakers could involve their own teenagers in planning the food budget and buying.

Donald D. Durost

Where Food Originates: the Farmer and His Farm

Few of us ever stop to think about how much food we eat in a year. And, probably, even fewer of us ever consider how much our more than 200 million Americans eat. You may find it hard to believe, yet each of us eats nearly three-quarters of a ton every 365 days! This amounts to nearly 3 tons a year for a family of four and a whopping 150 million tons to feed us all. It's the job of our farmers and commercial fishermen to provide most of this. The rest, around 10 percent of our total food, is imported from countries around the world.

So many of us live in cities that we tend to take for granted the lavish supply of foods at our grocery. As we wheel our carts around to select what our families want, we seldom consider what it has taken to get all this food to our neighborhood supermarket. We city folks frequently hear about farmers, but some of us have never been on a farm and few of us really know the part farmers play in getting food ready for its trek to market—to provide us with the most abundant food supply in the world.

Few nations are capable of producing enough food for all their people. For a country to do this, it must be blessed with a rich supply of natural resources, good workers, and money enough to keep pace with changing technology in this rapidly changing world of ours.

We've been very fortunate in having more than our share of natural resources. Our country is located in the temperate zone, has a wide range of climate and many types of land. This makes possible the great variety of crops and livestock that we produce—including wheat, corn, tomatoes, oranges, beef, and milk.

Production of all this food is not planned by some central agency. It is the result of 3 million sets of decisions made by 3 million farmers. It is they who decide what crops and how many acres of each will be produced. And a declining number of our farmers have been able to supply ample food for a constantly increasing population.

Our 50 States have a total area of nearly 2.3 billion acres, with about half of this taken up as farms. Forests and rangeland take another third and parks and wastelands, such as the western desert, about a sixth. The rest, only about 55 million acres, or a mere 4 percent, is used for our cities, towns, roads, and airports. Although farms take up a fair share of our land, there's still enough left that can be used for producing more food when it's needed.

Our farms come in different sizes, produce different kinds of food, and are managed in different ways. They fall somewhere between the extremes of small family farms with a few cows and chickens, a pig or two, a garden, and a few acres to raise food to sell, and the very large farms of a thousand acres or more, owned by individuals, cooperatives, or corporations and operated by managers and hired labor.

Accordingly, a farmer may run his

Donald D. Durost is an Economist with the Farm Production Economics Division, Economic Research Service.

Combine operator examines newly threshed soybeans on Ohio farm.

own small farm or a 320 acre spread where he raises grain and livestock. He may be a cattleman who owns a small farm and rents a thousand acres of range country. He may be a man who operates a big farm for someone else, or a sharecropper with a few acres. Yet in our country, farming is the only major industry where family groups make up the largest share of the labor force. Farmers and their unsalaried family members constitute almost three-fourths of the 5 million workers on farms. Only about a million are paid workers.

In addition to differences in size and the kind of employees, farms also differ in what they produce. Some grow fruits and vegetables, some produce livestock and poultry, and still others produce cotton and tobacco. Though some crops and livestock are produced in all parts of the country, the kinds and amount vary somewhat by region. Soil conditions, climate, and even how far it is to the nearest or best market influence decisions on what and how much to grow.

If we travel around the country, we find that the Northeastern States—from Maine to Maryland—and those bordering on the Great Lakes—from New York out to Minnesota—are the Nation's principal milk-producing areas. Climate and soil in these States are suited to raising grains and forage for cattle and for providing pastureland for grazing. Broiler farming has become important in Maine—and from New Jersey to Maryland. The half million farms in the Northeast and Lake States, which average about 190 acres each, provide 17 percent of our farm products.

The some half million farms a little farther south in the Appalachian region—West Virginia to North Carolina, Kentucky, and Tennessee—are somewhat smaller in size, averaging only 122 acres. Though these farms produce commodities such as peanuts, cattle, and milk, their main product is tobacco.

Going still farther south along the Atlantic Coast, farms start getting a little larger again. About a quarter of a million farms averaging 220 acres each are important for cotton and broilers. Some vegetables, such as sweetpotatoes, are grown in this area along with peanuts. And, of course, there are the big Florida citrus groves.

Traveling west to the Southern Delta States—to Mississippi, Louisiana, and Arkansas—we find another quarter of a million farms about the same size as in Appalachia, that concentrate on raising cotton. Some rice and soybeans are also grown and livestock is being produced in larger numbers than formerly.

As we turn and go north, we come to what is frequently called the "breadbasket" of America. The eastern part of this is known as the Corn Belt and the area a little farther west as the Great Plains.

The Corn Belt, extending from central Ohio to the Nebraska border, is a region with rich soil, good climate, and sufficient rainfall for excellent farming. And, its 643,000 farms provide nearly one-fourth of our food supply—corn, beef, and pork as well as soybeans and some wheat.

The Great Plains, which extend north and south from Canada to Mexico and from the Corn Belt on the east to the Rocky Mountain States on the west, are quite different in character from the Midwest corn country. Here the one-half million farms, averaging 680 acres in size, supply a fifth of our food. The flatness of the land, and the small amounts of rain in this area, greatly influence what can be produced. In addition, in the northern part—in the Dakotas and as far south as Kansas—winters are cold and snowy so the growing season is relatively short. Nevertheless, nearly 60 percent of our wheat is produced in the Great Plains. In the southern part—Oklahoma and Texas—cotton and cattle are important.

The Mountain States—from Idaho and Montana to New Mexico and Arizona—provide us with a still different terrain. Vast areas of this region are particularly suited to raising cattle and sheep. Irrigation in the valleys provides water for such crops as sugar beets, potatoes, fruits, and vegetables. The 134,000 farms and ranches in these States are the largest in the country as they average over 2,000 acres in size.

In our trek across the country, we now reach the West Coast. Farms are smaller here than in the Mountain States, but still large by most standards. The 151,000 farms in our Pacific Coast States average about 500 acres in size. Those in the south specialize in raising fruits and vegetables; wheat and fruit are important in the northern part. Cattle are raised throughout the entire region.

Finally, we come to the newest States in the Union, Alaska and Hawaii. These States provide only a small part of our total farm output. Dairy and poultry products are the major foods produced upon the 300 Alaskan farms. The long summer days make possible Alaska production of potatoes, lettuce, carrots, and cabbage. Hawaii has 4,700 farms. Pineapples and sugarcane are the major crops. The mild climate makes possible the production of bananas, coffee, macadamia nuts, and papayas.

This takes us around the country—showing us where most of our food comes from and why. Now let's take a closer look at our farms and farmers.

Our world has been changing fast and most of us have felt the impact of the changes that have taken place. Farmers are no exception. Probably no other major group in our society has had to deal with so much change in so short a time.

At one time, farming was a way of life; now it's a mighty serious business. Before World War II, farmers made up a large share of our population. Since then, more people have left the farms than now are living on them. Today, only one in 20 Americans lives on a farm. In the years gone by, a father could expect a son to take over his farm when he was too old to run it. Today, sons and daughters seek better jobs in the city and are likely to sell the farms they inherit to someone else who needs more land.

Since 1950, the number of farms has gone down significantly, but the amount of land being farmed has changed little. Today there are around 3 million farms, about half as many as in 1950. During these same years, the size of the average farm increased from 225 to 360 acres. And more than half of the farms sold in recent years were bought by farmers to enlarge their own holdings.

Though we have far fewer farmers today than what seems like only yesterday, those who have stayed have more than met the needs of a growing population. Since 1950, our population has increased 32 percent; our food supplies have gone up 41 percent. In addition, agricultural exports have nearly doubled.

All this has come about because farmers have adopted new technologies, mechanized their farms, and improved their management operations. It has been achieved because they have better seeds, insecticides, and fertilizers. They use more tractors, trucks, and harvesting machines. With this greater mechanization of their work, they plant and harvest more acres with fewer hired hands.

Family farms continue to be the backbone of our Nation's agriculture. These may vary considerably in size. On a family farm, more than half the work is done by the farmer and his family. According to this definition, 95 percent of all our farms are family farms. And they account for 65 percent of the products going to market.

But we have other kinds of farms, too—the large, commercial farms. These, larger-than-family-size, have an almost factory-type system of operation. Most of them are in California, Arizona, southern Texas, and Florida.

The decrease in the number of our farms and the increase in size doesn't necessarily mean that this trend will continue at the same pace as in the recent past. When a farmer increases the size of his farm to take advantage of new technologies, he also increases his investments and costs. Today, if farming is his only source of income, he must sell products worth at least $10,000 to provide his family with a minimum level of living.

Not all farms produce enough to bring in $10,000 a year. Many do not even try or want to do so. Some are meant to be part-time or retirement farms only.

On the other hand, some factory-type farms can produce enough to bring in hundreds of thousands of dollars a year.

About 43 percent of our farms have sales amounting to less than $2,500 a year. These account for only about 3 percent of our food. Some are retirement farms; others are subsistence farms where family members are underemployed. On the average, those living on farms with sales falling in this dollar range receive more than five times as much income from off-farm work as from farming.

About one-fourth of the farms sell between $2,500 and $10,000 worth of products and account for about 12 percent of all sales. Few of these will provide a satisfactory level of living unless supplemented by other income.

The rest of our farms, now less than 1 million, but gradually increasing in number, have gross sales of $10,000 or more and provide 85 percent of our farm products. Among these, however, are more than 30,000 farms with sales of at least $100,000 a year. Though such big operations represent only about 1 percent of all farms, they account for almost a fourth of all sales—over 60 percent of our vegetables; 45 percent of the fruit and nuts; and 35 percent of all poultry and poultry products.

To sum up, the average size of our 3 million plus farms is 360 acres; farmers sell livestock and crops valued at $14,000 per farm; and their average net income is $4,500 a year. As mentioned earlier, some farmers have regular work off the farm; others may take jobs during slack periods. Even families on farms with $40,000 or more sales average $5,000 a year from nonfarm sources.

Farmers are specialists, too. A major change that has taken place in farming is the trend toward greater specialization—raising fewer kinds of crops or livestock, buying more of the seeds and feed, and using more mechanical equipment—tractors and milking machines, and so on. Today, the average farm has between three and four major enterprises, compared with over five before World War II. Though there still are some advantages to diversified farming—raising more kinds of products—there are important reasons for specializing. It takes a high degree of skill and knowledge to compete successfully in producing one farm product. A farmer who does well uses knowledge of genetics, land and water conservation, and business management. He performs many jobs with complex tools and machines. He combines science and machine power with the ancient arts of tilling the soil.

A farmer must consider costs when deciding what to produce, and costs that must be met before he receives a return on his investment vary greatly by crops. For example, the cost per acre for the better-than-average farmer is $18.20 for wheat, $47.25 for corn, and up to $103.50 for cotton.

On the average, farmers spend 70 cents out of every dollar of sales for production expenses. This varies by size of farm, ranging from about 50 cents per dollar sales by small farms to 80 cents by farms with sales of more than $40,000 a year. As the size of a farm increases, farmers must purchase more fertilizers, pesticides, gas and oil, and other nonfarm goods. And the larger the farm, the more hired workers there are to pay.

Farmers are large purchasers of tractors, trucks, automobiles, and other equipment. They buy about one of every eight trucks that are sold. In a recent year, they spent over $1 billion for tractors, $1.3 billion for automobiles, and $2.5 billion for machinery like plows, planters, and harvesting machines. And, of course, as with other industries, as the years go by these wear out or become obsolete and have to be replaced.

Most crops have benefited from the use of new and improved technologies. For example, since 1950 corn yields have more than doubled—from 38 to 79 bushels per acre. Cotton yields also have nearly doubled, going from 269 to 511 pounds. Wheat yields went from 16.5 to 28.4 bushels an acre and soybeans edged up from around 22 to 27 bushels.

A major problem for a farmer, however, is the variability in prices he gets for his products. His income can fluctuate widely from year to year—and even within a season. Farm production is not a continuous process. Usually it covers a period of only a few months. During this time, crops can be badly damaged by weather, insects, or disease. And unlike most manufacturing industries, a farmer has almost no control over how much his farm will produce once the crop is planted—how many bushels of wheat per acre, for example. Wide swings in prices are common. In 1964, farmers received $14.80 for hogs, per 100 pounds. This rose to $22.80 in 1966 and then dropped back to $18.63 in

This Louisiana farmer increases his profits by storing rice in bins on farm, and selling it when the market is most favorable.

1968. The same and sometimes even greater ups and downs occur in prices of other commodities as well.

At the same time that prices may fluctuate widely, the things a farmer has to buy may be going up steadily in price. This increases his risk, already great. Some farmers, in an effort to reduce their risk, enter into informal or formal agreements with other agricultural-related businesses like feed dealers and processors. Such an agreement may let the related business share in management decisions. These arrangements are referred to as coordinated farming.

Various forms of farm and business arrangements have existed for a long time in commercial fruit and tree nut production. Contract farming now accounts for about two-thirds of the vegetables produced for canning and freezing. Most of today's broiler production is a joint undertaking between farmers and processors. Men employed by the processor do much of the poultry farm management. Production is concentrated in operations that make the fullest use of labor-saving equipment. In this way, poultry raisers reduce their risks and get a guaranteed income for themselves.

The sugar beet industry is another example of contract farming. Nearly all sugar beet growers have contracts with processors to insure a market. Sugar beets are heavy, bulky, and perishable. They are grown under contracts which guarantee a market for farmers and supplies for the processor. Negotiated contracts tie the price of the sugar beets to that of sugar. These specify the acreage to be planted, seeds and growing methods to be used, dates beets are to be delivered to the processor, marketing practices to be used, and even when the farmer will be paid.

All these changes calling for larger investments and more specialization have resulted in an increase in efficiency. Farmers have made the best record in this respect of all our industries. Since 1950, the amount of work, per man, per hour, working in agriculture has increased at a rate of nearly 6 percent a year compared with 2.5 percent for all other industries. In other words, one farmer now produces enough food for almost three times as many persons as he did back in 1950.

The share of workers employed on farms provides a good measure of a nation's productivity. In our country, only 6 percent of the total labor force works on farms. This compares with 10 and 18 percent in developed countries like West Germany and France. About 40 percent of all Soviet Union workers are on farms. In less developed countries such as India and Pakistan approximately three-quarters of the labor force works on farms.

What does all this mean to those of us who live in cities?

This abundance has helped raise our standard of living and to provide us with an unprecedented quantity, quality, and variety of food at the lowest cost in relation to our take-home pay in this Nation's history. This has left us more income for other things—houses, cars, college educations.

A second contribution of the continuing rise in agricultural productivity is the release of manpower to other sectors of the economy where they can make significant contributions in industry, the professions, and in the defense efforts of our country.

The release of manpower from our farms had its social and economic costs, however. Many of the released workers are poorly equipped in terms of skills, education, and personal resources for nonfarm occupations. As workers move from the farm to the city, some find the city has little to offer except unemployment or low paying, insecure jobs. They simply add to the already existing problems of unemployment and poverty.

A third benefit has been the creation of many jobs in the nonfarm section of the economy. Farmers spend more than $34 billion a year for goods and services to produce crops and livestock. Added to this, about $15 billion goes for the same things that city people buy—food, clothing, and

Wheat combines on the job in Nebraska. Farm machinery is constantly being modified and improved.

other consumer products and services.

Every year farmers purchase products containing about 5 million tons of steel and some 320 million pounds of rubber—enough to put tires on nearly 6 million automobiles.

They use more petroleum than any other single industry—and more electricity than all of the people and industries in Chicago, Detroit, Boston, Baltimore, Houston, and Washington, D.C., combined.

These are today's farms and farmers.

But what about the future? What is being predicted for farms and farmers?

It is forecast that by the turn of the century the American farmer will be freed from the arduous and time-consuming demands of planting and harvesting. Some see him sitting in an air-conditioned farm office, scanning a printout from a computer center. This computer center will help him decide how many acres to plant, what kinds of seeds to sow, what kind and how much fertilizer to apply, exactly what his soil composition is, and even what day to harvest each crop.

They foresee other things as well:

Automated machinery directed by tape-controlled programs and supervised by television scanners mounted on towers.

Robot harvesters to carry out high speed picking, grading, packaging, and freezing.

Crop yields per acre double and triple those of 1969.

H. E. Crowther

The Water's Harvest: Fish of All Kinds for Our Tables

The farmer must sow before he can reap. Fishermen can reap without sowing, for most fish are hunted rather than farmed. As with our farmers, commercial marine fishermen are affected by nature's whims. Not only are they concerned about the weather, but water temperatures and ocean currents as well. The farmer can protect his land with a fence and "posted" signs, and can brand his cattle as a sign of ownership. Coastal areas may be "posted" by State regulations, and sections of the ocean may be protected by international agreement; but there are no fences in the open sea.

An unnetted fish has no owner and no nationality. The American fisherman must take his chances, not only against the elements, but also against foreign competition.

Most of our Nation's fishing fleet is made up of small boats of less than 5 net tons. "Vessels," which are larger, account for about 15 percent of our fleet of around 82,000, and catch a large percentage of our fish. Though many craft in our fleet are at least 20 years old, the number of "vessels" being built is increasing. Recently, two trawlers were built, each 300 feet long—one to operate in the Atlantic, the other in the Pacific. These "factory ships" are the largest fishing vessels ever built in the United States. They are more powerful, have wider range. Most vessels have been built for shrimp and tuna fisheries, the two most prosperous segments of our fishing industry.

Around 225,000 persons are employed in the marine fisheries, about 60 percent as fishermen and the rest as shoreworkers. The number of these employees has been going down, even though the number of the processing plants has been increasing.

The commercial marine fishing industry is not a single entity. It is a combination of industries, and each industry may be broken down by location—as the Maine shrimp or the Gulf shrimp industry—and then within these by functional classes—producers (fishermen), processors, and distributors.

During the last 30 years, some major changes have taken place. Catches of Pacific mackerel, sardines, Atlantic cod, and haddock have gone down while landings of shrimp, crab, clams, flounder, and tuna have increased. Generally, declines have been greatest in the older fisheries, especially those off the New England and Pacific coasts. In 1967, the Pacific sardine fishery, once our largest, took only 100,000 pounds, less than one-hundredth of 1 percent of the record catch of 1.5 billion in 1936. By contrast, the Gulf of Mexico and the Gulf of Alaska are producing more than ever, and their potential still has not yet been realized.

In 1967, shrimp fishermen took a record catch of 312 million pounds which had a dockside value of $103 million. This was the first time that domestic fishermen had received $100 million or more for a single year's harvest. During this same year, the tuna industry had one of its best years. The catch landed in the continental United States and in Hawaii came to

H. E. Crowther is Director, Bureau of Commercial Fisheries, Department of the Interior.

At left, catfish raised in a big Mississippi fish farming operation. Below, harvesting catfish at Louisiana fish farm.

329 million pounds—valued at nearly $45 million, the largest since 1956. The tuna fishing industry has overcome some of its foreign competition through improved efficiency.

North Atlantic and North Pacific fisheries have been particularly susceptible to foreign competition on the fishing grounds and in the marketplace. Both haddock in the Atlantic and halibut in the Pacific have suffered the effects of heavy fishing by foreign fleets. Several years of poor spawning have also hurt the haddock fishery.

The last decade has seen the commercial catch increasingly supplemented through cultivation of both freshwater and saltwater species. In the freshwater "fish-farming," pond-grown trout and catfish have developed into multimillion dollar industries. On our West Coast, the salmon released by hatcheries are caught by sportsmen and commercial fishermen. In estuarine areas such as coastal bays and river mouths, managed beds produce more than half the oysters harvested in the United States.

Shrimp culture, already an old story in some Asiatic countries, has caught the popular imagination. All along the coast, a veritable frenzy of research by university scientists, government agencies, industry, and amateurs is aimed at adding this tasty crustacean to the list of our "home-growns." Work is also being done on pompano, clams, lobsters, abalone, and mussels.

While the U.S. catch has remained relatively static, some of the other nations have increased theirs steadily. Japan's catch is 50 percent larger now than it was a decade ago. The Soviet Union has doubled its catch. Peru has become one of the leading fishery nations with nearly 20 billion pounds a year—a fourfold increase within the past 10 years. It has made dramatic strides in its anchovy fishery.

The United States, with less than 7 percent of the world population, uses about 11 percent of the world's catch of fish—including around 44 percent of the tuna and about 35 percent of the world's shrimp.

About 70 percent of all our fish and shellfish is brought in from other countries—about 60 percent of the tuna, 50 percent of the shrimp, and 90 percent of the spiny lobster.

In recent years, total utilization of fish in the United States has climbed steadily. The total supplies (domestic catch plus imports) in 1957 were slightly above 7 billion pounds, but by 1967 this had increased to more than 14 billion pounds, a new record. Edible fishery products made up approximately 36 percent of the 1967 figure, and the rest went into industrial uses, primarily as a rapid growth additive in poultry and cattle feed.

Commercial fishing, like agriculture and other industries, has its expanding and contracting sectors. Government and industry are taking advantage of the latest scientific and technological advances. And improved transportation facilities are making fresh, wholesome products available to expanded markets. Considerable research effort is being directed toward the discovery and development of new fishery resources—a new shrimp fishery off the coast of Maine—a scallop fishery off Alaska with a high rate of catch and high prices—extensive calico scallop beds off the eastern coast of Florida—encouragement of the tanner crab fishery to partly offset the reduced abundance of the King crab.

Still, although Americans seem to enjoy eating fish, and although the United States is one of the world's most attractive markets, our narrow preferences make it difficult for any new fishery products to be developed quickly or easily.

Frederick D. Gray

That Coffee From Brazil, and Other Food Imports

Have you ever wondered, as you drank your cup of coffee or tea, and sprinkled cinnamon on your toast or pepper on your steak, where they came from? These foods have been around so long that you probably don't realize they may have traveled halfway across the world to get to your kitchen!

But coffee, tea, and spices are only a few of the many products we buy from 150 countries around the globe. Our food imports amount to more than $3 billion each year. They represent about 13 percent of all agricultural goods we buy abroad. Only the United Kingdom and West Germany import more food than we do. About two-fifths of our agricultural imports are products we don't raise in this country. Besides coffee, tea, and spices, our imports include cocoa, sugar, bananas, beef and pork, and some dairy products such as cheese.

Coffee is the most important food brought into this country. As one of the world's biggest coffee drinkers, we buy nearly half the world's supply. Over a billion dollars a year is spent to supply each of us with an average of 750 cups of coffee a year.

Two major types are imported—the milder flavored Arabica varieties, primarily grown in Central and South America, and more strongly flavored Robusta varieties from Africa and Asia. The milder Arabica varieties are used in roasted blends and represent about three-quarters of all coffee imports. Robusta varieties are largely used in instant coffees. But recently, increasing quantities are being used in roasted blends as well.

Though we can't compete with the English, we still drink a lot of tea, at least iced tea—143 million pounds of tea a year or nearly $60 million worth. About half of our tea comes from far-off Ceylon—the island which the inhabitants maintain was really the locale of the Garden of Eden. Some tea comes from Japan where it may have been grown on hillsides facing beautiful Mount Fujiyama. Both black and green teas are imported. The more completely fermented black teas represent most of what we consume.

Even more important than tea are imports of cocoa beans and semiprocessed cocoa and chocolate products. Each year the total imports amount to nearly $200 million. More than half of the cocoa beans come from Africa; most of the rest are from Central and South America. In general, there are two types, the regular beans which account for 95 percent of the imports and the flavor beans. This latter type, though small in quantity, sells for premium prices. The largest share of these products—85 percent—is used for candies, sirups, and similar items.

Sugar is the second most important food shipped into this country. Each year we import nearly half the sugar we use—over 5 million tons at a cost of more than $600 million. Latin America supplies over half of this, the Philippines around a fourth.

Altogether we take about 20 percent of the sugar that moves in world trade. Most of it is cane sugar, which typically comes in as raw sugar, and then is

Frederick D. Gray is an Agricultural Economist in the Food Consumption and Utilization Section, Economic Research Service.

"refined" to different stages—some to molasses, some to brown sugar, and some to the granulated sugar we buy at the grocery.

Bananas are another important food from abroad. In one year's time, we buy nearly 4 billion pounds at a cost of over $175 million. We take almost a third of the bananas shipped in world trade—most of which come to us from Central and South America. Even though we've been eating smaller quantities of fresh fruits in recent years, our purchases of bananas have changed little. Bananas are used in larger quantities—18 pounds per person—than any other fresh fruit.

Without spices, much of our food would be dull and tasteless. Although these products are important to us, their cost, by comparison, is relatively small—about $45 million a year. Black pepper leads the list. Others used in large quantities include mustard seed, vanilla beans, cloves, cinnamon, nutmeg, and ginger. In addition, we buy poppy seeds and sage and the less familiar capsicum, coriander and cummin seeds, and tumeric.

Our other food imports include fruits and livestock products. Beef imports total around 1 million pounds annually valued at over $400 million, while pork imports are typically valued near $200 million. Much of our beef comes from Australia, some from Argentina; canned hams and bacon are brought in from Denmark. Even so, imports of livestock products are small in total compared to purchases of crop products.

There are a host of imports that complement what we produce, some that add to our selection, and still others that provide gourmet touches to our meals. There are watermelons, cantaloups, tomatoes, peppers, onions, and garlic from nearby Mexico. We bring in canned tomatoes and tomato concentrates from Italy and canned pineapple from far-off Taiwan. Cashew nuts come from India, pistachios from Iran, filberts from Turkey, pignolias from Spain, and brazil nuts from Brazil (where else!).

Then there are such gourmet items as caviar from Russia, cheeses from the Scandinavian countries and Switzerland, bread from Syria, ludefisk from Norway, and turtle and elephant meat from other far-off lands.

Our farmers and fishermen, and those from other countries around the world, have provided us with a dependable supply of high-quality food. They are the ones who start our food through marketing channels and on its way to our tables, at home and away from home.

Picking coffee tree cherries in Latin America. It takes nearly 2,000 cherries to provide enough beans for a pound of roasted coffee.

John O. Gerald

Food on the Go: The Long Haul From Farm to Shopping Bag

Few of us realize the importance of the efficient transportation system we have in this country. It is a major reason why we can buy most of the same foods in a small town grocery as in a city supermarket; it is why we can have ripe tomatoes in February and fresh pork in July in any part of our country.

Without distribution, production would be useless in our land of vast distances; differences in climate, terrain, soil and crop specialization; and concentration of people in urban areas.

Every year, our transporters carry about 375 million tons of products off our farms. Less than 6 million tons of these are tobacco, wool, and cotton; the remainder is food and feed for livestock. Some of our food is exported, but most goes up and down and across our country. Sometimes the journey is direct, even when it's from coast to coast. Other times, it can be very roundabout—from farm to local buyers, to processing plants, and on to warehouses, wholesalers, and finally, to a supermarket or a plush restaurant on the upper east side of New York City, to cite an example.

Specialization of products by region benefits us all as well as farmers. But it wouldn't be feasible without dependable and rapid means of transportation. The cost would be prohibitive. With our system today, however, intercity transportation takes only about 6 cents of each dollar we spend for food. And for this we get untold variety along with the benefit of savings that come from the large scale production, processing, and marketing of food.

Our efficient transportation system didn't just happen nor did it develop overnight. Until railroads crossed our country and later built lines to small cities and towns, food raised on farms was eaten by the farm family, with any that was left over being sold nearby. What was eaten differed greatly from place to place, depending on what was produced locally. Families in towns raised much of their own vegetables, and usually some chickens, hogs, and a cow or two. When the railroads came, more and more people moved to cities. Then—and only then—we began to develop our present food distribution system. This was only about a century ago.

With the invention of the horseless carriage, small trucks became available. This made it possible for farmers to bring their products to the nearest railroad in a much shorter time than with old Dobbin hitched to a wagon. As trucks got larger and roads better, loads were carried longer distances. Then along came airplanes, and now the giant jets are carrying some food products.

Types of transportation vary widely—from small trucks to huge vans, from a single freight car to an entire train loaded with one product, from a section of a passenger plane to a giant superjet freighter, from a small barge to a seagoing merchant ship.

At times, food may be transported from farm to supermarket in the same vehicle. More often, however, it will travel by more than one and, even, by

John O. Gerald is Leader of the Transportation Research Group, Marketing Economics Division, Economic Research Service.

several different types. This means the cargo is likely to be transferred between vehicles one or more times on the way. Because speed and efficiency are important in getting most foods to their destination at a reasonable cost, there has been a rapid development of what is called "palletization." This consists of packing bags or cartons on a sledlike base that can be lifted and moved quickly and easily with a forklift truck. The chief advantage is that a product can be packed at the shipping point, transferred into warehouses or between vehicles one or more times, and not be unpacked until it reaches its destination. As a result, handling costs are lower.

"Containerization" is a further refinement of palletization, and will likely grow in the future. It is the putting of many small bags or cartons into one large container such as truck trailers without wheels.

Some products may require special equipment to control the temperature and humidity. This is especially true for fresh produce. Air must be circulated to remove heat from the fruit or vegetables and the small amount that comes through the insulated walls of the van, or car, or container. Humidity must be controlled to prevent drying or even the other extreme, too much moisture. Then, too, the temperatures must be controlled automatically for foods needing ordinary refrigeration and, at other times, for frozen foods. Foods like eggs and potatoes have to be heated in winter to prevent freezing.

In recent years, the pace of change in our modes of transportation has been speeded up by better communications—more roads, airfields, and even telephones and communication satellites. Roads span the country and airfields seem to be everywhere. Telephones at our elbows and wire services let marketing men know where they can buy and farmers where they can sell their foods. This eliminates hauling many products to faraway places and bringing them back to the same locality.

ANATOMY OF FOOD MARKETING

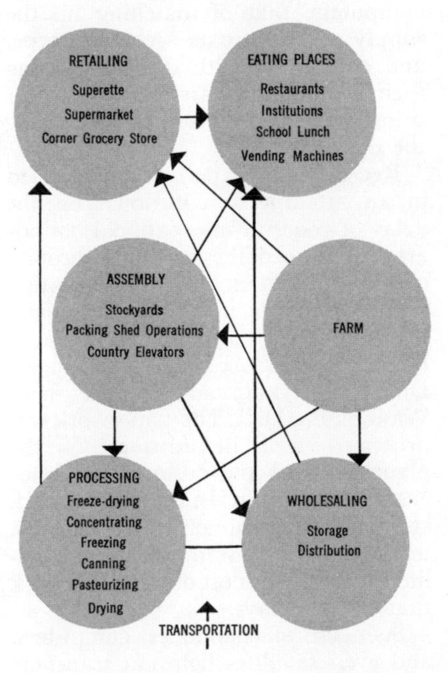

Communications also help in time of emergencies. For example, an egg shipper in North Carolina or Georgia may receive word from his buyer-to-be that a major wreck on the Pennsylvania Turnpike will delay the arrival of a few truckloads of eggs from Ohio that are needed for weekend customers in New York City. The shipper can reroute to New York his shipments of eggs going to Wilmington, Del. When the wreck on the Turnpike is cleared away, the eggs from Ohio can be sent to Wilmington. Customers in both cities will have eggs and will be unaware of all these "behind-the-scenes" maneuvers. This kind of diversion-in-transit is common for highly perishable foods.

The railroads and truck lines have begun to use computers to keep track of freight cars, trailers, and van containers. Shippers and carriers soon will have almost up-to-the-minute reports on the location of their equipment and shipments. A computer will receive these requests and send on the reports.

Railroads are testing another use of computers, that of matching up the supply of freight cars—location, type, and condition—with demand. Using their 1.8 million cars more fully for transport will be just like increasing the number.

Recently, an experiment was tried in an attempt to cut down on the delay of goods at international boundaries. To speed the products through customs, documentary information needed to clear incoming cargo was transmitted by communications satellite from Frankfurt in Germany to the Dulles International Airport near Washington, D.C. The paperwork was processed well in advance of the plane's arrival and customs clearance cut to a minimum. In the years ahead, computer and punch card may be teamed up with communications satellite to eliminate most of the paperwork that causes delays.

Such use of telephones, computers, and even satellites help cut transport costs and speed up the movement of products. They are particularly important for foods when a quick trip is essential to effective marketing.

Trains, trucks, planes, barges, and ships have their best function, but each is different in some respect. So let's see how they help in moving food.

Freight cars were the earliest form used for long-distance overland hauling of large quantities of products from one city to another. These could be loaded in California and unloaded in Chicago, all the while traveling over several different railway systems. Or the cars could be transferred at some point in between to other railway lines and then travel to the north or south.

At first, freight cars were simple boxcars. Today many of them are complex and specialized. We have refrigerated cars 50 to 60 feet long in which temperature and humidity are automatically controlled. Thermostats can be set so that fresh foods can be kept cool but above freezing one way and frozen food can be kept frozen on the return trip.

Insulated cars prevent temperature and humidity extremes and specially constructed cars can handle 60,000 pounds of bulk potatoes with a minimum of bruising.

A growing service is the "trailer-on-flatcar," or "piggyback" service as it's usually called. Flatcars transport huge highway trailers for long distances. It takes only a few minutes to lift and anchor two or three trailers on the flatcar, and the same amount of time to lift them off. Giant cranes that straddle two rail tracks pick them up, convey them to the side of the tracks, and set them down for a tractor to haul away.

Some large containers—big enough to be vans but without wheels—are also carried upon flatcars. These are lifted on and off and placed on flat trucks for the rest of their journey.

Large covered hopper cars are a fairly recent development. These can carry up to 100 tons of grain, sugar, flour, or other products in bulk. They are loaded through top hatches. When the hatches are closed, there is less chance of contamination and loss than is true of open hoppers. After the cars reach their destination, they are unloaded by opening gates which permit the product to flow out through grills into a pit where conveyors scoop it up and carry it to storage elevators, bins, or mills.

Not to be overlooked is the "train with a one-track mind" or the "unit train." This is a complete train loaded with a single kind of product, and sent to its ultimate destination without stopping at intermediate freight yards. Though so far these have been used primarily for coal, their use to ship grain from the Plains States to milling and export centers has been increasing.

Trucking is a big business today. Trucks can be equipped to haul a wide variety of products. They can start foods on their way at the farm gate and bring them to us from our home-delivery grocery. They have changed the way many foods move to market. For example, all cattle used to go by rail to the great central markets such as Chicago, Omaha, and Kansas City. Today, many packers have shifted to smaller plants located closer to livestock-producing areas and cattle are brought in by truck. Some of these trucks, called "possum-bellies," have three levels and can haul from 40 to 50 live steers or 100 calves in a single load. Others, for hauling up to 100 hogs, have sprinkling equipment installed for keeping the hogs from becoming overheated and dying. A cool hog is a perky porker.

Nearly all hogs are shipped by truck today and a large share of cattle and calves. After the animals are slaughtered at the plants, the carcasses are shipped to markets in specially designed refrigerated trucks or railcars.

Milk is delivered to large cities in big bulk milk trucks. This is quite a change from earlier days when milk was taken to the nearest milk depot in metal cans. These cans had to be stored, sterilized, filled, and loaded on trucks by farmers. At the receiving plants, the same operation had to be done in reverse.

Now farmers have lines running from milking machines to a refrigerated tank. Each day or two, a large tank truck comes by, pumps the milk out of the farmer's tank, and takes it to the receiving plant. There it is pumped again into various containers for further processing. On its journey from cow to final container, it hasn't been lifted once manually or touched by human hands.

This shows only what happens between the dairy farm and its market—the processing plant. Some milk may be sent in bulk a thousand miles or more, sometimes as far as from Wisconsin to Georgia or Alaska.

The newest method being used for transporting food is the cargo plane. The volume of food being shipped by air is still less than 1 percent of the total. Recently, around 25 million pounds per year of fruits and vegetables, mostly strawberries, were flown from California to large cities—some as distant as Frankfurt, Germany. Other fruits and vegetables that were flown to market included cherries, apricots, figs, asparagus, lettuce, nectarines, and more recently, carrots, celery, and oranges.

Occasionally, frozen foods and meat, poultry, eggs, and seafood have also been sent by air.

Though the cost of shipping food by air is still high, there are some advantages to sending perishables this way. The shorter travel time cuts down on spoilage, less expensive packaging is required, and shipping damage is apt to be less. Airlines are attempting to reduce air shipment costs.

Barges and ships continue to transport large quantities of food—particularly grains and sugar—on our inland waterways and across the seas. These carriers also can make use of containers to speed food along.

New procedures that are being tried by shipping companies include the so-called LASH (lighter aboard ship) vessels. These are large ships which can carry 30 or more barges, each being around 100 feet long and holding about 850 long tons of cargo. This makes it possible for barges to be loaded at river or other shallow water ports, towed out to deep water ports and put aboard seagoing ships. When the ship reaches a foreign port, these same barges are unloaded and then towed again to shallow water ports. This method tends to reduce the cost of transporting food.

These are the carriers of our food—the vehicles and workers that keep supplies moving. They are a necessary part of our modern food system that keeps us supplied with the gigantic abundance of food that we seem to take for granted. Probably we'd realize rather quickly, and quite painfully, what all this means to those of us who live in cities if, all of a sudden, these vehicles stopped running. Just try, for a minute, to imagine what you would do if, without any warning, all food stores and public eating places were to close for a week or even longer because all the trains, planes, trucks, barges, and ships had come to a complete standstill.

Kermit Bird

Food Processors and Packagers Put a New Cook In Your Kitchen

On a Thursday night, in a supermarket, in the town that could be yours, the wonderwork of our modern food processing system unfolded and came true. The shopping and the sales transactions which took place in that store are a culmination of modern man's endeavor to feed himself. Much of the miracle is a result of hard work, man's ingenuity, and the application of scientific techniques to food processing. Perhaps observing a young couple in a supermarket will provide us with a greater understanding and appreciation of our big U.S. food processing system.

Our young couple, who had been pushing their grocery cart through the aisles of the supermarket, approached the checkout stand. The wife made a last-minute check of her shopping list while her husband stacked the revolving counter with their weekly purchases—a large can of tomato juice, a pliofilm-wrapped sirloin steak, a small frozen turkey, a box of instant mashed potatoes, and some fresh carrots. Beside these he placed a package of frozen broccoli-in-a-bag with a cheese sauce, assorted frozen dinners, a loaf of sliced white bread, a box filled with envelopes of instant oatmeal flavored with apple and cinnamon, a half gallon carton of low-fat milk, and a quart of sherbet.

As more room on the counter became available, he unloaded the rest of the groceries—a large jar of instant coffee, a small jar of ripe olives, barbecue-flavored corn chips, assorted other groceries, and some miscellaneous nonfood items.

The couple ended this phase of their grocery shopping, and as the items were being added up on the cash register, their thoughts appeared to dwell solely on how the foods were to be used and the prices of the various items. Mentally, the housewife planned her next week's meals and hoped that nothing had been overlooked; her husband considered whether he had enough cash to pay for the mounting pile. At the moment, both seemed unaware of the "what" they were buying; of what they were really getting as they bought their groceries. Was it just the stack of food now being arranged in large brown bags, or was there more to this week's supply of groceries than meets the eye?

Actually, with each food item, they had bought some of each of the following ingredients:

- –the food.
- –preparation of the food.
- –processing: canning, freezing, drying, pickling.
- –seasonings, preservatives, and flavorings.
- –equipment used in preparation and processing.
- –maintenance of the equipment.
- –care needed to conform with health and sanitation standards.
- –research to develop and perfect the product.
- –packaging materials, with their associated labor and equipment.
- –transportation, storage, and food handling.

Kermit Bird is an Agricultural Economist in the Marketing Economics Division of the Economic Research Service.

Many things had been done to each food since it left the farm. Even the fresh carrots had been topped, washed, packaged, and kept cool. Other foods had undergone much more processing. Some, like the frozen broccoli, were prepared in a sauce and ready to cook. The olives had gone through long pickling stages. The jar of freeze-dried coffee, so casually selected from the shelf, had gone through many involved steps—roasting, brewing, evaporating, dehydrating, and packaging.

Our young couple may not realize the multitude of food choices they have. Main courses previously available only in restaurants can now be everyday items. Most any new bride can serve a variety of foods her mother never dared attempt! The saying was never truer than now that, "If you can read and follow directions, you can be a wonderful cook." How did this come about? What miracle has made it possible for this young couple to buy so much variety in their neighborhood store? How has food processing influenced our food marketing system?

Food processing, or food "manufacturing," is a multi-billion-dollar industry. Even more impressive than size is its complexity. Food processing includes pasteurizing, homogenizing, standardizing, and bottling of fresh milk. Freezing, canning, drying, pickling, curing, and salting are commonly used techniques. Blending, seasoning, and preserving are part of what takes place as are grading, inspection, and labeling. Packaging is another important function.

In short, food processing is all the things that make our foods easier and safer to use.

Food processing generally involves altering the composition or character of a food in some way. Processing usually makes the raw products more marketable by various kinds of treatment. But even before food can be processed, there is equipment to be thought of, designed, built, and installed. Afterward, this machinery has to be kept immaculately clean.

The processing industry uses the labor and talents of thousands upon thousands of people with a wide range of capabilities. Processed products are advertised and promoted so people like our young shoppers know they exist. To show how this system works, let's follow the procedures used in making a familiar, everyday product—the bread we eat.

Would your grandmother have believed it, when she was a girl, if she had been told that someday a series of coordinated machines would bake 13,000 loaves of bread per hour? To produce four loaves of bread, grandma had to sift the flour by hand, mix the ingredients, raise, punch down and knead, shape into loaves, let raise again, and then bake them about an hour. The whole process would take 5 to 6 hours, or about 1¼ to 1½ hours a loaf. The machines we will talk about bake more bread in an hour than she baked in her whole life.

The aroma of fresh-baked bread may make one nostalgic, but like other memories of the past, we forget the drudgery and the failures. In the case of homemade bread, we don't recall the coarse loaves full of holes, or those with soggy centers. Burned crusts are forgotten. True, we may no longer be able to enjoy the aroma of home-baked bread, but neither do we have to spend the better part of one or two days each week baking—unless, of course, we want to.

In most large bakeries today, bread is made automatically from start to finish. Imagine, for example, a bakery as large as two football fields. Here flour and the other baking ingredients go in one end of a series of integrated machines, disappear from view, and emerge at the other end as fully baked bread ready for cooling, wrapping, and delivery. These items of equipment and their associated techniques are called the "continuous-mix" process. "Continuous" means that the ingredients, dough, and loaves flow in a stream rather than in batches, as was the case in previous bread-making systems. Let's see how the idea works.

Train crews shuttle freight cars loaded with flour into the receiving section of the building where the flour is siphoned off into high storage silos. Upon a signal from one computer, quantities of flour move to interior silos. Computer No. 2 directs flour to mixers that "shimmy" when told to do so.

Even before the flour has started to shimmy, a "brew" is prepared to encourage the dough to raise. Brew consists of a ferment yeast, liquid lard, liquid sugar, and a liquid softener to help keep bread fresh after baking. The newly made brew goes to a special "proofing" room to raise. After being drawn out of the tanks, other machines add weighed quantities of flour. Then special machines whirl this doughy mixture around and around until it reaches a desired consistency. Enormous vessels convey it to molding machines.

Molding machines whirl the exact quantity of dough needed for each loaf and then drop each portion down a conveyor into another set of machinery. This equipment flattens the ball of dough, shapes it into a loaf, and drops it into a pan. After a controlled period of time, conveyors carry many of these pans of dough to gigantic ovens. Upon a predetermined signal, thousands of loaves of bread are baked. Conveyors take the bread to coolers, to bread slicers, and then to automatic wrappers and baggers.

But this isn't all. Wrapped bread travels by conveyor belts to the loading area where trucks stand in line waiting to take the newly baked bread to grocery stores, hotels, restaurants, and many other away-from-home eating places.

This sounds easy—as if bakers should or could have been making bread this way for ages. Not so! Developing a new system hasn't been that simple. The complicated equipment had to be

Bread loaves ride conveyor in a supermarket chain bakery.

designed, tested, and built. The freight cars which brought the flour were invented and manufactured just for this purpose. The tubes that unloaded the cars were tailored for siphoning the flour. The storage silos that hold the flour were engineered to be the right size and right shape. Each computer is exactly the right computer for the job to be done. The conveyor belts, pneumatic tubes, valves, elevators, molders, mixers, scales, softeners, flatteners, churners, ovens, wrappers, and baggers were all brought into existence with a specific job in mind. The vats, brewing rooms, and proofing rooms have to be kept at the right temperature and humidity. And each item of equipment has to be easy to clean.

But even before the equipment was developed, a special "formula" for bread had to be considered. Research laboratories scattered throughout the country devoted considerable effort to perfecting the required techniques. Years of intense effort yielded bits of data, so the total information could be used in this automated breadmaking process.

Even the type of wheat used in the breadmaking had to be determined, for only certain kinds provide flour with the precise mixing tolerance and stability suitable for these new continuous-mix bakeries. So, long before wheat becomes flour, laboratory technicians submit the flour to a series of intensive quality evaluations to determine its breadmaking characteristics. Millers have found they can literally tear a kernel of wheat apart and then reassemble the grain in a form more adaptable to the particular needs. Air-classification milling, based upon this principle, separates out the protein and glutens, and a miller can then put them back in the precise proportions he desires. Here are three tests commonly used in evaluating wheat:

- Wheat protein content. This test may be done by a dyebinding process.
- Sedimentation value. This tests the strength of a wheat. Strength is generally related to the gluten content.
- A farinograph predicts the quality and strength of gluten flour. Strong gluten indicates a good bread-baking characteristic.

Results of these tests may be outlined on charts, and a baker can examine them and tailor his bread to his exact specifications.

Other ingredients that are a part of the bread "formula" also had to be tested. Wrappers had to be developed that could be used on the high-speed wrapping machines. Wrappers keep the bread fresh and protect it during handling and in the household of the young couple.

We have described some of the many and complex arrangements involved in developing the new continuous way to produce white bread. But that is just one item. The same bakery may handle four or five other kinds of bread, each with a unique method of processing. Then, of course, there are rolls, buns, pies, cakes, and tarts that are equally complex in their manufacture. But none of these are as completely automated as white bread because their volumes are smaller.

All this background and developmental work called for considerable applied research and, of course, expense. The aim of all this is that we have our needs met in an efficient way. We must like the product and the price well enough to come back for more, and to be favorably disposed toward any other products made by the same company. This is what makes the system work, why engineers design the high-speed machines, why bankers are willing to risk investment funds for a costly automated system, and why the bakery owners go to all the bother and expense. By satisfying their customers, bakers can sell more loaves of bread, make more money, and retain or increase their share of the bread market.

For supplying us with our daily bread, bakers receive about 80 percent of the price we pay for our loaf of white bread. The grocer keeps the other 20 percent to pay his store expenses. Bakers pay out about half the money they receive from the retailer for employees' wages, fringe benefits, and social security payments. Ingredients take the next biggest slice—almost a third of the money bakers receive from the storekeeper. The rest goes for the package, delivery, equipment, and sundry items. Profits, of course, are important for they go to the owner of the business. In recent years bakers' profits have averaged about 2 percent of sales.

We have used baking as an example, but baking is only one part of our immense processing industry. Other examples could show equally well the complexity, size, and character of food processing.

Within the past two decades, food processing has adapted to different demands of the food market. Previously, processing was oriented toward procuring and preserving. Now food processing is more market oriented, with its new emphasis on food preparation, packaging, and convenience.

Even though procuring raw products and preserving are just as important functions as ever, greater emphasis is being placed on what the housewife wants rather than on what the farmer has to sell. This may be one reason for the current emphasis on ready-to-eat foods, for a processor tries to anticipate our wants and needs as consumers. He then develops, manufactures, packages, promotes, and distributes foods to meet our changing demands or desires. In taking this new tack, we find that the food processing industry acquired some of the tasks that formerly were thought of as farm duties. It's obvious, too, the processors have taken on many of the housewives' jobs, and processors now assume a multitude of the chores formerly in home kitchens.

Many factors appear to have brought about these modifications in our food economy. We don't always know which are causes and which are results of changes, for they seem to be intertwined. But the questions of how much processing, what types, where, by whom, and at what cost are the essence of the "economics" of the food processing industry. Each bit of processing must be coordinated with the rest, each processor must find the raw products he needs, and each food must get to where the customer can buy it.

Not only have consumer desires been changing, and increasingly reflected back to food processors, but technological advances have also played an important role in those modifications that have taken place. For example, newer type canning facilities are more specialized than formerly and require larger volumes to justify a much greater investment. The volumes needed to keep them busy may involve enlarging the whole food processing plant. The size of plants, where they are located, the kind of processing done, and the type of business which is evolving are all affected.

Transportation and communication developments have encouraged other changes. They have given processing firms a greater choice in the size of plants to be operated and where plants may be located. Trucks, trains, and planes move rapidly and continuously to get supplies from, and finished products to, almost any section of the country.

Early in this century, our meatpacking industry centered in Chicago, St. Louis, and Omaha. There was a reason. The packers built large-volume slaughter and packing plants so the plants could specialize and thus achieve lower packing costs. Slaughter and packing specialization, at that time, depended on large-volume operations.

Since the close of World War II, slaughtering has moved to country locations and become decentralized. Animals now can be slaughtered within hours of their shipping time. But while the slaughtering of meat animals has moved closer to the farm, range, or feedlot, other processing has tended to become more specialized and centralized. Weiners, bacon, sausages, and hams now may be processed in plants that specialize in these items. Imagine, if you will, a whole plant devoted to making sausage-type products—whole rooms filled with automatic wiener fillers. In this instance, the raw materials used are frozen meat, spices, dry skim milk, casings, and cartons.

Some meat processing plants do nothing but "quick-freezing" of steaks, chops, and roasts. No one knows the future of frozen meats, for at present there seems to be some consumer resistance to these. Yet, as if in contradiction, we buy frozen meats in prepared dinners, and even consider ourselves thrifty when we purchase fresh meat to freeze at home. We buy frozen turkey, although we prefer our broilers fresh. In future years, we may buy frozen cuts of meat and specialties like shishkabob as readily as we now do frozen vegetables.

Changes at other levels of marketing may affect who does the food processing, where the preservation is done, and how. Instead of sending whole meat carcasses to each grocery store, as was formerly the custom, some of the retail stores now cut and package steaks, chops, and roasts at their central warehouses. This cutting technique results in more efficient use of labor and less product waste. It is now technically possible for the complete cutting operation to be done back still another step—at the slaughter-packing plant. Research will show whether cutting at a packing plant is economically feasible. All this indicates that food processing is in a state of flux.

Meanwhile, back in the packing plant, food researchers have designed a new instrument to predetermine how tender the meat will be after having been cooked at home. A technician, using this device, can easily determine the best use of a beef carcass, and customers will know when they buy a steak, roast, or even stew meat, what the maximum tenderness will be "after cooking."

For most food processing industries, the prevailing trend is toward more centralization. The important factor in bringing this about is what economists call the economies of scale. This means, simply, that a bigger plant—by having a large volume—can find ways of lowering costs per unit.

Today, a large food processor has some distinct advantages over the small one. He can buy in larger quantities and may pay slightly lower raw material and supply prices. More important, he can afford some services that a small processor has to do without. He is large enough to have his own name brand, and in this country food processors find a nationally advertised brand to be a market advantage. Our TV networks, magazines, and even some U.S. newspapers have cross-country coverage. National promotion of food in these media is expensive per unit of sale unless costs can be spread over many sales.

Although a few processors have done so, a small food processor finds it extremely difficult to support a nationwide promotion campaign.

Another spur toward larger sized plants and companies is the advantage that results from team research. One member may work on texture, another on flavor, others on color, label, package design, closure, and so on. A product development man in a small research laboratory cannot specialize enough to achieve great success in any one field, and this limits his ability to develop new products.

The same reasoning applies to market testing. This is an expensive procedure, and small firms do it with difficulty. Generally, they need to hire a specialized company to do this for them. Large food processors, particularly those with a continuing flow of new products, have their own market testing staff and do market testing with comparative ease.

Adaptation of old and new technologies has spurred food processing firms to enlarge and centralize their operations. Fully automated plants can produce large quantities of food at lower cost in one place than when scattered around the country. Breakfast cereals are economically produced in large automated plants and the finished products sent to all parts of the Nation.

Other changes have been taking place in food processing, too. Some

On opposite page, oranges arrive by truck at Florida plant that makes frozen orange juice. Above, oranges in washer at a processing plant.

firms have expanded "vertically" by merging with their suppliers or buying them out. If a processor can't get his needed supplies or services at a reasonable price or one that meets his particular requirements, he then is under pressure to produce them for himself. Some fruit canners, to lower costs or to get the kind of cans they want, have begun manufacturing cans. Or a food processor may buy most of his bottles from a container supplier and still operate a bottle manufacturing plant as a safeguard against adverse labor problems or, perhaps, as a check on bottle prices.

Other processors have expanded "horizontally" by merging with other companies engaged in the same kind of business or making the same product. Some nationwide bakery organizations have used this expansion route by merging with local and regional companies. A current consideration is that the Federal regulatory agencies frown on mergers which lessen competition within an industry.

A variation of horizontal expansion is diversification through which a food processor acquires companies making different but related food products. Some old-line food processors have moved into the more rapidly growing sectors of the food processing industry by buying firms which make frozen and prepared foods, convenience items, snacks, and packaged products.

In "conglomerate" mergers, a firm combines with other companies having an entirely different kind of product. Food processors are in the toy business. Electronic, petroleum, and machinery companies have gone into food manufacturing. Tobacco firms have become food processors. Others have started making soaps, fertilizer, and leather goods. This type of expansion has been stimulated partly by the need for large investments in food processing plant facilities and supplies. Quite often the nonfood companies have the investment, research facilities, and promotional know-how to make a success of food processing.

In food processing, as in all other industries today, business management has become more complex, technical, and scientific. In the past, "management" was quite frequently the owner. And generally, the owner had a few "advisors" to help him make decisions. Answers, based on common sense and practical experience, were fairly simple. A new business venture of today requires enterprise, skill, and expertise to launch and manage it.

In a modern food processing establishment, a vast array of specialists and experts contributes to operation and management of the firm. Engineers, chemists, accountants, food technologists, purchasing agents, lawyers, advertising men, data processors combine their efforts toward more research. Working together, they look forward to successful new products and more sales.

As firms become larger, more complex, and geared to a nationwide market, innovations are the prime movers. Finding new products, new applications for existing foods, and using both to increase the quantity and variety produced—these have become ever-present goals.

Research, especially that directed toward developing new products or new processes, goes on continuously and takes many forms. Some research is just to improve a package; some to develop a new combination of foods. Still other research seeks to find something completely new to fill a specific need or develop a new process and find a way to use it.

Freezing of food, quite likely the greatest change in food processing since World War II, seemingly could have developed earlier, but several other changes had to occur at the same time. The commercial freezing of food, developed in the 1920's, went through various stages before costs were low enough and products reliable enough for mass production and distribution. Since then, newer freezing techniques and different types of refrigeration machinery have come on the food scene. Entirely new kinds of freezing media have been tested and put in general use. The IQF (individually quick frozen) method of freezing was one of these, and with some foods—like peas, french fried potatoes, and carrots—IQF freezing adds convenience for the housewife.

Other developments also had to occur at the same time. There was a need for new types of raw products suitable for freezing. Packaging materials had to be especially designed to protect and to preserve product quality. Ways to transport and store the food had to be adapted to the new processing situation. All these have affected the housewife, her home storage, her menus, her family's diets, and her general satisfaction with today's offerings. A simple change in the process of freezing snap beans has had far-reaching effects that stretch across the country to almost every town, every grocery store, and most homes in the Nation.

New ingredients, or old ones applied in new ways, have become increasingly important in today's food processing system. An example is the use of old-fashioned whey in modern prepared foods. Spray-drying removes most of liquid whey's moisture in seconds. A second drying process gives it solubility, storage, and handling properties that allow it to become a valuable ingredient in a variety of foods.

Spray-dried whey improves color, bloom, and texture of bakery products and gives added flavor to bread mixes. "Whey-breaded" shrimp taste "shrimpier." Frozen pot pies and fruit pies do less "weeping" and the whey helps to eliminate the watery effect often found on the bottom of pies. Sherbets and ice creams have a smoother appearance. Cheese sauces do less separating, and dried whey helps to maintain shelf life of many foods. One evidence of acceptance is that the use of this byproduct has increased 2½ times in the past decade.

Another and still different use of a familiar product is that of butter inserted in self-basting turkeys. One machine injects butter deep into the breast and thighs of freshly slaughtered turkeys. Other machines quickly freeze the birds and pack them in special-type plastic bags. From there they are stored in a freezer. Weeks later, when needed, the frozen turkeys arrive in our grocery stores. The advantage of all this extra process is that, while it's roasting, the turkey "bastes" itself by oozing the butter from deep inside to the outer surface.

Inspection of many foods is required by State or Federal law. Inspection of others is at a food processor's option, and the voluntary inspection programs may operate under governmental or industry standards.

While most food inspection work has been done in the past by the U.S. Department of Health, Education, and Welfare and the U.S. Department of Agriculture, many States will be doing more of this work in the future. Two recent laws, for example, provide a backdrop for more State activity in the fields of meat and poultry inspection. The Wholesome Meat Act of 1967 and the Wholesome Poultry Products Act of 1968 provide for fully cooperative Federal-State inspection programs.

Regulations governing food inspection programs vary to some extent from one product, or type of product, to another. Some regulations require inspection of materials coming into processing plants. Other rules deal only with the sanitation of processing plants. Still other inspections deal with the finished product to ascertain that minimum standards have been met. Food labels, too, come under scrutiny. Ham processed under Federal meat inspection, for example, must be labeled as "Ham, water added," if it contains up to 10 percent added moisture, and as "Imitation Ham" if the added water goes above this amount. Since Federal meat inspection standards limit the amount of moisture in cooked sausages, a laboratory test for this factor has become standard procedure. The amount of cereal or any other "extenders" in sausages is also analyzed, as is the protein content.

So far, we have looked at the present status of food processing. How about the future?

A much higher percentage of our meat, poultry, dairy, and fisheries products will be processed. Fresh red meats, as we know them, may become the high-priced, low-volume food items of the future. Most poultry meat of tomorrow will be frozen or processed by other methods. Fresh broilers may almost disappear.

The next decade will open increased possibilities for frozen snacks. Hostesses of tomorrow's superjets, traveling at much faster speeds than now, will not have time to provide a hot meal for their 250 to 400 passengers. A snack may have to do for some flights. These new planes with their multiple galleys and large food holding and thawing equipment will be able to handle a variety of frozen dishes. Snacks may include open-faced sandwiches, cold chicken, turkey, roast beef, and hors d'oeuvres—all processed. For desserts, there may be pudding, fruit salads and mixed fruit, rolls, pies, tarts, and puff pastry. Coffee may be the only hot item.

Another change to watch is that food processors will turn their attention more and more toward foods used in the away-from-home eating places. Some of these products will find their way into our supermarkets as well. The children of the young couple that we left at the checkout counter will be buying many foods in new forms, prepared by new processes, and sold in new kinds of packages.

Food Packaging

A grocery store presents a virtual kaleidoscope of color and design, with each packaged food item upon the shelves contributing to the overall mosaic. Every food package we see comes as the result of careful research to find out what is likely to appeal to us plus what will best protect the product and retain quality.

Back in the days of the local grocery, crackers, cranberries, and pickles were displayed in barrels. Aisles were lined with big bags of flour, potatoes, sugar, dry beans, oatmeal, and peanuts. Salted fish and oranges came in wooden boxes. Some foods were canned and pickled, but frozen foods were unknown. Consumer packages, as we know them, were unusual and clerks packaged most items in bags at the time of sale. These brown bags were meant just to carry the food and to hold up until the shopper got home. Food handling problems within the store were limited to such things as keeping the crackers dry and the flies away from the molasses. Packaging was a problem then, as it is now; but because of the new emphasis on convenience, our packaging ideas today take different forms.

What is there about our present food marketing system that encourages such wide usage of packages? First, our food itself has changed. Advances in technology have made many new kinds of processed food and food combinations possible. Convenience foods need the right type of package to be truly convenient. Many processing changes call for package changes, and finding the right package for each food is an essential part of our modern food processing and marketing system. When a new food is put on the market, a "right" package can help sell the product; a poor package can hinder sales and may even prevent a new food from getting nationwide acceptance.

Another basic reason for having a package is to assemble items. A jar of pickled onions becomes a unit of trade. A pound box of peanut brittle, a quart of milk, a 1-ounce bottle of dried chives, and a 10-ounce box of biscuit mix are other examples. Putting similar things together, or combining ingredients in handy sizes, allows for easier purchases and faster handling.

A special function of some packages is to protect the contents from mechanical damage. Most U.S. foods travel hundreds or even thousands of miles before coming to our supermarkets. They are packaged to keep them safe for the long trips. An egg carton keeps fragile shells from cracking. Special wrappings, fillers, and layers keep delicate fruits from bruising each other. Other packages provide stacking strength in handling, transit, and storage.

If a food has special consumer-use characteristics, a processor may have to cope with intricate packaging problems. Boilable-pouch foods need a pliable package which can be both frozen and boiled. This film has to keep the product dry inside and cannot react with the food. In common use for frozen vegetables for some time, this package now is used for cured meats and seafoods as well.

The foods sold in pressurized cans, like whipped cream, cake icings, and cheese spreads, were not ready to be marketed until market researchers devised a special nozzle for the can. Also, a propellant gas had to be discovered that would not unite with the food and would be harmless if eaten. These intricate problems of packaging were solved, and the concept has become a reality on the market.

A package needs to be convenient. The shopper may buy a food once, but no matter how well she likes the contents, she may not buy it again unless the package is easy to open up, easily reclosed, easy to store, and convenient to handle. There are many jokes about the plastic bag you tear open with your teeth, the key opener package which swallows the key, and the box that explodes or spills the contents.

But most of all, a food package must be a "silent salesman." A successful package must catch the shopper's eye, identify what the product is, and give her all the basic information she needs about the food inside. Some label information, like weight and contents, is required by law.

A food processor selects the most economical packaging materials and container that will meet his customer's product needs. He wants packages that do not adversely affect his labor costs or packaging equipment investment. When he has developed a package that will do the best job of protecting his product, then he must determine if it is economical to purchase, store, fill, stock, handle, and ship. He also wants a package design which requires an appropriate amount of shelf space; will attract people to buy it; prevent pilfering; and provide convenience to the consumer when used. A processor who has developed a package which meets all these requirements, and has also developed something good inside, may have a successful product.

Aluminum makes a unique food package. Resistant to greases and oils, it is odorless, tasteless, nontoxic, and does not shrink, swell, or soften. Nor does aluminum unite with the food or change the color. It is a good conductor of heat, but does not burn and won't crack in the freezer.

Aluminum is adaptable for the formed dishes used for frozen plate dinners since it can be pressed to many shapes. Aluminum lids for these same dinner containers seal tightly, but peel away easily. Aluminum pouches and bags are suitable for use with instant mashed potatoes since, unlike most films, they effectively keep out moisture, odors, and vapors. Aluminum cans, now coming on the market in larger volumes, are a competitor for the traditional tinned can. Manufacturers of tin cans counter by developing new lightweight steel cans.

The tin can we are all familiar with has been going through other evolutionary changes. Presently, food and beverages utilize 85 percent of the tin-plated steel cans turned out by U.S. suppliers. To maintain their share of the market, the can industry concentrates on research to lower costs while at the same time changing the can to improve performance and attractiveness. One way to reduce costs is to make cans from thinner sheets, or perhaps by using a tin-free steel can. Aluminum may also be deposited on the steel surface of the can. Chrome-plated steel is another possibility. Even the typical cylindrical shape may be altered in the years ahead. One manufacturer is experimenting with new contoured cans whose strong welded side seams will make many new styles possible.

Glass containers, long standbys in food processing, have many innovations to make them even more useful and durable in coming years. Here is an example: Surface scratches have been one cause of glass breakage. A recently developed surface treatment now makes glass containers virtually scratch resistant. Other special improvements in glass designs permit substantial weight reduction. Still another innovation: Glass decoration can be done at high speeds and low cost so, after use, these containers might serve other purposes.

Films like polyethylene or polypropylene and many others make excellent packing materials. The boilable bag is one adaptation. A temperature-resistant, disposable, film package for bread dough serves a secondary purpose as the baking pan. Other newer adaptations are the twist-tie bags for bakery foods and cured and processed meats.

Edible pouches now are technically feasible for instant coffee, tea, and soup mixes. In the last example, the pouch could serve as a thickening agent for the soup!

Individual portions of many foods—from potato chips to puddings—are ideal for the lunchbox or the person who lives alone. "Stack pack" crackers and cookies keep a product fresh after opening. "Pilfer-proof" closures help grocers maintain fresh packages and minimize losses. Vacuum-sealed food jars are one example—a gentle twist of the lid tells the shopper whether the vacuum is still there or if the jar has been opened. Reusable containers—like those tubs used for margarine, salad, and ice cream—make excellent refrigerator storage dishes. Molded handles—like those now used on gallon milk jugs—make these containers easier to handle and store.

The variety of new food containers streams on endlessly. In future years, we anticipate that these will provide even more convenience, better appearance, easier handling, and lower costs.

Harry H. Harp
William S. Hoofnagle

Thousands of New Foods Give You a Wide Choice

When Abraham Lincoln clerked in a country store, his customers had around 900 food items to choose from. Until as recently as 1940, a family shopper had only about a thousand food items from which to make selections. Contrast this with the average supermarket today with 8,000 or more items—many of which were not available 10 years ago.

So many new forms of food products have been produced during the past few years that supermarkets have to limit the number they can carry. If a grocer tried to stock all that have been developed, his store would probably take up a whole shopping center. Though supermarkets must limit to some extent the number of items they stock, we still have an amazing array of choices. It's often fun just to wander about and look for new items which seem to appear almost daily.

Today we can find cases and cases of frozen foods, rows upon rows of bakery mixes and icings, sauces and sauce mixes, beverages and beverage mixes. There is virtually an endless number of easy-to-cook foods which were not in our grocery stores just 5 years ago. And, though it seems that every possible food, for every possible use, has been developed, many more are "in the works."

In a few years, our weekly market order may be made up almost entirely of the so-called "convenience" foods with their built-in maid or chef services. Many of these will be for dishes we have prepared at home, yet they may contain ingredients we won't recognize. Even now, names appear in lists of ingredients on packages that seem strange to many of us. New items today are not only new or different combinations of foods but some are actually "synthesized" to represent the "natural" foods. Many contain emulsifiers, stabilizers, and preservatives of various kinds to provide desired textures and flavors, and to insure better keeping qualities.

Some of our grandmothers who had cleaned, washed, diced, chopped, stewed, fried, and baked for hours at a time are bewildered by how readily the younger generation accepts each new food—frozen plate dinners, pizzas, pot pies, chow mein, shrimp creole, cake mixes. But, in her busy life, our young homemaker is happy to heat and serve important parts of her meals. If she wants to, she can still express her own individuality by adding another seasoning or flavoring, using a sauce, or combining two items to make a third.

All of these new products make us wonder why so much has happened in so short a time, particularly when for decades Americans followed almost the same pattern of shopping for food and in preparing meals. As with most dynamic changes, these have resulted from a combination of factors. But, trying to identify what actually started it all is difficult, for each change seems to have depended on another occurring at about the same time—or nearly so.

Perhaps all these changes have been

Harry H. Harp is an Agricultural Economist in the Marketing Economics Division, Economic Research Service.

William S. Hoofnagle is Deputy Director of the Marketing Economics Division.

speeded up because more of us live in cities, more of us have more money to spend as we like, more women work away from home, and our younger homemakers appear to have a multitude of outside interests. Underlying all this is the value being placed on the use of time—and enough money to allow considerable latitude as to how we spend it.

Many of us, and this includes a fair share of today's homemakers, travel considerable distances to our work. We leave home early, and arrive home late. This brings in more money, but it uses up more of our time. Even young mothers who stay at home may have to take the children to school, go to the bank, to the cleaners, and so on. All these factors have helped to put a premium on "time."

To meet demands for time-saving foods, new equipment had to be designed along with new methods for processing, new preservatives, new packages, and even new methods of getting these foods to the grocery. Then, too, family shoppers had to be alerted that such foods were available. All this has contributed to the development of mass markets. In terms we often hear, this has called for mass production, mass distribution, and mass consumption.

The effect of the increasing demand for new foods has been felt way back to the farm. There have been new varieties of products developed which can be mechanically harvested and ones which can be shipped long distances—often clear across the country. New varieties of tomatoes for processing have been developed which can be harvested by machine. These tomatoes are uniform in size, they all ripen at virtually the same time, and they have tougher skins so that they will stand machine handling.

Because of consumer demand for tender, juicy, flavorful beef, farmers have selected breeds of cattle which give these qualities. The animals are fed special rations and marketed at younger ages and lighter weights than formerly. Farmers are also raising breeds of hogs with less fat. Then, too, whole farms are devoted to producing broilers that come to market when they are young, tender, fresh appearing, all cleaned and ready to cook. With our larger, more mechanized farms, one farmer now feeds about twice as many people as he did 10 years ago.

Though many changes have taken place on our farms, probably the greatest changes have occurred in food processing, packaging, and distribution. We've made great strides in controlling food texture, taste, tenderness, and storage life. Sometimes years of experimentation are necessary to solve the technical problems related to development of a new product form—to perfect recipes which will have a general appeal. Many products now coming to market are the result of research initiated in the late forties or early fifties, like boil-in-the-bag items and dehydrated salad mixes. Today, lots more food products are in the experimental stage.

Many new methods are being used in processing foods. Even the older techniques have changed somewhat. Fresh foods are still kept in cold storage, but now even temperature and moisture are controlled—and even the oxygen or carbon dioxide of the air. This keeps the foods from spoiling or ripening too fast.

Canning, as in previous years, is important for preserving fruits, vegetables, and meats. But, added to these, we now have a much wider assortment of ready-to-serve forms ranging from soups to desserts—from soups of the gourmet type to the cornstarch puddings that mother used to make. A new adaptation of this process is called aseptic canning where the container and the contents are sterilized independently of each other. Sterilized milk aseptically canned will keep for several months without a significant flavor loss. Milk processed this way is now being shipped to the Far and Middle East.

One of the most successful new kinds of dairy products on grocery shelves are the aseptically canned puddings. These precooked puddings come in various flavors. Some can even be used as ice cream topping.

Frozen foods are becoming commonplace. Our young shoppers have been able to buy them most of their lives. Quick freezing has done much to lengthen the season of foods, to provide us with fresh-tasting foods in numerous convenient forms the year around. Recently, however, even this process is providing new foods and taking on new forms. New combinations of foods are in the supermarket cases—vegetables in cream sauce, frozen plate dinners, entrees for one person and even for families of five, shrimp and lobster newburg, frozen egg noodles, and a wide variety of canapes. Almost every food prepared at home can be purchased frozen.

New cryogenic freezing techniques are being experimented with that may provide us with frozen lettuce and salad mixes. This method uses temperatures below minus 100° F. Mushrooms, seafoods, onion rings, and bakery products are being frozen in this manner along with such hard-to-freeze foods as tomato slices, melons, and bananas.

Dehydrated foods now are respected members of the convenience food line—instant potatoes, nonfat dry milk powders, fruit juice powders—that are made ready for serving by just adding boiling or cold water. Current research promises dry whole milk in the future.

Freeze-drying—which combines both freezing and drying—is becoming increasingly important as a method of food preservation. Foods processed by this method are used as ingredients in other products, like chicken in dry soup mixes and fruit in dry cereals. Campers can purchase a variety of dehydrated meats, dairy foods, eggs, vegetables, fruits, and desserts that take up little space and can be reconstituted rapidly. Some day we may have such exotic items as freeze-dried catsup, barbecue sauce, gravy, pickle relish, chives, and sirup—easy to keep without refrigeration and quick to reconstitute.

Some processes, which were developed for specific products, have now been extended to others. The "puff" process, first developed for cereals, and which popularized the expression "shot from guns," was once actually made by equipment that looked much like guns. Now a similar procedure is being used for carrot pieces and is being tried out on apple slices, blueberries, and beets.

But special processing techniques are only one aspect of the innovations that have brought us so many new products. Equally as important and probably newer is the widespread use of "additives" and the development of the "synthetic" foods.

Today, when we read the list of ingredients in a product, we meet names that may have little meaning to us. For example, monosodium glutamate, lecithin, mono- and diglycerides, ascorbic acid, and sodium benzoate. These are additives, some from natural sources, and some manufactured. They have a big variety of uses—to improve nutritive value, like the addition of vitamins A and D to margarine; for enhancing flavor and color; to keep a product from spoiling; or as emulsifiers. One or more of these additives are found in a wide range of foods—from meats, flour, cake mixes, and bread to cheese, margarine, salad dressings, ice cream, and beer. They are safe when their use is approved by the Food and Drug Administration.

We have antioxidants which help keep cooking oils and shortening from becoming rancid; mold inhibitors in bread, such as sodium and calcium propionate.

Emulsifiers, stabilizers, and thickeners are used in bakery products, cake mixes, ice cream and other frozen desserts. They affect the volume, and help to give a product the right consistency—smooth and uniform texture—and to keep it that way. Lecithin, mono- and diglycerides, and vegetable gums are names of commonly used emulsifiers. Gelatins are used for thickening and as a stabilizing agent. Starches are used in whipped

Dehydrated foods are versatile. Left, camper cooks with dehydrated food in a national forest. Above, precooked dehydrated sweetpotato flakes, developed by USDA. Below, orange juice disc made by drying concentrated citrus juice in a new USDA process.

products, chilled desserts, cream pie fillings, and soup mixes.

Saccharin and calcium- and sodium-cyclamates are used as nonnutritive sweeteners in a wide variety of products for diet-conscious consumers.

We could go on and on. But these illustrate just a few of the unfamiliar names on packages. And some of our newest foods use several of them.

Probably the most recent items to come to the forefront are imitation foods. These resemble well-known natural foods in flavor and appearance but are manmade by combining constituents from different products. Most "imitation" foods are made using agricultural products. Examples include meatless meats, filled milk, and imitation or nondairy milk.

Meatless meats, like imitation bacon bits, are made from soybeans. They are tasty and have a good aroma. In contrast to meat, this simulated product can be stored a long time without refrigeration. Some of these products, which have been sold through health stores, are now finding their way into grocery stores.

"Filled" milk contains skim milk and a vegetable fat instead of butterfat. It is being produced and sold in some States. At present, however, it can't be shipped across a State border.

"Imitation" ice cream consists of vegetable fat and nonfat milk solids. Mellorine is probably the most widely used term for this product.

Among the most recent imitation foods are the substitute fresh fluid milk products. "Imitation" milk is made by combining vegetable fats, vegetable protein, corn sirup solids, sodium caseinate, stabilizers, and emulsifiers.

Imitation and filled milks look and taste like regular milk but usually will sell for less. However, these products—particularly imitation milk—may have smaller amounts of some nutrients.

Nondairy coffee whiteners and whipped toppings are examples of other imitation products. Some of these products can be kept for quite long periods without refrigeration.

These are some of the newer processes and substances that have given us many new foods. Along with them have come packages of every description. Changes in food packages are so closely associated with the changes in food processing that neither could have developed to any great extent without the other.

Packaging materials have been developed which will keep products a long time. Some have been fashioned into containers that can be used and even reused at home.

Packaging has also cut down on the space needed for transporting products from the processor to the grocer. It has made our self-service system work more smoothly.

In recent years, cans have been made easier to open by adding the tab-pull opener, pull-strip, and plastic lid. These containers are used for such diverse products as mustard, mayonnaise, and more recently milk. And, although plastic bottles now represent only a small percent of milk containers, their share is increasing.

Aerosol containers, originally developed for fly sprays, are being used for such products as whipped topping, cheese spreads, and decorative cake icings. These are proving quite popular, and we may find many more foods adapted to this type packaging.

Sauce mixes and instant mashed potatoes packaged in laminated aluminum envelopes can be kept on kitchen shelves for long periods. Extra ingredients, like flavorings or cheese which are to be added during home preparation of mixes, are often put in these containers.

Packaging has become so vital to the success of a product that the proper material and type of package to be used is generally decided upon simultaneously with development of the new item.

With all the new products coming on the market, advertising has been playing an important role. As it would be difficult for us to find time to discover these products on our own, TV, magazine, and newspaper ads tell us what is new, what these items can do, and where they can be purchased. Packages usually carry directions on "how to use."

Advertising also helps processors to build a market. For companies to continue to spend time and money in developing new foods, markets must be found and enough products sold or they will disappear from grocers' shelves.

One more point of interest to most of us is the cost of these new foods in comparison to their made-at-home counterparts. Some are less expensive. But, so far, most are more costly. Whether they are too expensive or not has to be decided by each family shopper. In the end, it will probably revolve around the value, monetary or otherwise, which she puts on her time. One thing for sure, with these new foods a homemaker can regularly give her family a wide variety of foods. She also can prepare interesting and different company dinners, and still be rested enough to enjoy her guests.

All of this—the development of new varieties of foods on our farms, new processes by our manufacturers, and new ways to get these products to us—is a preview of the future. As our population grows in number and in affluence, the demand for more and better food and marketing services will continue.

Above, California store displays mixes that typify the constant flow of new food products. Left, crawfish for today's food market, raised in flooded Louisiana rice fields. A few farmers have begun producing these "crawdads" as a new rotation crop with rice.

Alden C. Manchester

Wholesalers and Brokers: Buyers by the Carload

Eggs in the nest, milk in the bucket, beef on the hoof, apples on the tree, and wheat in the field are of no immediate value to us who live in cities. Before we can buy such products, they must be harvested, processed, packaged, and transported. And to do this for 200 million people takes many hands and many businesses. Each of these has its own part to play; each is important in its own way. And wholesalers and brokers, the last to handle food on its way from the farm to the grocery, have significant roles to play in keeping our food industry running smoothly.

Can you imagine what it would be like if each of the tens of thousands of food packers and processors had to do business with each one of the 200,000 grocery stores, plus an ever larger number of away-from-home eating places? If every one of these companies had a salesman visiting the same retail store, the grocer wouldn't have time to sell us what he buys. A virtual bedlam could result.

Someone must bridge this gap—to bring together a wide assortment of products ready for delivery on short notice. This is the job of our wholesalers and brokers. Though both are go-between agents or middlemen, their methods of operation are quite different. The wholesaler physically stocks and sells food while the broker is a modern version of the traveling salesman—bringing buyers and sellers together without physically handling a single product. With this introduction let's take a closer look at how each of these "go-betweens" does his job.

The wholesaler buys by the carload and sells by the case. He keeps the merchandise in some kind of a warehouse located in the area he serves. This warehouse may be a large building with racks upon racks of cartons, or it may be one equipped with sophisticated equipment that controls the temperature and even the nitrogen or oxygen content of the air. He may have an office force that checks out orders to grocers, carton by carton, or an automated operation that seems to have a mind of its own. He may stock only nonperishables—"dry groceries"—or a much wider assortment of products. As in other business, the owner determines the kind of wholesaling and warehousing and the products to be stocked.

Some larger processors operate their own "distribution centers" which perform the wholesaling function for the items that they produce. Large- and medium-size chains often have their own warehouses; some retailers are "affiliated" with wholesalers which do the buying for them. And, then, there are the independent wholesalers with no special affiliation. They buy products for, and they sell to, any or all customers that come their way. While about three-fourths of all the nonperishables—canned goods and the like—sold in grocery stores are channeled through warehouses of processors, chains, and affiliates, most of the perishables are still handled by independent wholesalers.

Many warehouses may have racks

Alden C. Manchester is Chief, Animal Products Branch, Marketing Economics Division, Economic Research Service.

upon racks of cartons waiting to be sold. But there are many other types as well. For example, nearly a third of our food now goes to restaurants, cafeterias, school and factory lunchrooms, hamburger stands, vending machines, and the like. Because of the growing importance of these away-from-home eating places, unique businesses have developed to serve their special needs.

Some wholesalers specialize in supplying ready-to-cook roasts, steaks, and chops. Meats are selected, cut, and packaged according to exacting specifications so restaurant managers can have better control over their costs. Other wholesalers specialize in supplying hamburgers. They buy the beef, grind, season, and even shape the patties ready for the grill. Several hundred companies peel potatoes; others prepare salad mixes so that all the cook has to do is add the dressing. Though these specialists provide a sort of glamour to wholesaling, those who stock the thousands and thousands of items sold in our supermarkets are still the backbone of these operations.

Grocery warehouse elevator rolls along narrow aisles, allowing operator to pick store orders from either side. As each case is picked, it is automatically identified for an individual store and then moves on conveyor to where the orders are assembled.

To perform the job of wholesaling in an age of rising costs, changing foods, and increasing customer demands, these businesses must be run as efficiently as possible. In recent years, companies have been trying to streamline many of their operations—the size of orders, number of deliveries per week, and so on. Some use complicated machinery to shorten the time and reduce the personnel needed to fill orders.

Though many changes have been made, visionaries are projecting the concept of efficient management much further. They foresee an automated system of food distribution starting at the supermarket checkout counter and winding up at the farm. It would go something like this: The first step would be to assign a code number to each item, designating the processor, product, brand, grade, and package size. This number would be stamped on each package using a special ink so that as we pass the checkout counter an electronic scanner could record our purchases, item by item. These records would be checked automatically against inventory lists. When the inventories dropped to a predetermined level, the list of items needed would be transmitted to a wholesaler. His computer would print out the order and start it on its automated journey back to the supermarket.

But this isn't all! When the wholesaler's inventory drops down to a specified level, his computer would relay an order to the food processor. And, finally, to carry this process to its conclusion, the food processor's computer would be joined with the farmer's to tell him what to plant or raise. This may seem rather far out, but so did circling the moon just a few short years ago.

Before leaving the wholesalers, we should recognize some of their other contributions. Our modern wholesalers also provide a variety of services for their customers—the "specialized" wholesaler, for the department he supplies in a supermarket; the "general line" wholesaler, for the whole store. If a retailer wishes, a wholesaler of fresh fruits and vegetables will virtually take over the entire management of the produce department, including ordering, displays, and pricing. Some meat wholesalers provide a similar program.

Many "general line" wholesalers offer a complete range of services from helping to design stores and to obtain financing, to merchandising, advertising, and pricing. In many ways, these services are identical to those offered by chains to their retail stores.

Last but not least, supplies in wholesalers' warehouses are a reserve which could keep us in food for some time in case of a breakdown in our transportation system due to some national disaster. It provides us with a modest insurance against such events.

Wholesalers may have warehouses that cover acres; most brokers operate out of offices that are small by comparison. This is due largely to the different methods employed by these two kinds of middlemen.

Our 3,000-plus food brokers are local businessmen whose job is to find a market for the products that packers and processors want to sell and the items that the grocers and wholesalers want to buy. Processors expect a broker to be an authority on local market conditions; grocers look to him as a reliable source of supplies and a wide selection of items from which to choose.

To get a general idea of what our grocery brokers do, let's look at a composite picture of how they operate.

The average broker serves 22 companies, none of which sell the same kind of products. He sells and merchandises 25 brands and 245 items, employs 8 salesmen, and has a sales volume of around $5 million a year.

A food broker operates in or near the city where his office is located. As a rule, he is the only local agent for the companies he represents. He works on a commission basis, and hence receives no pay for his efforts until sales are made.

The broker's salesmen visit local chain headquarters, wholesalers, and retailers to get orders for future deliveries. These are mailed to the respective processor; when urgent, they are telephoned or teletyped.

These salesmen provide customers with information about new products, discuss their merits and the types of promotions and advertising provided. Later, they report back to the company about the degree of acceptance of the new products and the problems encountered. At times, they offer suggestions on changes in package sizes and advertising programs that might better suit local situations.

When a retailer is given a special allowance to feature a product in his newspaper ads or for in-store displays, the broker has to furnish the company proof that this has been done—usually a copy of the ad or a picture of the store display.

The broker's strongest traits are his intimate knowledge of local market conditions; close personal relationships with local buyers; and awareness of the likes and dislikes of both grocers and consumers.

Wholesalers and brokers bridge the gap between us and those who prepare our food. They are the necessary links between the many packers and processors of food products, retail stores, and away-from-home eating places. While the particular arrangement under which they provide these services can and has changed over the years, their function is essential and must be performed.

D. B. DeLoach

A 'Showcase' for Food, at Your Local Supermarket

Most of us think we have a herculean task just to provide the variety of food which will keep our family happy. Think, then, what a task it must be for a grocer who has to provide a variety of food which will satisfy a thousand or more shoppers!

Each of the many Marys, Marthas, and Pauls that make up the present and prospective market of a grocery store has preferences based upon his or her own background and present income. None is ever a "typical" or "average" shopper. Nevertheless, satisfying all our needs is the job that faces the owner or manager of each of more than 226,000 grocery stores. It is our grocer who must try to please us at any hour, of any day, of any year as we shop in his store.

We have always had some kind of a shopping mart, but the present type—the supermarket and the super-supermarket—are largely products of the past 25 years. This growth has been stimulated largely by the relatively greater efficiency and profitability of large versus small volume stores. Apparently, the large stores now fulfill best our desires for a wide variety of products and other services.

Today, we seem to take supermarkets for granted, yet at the same time, expect them to do a multitude of tasks for us. We expect them to stock the items we want, change these as the seasons and our wants change, guarantee the quality of the products which they sell, and take all the risks involved in trying to balance their supplies with our demands. This is not a simple task, as a closer look at several of their responsibilities and problems will show.

Food retailing is a service business. Though the kind and number of services may vary greatly from store to store, each grocer has two jobs—providing adequate supplies and selling them to us. He must anticipate our demands for the thousands of items he stocks as well as the services he must provide to make a sale.

Supplying the items that we want requires him to locate, purchase, and store a multitude of products. Selling involves proper pricing of these and determining how they are to be paid for—cash or credit. In fulfilling those functions, a grocer acts as an intermediary between his customers and the rest of the food industry. As such, he must establish and maintain good working relationships in both directions.

A retailer who strives to build his business must find an economical and feasible way to cater to his present customers and, at the same time, try to get others to shift their patronage to his store. One of the most successful ways has been to stock a wide assortment of products and brands—both food and nonfood.

This trend toward almost unlimited selection characterizes most modern supermarkets with their 8,000 items compared with around 3,000 just two decades ago. Despite the rapid increase in the number and kinds of items offered, there are indications that our insatiable desires may not even be fully satisfied by supermarkets offering as many as 9,000 to 10,000 different items.

D. B. DeLoach is Professor of Agricultural Economics, University of California, Davis.

This desire and willingness to pay for greater customizing of both products and services has spawned specialty bakeries and gourmet shops that cater to those of us who want "something different."

Supermarkets are constantly offering a different assortment of items. But so many new ones become available each year that a retailer could not possibly stock them all. Through constant testing of customer responses, decisions are made as to which will sell best in a particular locality. As a result, many new products never reach our supermarket shelves. Even with this restriction, more than half the items now stocked were not available 10 years ago.

With all of the choices provided in supermarkets, some shoppers still complain they are being forced into a product-use pattern by retailers. The opposing view is that a grocer cannot afford to handle all items offered him, and thus must choose among them. Nevertheless, this process of selection still provides us with a wider variety from which to choose than would be economically feasible under any other supply system.

Another successful method used by grocers to keep or increase their sales has been to provide a wide range of services. The most important of these include check cashing, air conditioning, offstreet parking, longer store hours, and carryout services.

With grocers basing most of their competitive strategy upon the wide variety of products, brands, and services they offer, one wonders just how important these actually are to the customer in choosing a store. Interviews of shoppers show that eight factors ranked above prices as absolutely essential or important. Of these, location of the store and the assortment and quality of items offered were at the top of the list.

Items Important or Essential to Shoppers in Their Choice of Food Stores

Store attribute	Percent of shoppers interviewed: Absolutely essential	Percent of shoppers interviewed: Essential or important
Is easy to shop	45	75
Has wide selection of items	43	71
Has best quality of meats in area	54	67
Is easy to get to	39	63
Has top vegetable and fruit department	43	62
Has favorite brand	38	62
Is nearby	34	53
Gives best value on canned products	32	52
Has low prices in area	31	52

There are all sorts of difficulties in trying to balance supplies and services with customers' demands. Nevertheless, the job of a retailer is to solve these problems. How well he does determines his success or failure. The firms that survive and prosper are those that buy and sell as efficiently as possible. Such firms are successful in both assembling supplies and using their money and personnel resources to achieve their business objectives. This requires good planning.

Because of our consumer acceptance of—or preference for—large supermarket-type grocery stores, most sales are made through this type of market.

Retailers often try to lower their unit output costs by selling more merchandise without a corresponding increase in such inputs as labor, facilities, and maintenance. When such "economies of scale" are possible, total net profit will rise. In fact, total net profit might increase even though both the unit price and total price received from sales are lowered. Generally, "economies of scale" are possible in grocery stores and firms.

Widespread acceptance of the principle of economies of scale, the more favorable net profits of large as compared to small firms, and the greater ease with which medium and large chains can obtain investment capital have brought us fewer but larger stores and companies. An indication of this is that supermarkets now represent around 15 percent of all grocery stores, compared with 6 percent in 1954. Contrary to what many may assume, all supermarkets are not owned by the chains. According to recent information, those independ-

Gourmet section of a food store.

ently owned represent about half of all supermarkets—which is the same as 15 years ago.

With the growing importance of supermarkets, we are now spending a larger share of our grocery money in these big stores than ever before—nearly three-fourths today compared with a little more than half in 1954. Independently owned supermarkets have around 40 percent of these sales.

Some people are concerned about the impact on communities of the decline of the small grocery store; and others are concerned about the increase in economic power in the hands of fewer companies. However, most of us appear to ignore such issues and shop where we wish as long as we can buy what we want at satisfactory prices. In other words, if shopping and sales patterns are indications of our preferences, most of us have chosen to shop in supermarkets regardless of type of ownership or business organization. Furthermore, the pronounced and fairly rapid shift of patronage from small to large stores since World War II indicates a favorable attitude toward the supermarket-type grocery.

Much of the reason for the increased sales of supermarkets can be found in the changes in where we live, our shopping patterns, and our incomes. Nearly three-fourths of our population lives in or near large cities. And the recent trend for more of us to move to suburban areas has affected the grocery business considerably. Furthermore, we don't want to move to an area unless there is reasonably easy access to supplies and services, particularly food.

New communities are often built on land formerly used for farming, and there are few, if any, old stores large enough to serve the influx of people. Hence, this is ideal for building new modern stores. The investment in both buildings and equipment is relatively high as modern refrigeration space, frozen food display counters, parking lots, and air conditioning are standard for these suburban stores. Supermarkets today in these new communities usually offer both food and nonfoods, the latter ranging from clothing to household appliances. If a wide range of items are not provided, satellite shops usually open up and a shopping center results which fulfills practically all supply-service needs.

Inasmuch as three of the first four priorities for choosing a place to shop for food are that it must (1) be easy to shop, (2) have a wide selection of items, and (3) be easy to get to, competitive zeal often results in too-large stores, an unduly big inventory, and a notion that the supermarket must handle "everything."

Another competitive excess arises from "overstoring," which comes from misjudgments of the number of stores required to meet our idea of "easy to get to." Overstoring has often created competitive problems which merchants have sought to solve through additional types of promotion which have either increased marketing costs or reduced profits. One evidence of the trend toward overstoring is the fact that in the midsixties, consumers were within reach of 5 to 6 supermarkets—compared to 4 or 5 some 10 years earlier. This ease of access to more supermarkets results mainly from more automobiles, good roads, and parking facilities provided by the supermarkets.

About three-fourths of our grocery sales are made by chain or independent supermarkets that are competing for the same customers. In general, these retailers must depend on the same sources of supply for most of their merchandise, equipment, and buildings.

Except for the private brands of chainstores and of a few independent supermarkets, most grocers handle the same brands. Even their store equipment and buildings may be built by the same companies, using the same plans. This leads to a high degree of standardization of merchandise and facilities of various types. Hence, it is evident that something unusual has to be done to induce customers to shop at one store in preference to another. The most vital question for an individual grocer is how best to get and to keep enough customers to make his business profitable.

Given the amount of standardization of products and services that are found in all our grocery stores, it would seem that prices would be the logical method of competition. To be sure, there is a considerable amount of similarity in the prices of a number of products. But, because "across-the-board" price cutting is regarded as too risky and self-destructive, grocers have tended to be conservative in the use of this practice.

With the advent of "discount" grocery stores, the barrier to "across-the-board" price cutting may be weakening. Recently, some rather noticeable downward adjustments in pricing policies have occurred. Because of the lowering of prices and resulting gross margins, there have been severe pressures upon the retailers to reduce their operating costs. This has made necessary substantial cutbacks in so-called services, or an increase in total sales.

A quick examination of the practices of five chainstore firms which have adopted a lower markup policy shows they tried to compensate for the lower margins by reducing the number of items handled, eliminating promotions such as trading stamps and games, cutting down the number of hours and days their stores are open, eliminating carryout services, and cutting back on their maintenance costs. It was assumed that such economies and the increase in customers resulting from lower prices would yield greater net revenue. Some of the first companies to adopt this pricing policy did achieve good results. The main question, however, is whether "all" our grocers can follow this practice and get the same favorable results.

The National Commission on Food Marketing estimated that it would take an average of a 21-percent increase in sales to obtain a 5-percent decrease in store-operating costs. If this is correct, it is evident there will have to be substantial reductions in the number of grocery stores to have an increase in sales of this size per store, or the total demand for food and services will have to rise.

Because the expenditures in grocery stores directly affect most of us, prices and profits are watched closely. Despite all efforts to keep prices from increasing too much, the retail food price index has been going up. This, of course, has stimulated consumers and government agencies to try to find out the cause. One of the most recent inquiries, made by the National Commission on Food Marketing, found that the chainstore margins had increased 28 percent in the past 20 years. Since gross margins (difference between the cost of the products and the selling price) accounted for only around a fifth of the increase in prices, the remaining four-fifths had to be due to the higher prices paid out for supplies and other needs.

In order of importance, the primary contributing factors to higher gross margins have been the costs of labor, rent and real estate, and promotion. Though this has been the case, many people have blamed rising prices on the domination of a few firms in the retail food business. Since the gross retail margin includes whatever profits remain after paying all expenses, the real question is whether margins rose because of higher net profits.

The Commission's data show that, because net profits per dollar of sales average about one cent, higher retail store profits have not been the major reason for the gradual rise in prices and margins. Nevertheless, the Commission concluded that, during most of the postwar period, profits of retail food chains have been high in relation to other industries. Moreover, large profits in relation to dollars invested have contributed to the overstoring that plagues the grocery business.

Retail food stores employ about 1.6 million workers, about 45 percent of them women. Based on current statistics, wages paid to workers in retail food stores amount to around $5 billion. The administrative employees probably add in another $1 billion.

While these are rough approximations, they do indicate the magnitude of the labor bill in the grocery retailing business.

The growing importance of grocery chains and independent supermarkets which operate under fairly uniform labor contracts has tended to raise the level of wages and employee benefits. Today, these compare favorably with other industries that require comparable education, skills, and experience. In addition, competition for workers has had a beneficial influence on other conditions of employment, particularly fringe benefits. Because the retail grocery business, like many others, is undergoing rapid technological change in almost every phase of its operations, it is now competing with other industries for highly trained people, skilled workers, and managers. The larger retail grocery firms can also offer employees opportunities for on-the-job training and advancement into managerial positions. Such opportunities were much more restricted in small, family-operated stores.

Other costs have been rising, also. Rent and real estate costs have been going up and on the average, account for about 10 and 13 percent, respectively, of the operating costs of food retailers. Significantly, the increase in promotional costs for single-store owners has almost doubled in the past 15 years, which reflects the competitive conditions in the retail grocery trade.

The shift of our purchases from small retailers to supermarket-type stores is exerting an unrelenting competitive pressure upon the small, single-store firms. Unless our shopping patterns begin to change, the very existence of the small grocery is seriously threatened. This in turn implies still further concentration of retail sales in larger establishments.

We have discussed the past and present status and problems of our grocery stores. This makes us wonder what the future will bring. At times, it seems that all possible changes must have taken place, but in this technological age, such conclusions can prove quite naive.

"Company cuts" and aged prime beef are featured at this meat counter.

Those who try to look into the future anticipate many changes in our grocery stores—in size, location, items stocked, and use of automation. Here, in brief, is what is frequently predicted:

In new suburban areas, many supermarkets have been turned into a modern version of the old general store. This trend will probably continue until food may represent only half or less of total store sales. Food may be a department in the store—rather than its chief purpose. To balance this, the current trend toward convenience or bantam stores will accelerate. These will take the place of the corner or neighborhood grocery. Some of the bantam stores may be located in high-rise apartments and even in office buildings to make it still easier to shop.

New food items will appear and disappear in a much shorter time than in the past. They will be advertised in a way to bring customers into a particular store since competition will have become more intense.

Competition to keep up sales volume also increases as more people eat more meals away from home. Stores will carry more ready-to-eat items, and family sized, precooked, frozen food entrees will be offered to entice people to fix quickie meals at home rather than eating out.

Because innercity supermarkets cannot expand in size as much as those in suburban areas, shelf space will be at a premium. This should lead to stricter inventory controls. Fast-selling items will be given more space and slower moving ones less. The actual amount allotted various products will be determined by formulas, and computers will be used to signal the point for replenishing of stock and transmitting orders to a warehouse or wholesaler. This will help keep in-store inventories at a minimum.

Automation may be carried even further. Some predict we will put a card in a slot beside each item we want as we travel around the store. When we reach the checkout counter, our purchases will be ready and the bill totaled. But different from today, we may not pay our bill with cash. It may be automatically transferred to our checking account or to some central credit system.

It will be interesting to see how these predictions work out.

Stephen J. Hiemstra

Telescoping 20 Years of Change in the Food We Eat

Many things have been happening during the past two decades. We have fought two wars. Cars have become more powerful. Social problems have grown more acute. The stock market has boomed. Prices have risen. Our incomes have doubled. And we're eating differently, too.

Though changes in what we eat may not be in the same league with the others, they're equally important to each of us, or possibly even more important. So, let's look at the broad changes that have taken place.

There are many ways to look at what has happened to our food buying. We can examine our own buying and stop there. Or we can see what kind and how much food is used by families with different incomes; by small and large families; or by those living in cities and on farms. As a starter, let's see how we, a Nation of some 200 million people, eat differently now than we did just 20 years ago when there were 50 million fewer of us and our incomes were about half as big.

Probably the one change we notice most is the arrival of a host of new and radically different items on our grocery shelves. Some of these are old foods in new sizes, shapes, or packages. Others are new products. For example, consider the large variety, many sizes, and strange shapes of breakfast cereals. These come presweetened and unsweetened; plain or with freeze-dried fruit added; uncooked and precooked; and even specially prepared for babies. Some cereals snap, crackle, and pop. Others just lie there and soak up milk. But most are still made from wheat, corn, or rice.

Less noticeable, but perhaps even more important, is the change in the relative amounts of different kinds of foods we're buying. Today, we use more meat and poultry per person; more processed fruits and vegetables, margarine, and salad and cooking oils than we did back in 1950. While increasing use of these foods, we've cut down on fresh fruits and vegetables, dairy and cereal products, eggs, and some of our beverages.

While our buying patterns have changed, we are bringing home from the supermarket only about 5 percent more food per person than we were 10 years ago. But during this period the population of our country has grown by a third. So as a Nation we are buying much more food.

Beef and broilers have been the big gainers in our increased individual buying of meat and poultry products.

The rise in our use of beef has been due mainly to our growing preference for steaks and hamburgers. We are buying more beef despite an increase in beef prices.

Pork chops and ham are not as popular as they were at one time, although they have risen in price no more than beef. The amount we buy varies considerably from year to year, but pork chops and ham don't command the prestige of steak. Our preference for beef is indicated, also, in the smaller amount we buy of veal and lamb.

Chicken and turkey have become

Stephen J. Hiemstra, an agricultural economist, is Head of the Food Consumption and Utilization Section, Economic Research Service.

year-round items—not as much the Sunday, Thanksgiving, or Christmas treat they used to be. We're buying nearly twice as much of these as we did back in 1950, mainly because the prices are much lower. But as before, we still use much more chicken than turkey.

And we aren't the "eggheads" we used to be. The popularity of eggs has declined along with our traditional American breakfast. Toast and coffee for adults and cereal and milk for the kids have become the standard fare. Rising prices for prepared cereals and the declining prices for eggs have not stemmed the tide.

Most dairy products have gone the way of eggs. Fresh whole milk, cream, evaporated milk, and butter have borne the brunt of this drop. To an increasing degree, nondairy products—coffee creamers and whipped toppings—are being used in place of cream. But in the process, these new products have enlarged the total market for creamers and toppings. More recently substitutes like "filled milk" have started to make inroads in our purchases of whole milk. Vegetable fats are used in this product to replace butterfat. On the other hand, cheese and low-fat milk have gained in popularity.

One of the biggest stories, however, is our shift from butter to margarine. But our purchases of total "table spreads" haven't changed very much. Twenty years ago, we bought around twice as much butter as margarine. Today, it's just about the reverse.

Along with increasing our use of vegetable oils in the form of margarine, we are buying larger quantities of these oils as cooking and salad oils. Lard, an animal fat and a longtime favorite, is being used less for cooking, but is gaining in importance as an ingredient in solid shortenings and other products.

Contrary to what we might expect in this age of affluence, our total use of fruits and vegetables has gone down. In spite of the fact that most fresh fruits and vegetables are available the year round, they are not used in as large quantities as they were 20 years ago. Instead, we are buying more processed products, with frozen vegetables and citrus concentrates leading the way. Then too, some of the newer methods of processing, such as freeze-drying, are being used on some of these foods. We have freeze-dried strawberries in cereals, freeze-dried vegetables in dry soup mixes.

Oatmeal prepared in cereal dish. Just adding hot water to this new product makes old-time favorite an "instant" breakfast food.

Price and convenience helped bring about this change in our food buying. Prices for fresh fruits and vegetables have gone up much faster than for processed products, even though processed product prices have risen faster than for most other foods. And the processed products offer us more convenience and variety.

What has happened to our old standby the potato is almost sensational. After a long period during which we used smaller and smaller quantities each year, potatoes now seem to have come into their own. Though we still haven't increased our use of fresh potatoes, our purchases of processed products are more than making up for this. Today, we can buy them canned, frozen, and dried. And, within each of these kinds, there's a wide enough selection to fit into almost any menu from breakfast—if you like hash browns or fried—to the most elegant dinner.

Finally, we are purchasing smaller quantities of flour, some cereal products, and coffee than we did two decades earlier. The amount of wheat flour used in all consumer products has been going down at a rate of about 1 pound per person per year, though now the rate appears to be slowing up somewhat. On the other hand, we're buying more rice and corn products. Though purchases of cornmeal have gone down along with the drop in home baking, the use of corn in breakfast cereals has increased.

In addition, much more corn is being used for making sugar and sirups, most of which goes into candy and processed foods.

Despite the growing importance of corn sweeteners and the rising popularity of noncaloric sweeteners, our total use of sugar has remained fairly stable. Soft drinks take the largest amount of the noncaloric sweeteners as our weight watchers continue to buy more and more of these. Altogether, over two-thirds of all sweeteners are being used in processed food and beverages.

Though it seems it can't be true, we are drinking less coffee than we did—at least we've been using smaller amounts of coffee beans. Part of this change is due to the introduction of "instant" coffee during the fifties, which now has stabilized at nearly a fifth of our coffee consumption. But use of "instant" tea continues to expand.

All of these shifts in our food purchases make us wonder why we made them. There are probably as many reasons as there are families, but here are some that are important. First, there's the size of our paycheck. As our income goes up, we tend to buy a little more food—but not too much more. If there's no change in prices, we tend to increase the total quantity purchased by 1 or 2 percent for each 10-percent increase in our income. Added to this, we tend to buy higher priced items.

By contrast, if prices go up and our income stays the same, we tend to buy 2 to 3 percent less food with each 10-percent increase in price. In this case, we tend to shift to lower priced food items.

As we all know, during recent years we've had rising incomes and rising food prices. So let's see what effect this combination has had upon our buying practices.

During the past 20 years, prices of meat, fruits and vegetables, cereal and bakery products, dairy products, and vegetable oils have increased. At the same time, those of poultry, eggs, and coffee have gone down. Our use of fresh fruits and vegetables, cereals, and dairy products went down as prices went up. But we ate more meat, used more processed fruits and vegetables, and used more vegetable oils despite their rise in price—showing our preference for these foods.

We bought larger quantities of poultry products as prices went down. But even though prices went down, we bought fewer eggs. Our change in breakfast habits may be responsible for some reduction in the use of eggs.

All of us together spend more than $100 billion a year for food—yet today, this represents only a fraction more than 17 percent of our take-home pay. In 1950, we spent 22 percent of our incomes for food; in 1960, we spent 20 percent. To make today's 17-plus percent even more significant, note that we are having a larger share of our food preparation done for us now than two decades ago.

So far, all the figures given have been

Researcher studies effects of microwave heating on a frozen precooked hamburger. Many foods are dispensed from refrigerated vending machines and brought to serving temperature by customers placing them in microwave oven.

averages for our Nation as a whole. This is one way we determine the economic direction we're traveling. But, each of us is likely to face a somewhat different combination of circumstances. We may have had smaller or even larger increases in our incomes than the average or a larger-than-average-size family. We may have moved from one part of our country to another or from the farm to the city. Then too, some families attach more importance to gourmet foods than others. Any of these things will affect an individual family's purchasing, and make it vary from the "average."

A recent study found that the percentage of income spent upon food varied from around 30 percent for families with incomes below $3,000 to around 12 percent for those earning $15,000 or more. About a third of the money spent for food by the highest income group went for meals and snacks eaten away from home. Low-income families spent a much smaller share of their food budget away from their homes.

Two-person families spent an average of 19 percent of their income for food compared with 26 percent by families with 6 or more persons. Of course, part of these differences were associated with income variations—the larger families having the higher total incomes but smaller incomes per family member.

The study also showed that after allowing for home-produced food, farm families used a larger share of their income for food than families living in cities. Again, part of this difference was due to variations in level of income.

Though regional differences were small, families in the north-central and western regions spent less of their incomes for food than those in the Northeast and South.

This is a telescoped picture of our use of food as a Nation over the past two decades. If current predictions come true, the next two decades will bring large additions to our incomes and many more changes in the kind of foods we buy.

Denis F. Dunham
Robert E. Frye

Shedding Light on the Prices We Pay for Our Food

How often have you heard a neighbor say, "Aren't food prices high these days?" Or had her imply that by remarking, "I spent $35 at the grocery yesterday and don't have a thing for dinner." Chances are each of us has made these or similar comments. But why is it, in a country where many have two cars, two television sets, and even a boat, that we are so aware of food prices and express so much interest in them? And why is it we seem to be more aware of prices that go up than those that go down?

There are probably lots of reasons why we are so conscious about increases in food prices. For one thing, food is a major item in most family budgets. Then, too, it's purchased frequently, and any price changes are quickly reflected in our pocketbooks. For something that touches our everyday lives and affects our finances as much as food, we are almost always comparing prices.

Price by itself is a relatively simple word, but it can have a variety of meanings. It can have one meaning to those who examine the state of the Nation's economy; another to farmers, processors, and retail store owners. And still another to each of us as consumers. Food prices may be the figures stamped on packages or cartons, but if we are to understand their real meaning, we have to know what they represent and what it is that makes them change.

Food prices represent the sum of the costs incurred and profits earned by farmers, processors, and retail store operators in providing us with a host of products and services. And in one way or another, all these prices are affected by the same economic conditions that determine those of other goods and services important in our day-to-day living. Because the food industry is interconnected with every other segment of our national economy, it must compete in the national market for labor, materials, equipment, and other needs. Thus, food prices tend to follow the general price trend in the Nation.

Though this is the overall situation, the value assigned to a product may be different for the farmer, the processor, the neighborhood grocer, the supermarket operator, and the low- or the high-income shopper. In these various capacities, each will have a level, real or imagined, that becomes the basis for determining the reasonableness of a price. And at each of these stages—producing, marketing, and purchasing—the value placed on a product may be different tomorrow.

Most everyone knows that food prices have been going up—sometimes at a slow pace, sometimes at a faster one. While we may not have all the facts needed to explain why, most of us have opinions about who and what are causing the changes. So let's look at food prices from the various viewpoints, starting with their relation to our Nation's economy.

One way to compare changes in the food price level is to see what has happened to prices of other goods and

Denis F. Dunham and Robert E. Frye are agricultural economists, Market Development and Performance Branch, Marketing Economics Division, Economic Research Service.

Checkout counter at Washington, D.C., supermarket.

services. Since food is but one item in our family budget, it should not be singled out as the sole reason—or even the most important reason—for changes in the cost of living.

On the national level, comparisons of prices are made using the Consumer Price Index. This index measures the changes from month to month in the overall level of prices of all goods and services, and those of major groups, such as housing, apparel and upkeep, transportation, health and recreation, and food. These major categories are also divided into important subgroups. For example, the Food Index has two, one designed to show changes in the price of food used at home and the other to show changes in prices of food eaten away from home. Each month, the same list of foods is priced in cities around the country. Then, these are compared with the average price of the same item during the 3-year period 1957–59, to determine which foods have changed in price and how much this has affected a family's food bill.

The index for all items, the one that

indicates how much the cost of living has changed, shows that during the past 10 years the prices of all goods and services important in our day-to-day living have gone up 21 percent. During the same period, food, housing, apparel and upkeep, and transportation went up about 20 percent. In contrast, the index for health and recreation went up 30 percent.

The Consumer Price Index may have more meaning to us if we look at changes in prices of the subgroups. For example, prices of food at the grocery have gone up only 16 percent in the past 10 years compared to 36 percent for food in public eating places. During these same years, footwear went up 32 percent in price; homeownership, 27 percent; public transportation, 38 percent; and medical care, 45 percent. The index for gas and electricity changed the least, going up only 10 percent.

Prices of goods and services have been going up for many reasons. The decade of the 1960's has been a period of rapidly rising incomes and falling rates of unemployment. Such conditions are usually associated with some degree of inflation, for as the number of persons without jobs goes down, wages tend to be bid up and incomes rise. If these higher wages and other costs are not offset by gains in production efficiency, prices usually rise.

Fortunately, for a large share of Americans, higher prices have been accompanied by wage increases. On the average, our incomes have more than kept pace with prices. If they didn't, we would not have the new homes, the two cars, or the two television sets many of us enjoy today.

Price changes are also measured in other ways. The U.S. Department of Agriculture measures trends in prices of foods that originate on U.S. farms by changes in the cost of a "market basket." This market basket is based upon the average quantities of food purchased per year in 1960–61 by urban wage earner and clerical worker families and single workers living alone. It excludes imported foods and

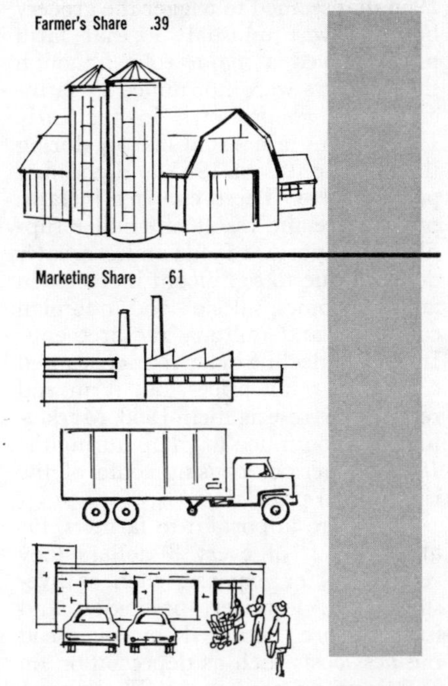

seafoods which are not produced on U.S. farms. Quantities and qualities of foods in this market basket are held constant so that price changes are not affected by shifts in our purchasing patterns. The cost of this basket of food is estimated, using retail prices that are published by the Bureau of Labor Statistics.

During the past 10 years, the retail cost of the market basket has increased about 14 percent. This means that for every $10 spent upon these foods a decade ago, we spend $11.40 today. However, three-fifths of the rise occurred in 1965 and 1966, and the consumer boycotts followed. If this increase had been evenly distributed over the entire period, we probably wouldn't have been as aware of the rise in prices.

For most of the past decade, rising marketing costs have been the main cause of higher food prices. Moreover, since 1957–59 marketing costs have caused two-thirds of the increase in the retail cost of the market basket.

The rise in food prices in 1965 and 1966 that seemed to trigger the grocery boycotts was unusual in that farm prices played a major role, although the boycotts were not aimed at farmers. After going down in the early 1960's, farm prices rose sharply during the last months of 1965 and the first part of 1966. These changes in farm prices were the result of smaller supplies of important foods and a greater demand due to significant increases in family incomes, sales of food to foreign countries, and military requirements. In 1967, a decline in farm prices caused a drop in retail prices, but farm and retail prices rose again in 1968. Marketing costs continued to go up during the 1965–68 period, causing some of the rise in food prices.

Prices are important to farmers, for about 2 out of every 3 dollars they receive go for expenses such as livestock feed, fertilizer, pesticides, and fuel, or are absorbed by overhead business costs such as depreciation on buildings and equipment. The other 1 dollar is the return for their work and on their capital investment. So far, prices of things needed to operate farms have increased much more than those farmers have received. Fortunately, some farmers have been able to expand production enough to offset part of these increases in costs.

To add to the problems of farmers, prices of farm products are unstable compared to those of automobiles, furniture, newspapers, and haircuts—to name only a few goods and services important to us. This is largely due to the limited control over supplies of farm products and the demand for food which is exceptionally stable. Most farmers produce as much as they can since the amount produced by any one seldom affects the market price. Hence, there is a tendency to over- or under-produce and, as a result, for farm prices to fluctuate. When food supplies are plentiful, farm prices may be relatively low. The reverse is true when foods are in short supply.

On the average, farmers receive less than half of what we pay for food. In recent years, they have received about 39 cents of each dollar we spent at the grocery for farm foods. A farmer receives such a small part of the retail price of some foods that, even if he gave them away, the price at retail would be reduced by less than a fifth. For example, in 1968 the average price of a 1-pound loaf of white bread at the supermarket was 22.4 cents. Only 2.6 cents of this went to the farmer for the wheat used in the loaf. Thus, if he had been paid nothing for his wheat, the bread would still have cost 19.8 cents.

Farmers also receive only a small part of the retail price of such foods as cookies, corn flakes, canned peaches, and frozen french-fried potatoes. Changes in farm prices of these items have little effect on retail prices. On the other hand, farmers receive more than half the prices we pay for such major items as meat, eggs, and butter. Moderate changes in the supplies and farm prices of these products will affect retail prices more. The difference in what a farmer receives from our food dollar is largely a matter of how much processing and packaging is necessary before his product reaches the grocery store.

Farmers have not been making large profits. Although their incomes have been improving, they still lag behind those of most other workers. In addition, incomes are not evenly distributed among farmers. This distribution differs greatly from one area to another, one year to the next, and one kind of farm to another.

Foods go in many directions after they leave the farm and pass through many hands before they reach our grocery shelves. The task of getting food to us in the right form, at the right time and the right place is the function of the food marketing system. Doing these jobs for us takes the remaining 61 cents of each dollar we spend at the grocery. The businesses that do all this work number in the thousands and include grain elevators, milk processing and bottling plants, fruit and vegetable canning factories, bakeries, and retail food stores.

What happens to products after they leave the farm determines, to a large extent, the appearance, variety, and quality of the foods we buy and the prices we pay. Without the marketing system, our steaks would be standing in a feedlot in Iowa, our cheese and butter would be milk on a dairy farm in Wisconsin, while our orange juice would still be on the tree in Florida or California.

Of course, as is true for other things we buy, we must pay for the services provided by the marketing system, and the cost of these has been increasing. During the past 10 years, the cost of an hour of labor used by processors, wholesalers, and retailers has gone up almost 50 percent. And because labor is usually the largest item of cost, increases in labor cost have had a significant effect on retail food prices. The sharp rise in food prices since 1964 has been caused, in part, by labor costs that have risen at a faster rate recently than during the previous years.

Preparing frozen turkey dinners at Minnesota processing plant.

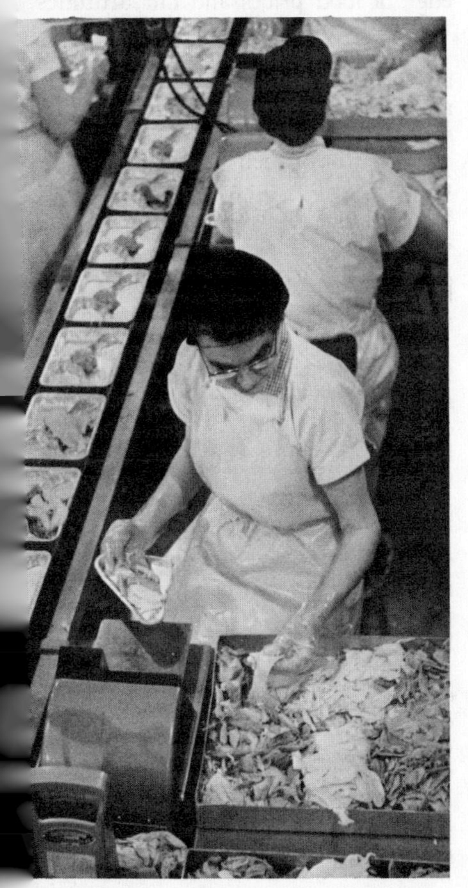

The marketing system has been able to offset part of the increase in the cost of labor by adopting new methods and equipment, by improving skills of workers and management, and by combining or eliminating small, inefficient units. As a result, instead of increasing by 50 percent, the cost of labor per unit produced has gone up only 18 percent.

Another measure of increased efficiency is that, while the amount of food being marketed has increased 21 percent during the past 10 years, only 6 percent more persons have been needed to do the job. And the number of hours worked per week per person has actually declined. So, while hourly labor costs have been rising, the marketing system has been able to minimize the effect of the higher labor costs on the prices we pay for our food. If this hadn't been done, our food would have cost much more.

During the past decade, other marketing costs have gone up, too. Items like rent, insurance, maintenance, and telephone services have increased by nearly a third. The cost of new plants and equipment are 17 percent higher, and prices of food containers, packaging materials, and electricity have gone up 8 percent.

Over the years, profits of the food marketing industry have been lower than those of many other industries. Profits, before taxes, now take only 3.6 cents of each dollar we spend for food—about the same as a decade ago. Though some marketing firms have been more profitable than others, higher industry profits have not been the major reason for rising food prices.

During the past 10 years, profits of leading retail chains have been declining. While increased sales have brought in more dollars, the returns on their investments (after taxes) have dropped to around 10 percent or about two-thirds of what they were a decade ago. To put this another way, profits now amount to approximately 1 penny of each dollar spent at the grocery. So eliminating the retailer's profit entirely would not appreciably lower food prices.

As in other businesses, food firms must make a profit, at least over the long run. Profits are quite variable, and at times may seem excessive. Whether they are too high or too low is impossible to judge without knowing all the facts.

Profits may be thought of as an investment in the future, for they are necessary to stimulate investment in more efficient facilities and for research on new and improved products. With no extra funds to use in this manner, it would be difficult for our food industry to keep pace with other industries in a rapidly changing age.

For the most part, the functions of marketing—processing, transporting, wholesaling, and retailing—are essential to our urban-oriented society where most of us have little or no contact with agriculture. Since World War II, our food industry has established a good record of efficiency. And it has provided us with a steadily increasing variety of wholesome, nutritious, and appetizing foods at a reasonable cost while adjusting to our ever changing demands.

During recent years, we have also shifted many of our food preparation tasks to the marketing system. Because of the cost of developing these more highly processed foods, large sums of money have been spent to advertise and promote individual brands. Overall, however, such costs must be viewed in the light of our competitive economy. One company may be able to increase sales and profits by using advertising to differentiate its products from those of another. This tends to make companies strive to improve their products, so they can remain competitive. We, as consumers, benefit from advertising to the extent that competition results in the development of new and better products and a more stable mass market. Advertising may also provide information about new products that are available.

We have seen that to farmers and to those who process, transport, and market our food, prices represent what they will receive for their work. To the rest of us, the price on the package indicates what we may have to pay out. This is probably the main difference in our approaches to food prices.

Undoubtedly, most of us think we know prices. But do we, or can we, know them as well as we think we do? Do we know enough about the behavior of prices to make good judgments about their current levels? How do we decide when prices are reasonable or too high? What are some of the factors that influence our knowledge of food prices and our attitudes toward them?

Most of us as family shoppers buy around 30 to 40 items a week of the many thousands stocked in a modern supermarket. But some of these items change from week to week, so—in reality—we buy many more kinds over a period of a month or so. We may be able to remember the last price we paid for a few of these—the ones we buy regularly—but it's doubtful that we can do so for every item purchased. Added to this is the effect of normal fluctuations in prices. Because of the seasonal nature of production, prices of foods like pork, eggs, and fresh fruits and vegetables change more often than many others. Then there are the promotional changes in prices—the "specials," and "cents off." Through all this, we seem to have a better memory for prices that go up than we do for those that go down. And, though food prices have been trending upward, those of some important foods have declined. Such items as frying chickens, eggs, frozen orange juice concentrate, and ice cream cost less today than a decade ago.

Prices are responsive to changes in supplies. When supplies of food are scarce, we have to pay higher prices

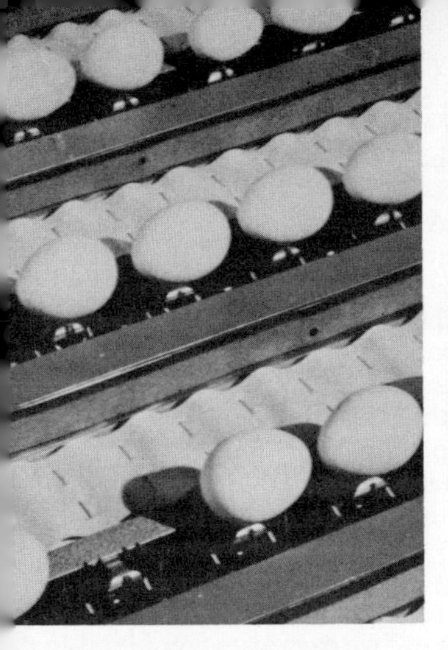

While prices were generally up, frozen orange juice concentrate and eggs cost less in 1968 than decade ago. Eggs, left, are pictured on automatic egg-weighing machine.

—or change to another product. At times, even small changes in supplies caused by bad weather can have a noticeable impact on prices. On the other hand, when supplies are plentiful, prices usually go down because we only want so much food.

Discussions of prices frequently center on convenience foods. Here, again, reactions differ. Because of the value one homemaker places on her time, she may consider partially prepared or ready-to-serve foods reasonably priced. Another homemaker may think they are too expensive. Yet, studies have shown that, when a reasonable value is placed upon a homemaker's time, many of these foods are no more expensive than the same item prepared at home from basic ingredients, and some are less expensive.

The store where we buy can affect our ideas about food prices. Because small neighborhood groceries have too few customers and can't buy in large enough quantities for efficient use of labor and facilities, they will usually charge higher prices than supermarkets. Prices also vary among large supermarkets. Higher prices in one may be justified by differences in the kind and quality of products stocked and the customer services offered—like check cashing, carryout services, shopping hours.

The continually changing character of our grocery stores—the ever changing array of new foods and more and more nonfood items—makes it hard for us to be precise in our knowledge of many prices.

Saying prices are high indicates a comparison, and usually this is in relation to what we have to buy with. Being human, we tend to think of all the things we want—and these may add up to many more things than we could purchase with our take-home pay even if all prices stayed the same.

One way to make this comparison is to look at the quantity of individual foods which can be purchased with an hour's pay:

Amount of Selected Foods the Average Hourly Earnings of Factory Workers Would Buy

Item	Unit	1948	1958	1968
Round steak	lb.	1.5	2.0	2.6
Pork chops	lb.	1.7	2.3	2.9
Bacon, sliced	lb.	1.7	2.7	3.7
Bread, white	lb.	9.6	10.9	13.4
Butter	lb.	1.5	2.8	3.6
Margarine	lb.	3.2	7.2	10.8
Eggs	doz.	1.8	3.5	5.7

Of course, prices will always be important to us. What we have tried to do is to present a few facts about what can happen to food prices and why. Clearly, the increase in food prices in recent years has been caused, to a large extent, by higher production and marketing costs. At the same time, we are buying more expensive and higher quality foods. Compared to our incomes and to prices of many other things, food is still a good buy for most of us Americans.

Eileen F. Taylor

100 Million Times a Day, Americans Eat Out

More than 100 million times in each day, someone has a meal or snack in a fancy restaurant, a college cafeteria, a snackbar, or a hospital. If we picked up the check for all the meals and snacks we Americans eat away from home in a year, it would amount to a whopping $22 billion.

Sounds impressive? Well, it is—and it's getting more so every year. We like to eat out, and just about everyone does so at one time or another. At least once a month, about 100 million of us have dinner at a restaurant; 66 million go out for breakfast and twice this number eat lunch away from the home.

Among us, however, "who" eats out and "when" varies considerably. During the day, working people represent the largest share of customers, but in the evening, students are important, especially at the informal eating places like drive-ins.

Men alone or in groups make up the bulk of customers during breakfast and lunch hours. At dinnertime, family groups take over. Later in the evening, couples predominate.

We Americans like to take the whole family out—to give mother a break once in a while. Our children go along about half the time. Those between the ages of 6 and 12 are included most often. As most parents would guess, the younger ones are at home with a babysitter. Teenagers tend to want to go on their own.

Overall, the postwar "baby boom" has provided millions of new customers for the restaurant industry. In fact, total spending for food away from home has gone up at a faster rate than population. And restaurants catering to the under-35 groups have been growing even faster than the food service industry as a whole.

"Where" we eat varies considerably. However, basically it is at one of two types of places—at an institution like a hospital, college, or camp or at some kind of public eating place—a restaurant, cafeteria, snackbar, drive-in, and the like.

Although institutions represent a small share of all eating places, they are important in the number of people they serve. For example, the average college serves 10 times as many meals and snacks each day as the average public eating place.

But the typical American looking for a place to have lunch or one to take his family to for dinner isn't concerned about the meals being served in institutions. He will choose one of the 344,000 public eating places. It could be a spot to get a sandwich in a hurry, to take home a bucket of fried chicken, to stand in a cafeteria line for lunch, or to enjoy a leisurely dinner in a softly lighted dining room.

The family going out for dinner is apt to go to a restaurant located near home. They shouldn't have a difficult time finding one open because the average restaurant operates more than 13 hours a day, 6½ days a week, throughout the year. This restaurant is likely to have tables or booths, and possibly counter and carry-out service as well. Usually the menu will offer a

Eileen F. Taylor is a Food Economist in the Office of the Director, Marketing Economics Division, Economic Research Service.

variety of American plate meals rather than a particular food like seafood or oriental dishes.

But many kinds of eating places make up this average. For example, drive-in service is much more important in suburbs and rural areas than in central business districts. Counter service is more important in these areas. In small eating places—those with yearly sales of less than $20,000—sandwiches and refreshments are the most important specialty; those that specialize in seafoods, chops, steaks, and roast beef are likely to have sales of $100,000 or more.

Although most eating places are still independently owned, chain operations are growing in importance. A major reason for this is customer recognition. As we get accustomed to the style, the food, and the service associated with a certain name, we quickly recognize these wherever they are located—in our city or far from home. The golden arches and the orange roof have become landmarks because they are easy to recognize.

There are other reasons, too—chains have the necessary staff and resources to do research and invest in market studies. They have the experience and the talent to open a new eating place and make a success of it. Some chains have taken advantage of the rapid growth in the suburbs and specialized in drive-ins that appeal to young families. Some have diversified into the institutional field. Some offer prepared food for the customers to take home; others have developed their own brand of frozen foods so that their name is seen in grocery stores as well.

Urban living, working far from the home, increased travel around the country and the world, and even television have helped to make our tastes more diverse. Our away-from-home eating places tempt us by featuring everything from a full course steak dinner to shrimp creole to chow mein to a 20-cent hamburger. Though the largest share of eating places feature American-type meals, or sandwiches and refreshments, some specialize in Italian or oriental foods, roast beef, seafood, chicken, and steaks.

And our tastes are somewhat fickle. We always seem to be searching for something new or different. Last year's standbys—beef stew, creamed dishes, hash, and liver—appear to be "out" these days. Main dish salads, barbecued foods, pizzas, feature sandwiches, and diet specials are "in." So are a la carte menus, and especially those that include extravagant desserts.

The owner of a restaurant has to be constantly on the alert for changes in the kinds of food that will please his customers. A look at what's popular with the school lunch crowd—pizza, barbecued beef, or hamburgers—helps to guide the menu planner aiming at family groups. Even sales by his competitor—the grocer—can help. For

A family dining out.

example, young marrieds with small children may not have much extra money. But they remember how they ate at home before they were married. Gourmet foods and sauces appeal to them, and they tend to choose these when they get a chance to eat out. Small town residents who do lots of baking at home may be intrigued by the eating place that features "home-style pastries."

The widespread popularity of certain foods has led to the growth of eating places featuring limited menus. Some drive-ins offer only one type of sandwich and a choice of beverages.

In some chain organizations, the technique of preparation and service has become such an exact science that we can expect a roast beef sandwich or hamburger we buy in Denver to taste the same as the ones back home in Baltimore. The menu, the surroundings, and the advertising too are all designed to attract those who want quick, informal, and inexpensive food served in a familiar atmosphere.

But what may be even more interesting than the menu in your favorite eating place is how the cook prepares your meal. New food processing techniques and high cost of labor have combined to make partially and fully prepared foods very attractive to restaurant owners. It is quite possible that the delicious looking beef stroganoff you are eating in California today was prepared and frozen in Connecticut weeks before, and possibly even months ago. When a waitress takes your order, the cook gets the entree from the freezer, puts it in a microwave oven, and it is ready to serve in seconds. If chicken salad is on the menu, the cook will open a can of dehydrated salad mix, add water, and chill. If you'd like an egg salad, he might open a bag of frozen diced eggs and use these in his favorite recipe.

Some restaurants have achieved what might seem to be the impossible—virtually no kitchen at all! With specially selected menu offerings, one employee can take frozen food from storage, heat it in a microwave oven, and seconds later, serve it to the customer. This means that more space can be devoted to selling instead of being used for oversized preparation areas.

Many factors have combined to foster more eating away from home—to build an industry that, in a few years, may be serving us half our food. Important among these are the level of our incomes and where we live. Of these, our income is probably the most important. The more dollars we make, the more we spend for food away from our homes.

Studies have shown that the families with incomes of $10,000 and over a year spent more than 25 percent of their food money for meals away from home; those with less than $3,000 spent 10 percent. In actual dollars, the higher income families spent 10 times as much each week eating out as those in the low-income group.

When the wife works—as more than a third do now—the family is likely to eat out more often and to spend more doing so than a family having the same level of income with the wife not employed outside the home.

On the average, we spend about 5 percent of our household budgets for food away from home. There is some variation in this depending on where we live, however. Families in the West spent the most dollars. Families in the Northeast were the second biggest spenders, followed by families in the North Central States. Families in the South spent the fewest dollars, but in the last decade they have been increasing what they spend to eat out much more than families in other parts of the country. If we live in the city, rather than on the farm, we probably will spend more on eating out. But these differences, like those between the various regions, are becoming less pronounced.

This is our food service industry today. What will it be like in the years ahead?

To begin with, there will be more restaurants as the population increases and our take-home pay gets bigger. Today, there are more than 200 million

Americans. By 1975, there will be 25 million more of us, and 10 million more households. Younger families—those that are on the move and likely to eat out—will make up an even larger share of our population than they do now. Today, our median family income is a little more than $8,000. A third of our families earn more than $10,000. And it is predicted that by 1975 more than two-fifths of us will have incomes over $10,000. Unless the cost of eating away from home goes up more rapidly than incomes, we'll have more people with more money to dine out more often.

More married women will be working away from home, so restaurants will be geared to demands of the working wife. Perhaps we'll see substantial growth of restaurants in the suburbs, because this is where many working wives live. New restaurants will be designed for evening dining out for the whole family, at a place close to home. In addition, many of us like to use dining out as an occasion to entertain friends—especially those of us who live in apartments with limited space. Some experts are suggesting the possibility of a modified American plan—a system of special pricing for five dinners a month eaten in the same restaurant, with the same couple as hosts and different guests for each dinner.

Our tastes will become more and more discriminating, so eating places will have to meet those ever higher standards of excellence that we expect.

Except for luxury-type and specialty restaurants which feature fine cuisine, chains and franchised operations will continue to grow rapidly. We'll be able to identify even more establishments and types of eating places as we travel across the country.

Growth of the chains and the continuing importance of independently owned eating places mean that more and more people will be needed to work in and manage food service units. More than 150,000 openings a year are expected in the restaurant industry throughout the 1970's. Some of these will be new jobs as the industry grows, but most will be due to turnover. Even all of the new equipment and ready-to-serve foods won't ease the industry's need for good talent.

Restaurant kitchens will be smaller—some may even be virtually eliminated. Kitchen work will be cut down, but capable personnel to do the final preparation and serving of food will still be in demand. Opportunities for skilled chefs and restaurant managers will be expecially favorable. For the restaurant industry of the future will service an even more sophisticated market and will need highly trained management people.

Finally we, the customers, will be eating out more and more. Retail grocery stores are already feeling the impact of the increased away-from-home spending and are trying to cope with this new competitor by offering such services as a delicatessen, ready-to-eat barbecued chickens and an expanded frozen food department that includes family size entrees.

As long as the present trends last, we will continue to spend our extra dollars for service—and one of the services we like the most is having someone else do our food preparation and cleaning up for us. The organization that provides that service best—restaurants, drive-ins, vending machines, or even grocery stores—will prosper in the 1970's.

M. L. Upchurch

Farm Programs: Their Role in Assuring Our Food Supply

We Americans are lucky to be able to walk into a well-stocked supermarket at almost any time and choose our food from the wide variety offered. But fortunate as we are, we still need a farming industry that will assure us of plentiful supplies in the future.

Modern farming requires heavy investments of capital, along with heavy expenditures for seed, fertilizers, machinery, and fuel. The prices farmers get for what they plant or raise must cover all these costs and leave enough extra to pay for their efforts. If they can't cover these costs, farming as a business is in trouble, and our food supply is in jeopardy.

Like many other businesses today, farming has experienced vast changes. Most farms of the past were highly self-sufficient. They provided a way of life and some cash money to buy necessities. Modern farms are commercial businesses. During this change, farmers have often been perplexed; and many have been forced to leave their farms to seek other ways to earn a living.

Most of the change in farming has been brought about through improved machines, seeds, feeds, and fertilizers—by the so-called technological revolution. Machinery now does much of the work formerly done by men and work animals. Better seeds and new fertilizers have increased the amount produced per acre.

Modern farmers have the capacity to operate larger farms. Their desire to increase incomes encourages larger operations, and larger farms are required to use the new developments efficiently. As a result of these changes, about a third of the farms now produce four-fifths of our food. The other two-thirds—the small farms—seldom produce enough to provide sufficient income for even a minimum level of living. As a rule, these farmers supplement their income with off-farm jobs.

Farmers, as primary producers, face problems unlike those of most other businesses. A manufacturer can control his production to approximate demands. He can slow or step up his output in response to sales. So far, however, farmers have had difficulty balancing supplies of their products with demand well enough to prevent violent ups and downs in prices and farm incomes. The individual farmer cannot improve his income by not producing, by letting his land remain idle. Moreover, the size of his crops are subject to the whims of nature. He can have a bumper crop, or a hailstorm can flatten his wheat just before harvest.

Because of our needs for ample supplies of food for our ever increasing population, the farmer's plight must be our concern. For this reason, if for no other, various programs have been devised in an attempt to help farmers meet problems of erratic supplies and dislocations brought on by technical improvements. A look at some past problems may provide an insight into the rationale behind programs which have been devised to help the farmers and, at the same time, provide us with an adequate and continuing supply of foodstuffs.

M. L. Upchurch is Administrator, Economic Research Service.

For a few years prior to World War I, farmers were relatively well off. Then, following that war, prices of farm products dropped sharply while those of other products stayed about the same or went up.

At the time, some people regarded this change as a normal readjustment from pre-World War I levels. Others disagreed. One way suggested to show the relative well-being of farmers was by the use of a so-called "parity ratio." Parity was defined as the relationship between the prices received and prices paid by farmers during the period 1909–1914. In general then, a parity ratio of 100 would mean that farmers were or are as well off at a particular time as in this pre-World War I period.

Congress, too, was concerned about the plight of farmers and twice passed the McNary-Haugen bills which were twice vetoed by the President. Then, in the late 1920's, the Federal Farm Board was created to give farmers relief from low prices, but it was "too little" and almost "too late" to help out very much.

The advent of the Great Depression demanded action for relief of farmers. The days of ". . . ten-cent cotton and forty-cent meat . . ." had become "five-cent cotton and twenty-cent meat." Farmers were burning corn for fuel instead of coal, as there was no market for their corn and no money with which to buy coal. Many lost their farms because they couldn't pay their debts. It was during this period that Congress enacted the Agricultural Adjustment Act, commonly called the AAA, as one of a broad range of tools to fight the nationwide economic depression.

This early AAA program called on farmers to reduce production of basic commodities in return for price supports guaranteed by the Government. Variations on this theme have been the core of farm legislation and programs ever since. In addition, prices of commodities other than the basic grains, cotton, and tobacco have been supported, when necessary, by direct purchases in the market. Some of these purchases have been financed by a portion of the import duties which legislation has decreed to be used for this purpose. In recent years, producers of feed grains and wheat have been offered the opportunity to reduce their production below the former levels in return for price support loans and direct supplements to their income.

These arrangements and other variations have been used to try to restrict production of major crops and to increase incomes of farmers. They have been necessary because of the chronic tendency of farmers to produce more than our markets will take at satisfactory prices.

You might ask, "Why don't farmers reduce their output without Government programs if prices and incomes can be improved by restricted production?" The answer is that with 3 million farms, the influence of any one farmer on production and price is negligible. No individual farmer can reduce the amount he produces and gain by increased prices unless all the farmers go along with him.

Again, we might ask, "What would happen if we did not have such programs?" As an example, let's examine what could have happened during the past decade if we hadn't had these programs.

A decade ago stocks of major farm products held by the Government were excessively large. It was evident that changes in programs were needed to bring about a better balance between supplies and demands. As a result, during recent years, farm programs have included price supports, acreage diversion policies (which affect both supply and income), and promotional programs designed to stimulate domestic and foreign demand. Export subsidies were also used in the early 1960's, but more recently these have been reduced or dropped.

Records were kept of the volume of production, prices, and incomes that occurred under these circumstances, and studies have been made to ascertain what would have happened during this period without the various programs. As a basis for these analyses, we assumed a balance between production and demand for farm products. Besides, we assumed that land held in the Conservation Reserve at the beginning of the 1960's would gradually return to production.

According to these studies, without the programs the production of farm commodities would have increased and prices would have gone down. Lower prices would have boosted domestic consumption and exports. Lower feed prices would have boosted livestock production which, in turn, would have lowered prices of livestock. We would have had more land in wheat, feed grains, and cotton than we actually had. Prices of such crops as soybeans, rice, and tobacco would have been much lower than they actually were.

There has long been concern about our farmers and their problems, and many diverse opinions as to how best to solve them. Because of this, in 1965, the President set up a National Advisory Commission on Food and Fiber. In his initial charge to the Commission he said:

"New ways must be explored to keep agriculture and agricultural policy up-to-date, to get the full benefit of new findings and of new technology, to make sure that our bountiful land is used to the best of our ability to promote the welfare of consumers, farmers, and the entire economy.

"I am asking you as a Commission to make a penetrating and long range appraisal . . . to construct a thorough and searching study of the effects of our agricultural policies on the performance of our economy . . . ."

The report to the President by the Commission said—

". . . the pursuit of efficiency in a dynamic economy means adjustments for some of our people, and perhaps the need to look objectively at some of the long-held concepts we have associated with work and achievement on one hand, and social and economic organization on the other . . .

"We have reached the stage when the nation must clearly separate its policies directed toward commercial agriculture from those designed to deal with poverty in rural areas. Analyses and solutions for one sector have no particular significance to the other . . .

"The Commission is in almost total agreement on a number of modifications needed in the present agricultural commodity programs to bring U.S. farming closer to a market orientation, help to alleviate excess capacity, and become still more efficient and responsive to changes in productivity and markets. These include changes in the parity concept, price supports, deficiency payments, acreage allotments and quotas, reclamation programs, conservation payments, strategic reserves, export subsidies, and import quotas.

"The main difference between the majority and minority of the Commission lies in the policies that should be followed after these initial steps are taken.

"The majority of the Commission recommends that the modified programs be retained until the problem of excess capacity in farming is alleviated, and farmers are able to earn incomes from the market that are comparable to nonfarm incomes.

"They feel such programs may well be desirable as safeguards for farmers on a standby basis, even after excess capacity has been alleviated.

"The minority believes that, following an appropriate transition period, the United States should rely on temporary income supplements or a moderate level of price deficiency payments, to protect farmers' incomes against temporary declines with a minimum of interference in the operation of the market."

Changes of the magnitude suggested will take time. But, if we are to continue to visit our supermarkets and have the same choices tomorrow and the many tomorrows, future programs must make sure that the primary producers of food—our farmers—stay healthy, economically.

Samuel C. Vanneman

School Lunch to Food Stamp: America Cares for Its Hungry

Hunger hurts. It hurts physically, mentally, and emotionally. It is a harsh and ugly word that has no place in the American scheme of things.

Nutrition is a quiet word—a grey word—it carries no image of anger or harshness. It is a positive word, and it has an important role in the American scheme of things.

Americans are gradually becoming aware that hunger and, more particularly, poor nutrition still do exist within our borders.

In the last 30 years, the United States has steadily expanded and improved its programs to improve nutrition among children and low-income families.

One example is the national school lunch program, enacted in 1946. Congress, in the National School Lunch Act, declares its policy to safeguard the health and well-being of children and encourage consumption of nutritious foods.

The Act authorized giving cash and foods to schools that offer a nutritionally balanced lunch to children, without profit. Such lunches include a half-pint of milk, a protein-rich food, a vegetable and/or fruit, and enriched bread with butter or margarine.

The National School Lunch Act also requires that a child who cannot pay the full price of the lunch shall get it free or at a reduced price. The lunch program is further intended for all children, regardless of their ability to pay.

The special milk program—a dual-purpose program—was enacted in 1954. By providing Federal cash assistance to help reduce the cost of milk served to children, nutrition would receive a boost while at the same time strengthening the market for sales of fluid whole milk. This program was, in many respects, a stopgap until a complete lunch, including milk, could be made available to all children.

The oldest of our food assistance programs is the commodity donation program for low-income families. It was started some 30 years ago, when an amendment to law authorized encouraging consumption of agricultural commodities through donating them to low-income persons, among other means.

Originally, the foods offered to State and local governments for donation to needy families were limited to foods acquired by the Federal Government under price support and surplus removal programs.

For many years, the foods offered depended, primarily, on supply factors and bore little direct relationship to the nutritional needs of the family. In late 1960, for example, the donated foods included lard, flour, cornmeal, nonfat dry milk, and rice. The assumption had always been that donated foods would provide some help and free some of the family's food purchasing power to buy other foods needed.

Over the postwar years there had been little awareness of how many people—or how many families—were trying to live, trying to survive on the donated foods and little else.

Early in 1961, steps were taken to build on what had been done, and

Samuel C. Vanneman is Assistant Deputy Administrator, Consumer Food Programs, Consumer and Marketing Service.

try some new approaches to improving nutrition. The first step was to increase the quantity and variety of the donated foods offered—with special emphasis upon assuring the continuing availability of protein items.

The second step was to introduce the food stamp program on a pilot basis. The food stamp program uses a different technique from that of the donation program. Food stamps are used to increase a family's existing food purchasing power. Families are required to purchase food coupons in amounts that reflect their normal level of food expenditure based on family size and income. This on-going food purchasing power is then supplemented by additional food coupons provided free of charge. On the average, families pay about $6 for every $10 worth of coupons they receive. Families shop for food in the food stores of their choice that are authorized to redeem the food coupons. Virtually every food store in every community which has the program is authorized to accept food coupons. Families may buy any food they wish with the exception of a few imported products.

Here again, we have a dual-purpose program. Families have an opportunity to improve their nutrition while broadening the demand for farm products—particularly for perishable items such as meat, poultry, dairy products, and fruits and vegetables.

The food stamp program was tested on a gradually expanded basis before enactment of substantive legislation in 1964. This legislation contemplated a continuing gradual expansion of the program so it could be made available to every county and city that wanted it. Under one provision of the Food Stamp Act, a local jurisdiction may have the commodity program or the food stamp program but not both, since essentially they are directed toward the same end—improved family nutrition.

During these years, every effort was made to encourage State and local governments to join one program or the other. Funding of the food stamp program has never been sufficient to cover all of the counties that have wanted the program, but these counties have been urged to initiate a donation program as an interim step. Rates that many families had to pay for their stamps were reduced, effective in February 1969.

In mid-1967, a review of program coverage, geographically, revealed that many of the thousand lowest income counties in the country did not have a food assistance program for the low-income families. Many of these, with a limited tax base, felt they could not afford the donation program under which the costs of storage, distribution, and certification are borne by local governments with, in most instances, very limited help from the State. The U.S. Department of Agriculture moved to offer these local governments assistance in meeting local costs for the donation program. Similar assistance for a food stamp program is barred by language in the Food Stamp Act that limits financial assistance for administration to a portion of certification expenses.

Many counties accepted the offer of financial assistance. Many managed to find funds, locally, to join the program. But some counties simply said they did not want a food assistance program under any circumstances. In these instances, USDA moved to meet the larger responsibility to all our low-income families by using its own personnel to operate a commodity donation program in these counties. At the same time, USDA said it would stand aside any moment that the local government would agree to operate the donation program with or without financial assistance.

Meanwhile the nutritive value and the variety of the foods offered under the donation program were stepped up. In early 1969, 22 foods were offered which, if they are all accepted by State and local governments and used by eligible families, will provide from 80 to 150 percent of the minimum daily requirements for all nutrients as recommended by the Food and Nutrition Board of the National Research Council. Since these foods amounted to some 35 pounds per person, each month, and most areas provide only a monthly distribution, some very practical limitations are encountered in terms of a large family's ability to get the food home and store it.

Also, in mid-1967, modifications were made in the food stamp program to make it more fully responsive to the needs of participating families. The purchase requirement for the lowest-income families was dropped to 50 cents a month per person, with a maximum of $3 for a family of six or more. The first month's purchase requirement for all families was reduced by half to give them time to adjust their budgets to the purchase requirement. Adjustments were made in the determination of farm income so that farm laborers and others would not be priced out of the program.

In February 1969, the price of stamps was further reduced, but the reduction was limited by the appropriation available. Some further modifications are now under consideration.

As indicated above, modifications have been made whenever food stamp program experience has demonstrated a need for change. Still further changes are under consideration to assure that the program is as effective as possible in assisting low-income families toward the goal of an adequate diet.

To further emphasize the national commitment to improved nutrition, the President has issued a call to convene a White House conference on nutrition in the fall of 1969.

Mother pays at checkout counter with food stamps. Back home, she uses purchases to feed baby.

It has become increasingly clear that total community involvement is necessary if malnutrition is to be eliminated. The 1969 White House conference will summon the thinking and the ideas and the recommendations of the widest possible range of concerned people from both the private and the public sector toward this end.

An additional supplementary food program is underway in both food stamp and commodity donation areas to provide the low-income pregnant

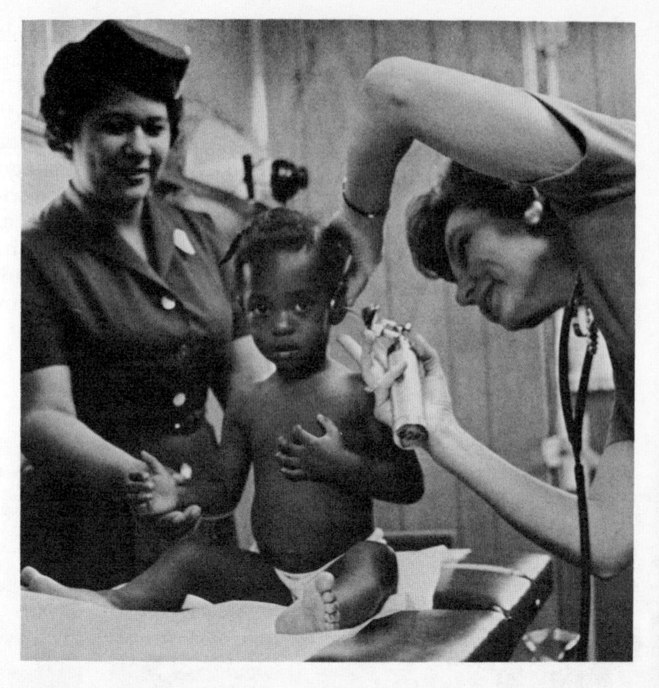

Mother and young child get extra food as part of free health care at public clinic in North Carolina. Above, child is examined at clinic. Doctor then writes food prescription as preventative measure or to treat specific health condition. Health official, below, checks records. Family will receive foods from USDA-donated stocks.

women and new mothers and their young children with special foods to meet their special needs.

The goal over the next several years is to have a family food assistance program operating in every county and independent city in the country—there are still more than 400 that do not participate.

Child Nutrition. Hand-in-hand with the evolution in family food assistance programs has been a similar development to improve child nutrition. Program growth under the school lunch program since its start in 1947 had been steady, but the progress made was deceiving.

Behind the pleasant growth figures of 6 to 7 percent annually lay the unpleasant truth that millions—literally millions—of children had been bypassed. The students in small rural schools and the students in the urban elementary schools had become the forgotten children. The free and reduced price requirement in the National School Lunch Act was impossible to meet in the absence of greater funding. Many schools, knowing that their youngsters couldn't pay enough to make a viable lunch program, had declined to sign up. Others did come into the program but were only able to offer a fraction of the free and reduced price meals that were necessary.

The first major forward step of this decade was taken in 1962 when the school lunch formula for apportionment of Federal funds to the States was revised to reward those States making the greatest effort to increase participation. The previous formula had tended to reward the stand-patters and discourage increased participation—the more meals you served, the less you received per lunch. The second major step in that amendment was one authorizing a higher rate of reimbursement, per meal, in those schools drawing attendance from low-income areas. This provision was much needed and was enacted rather easily but was not funded until the 1964–65 school year and, then, only to a very limited extent.

It was apparent that many schools could not participate in the lunch program because they were unable to finance the cost of even simple, basic food service equipment. At the same time, increasing numbers of educators were finding that all too many children came to school without breakfast or with a totally inadequate one. They fell asleep at their desks—they became listless and inattentive or bored and restless. In the Child Nutrition Act of 1966, the Nation moved to meet this need. Legislation authorized a pilot school breakfast program. It authorized assistance in financing school food service equipment in low-income area schools. And it authorized help to the States in strengthening their technical assistance capabilities so as to get food service programs into a substantial number of schools that either had no programs, or where an on-going program was eking out a quite precarious existence.

In 1968, still another forward step was taken with legislation that authorizes food service assistance to day-care centers, summer day camps, neighborhood houses, settlement houses, summer recreational projects—almost any situation where children are gathered together in organized groups and can be reached with a food service. This bill also extended the school breakfast program which during its pilot stage had proved its value many times over.

Meanwhile, during these past several years, the Congress has provided a level of funding for the regular lunch program that will assure a steady rate of reimbursement per meal and allow for expansion of the regular program. For fiscal 1969, the Congress provided $45 million over and above the money appropriated for what might be considered the regular child food service activities. The major share of these funds—$43 million—was allocated to provide free and reduced price meals to around 2 million additional needy children who could not have been reached with the money available under the regular child food service appropriations.

Above, a young charmer with her school lunch in the Nation's Capital. Below, child at Indian reservation in Oklahoma gets energy for class under pilot school breakfast program.

We have, then, a situation where the regular school lunch program can continue to grow and expand while additional and new resources are being applied to get to the neediest children. And, as child food service grows, so does this big market for the Nation's farmers—nearly $1 billion is spent locally for foods needed in the lunch and breakfast programs.

Our national goal is a food service program available to every school child, priced at a level so that every child may participate. New approaches are being tested to minimize the cost of equipment, for example, through the use of centralized kitchens serving a number of satellite schools.

There is one more major drive under way that affects both the family food assistance programs and the child nutrition programs—an all-out effort to get across the nutrition message. This drive seeks to explain why good nutrition is important and to make good nutrition part of everyone's life. The actual existence and participation in the food programs is not enough—people need to know why they should eat certain foods. And this applies to all of our families, however poor or however affluent.

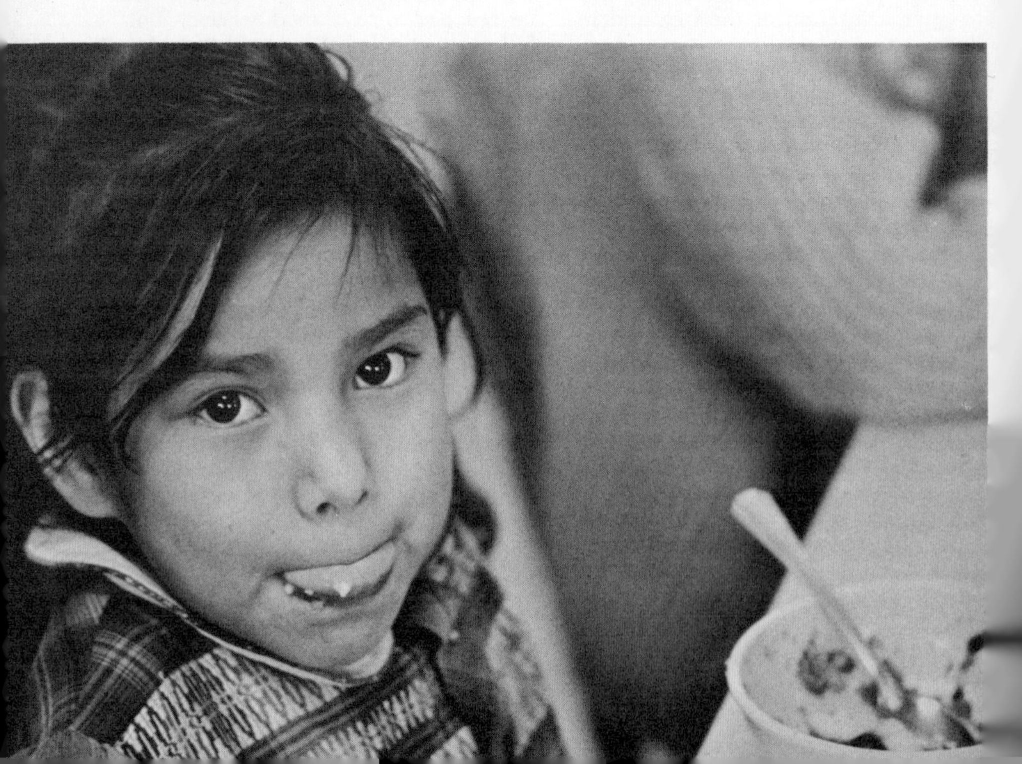

Kenneth W. Olson

U.S. Farmers, Suppliers of Food for the World

American farmers produce such a large volume of agricultural products that there is plenty for all of us, with large amounts left over to share with the rest of the world.

Our country is the world's biggest exporter of farm products. The harvest from 1 in every 4 acres goes abroad.

Travel to Spain, and the eggs you eat for breakfast may have come from hens fed on American corn. Travel to Brazil, and the bread you eat for lunch may have been made from American wheat. Travel to Japan, and the fried shrimp you eat for dinner may have been cooked in vegetable oil from American soybeans.

In nearly 125 countries, you have but to look and somewhere—on the shelves of the food shops, in the feed mills and flour mills and bakeries, in the cotton mills, even in the shoe factories—you will find products that originated on American farms.

The farmers of the United States, through exports, have established a presence in the world that is unique, helpful, and profitable. It is unique because no other nation exports such a variety and volume of farm products as we do. It is helpful because without our farms as an auxiliary source of food, millions of people in Europe, Latin America, Africa, and Asia either would have a lower standard of living or actually would be hungry. It is profitable because foreign trade is good business for the United States; it provides additional markets for our fertile acres and additional income for our farm and city people.

Our three biggest exports are wheat, feed grains, and soybeans. Mainly, although not entirely, these products move to foreign ports in large bulk shipments, and sometimes completely filling the holds of ships. To a lesser extent, they may move in processed form—the wheat as flour, the feed grains as specially formulated mixed feeds, and the soybeans as soybean oil or meal. These three have been called members of the Billion Dollar Export Club, since exports of each recently have been totaling more than $1 billion a year.

Our country has such a diversity of soil and climate, however, that our farmers are able to produce for export a wide range of products besides wheat, feed grains, and soybeans. Last year's official trade listings show that 466 different American agricultural items moved into foreign commerce. Among them, naming only a few, were rice, dairy products, red meats, poultry, fresh and canned fruits, lard, and frozen foods.

In total, the United States exports as much as $6 billion or more worth of farm products each year. Somewhat more than three-fourths of these shipments move as dollar-earning commercial sales; somewhat less than one fourth of the shipments move under foreign aid.

Even though it represents the smaller segment of our agricultural exports, one of the dramatic parts of our foreign agricultural trade is the food aid we make available to the less developed countries. Through this program we

Kenneth W. Olson is Director of the Foreign Market Information Division, Foreign Agricultural Service.

have helped to prevent starvation among millions of people and we have helped to build better living conditions for millions of others.

During India's two bad drought years, 1965–66 and 1966–67, about a shipload of wheat moved daily from American ports to Indian ports. Some 60 million people of India received most of their nourishment from this American grain.

Food aid shipments are made largely under authority of Public Law 480, the Food for Peace program. Under this program, food reaches the needy in several ways—through donations, concessional sales in which the receiving country pays with its own "soft" currency, and sales for dollars under long-term credit arrangements. Between 1954, when Public Law 480 was enacted by the Congress, and the end of 1968, a total of $17½ billion worth of U.S. farm products moved to needy countries under its provisions.

Throughout the years of Public Law 480, however, there has been growing recognition that this food aid alone is not an adequate answer to the gnawing question: "Can the world feed itself?" Two years ago an important addition was made to the program. A "self-help" stipulation was added which says that a developing country, to be eligible for our food assistance, must be making a determined effort to improve its own farm production and general economic status—in other words, must be trying seriously to get off the relief rolls and become self-supporting.

Today our food aid program not only is helping to feed hungry people but is giving encouragement and support to their own efforts to do a better job of feeding themselves.

We noted earlier that the big part of U.S. sharing of food supplies with the world takes place not under aid but under traditional methods of sell-

Sharing Our Abundant Food Supplies with the World

[Billion dollars]

Year ending June 30	U.S. agricultural exports		Total	
	Government programs	Dollar sales	Agricultural exports	All U.S. exports
1946	1.8	1.1	2.9	8.5
1947	0.9	2.7	3.6	12.7
1948	1.6	1.9	3.5	13.8
1949	2.3	1.5	3.8	12.7
1950	2.0	1.0	3.0	10.1
1951	1.2	2.2	3.4	12.6
1952	0.6	3.4	4.1	15.6
1953	0.5	2.4	2.8	15.1
1954	0.6	2.3	2.9	15.2
1955	0.8	2.3	3.1	14.9
1956	1.3	2.2	3.5	16.9
1957	1.9	2.8	4.7	20.7
1958	1.2	2.8	4.0	18.7
1959	1.2	2.5	3.7	17.4
1960	1.3	3.2	4.5	19.1
1961	1.5	3.4	4.9	20.5
1962	1.6	3.6	5.1	21.4
1963	1.5	3.6	5.1	21.6
1964	1.5	4.6	6.1	24.7
1965	1.7	4.4	6.1	26.3
1966	1.6	5.1	6.7	28.9
1967	1.6	5.2	6.8	30.8
1968	1.6	4.7	6.3	32.0
Total 1946–68	31.7	68.9	100.7	430.1

Figures may not add to totals due to rounding.

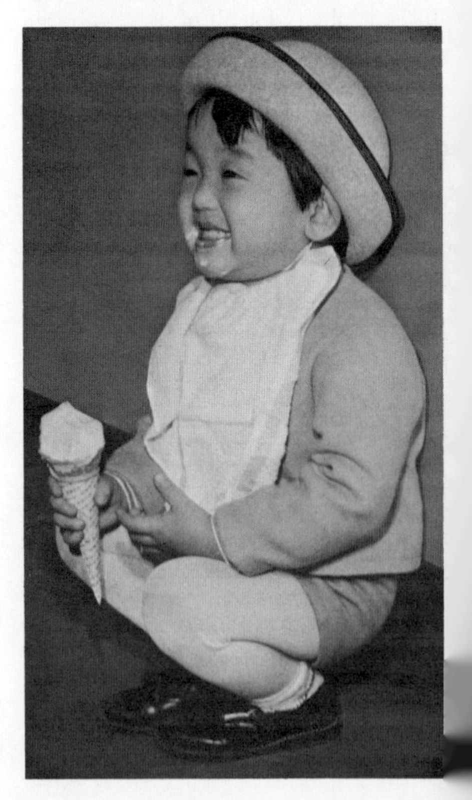

Kyoto boy enjoys his first taste of soft "ice cream" made of soybean products. This taste treat is becoming increasingly popular in Japan, world's No. 1 importer of U.S. soybeans.

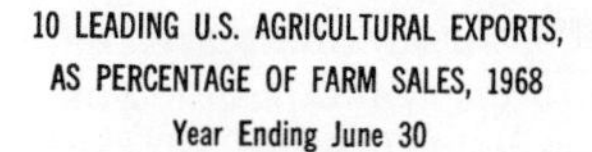

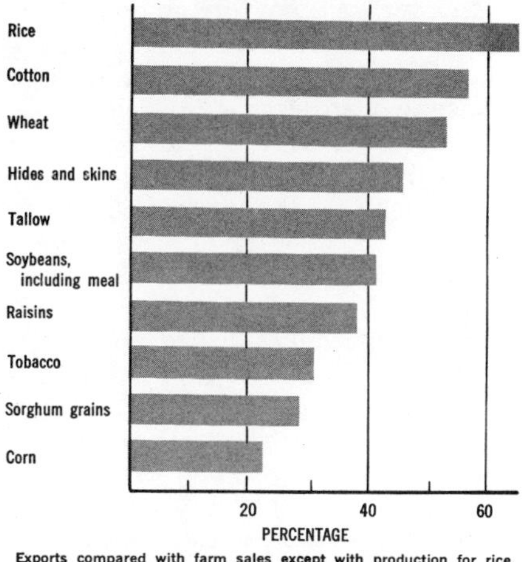

Exports compared with farm sales except with production for rice, hides and skins, tallow, cotton, and tobacco.

ing in the world market. And we noted that three-fourths of our agricultural exports move as commercial sales. An additional fact of which many people are not fully aware is that these dollar-earning commercial sales—averaging $5 billion a year during the 1966–68 fiscal years—have become the strongest single contributor in easing our Nation's troublesome balance of payments problem.

American agriculture's positive contribution to the Nation's international payments position comes about because our dollar-earning agricultural exports have been considerably larger than our dollar-costing agricultural imports. The difference between them, known as the favorable trade balance, has helped to offset balance of payments deficits incurred by the non-agricultural part of our economy. In this way, American agriculture has contributed a net plus of about $1 billion a year to our Nation's balance of payments during some recent years.

American agriculture and foreign commerce are not new to each other. In colonial days, the pioneer farmers sold their tobacco, cotton, rice, jute, and indigo to markets in England. What is new about today's U.S. agricultural export flow is its size and diversity. Every American agricultural product finds part of its market abroad. Half or more of our production of rice, wheat, and hides and skins is exported. A third to a half of our cotton, grain sorghum, tallow, soybean, and tobacco production is exported. A fourth of our corn is exported.

These large foreign markets for American farm products are a comparatively recent development. Much expansion has taken place within the past 10 years. In fiscal year 1958, we exported only $4 billion worth of farm products. In fiscal year 1967, we exported a record $6.8 billion worth, a gain of 70 percent. And the long-range outlook for future gains is good.

The expanding of foreign markets for our farm products is one of the outstanding success stories of modern American agriculture. As every successful businessman knows, however, market expansion is not a process that takes place by itself. The "e" in expansion requires an additional "e" for effort. The effort behind this expansion has been in two directions.

• Access to foreign markets. Trade barriers are the bane of any exporter's existence. No matter how good his

American Rice Council representative talks prices with Saudi Arabian sheikh, who ordered large quantities of U.S. rice at display in Beirut.

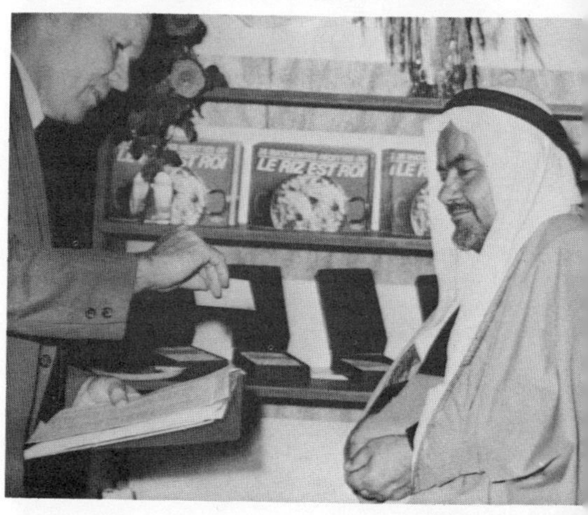

product, or attractive his price, his selling efforts are frustrated unless the doors of an importing country are open. The United States has worked hard for many years—and with considerable success—to open doors and bring about a freer flow of agricultural products in international trade channels. The Kennedy Round of trade negotiations was only one example of such efforts. Work goes on continuously to get foreign governments to permit our farm products to enter their countries and compete for sales to their consumers.

• Promotion in foreign markets. With access to a foreign market, the exporter of American farm products is able to promote sales. This he is doing today more aggressively than ever before. And in doing it, he is given a helping hand by the U.S. Department of Agriculture and a large number of cooperating private trade and agricultural producer associations.

A new chapter in U.S. agricultural export promotion was begun when, somewhat more than 10 years ago, USDA and cooperating agricultural and trade groups set up a joint-venture foreign market development program. Gradually the program was expanded until today sales promotions are being carried out abroad for every major agricultural commodity produced in the United States.

The list of countries in which the promotions are carried out has grown to 70. Much of the actual promotion work is done by the cooperators, and they use a variety of techniques: Market surveys, demonstrations, technical assistance to foreign users, advertising, test shipments, and many others.

A prime means of attracting foreign tradespeople and consumers is through exhibits of U.S. farm and food products at international trade fairs. Since 1955, USDA and cooperators have sponsored more than 200 such "showcases" in almost 40 countries. Among target cities have been London, Paris, Munich, Cologne, Brussels, and Tokyo.

Permanent trade centers for promotion of U.S. products are maintained in London, Milan, and Tokyo, and they too help to stimulate sales.

Another way that foreign consumers are being reached is through "America Week" U.S. food promotions in large department stores and in self-service chainstores. This type promotion in Tokyo in April 1968 resulted in sales of American foods that totaled nearly $1 million.

Still another export promotion technique is the foreign trade mission. Teams of specially selected marketing experts, representing both our Government and private business, from time to time visit countries that are active or potential buyers. The evaluations and advice they bring back provide important guidelines, both to exporters selling in the areas and to Government efforts to assist such sales. In similar fashion, teams of foreign buyers are brought to the United States to get acquainted with our producers and our products.

The success we have achieved in foreign agricultural marketing has not always come easily. For the sun never

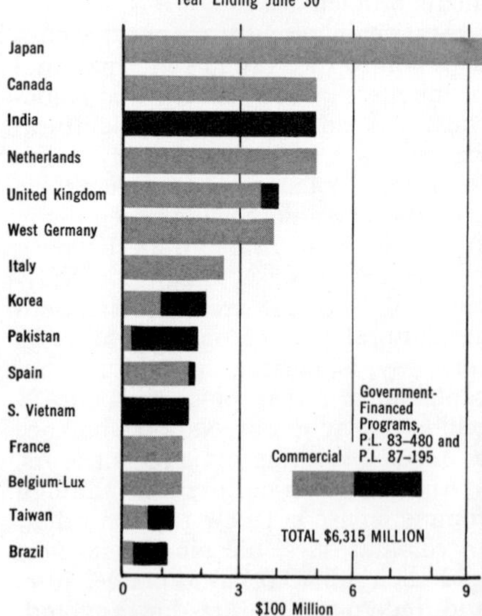

Data not adjusted for intransit shipments; U.S. shipments through Canadian ports, for example, were $79 million

Foreign promotions of U.S. foods. Above left, country singer introduces West Berlin boy to American hamburger. Above right, "bride" samples U.S. food at British food show. Right, film star Dana Andrews autographs cake at U.S. food promotion in Spain.

sets on the flags of our competitors. Wherever American farm products go, there also are the products of others—Canada, Australia, New Zealand, Thailand, Communist China, Denmark, France, the Netherlands, South Africa, Argentina.

Adding to the problems of competition, there also is an increasing trend toward protectionism and self-sufficiency in some of our major markets, particularly those of Western Europe. This trend in the six countries of the European Economic Community already is hurting some of our agricultural sales there, and the impact may be even greater in the years ahead of us.

In Japan, our largest single market for agricultural products, there is a definite trend toward diversifying the sources of supply. That is, Japan is seeking to spread its buying around among a number of agricultural exporting countries instead of depending so heavily upon a single country such as the United States for its supplies.

Even the developing countries are increasing their trade barriers against American farm products. In a number of instances they have set up special trading arrangements with other suppliers, thereby cutting off that much of their markets for our agricultural exports.

Though many problems lie ahead, however, the fact is that at this particular period of history, our Nation is enjoying rewarding returns from its agricultural exporting operations. Look at a map and you will see that we have only a relatively small share of the world's land area. Yet, our farmers supply nearly a fifth of all the agricultural products that move in world trade. We produce abundantly and, mainly through trade, we now share and can expect to continue to share abundantly with a world that needs and welcomes our products.

For further reading:

U.S. Department of Agriculture, *Handbook of Agricultural Charts*. Agricultural Handbook 359, Washington, D.C. 20250, 1968.

U.S. Economic Research Service, *Foreign Agricultural Trade of the United States*. U.S. Department of Agriculture, Washington, D.C. 20250.

U.S. Foreign Agricultural Service, *Foreign Agriculture*. U.S. Department of Agriculture, Washington, D.C. 20250.

American foods are popular in grocery stores around world. Here, shoppers examine Hawaiian pineapple at Tokyo supermarket.

Quentin M. West

The Revolution in Agriculture: New Hope for Many Nations

Antonino Eldemida is a rice farmer in the province of San Isidro in the Philippines. He is a tenant on 12 acres of land. He is probably the first farmer to plant "miracle" rice. His yields more than doubled. He sold the new rice for 23 pesos ($5.90) per cavan (100 lbs.). He bought an acre of land and a tractor; he sent two children to college. He improved his irrigation system as well.

This year there is a surplus of rice in the Philippines. The government has a lot of money in rice it bought last year and cannot export. It has not been able to support the price this year. Senor Eldemida only received 11.5 pesos per cavan this year. He still makes more money than with the old varieties, but some of the bloom is off the "miracle."

H. S. Grewal is a wheat farmer in the Punjab state of India. He is a retired army major and owns 30 acres of irrigated land. He adopted the new dwarf wheat 2 years ago. Yields increased more than 50 percent. He has replaced his Persian water wheel (operated by buffalo) with an electric pump. He has ordered a tractor, but it will take 2 to 3 years to get it.

The Punjab has produced a surplus of about 2 million tons of wheat the past 2 years which has helped feed the deficit areas in India. However, it took a long time to move it, and there was not enough storage. If the monsoon had not been 2 weeks late last summer, thousands of tons of harvested wheat would have been rained on.

It is important to be clear what today's world agricultural revolution is and what it is not. It is a tremendous accomplishment. It is a new hope for developing nations. It is not a total solution to the hunger problem, but it should make substantial additions to food supplies in countries where there have been food shortages. It should relieve the pressures to produce or to import grains to provide sufficient quantities of food and enable these countries to begin to plan for better quality of diet, including the livestock products, pulses, fruits, and vegetables.

Today's hope for hungry nations starts with their growing awareness of the necessity for agricultural improvement. More of their national budget is being allocated to agriculture. More foreign exchange is being made available for fertilizer imports. Some governments have scrapped their cheap food policy and are supporting higher farm prices. But an important factor in present prospects is the new high-yielding varieties of wheat and of rice.

Dwarf varieties of wheat, developed with the support of the Rockefeller Foundation in Mexico, are now being planted across South Asia and in North Africa. In West and South Asia, these improved varieties now cover an estimated 16 percent of the total wheat acreage.

Two new tropical varieties of rice (IR–8 and IR–5) have been developed by the International Rice Research Institute in the Philippines, a combined Ford-Rockefeller Foundations venture. They have been planted on about 13 million hectares or about 7

Quentin M. West is Director, Foreign Regional Analysis Division, Economic Research Service.

percent of the rice land in South and Southeast Asia this year (1968/69).

These new grain seeds are especially responsive to heavy application of fertilizer, as many old varieties are not. When grown under proper conditions, they produce yields which may double or more those of the old seed. A rough estimate, based on very limited information, is that the new varieties of rice will add about 9 percent to the total production of South and Southeast Asia in 1968/69, compared with what production would have been without them. Wheat production in West and South Asia in 1968/69 may be 20 percent higher due to the new dwarf varieties. This is difficult to estimate because this year and last have seen good weather following 2 years of drought in several countries. Also, fertilizer consumption has been rising sharply and grain acreage has gone up.

Several factors will impede expansion of the new varieties. They are new to the regions where they are being introduced and may become susceptible to local diseases and insects. Plant protection services are primitive in most of these countries. Without large investments in irrigation facilities, the potential of these new seeds will not be realized. Since the new rice matures early, during the latter part of the wet season, drying facilities must be supplied.

Also, priorities given to agriculture could weaken as the food crisis of the past few years abates. Farm prices could fall and reduce farmers' incentives. If internal marketing and distribution facilities are not improved, increased food supplies may not reach the people who need them. Also, as countries begin to produce a surplus over their effective domestic demand, problems of finding export markets at satisfactory prices soon develop.

From our own history, however, we know that the path of agricultural development is not always smooth. It would be too much to expect unruffled progress in the developing countries. The important thing is that agricultural development has gotten off dead-center and is moving. With hope, we can expect the progress to be greater than the problems.

World Food Situation

What is the size and scope and history of today's world food problem? Where is it centered? And what are we of the United States doing to help to solve it?

Opinions on the magnitude of the world food problem have often swung between extremes of pessimism and optimism. In the late 1940's, considerable concern existed about world food shortages. Fears lessened as surpluses accumulated in the early 1950's. However, by the mid-1950's, supply management and food aid programs began to reduce the large U.S. reserves. Then in 1966, there was a rapid drawdown of world grain stocks and an increase in grain prices largely as a result of expanded imports by India and the Soviet Union. India had 2 successive years of drought, and the Soviet Union had two crop failures in 3 years.

These events were taken by many as evidence that the world food problem was worsening, and again raised the question whether there would be sufficient food in the future to supply the rapidly growing world population at acceptable levels of nutrition.

In 1967, the situation was somewhat different. Record grain crops had been produced in the Soviet Union, Canada, and Australia (1966/67). India harvested almost 100 million tons of food grain (1967/68), compared with 73 and 78 million in the previous 2 years. Western Europe and South Africa also had record grain crops. Crop production gains in 1967 were especially marked in the less-developed countries of the free world. Per capita food output increased by about 5 to 6 percent, a recovery to the previous record level of 1964 or slightly above.

Record crops in the developing countries in 1967 and the successes of the new high-yielding varieties of wheat and rice have led many to be more optimistic about development possibilities in these countries. They feel that the new grain varieties, plus a whole new agricultural technology involving large fertilizer applications, irrigation, and double (or even triple) cropping can revolutionize agriculture and food production in many of the developing nations.

Food production again increased in the developing countries in 1968 but only at the same pace as population. Per capita production remained at practically the same level as in 1967.

It is hard to determine with any degree of accuracy the current food situation in the developing countries and project how it will change in the future. Statistics do not exist, or at the best are rough estimates, in many nations for even the most basic elements of population, production, and trade. Weather may cause fluctuations in agricultural production as great as 25 percent and obscure other changes. The U.S. Department of Agriculture is doing research on the world food problem because it is essential to our programs for food aid, agricultural trade, and domestic production to have the best estimates possible of developments in these countries. The major reports on this research are *The World Food Budget, 1970,* (FAER 19), and *World Food Situation; Prospects for World Grain Production, Consumption, and Trade* (FAER 35). Some highlights of these studies follow.

The Food Gap

Probably two-thirds of the world's people live in countries with nutritionally inadequate national average diets. The diet-deficit areas include all of Asia except Japan and Israel, all but the southern tip of Africa, and most of South and of Central America. The calorie level of the diets of people in these less-developed countries averages about three-fourths that of people living in developed countries, and is 150 to 200 calories below the minimum standard of 2,400 calories required for normal activity and health.

Consumption of about 40 pounds additional grain per person annually would be required to meet this calorie deficit. The total additional grain required for the free world developing countries would amount to about 25 million metric tons of grain, or about 10 percent of their present production of grains. Almost two-thirds of this requirement is in four major food-aid countries—India, Pakistan, Indonesia, and Egypt, with over 45 percent in India alone.

There is also a deficiency of protein in most of the developing countries. Daily consumption of protein by the people in these countries averaged less than two-thirds of the level in the developed nations.

Food production has been increasing at a slightly faster rate in the developing countries than in the developed countries, but the per capita trend in developing countries has been slowed by a high rate of population growth. Annual population growth has reached 2½ to 3 percent in many developing countries, as widespread application of medical technology and improved food supplies have reduced death rates.

An important aspect of the world food problem is to bring birth rates into balance, and some progress is being made in this effort. The most encouraging signs come from Chile, Hong Kong, Singapore, Taiwan, and Trinidad, where birth rates have fallen so fast that the number of babies born in 1966 was less than in 1960. Fairly clear signs of a decline in the crude birth rate are now reported from Ceylon, West Malaysia, Jamaica, and Costa Rica.

Over the past two decades, food production per capita has increased in the developing countries at an annual rate of only about one-third of 1 percent, whereas food consumption has been increasing at almost one-half of 1 percent per capita.

The gap between production and consumption has been made up by increased food imports from the developed countries. Food imports by the developing countries have been mostly grain to increase calorie intake.

Before World War II, the free world developing countries (excluding the grain exporters—Argentina, Mexico, Burma, Thailand, Cambodia) were net importers of only 2.3 million tons of grain. But for the past few years they have imported nearly 30 million tons annually. More than one-fourth of this has gone to India.

What have been the forces responsible for this gap between production and consumption in emerging nations?

Higher Levels of Living—Before World War II, there was little concern about the welfare of people in the developing countries. The great mass of people in these areas subsisted as they had for centuries, at the hunger margin; this was more or less a fact of life.

Since then, 66 of these developing countries have become independent. Almost without exception, they have immediately embarked on a program of economic development. These have had varied success, but in general they have brought about some improvement in the per capita income; 1 to 2 percent annually. With rising incomes, people demand more food. They also desire higher quality food which requires greater agricultural resources for their production.

As incomes rise, if increased supplies are not available, food prices go up, and the poorer people—whose ability to buy has not improved—can obtain even less food. Because of the great importance of food prices to a large majority of the population, sharp rises in prices are likely to have political repercussions. Under such circumstances there are strong pressures to expand food imports. With food aid available, this expansion has been possible without diverting scarce foreign exchange resources.

Urbanization—The impact of population on food supplies in the developing countries is accentuated by the concentration of people in cities. The extremely rapid growth of urban population compounds the problem because it imposes the difficult task of improving the distribution system so food can be moved from producing areas to urban areas.

To accomplish this task, incentives must be used to bring farmers into the commercial economy. Not only must there be an increase in production of

Seed testing laboratory in India, left. Right, Bolivian woman compares small native potato with improved variety now grown with help of Alliance for Progress program.

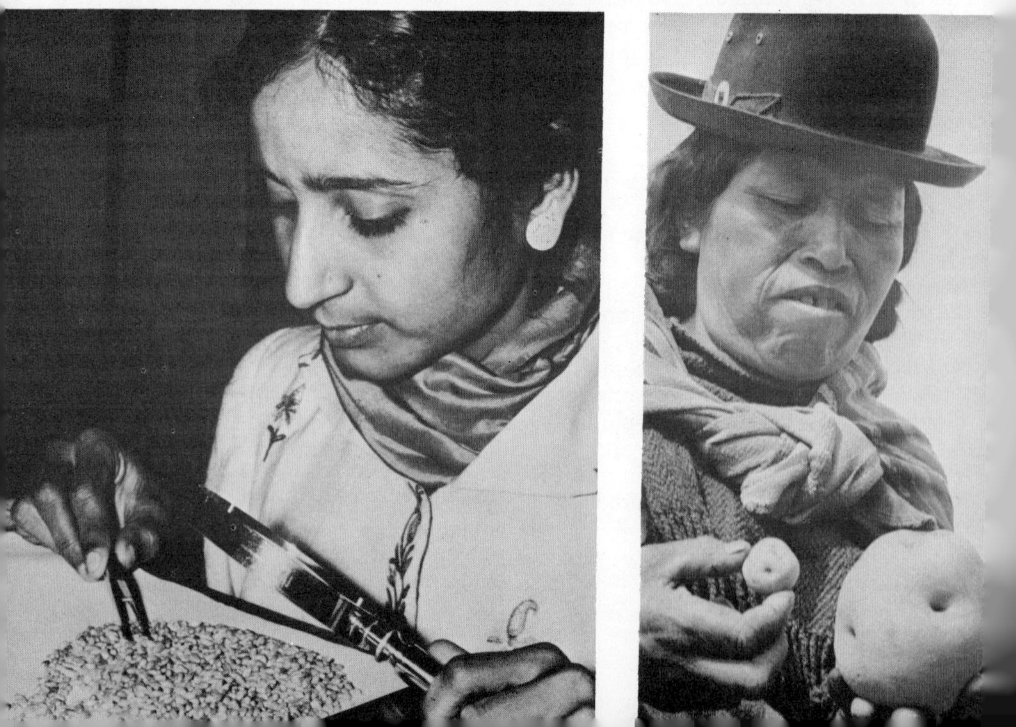

food, but marketing facilities must be built to transport, store, process, and distribute the farm products. When this task is not accomplished, urban centers have to rely on imports for much of their food supplies.

Availability of Food Aid—The United States has long shown a great concern for the hungry people of the world. Immediately after World War II, agricultural aid programs were instituted to supply food to war-torn areas of Europe. In the early 1950's, following a severe drought in India and Pakistan, special wheat loans were made to these countries.

During the 1950's, American farm output increased much faster than did consumption, and surpluses of several agricultural products began to build up. In an effort to dispose of these surpluses and at the same time give foreign countries an opportunity to obtain agricultural products which their limited foreign exchange would not permit them to buy, Congress in 1954 enacted Public Law 480: "To increase the consumption of U.S. agricultural commodities in foreign countries." Since that time, the United States has shipped over 135 million metric tons of wheat and about 40 million tons of other grains under this program.

This U.S. food production capacity and the large accumulation of U.S. grain stocks has made it possible for the developing countries to expand their consumption faster than their production over the past decade.

Should We Feed the World?

The policy of the United States is to encourage and assist the developing nations of the free world to develop economically and improve their own food production so they will become less dependent on food aid. A significant feature of the Food for Freedom program is the requirement of self-help efforts to accelerate food production within the food-deficit countries themselves.

Food aid probably will continue to be needed for the next decade. But dependence on food aid should diminish as these countries accelerate agricultural development and economic growth to the point where they can produce or commercially import their food requirements.

If the developing countries raise

India extension guide estimates size of corn raised by farmer at right, who achieved highest yield in his area.

their rate of increase in agricultural production to 4 percent annually—a rate already reached by a few countries—they would be achieving a high enough rate of growth in food production to provide minimum adequate calorie levels for their people by 1980 and break their dependence on food aid. However, this would require unprecedented increases in resource commitment to agricultural development. It would require massive efforts by developing nations and considerable assistance by developed countries.

National leaders have emphasized that "hunger is a world problem. It must be dealt with by the world." They have called for a "truly international effort to combat hunger and to modernize agriculture." The Food for Freedom Act affirms the "sense of Congress that the President should encourage other advanced nations to make increased contributions for the purpose of combating world hunger and malnutrition, particularly through the expansion of international food and agricultural assistance programs." The Food Aid Convention under the International Grains Arrangement of 1967 is a step in this direction.

Although faster progress is needed among developing countries, there is no immediate likelihood of a world food shortage. It is estimated that the production capacity in the developed nations will be more than ample to meet import needs of the developing nations in the foreseeable future. In fact, even if there were no improvement in the rate of agricultural development in developing countries and their grain import requirements doubled over the next decade, the developed countries would still possess some excess grain production capacity.

South Vietnam boy with American Sugar Baby watermelon grown in his country under the U.S. aid program.

Rex F. Daly

Food Enough for the U.S.? A Crystal Ball Look Ahead

Chances are small indeed that you or I will live to see famine conditions in the United States. Many of us may eat poorly by habit; a few of us may be hungry at times. But food has been, and will very likely remain, relatively abundant for most of us during our lifetimes.

The very word "future" intrigues us. And properly so, for everybody has a vital interest in the subject. The future is where we will live, work, and play. Our interest is genuine; and our actions in the days, months, and years ahead will determine to a considerable extent the kind of 21st century we will have. If we are able to be more than passive agents in the overall scheme of things, well thought out plans and goals will form a rational bridge between our present and our future.

It is a risky business, at best, to try to predict the future, and of course, we can't presume to do so with any great degree of accuracy. Projections should not be considered an attempt to anticipate some inevitable unraveling of coming decades. Rather, they should be thought of as a sketch of the future, as tools to help us to anticipate changes, possible imbalances in supplies, and other likely problems. A chart of the future may turn out to be a red flag that warns us of undesirable consequences if current trends or policies are continued. Or, it may be a goal or blueprint for future actions.

In general, long-term prospects for plentiful supplies of food, while favorable to us, are by no means assured. And for most of the remaining world, the prospects are hopeful but not optimistic because of the continuing population-food imbalance. Food in our future will depend on the outcome of the race between domestic and foreign demand and our potential for producing food in the United States. So as a prelude to what the future may hold for us, let's take a look at our past and present achievements, policies, and problems.

Food production is an economic process in which the farmer brings together resources to produce food. Accordingly, he is interested in demand for his products backed with buying power. He likes to grow things, but he also must make money to stay in business.

Production is an economic process because it depends upon the cost of resources, demands for food, and the prices these will bring. But it is partly physical in the sense that it depends on natural resources and the state of technology. Thus our food supplies depend, in part, on how hard and in what way we as a society wish to push to increase them.

Larger quantities of most crops could be produced now, but this would be a costly and unprofitable venture. Similarly, if we ever chose—or were forced—to have a "no meat" diet, our current production capacity would feed four or five times as many people as it does. Feeding animals to furnish us with meat is less efficient than direct use of crops for food.

Rex F. Daly is Director of the Economic and Statistical Analysis Division, of the Economic Research Service.

In the past, our supplies of food have been large enough to depress farm prices and incomes. In the last three decades, farm production has increased nearly 80 percent. This was accomplished using fewer acres, fewer farmworkers, more mechanical power, more fertilizer, and greatly improved "know-how." These bumper crops and the huge carryover stocks have spawned programs designed to expand our markets for food and to limit production.

Our U.S. agriculture is in an excellent position to provide us with what we need as well as to help people in other nations. In addition to the millions of acres currently being withheld from production, there are millions more which are suitable for farming. At present, however, it would require either higher farm prices or more public expenditures to make this worthwhile to farmers.

Higher farm prices and higher returns to farmers would also step up the use, if not the tempo, of technological developments. Research in breeding is resulting in more productive hybrid seeds, better disease and insect controls, and genetic modifications such as high-protein corn. Similar research on livestock is resulting in vigorous crossbreeds, multiple births, improved use of feed, and meatier cuts.

In addition to the ordinary means of expanding our food supplies, synthetics are indirectly serving the same purpose. These have cut into usual markets for such foods as sugar, fruit juices, and several protein foods.

Another recent development with an impact on supplies similar to that of synthetics is the current substitution of lower priced farm foods for milk products, meat protein, and animal fats. This kind of substitution may affect potential food supplies even more than synthetics. For example, the consumption of dairy products would be about 50 percent larger than it is if the industry still had its prewar markets for butter, cream, and some of the other high-fat products.

The primary reason for shifts to crop products is that they are usually cheaper and require fewer resources than animal products. About a third of our calories now come from animal products. To produce these 1,100 calories, animals require more than 10,000 calories, some of which come from products which could be used directly for food.

The world could support many times its present population if the photosynthetic process could be more fully used. This is the process which transforms carbon dioxide from air and water into energy. Though we now use a very small proportion of annual photosynthetic output for food and feed, it has great potential. The leaves of many plants are substantial sources of energy and protein. And, the chlorophyll-bearing algae of the sea are reported to be around 100 times more efficient than corn in the use of solar energy. The day will surely come when we will better understand the "miracle of the green plant" and, perhaps, be able to make more efficient use of this receiving set for solar energy.

All these are rather rosy possibilities for our food supplies in the next few decades. Nevertheless, there are some gnawing uncertainties about how we can resolve—not only the publicized world food-population race—but also two other questions. One of these relates to the longer run potential for productivity and yields in agriculture; the other considers results of imbalances being created by erosion, waste, and pollution.

Charting longer run productivity is difficult. With the moon within reach, there's a great temptation to be optimistic in all assessments. Also, in the past we have usually understated long-run technological possibilities and productivity. Even so, we should not let this tendency to be conservative blind us to some of the constraining factors that may be with us.

The revolutionary advances in output per man-hour in agriculture, about double the productivity gains in the nonfarm sector, are in part a fiction. A rapid decline in number of farms is due to combining several smaller, and often less efficient, units into larger and more efficient units. The result is a sharper rise in productivity for agriculture as a whole than for individual farms or size groups. If the size structure of agriculture continues evolving into an industry of fewer and larger optimum-size farms, does not this imply some slowing in the growth of productivity?

Questions about waste and pollution demand answers, for they bear on our food supply potential. In recent years, a growing body of evidence suggests that, along with industry and huge population concentrations, agriculture is contributing to the wastes and pollution of our soil, water, and air. The dimensions of these problems are not known, but the private and social costs of correcting them are expected to be immense. The potential threat to our future supplies of food is clear.

Most large rivers and lakes are polluted with wastes and sediment. Appraisals of Lake Erie read almost like an obituary. Possibly a similar fate lies ahead for Lake Michigan. Its basin States recently signed an agreement to protect the environment of the lake. Such pollution problems go ". . . beyond the development of new technology; beyond sophisticated analyses of benefits and costs in the economic arena; and beyond the police power of legislation."

The U.S. Department of Agriculture's 1967 report on pesticides and related activities attests to the magnitude of the problem and the concern about contamination. Random research titles indicate the nature of current questions such as management and removal of pesticides from food; contamination of soil and of runoff water; and the effects of feeding contaminated forage.

Some biologists are alarmed over the heavy use of nitrogen fertilizers. Because of their relatively low prices, these have been replacing the use of animal manures. Apparently, the increasingly massive use of high-nitrogen fertilizers has forced considerable amounts into the air and runoff water. This added emphasis on the use of inorganic nitrogen may also contribute some toxicity to feeds and other crops used for food.

A recent USDA report states that a serious consequence of contaminations by insecticides is that, through the "food chains" from plants to animals to man, residues may progressively accumulate to higher levels.

As fertilizers, insecticides, and other chemicals form a vital link in our capacity to produce food, solutions to the problem of contamination may have to come from greater biological controls over disease and insects, by the using of new and possibly safer chemicals, and, possibly, by reduced applications. Solutions may increase production costs and slow the present upward trend in yields. As a result, during the next quarter century we may not be able to plan with complete certainty on ample supplies of relatively low-priced food. Our research programs and plans must continue on the side of caution because the costs of being too optimistic could be mammoth.

What kind and how much food we will be eating after the turn of the century will depend on many factors. Important among these is the rate of increase in world population. Our postwar program, which reduced disease, insects, and malnutrition in the less developed countries, sharply reduced death rates and contributed to a worldwide population upsurge. In the first two-thirds of this century, world population more than doubled to around 3½ billion people. If recent growth rates continue, it will double again by the end of this century.

The United Nations recently reported an annual growth in population of between 2 and 3½ percent in the less developed parts of the world, which now includes three-fourths of the earth's inhabitants. Annual growth rates for Europe, North America, and the Soviet Union ranged from 0.8 percent to about 1.25 percent. To put these in perspective: At a 2-percent growth rate, population will double in 35 years; at a 3-percent-a-year rate, it will double in less than 24 years. The rapidly growing regions harbor most of the hunger and malnutrition, and some of these areas are not well endowed with natural resources. As a result of rapid growth in population, fewer working-age people must provide for, and train, many more of the young people if these areas are to assume a viable role in tomorrow's world.

The implications of unrestricted population growth are not generally understood. Any population growth rate, if sustained, will ultimately push world population to an unacceptable level. Though it will never arrive at a "standing room only" crowd, uninterrupted growth does imply this or a somewhat less but still unpleasant fate. Birth rates needed for a stable population depend on average life expectancy. If we want an average life expectancy of 60 years and a stable population, both birth and death rates would have to average around 17 per 1,000 people or about the present U.S. birth rate. Uncontrolled births probably average around 40 to 50 per 1,000 people.

Attitudes toward population planning are tied up with religion, folklore, and politics, and many nations see population controls as weakening their vitality and political influence. Despite all the publicity regarding the need for world population control, this problem may remain the critical barrier to righting the population-resource equation in much of the world.

In the years ahead, economic growth in the United States and the world will increase consumer buying power. This will accelerate the demand for food in the less developed regions of the world. On the other hand, in the United States and other high-income nations, rising incomes may have less impact on per capita food use than in the past.

In general, some current and persistent trends in U.S. diets will moderate due to changes in prices, inroads of substitute products, and, perhaps, to health considerations. Whether due to any or all of these factors, it doesn't seem realistic to expect a continuation of past big gains in per capita use of beef and poultry meat. Similarly, the current downward trend in per capita use of grains and animal fats may be slowed.

Synthetic foods and substitute vegetable proteins and oils will become more widely used in place of animal proteins and fats. Laws, controls, and other institutional barriers probably will be overcome, much as they were for the margarine versus butter controversy. Even so, there is no reason to expect a revolutionary change in our diets unless the world population is unchecked, or there is a slower rise than is expected in the U.S. food supplies. If, for example, we were forced back to the type of meals we ate in 1930 because of tight demand-supply balance and high prices, per capita demand and need for food production resources would drop about 7 percent. This would reduce per capita demand for livestock products by 16 percent and raise the use of crops by about 10 percent.

Despite impacts of the problems already described—unrestricted growth of population, increased waste and pollution, and the possibility of slower productivity advances in agriculture—some qualitative views will be presented about supply and price prospects for food. These projections should be looked on as largely illustrative.

Population in the United States will continue to grow. The sharp decline in birth rates since 1955 has slowed population growth to about 1 percent per year. However, these birth rates are expected to increase during the next several years as a rising number of women reach the most fertile childbearing ages.

The Census Bureau projects four levels of birth rate, with the next-to-the-lowest of the levels projecting around 308 million people by the year 2000 compared to around 200 million today. This is considered a reasonable projection, and represents an annual population growth of 1.3 percent, the same as the past 3½ decades. The next highest level projects 336 million people, and this may be entirely as reasonable.

During the next 30 to 40 years, the economy is expected to grow somewhat faster than during recent years. Projections of the labor force, hours worked, and production per man-hour for the year 2000 indicate a potential gross national product nearly four times the 1964–66 average. Consumer buying power will grow more rapidly than the 2 percent per year rate during the past 3½ decades.

tion of grain products will continue to decline, but at a slower rate than in the past.

It is likely that, in the upcoming decades, exports of farm products will continue to be the most expanding part of the total demand for U.S. farm products. This, of course, is based upon the assumption that our agriculture will continue to have an excess capacity to produce. The economic, social, and political forces which can affect exports are difficult to identify and virtually impossible to measure.

Probe used to get wheat sample from railroad car of grain in Ohio, first step in grading wheat.

In our expanding economy, most of us will be able to buy the foods we want. Though advances in food prices would have little effect on how much food each of us eats, changes in the prices of individual items may alter the foods in our diet. Since income and price may have progressively less effect on what we buy, we might reasonably sketch a diet for the 1980 decade. It will include even more red meat—particularly beef, more poultry, and more processed fruits and vegetables. The projected diet includes about the same amount of pork, less milk, fewer eggs, and a smaller amount of animal fats such as butter and lard. Consump-

To illustrate what could happen to farm prices, incomes, expenditures for food, and resource requirements, we can assume two levels of future exports. The first projects the volume of crop exports in the year 2000 to nearly five times what they were in 1964–66. This would be equivalent to more than 40 percent of total crop production, compared with 22 percent in 1964–66.

The second assumption projects crop exports by the year 2000 at about three times the 1964–66 volume. That would equal about 30 percent of projected crop output. This latter and less optimistic projection would

Food Consumption Trends

Commodity	Unit	Average per person, per year 1929–1931	1949–1951	1964–1966	Projected
Red meat (carcass weight)	lb.	130	142	171	192
Poultry (ready-to-cook)	lb.	16	25	41	60
Eggs	doz.	28	32	26	24
Milk (milk equivalent)	qt.	383	339	287	245
Food fats and oils (fat basis)	lb.	45	44	48	47
Fruits, vegetables and potatoes (fresh farm weight)	lb.	502	517	489	520
Grains (farm weight)	lb.	339	257	230	215

suggest little change in prices assuming the full use of land now available for crops. The higher export projection would result, to start with, in sharply higher prices until additional acreage and other resources could be drawn into production. Adding another 100 million acres would increase production and moderate the price increases. There is, of course, no way to judge how much additional land and other resources would come into production. And, there is little basis for estimating how productive these new resources would be. But we can mull over some probable consequences.

Farm prices projected under the more modest export projection would average about 10 percent below those resulting from the higher one. Lower crop prices would reduce feed costs, increase use of feed, and step up production of livestock products. Also as a result of lower prices, domestic food use of both crops and livestock products would be a little more than if a larger share were exported. However, moderately higher prices probably would not greatly alter the U.S. diet that is sketched above unless there were large price differences among important foods.

If we can avoid big increases in demand or a marked slowing in food production, food bills will take a still smaller share of our incomes (after taxes). If food prices increase at about the same rate as those of other goods, as they have over the last 3½ decades, expenditures for food will have to shrink as a share of consumer income. The decline is an inevitable consequence when food expenditures go up at a slower rate than incomes.

By the year 2000, the percentage of income spent for food might be down by four or five points from the 17.3 percent in 1968. However, increased demand or slower gains in production could slow, halt, or even reverse the downward trend in the percentage of income spent for food.

Farm production in the year 2000 is projected to a level about double what it was in 1964–66. This will be accomplished with around half the work force, somewhat more land, and possibly two to three times the volume of nonfarm resources that were used in the midsixties.

The number of farms are expected to continue to decline in response to gains in efficiency and farm consolidation. A continuation of this trend would suggest around 1½ million farms by 2000. Perhaps less than half these farms would account for the commercial output of agriculture. Certainly changes in number and size now underway and in prospect for agriculture, along with technical advances, point to fewer, larger, and more efficient commercial farm units.

This discussion was started by asserting that the possibility of famine in the United States was very remote, and it should end on this note as well. At the same time, however, uncertainty does exist about the potential of our food production capacity and about our role in the outcome of the world population-food race.

In planning for the future, the costs of being too optimistic are great indeed. The stakes are high, not only in dollars but also in terms of adequacy and purity of our food, our health, and perhaps our vitality as a Nation.

Buying and Cooking Food

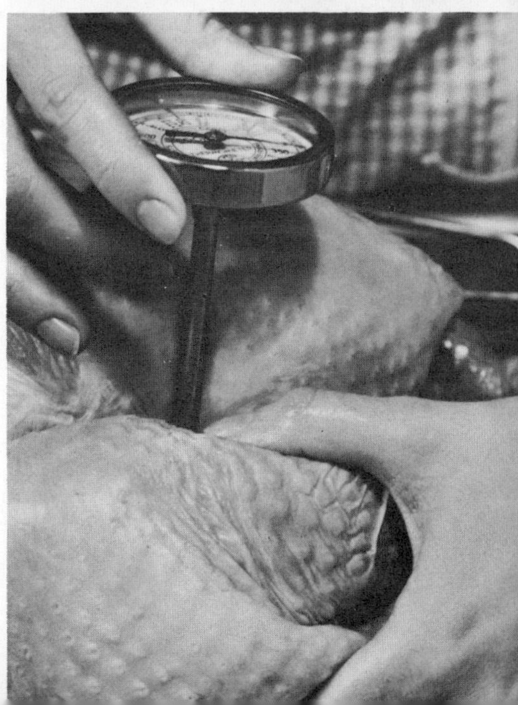

Olive M. Batcher
Charles E. Murphey

All About Meat, That Key Item in Food Buying, Meal Planning

Very few people realize that there are enough different kinds and cuts of meat available in today's supermarkets so a homemaker could prepare a different meat dish for her family every day of the year. This variety should make meat buying and meal planning a real pleasure.

Since meat commands a large share of today's food dollar, the consumer should know as much as possible about its selection and preparation.

As assurance to consumers that their meat is wholesome, all meat and meat products prepared in plants which make shipments into other States must be federally inspected. This assures us that the meat comes from healthy animals, is processed under sanitary conditions, is properly labeled and packaged, and it is not adulterated or contaminated. A round stamp identifies meat which has passed this inspection.

Although meat and meat products from plants that do not ship out-of-State usually will not be federally inspected, many States and municipalities have their own inspection systems. However, under the Federal Wholesome Meat Act of 1967, each State must provide, by 1970 at the latest, inspection equal to Federal inspection for plants which sell meat solely within the State. If this isn't done, these plants will become subject to Federal inspection.

In this country, "meat" means the "red meats" or those produced from cattle, sheep, and hogs. Our beef, calf, and veal are all produced from cattle—they differ in the maturity of thc animal from which they are produced. Veal comes from very young animals—usually 3 months of age or younger. It has a grayish pink lean which is very smooth and velvety and it usually has very little fat. Veal is prized for its delicate flavor. Calf is produced from slightly older animals—usually 3 to 8 months of age. Its lean is grayish red in color, fine in texture, and mild in flavor.

Beef is from still more mature animals. Most beef sold as cuts in retail stores is from animals 15 to 30 months of age. Most of the beef from the older animals is used for making processed products like frankfurters, bologna, and luncheon meats. Fresh beef is available at all times in every section of the United States.

Lamb is meat from young sheep usually less than a year old. Tender, juicy, and flavorful lamb is available throughout the year. Meat from older sheep is called mutton, but very little of this is sold as fresh meat in retail stores.

Pork, mostly produced from young hogs, is always available in quantity. Although the total fat content of some pork cuts may be higher than for most other meats—depending upon how it is trimmed—the lean of pork is not any higher in fat than is beef.

Success in preparation of all meat dishes—the concern of every cook—begins with selection of the meat. One

Olive M. Batcher is a Research Food Technologist, in the Human Nutrition Research Division, Agricultural Research Service.

Charles E. Murphey is Assistant Chief, Standardization Branch, Livestock Division, Consumer and Marketing Service.

INSPECTION STAMP FOR PROCESSED MEATS

of the more important factors affecting the desirability of meat is the portion of the animal from which it came—the lean meat in some parts is naturally more tender and palatable than in others. Also, cuts from various parts differ in the number and size of muscles and in the amount and location of bone. Cuts with only one or two muscles, and which do not contain any bones that interfere with carving, are more attractive and convenient to serve.

There are no Federal or other laws or regulations which relate to the names of meat cuts prepared in retail markets. However, the names of most of the more popular cuts have become fairly well standardized. But in the case of the less popular cuts, different names—many of which are not really descriptive—are frequently applied to the same cut.

The muscles and bones of all our meat animals and the relative desirability of cuts from the various parts are quite similar. This simplifies learning how to recognize cuts and how to use them to best advantage. Names of cuts frequently reflect the name of a portion of the carcass or the shape or name of a bone.

In general, cuts from along the back of the animal are naturally the most tender and palatable. They include the "ribeye" or "loineye" muscle—the largest muscle in the animal and also one of the most desirable.

Cuts from the back between the hip bone and the last rib contain the familiar T-shaped bone and two major muscles. The larger muscle is the loineye and the smaller one is the tenderloin. These are separated by the upright portion of the "T" shaped bone. In pork and lamb, this portion usually is made into center-cut loin chops. In beef, it is nearly always used for steak. When prepared "bone-in," these are referred to as porterhouse, T-bone, or club steaks.

In porterhouse steaks the tenderloin is large, in the T-bone it is intermediate in size, and club steaks contain, at most, only a very small portion of tenderloin. Retailers leave varying amounts of "tail" or flank meat on these steaks. This is definitely less desirable than the rest of the steak. If this flank portion has not been removed, the steak should be priced cheaper. When the bone is removed from this section, steaks from the loineye muscle are called strip steaks.

The tenderloin usually is made into filet mignon or tenderloin steaks. However, the tenderloin is sometimes made into portions several inches in length to serve two or more. Such a cut is frequently called "chateaubriand."

In the section of the back which contains ribs, the bone structure includes the thin backbone vertebrae and a short section of attached rib bones. In beef, this section usually is made into roasts. When the bones are not removed, it is the ever-popular standing rib roast. These usually are further identified as 5-inch, 7-inch, or 10-inch cuts to reflect differing amounts of rib ends or short ribs left on the cut. If the bones are removed it becomes a boneless rib roast.

The large, ribeye muscle together with a few small, firmly attached muscles are sometimes removed and sold as a roast—the ribeye roll—or as ribeye or delmonico steaks. Many consider this the premier cut of beef.

In lamb and pork this rib section usually is made into rib chops or rib roasts. The crown roast of pork or lamb is fashioned from two such rib sections. In pork, when the large ribeye muscle is removed and cured and smoked it is Canadian style bacon.

Immediately below (as the animal

BEEF CHART

Wholesale Cuts of Beef and Their Bone Structure

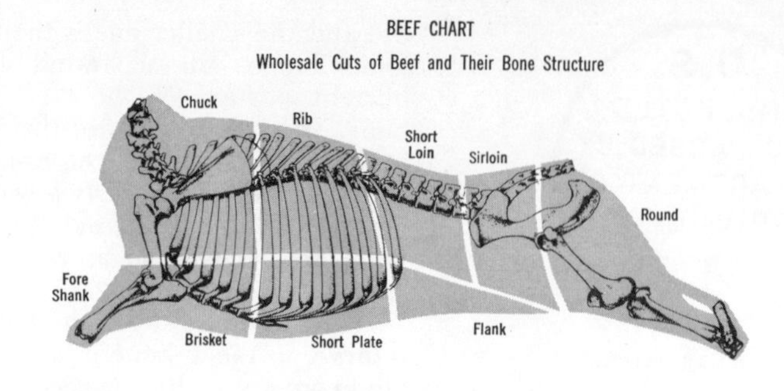

Retail Cuts of Beef and Where They Come From

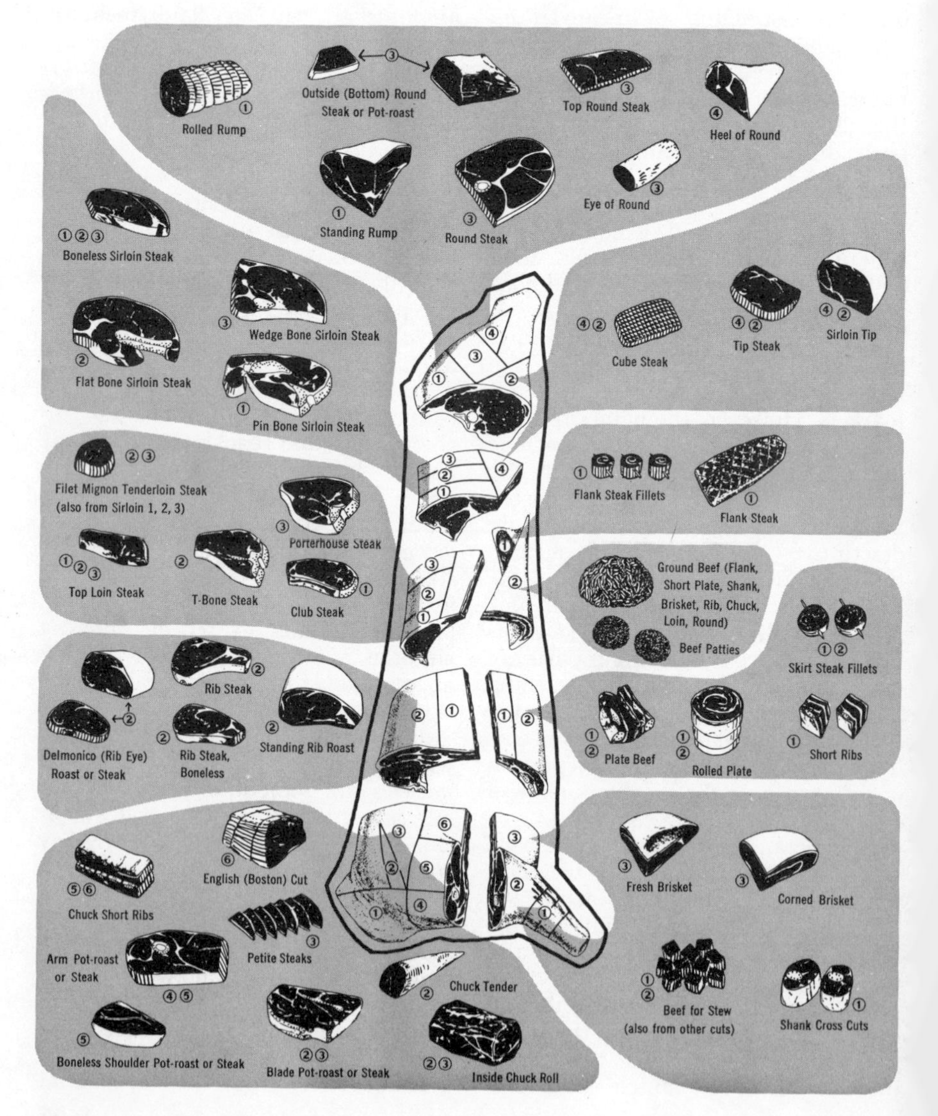

stands) these two back sections are thinner portions which, except for pork, are much less desirable. In pork, this is where bacon and spareribs originate. In beef, these portions are made into a variety of cuts—ground beef, beef stew, short ribs, beef bacon, and corned beef. (Corned beef is cured similar to pork but it is not smoked.) The flank steak also originates in this section. In lamb, these portions are normally sold for stewing or as ground lamb.

In the region which contains the hip bone, the muscles are highly desirable—large and tender. In beef, this portion usually is made into sirloin steaks. In lamb it is included as a part of the leg or sold as sirloin chops. In pork it is made into a loin end roast or into sirloin chops. The hip bone is quite variable in size and shape. In beef, the back bones are frequently removed, especially from steaks in which the hip bone is large.

The hind leg portion—round in beef, ham in pork, and leg in lamb—also contains large muscles and the main part of this portion includes only a small round bone. In beef, the round is made into rump roasts and round steaks or roasts. Because of its size, the main part of the beef round frequently is separated into its three major sections—the top round, bottom round, and round tip or knuckle. The bottom section contains two parts of which the "eye of the round" is more desirable. When the eye of round is sold separately, the remaining portion is still referred to as bottom round.

In pork, the ham is merchandised whole, separated into butt and shank halves, or made into a center cut roast or center slices and the remainder sold as butt and shank ends. The center cuts contain only the small round leg bone. In lamb, the leg may be sold in one piece or made into butt and shank halves. When sold in one piece but with a small end of the shank meat removed, it is a "Frenched" leg. When the shank bone is removed but the shank meat is not, it is an "American" leg.

There is considerable variation in the way cuts are made from the forepart of meat animals and in the names given these cuts. In lamb, the fore shank is sold as such—and one shank makes a generous serving. In beef, the shank usually is made into ground beef. To the inside of the shank on beef is the brisket—and in lamb, the breast. Beef brisket is the cut which is most frequently made into corned beef. When purchasing corned beef it should be remembered that, as a result of the curing process, it may have some added moisture. Corned briskets produced in federally inspected plants may weigh up to 20 percent more than their uncured weight, but the other corned cuts are limited to an increase in weight of 10 percent.

Immediately above the shank and the brisket or breast is the chuck (beef) or shoulder (lamb). Rib and back bones are located on the inside of these cuts and the arm bone and shoulder blade are nearly in the center. This portion contains a large number of relatively small (thin) muscles which run in many different directions. In beef, the chuck is made into arm and blade roasts or steaks. The neck portion usually is made into ground beef or boneless stew meat.

Arm cuts resemble round steak in shape and also usually have only a single round bone. However, the arm cut has a distinctive round muscle close to the bone which also is darker red than the other lean and contains a noticeable amount of heavy streaks of connective tissue. A similar muscle is not found in cuts from the round. Blade cuts contain a portion of the shoulder blade. The first blade cuts include the same muscles which make up the very desirable ribeye roll. With just a little practice, these can be removed and made into delicious steaks.

To facilitate carving and serving, the arm and blade portions frequently are boned and further separated into sections in which the muscles run in about the same direction.

LAMB CHART

Wholesale Cuts of Lamb and Their Bone Structure

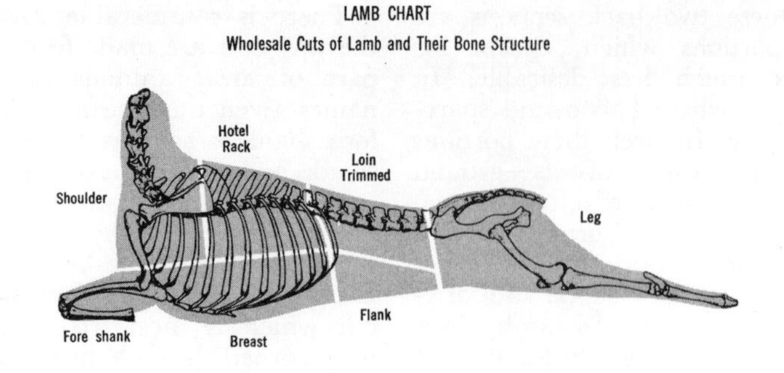

Retail Cuts of Lamb and Where They Come From

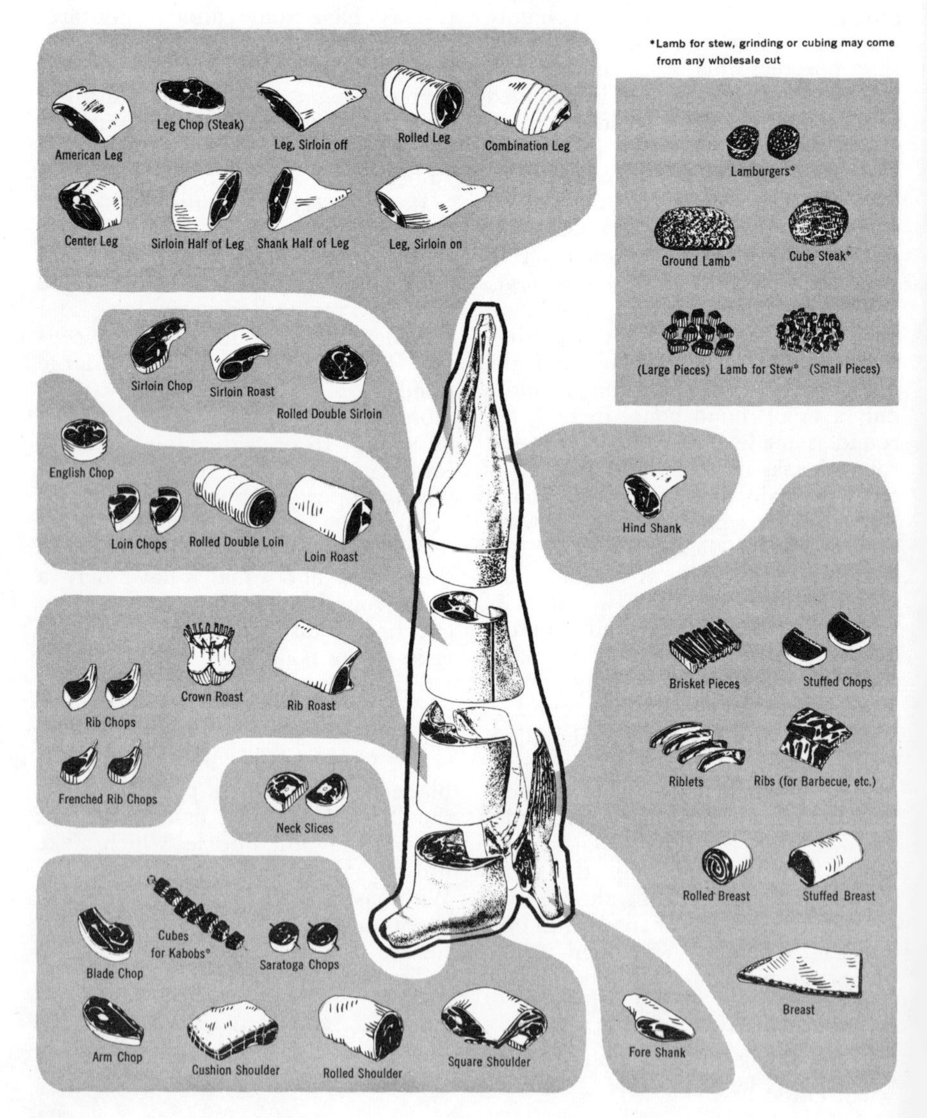

USDA meat grader rolling a Choice veal carcass. The grade and the letters "USDA" are enclosed in a shield and the word "veal" also is included.

In lamb, two or three blade chops and arm chops usually are removed from the shoulder and the remainder is then sold as a bone-in or boneless shoulder roast. The neck may or may not be removed.

In pork, this forepart produces two major cuts—the lower part is the picnic shoulder (it is not a picnic ham) and the upper part is the Boston butt.

The Boston butt's inside portion, when cured and smoked, is the very desirable smoked shoulder butt—more frequently referred to as a "westphalia" or "daisy." The cured and smoked jowl is sometimes termed a "bacon square." It is satisfactory for seasoning but is not a good substitute for real bacon.

Quality Factors. Learning how to select for quality—tenderness, juiciness, and flavor—is also an important aspect of meat selection. The most reliable factors for indicating meat

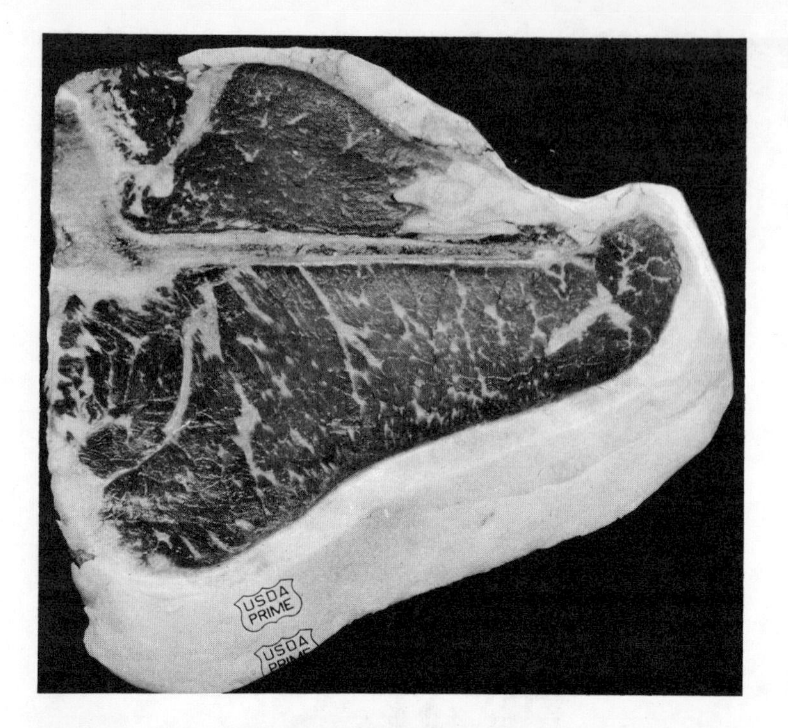

U.S. Prime, above.—Prime grade beef is the ultimate in tenderness, juiciness, and flavor. It is produced from young animals and has a liberal amount of marbling. Most Prime beef is used by exclusive hotels and restaurants, but it is also available in some retail stores. U.S. Choice, below.—Choice is the grade in greatest supply and is the one most commonly sold in retail stores. It has slightly less marbling than Prime but still is of very high quality.

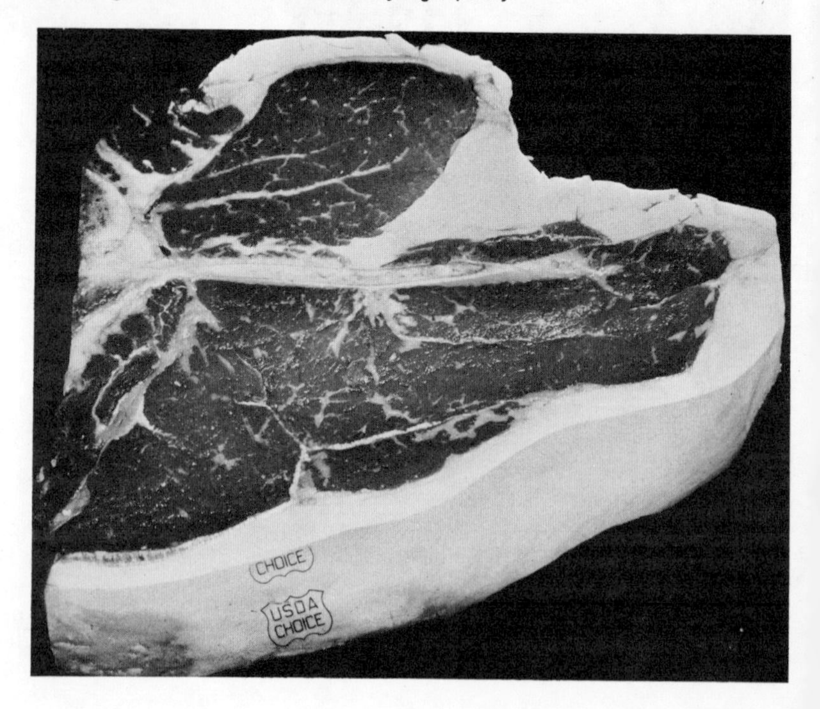

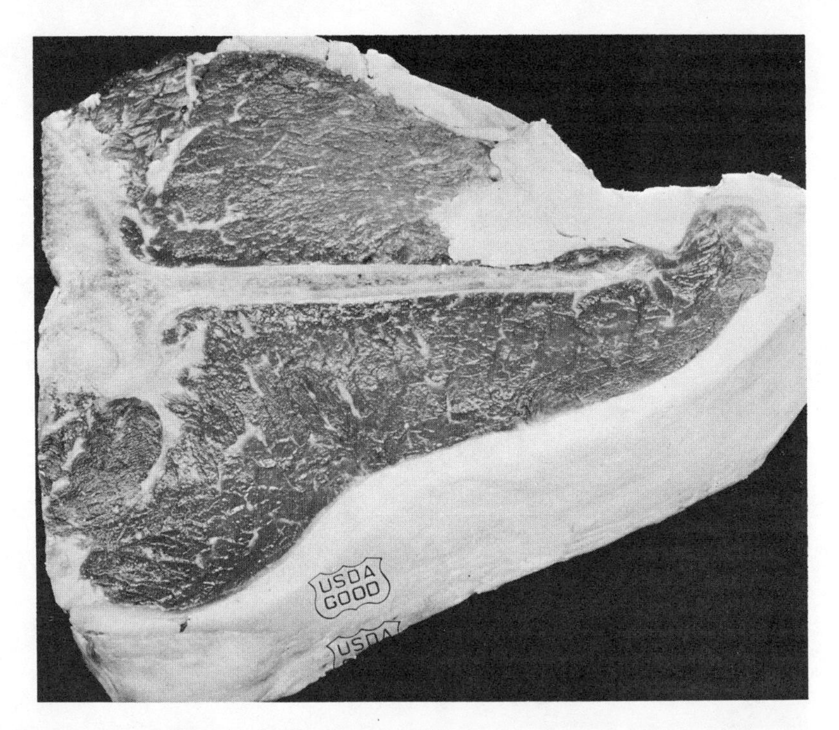

U.S. Good, above.—Good grade beef often pleases thrifty shoppers because it is somewhat more lean than the higher grades. Some stores sell this quality of beef under their own or a packer brand rather than under the USDA grade name. U.S. Standard, below.—Standard grade beef has a high proportion of lean meat and very little fat. Because it comes from young animals—the same as Prime, Choice, and Good—beef of this grade is fairly tender.

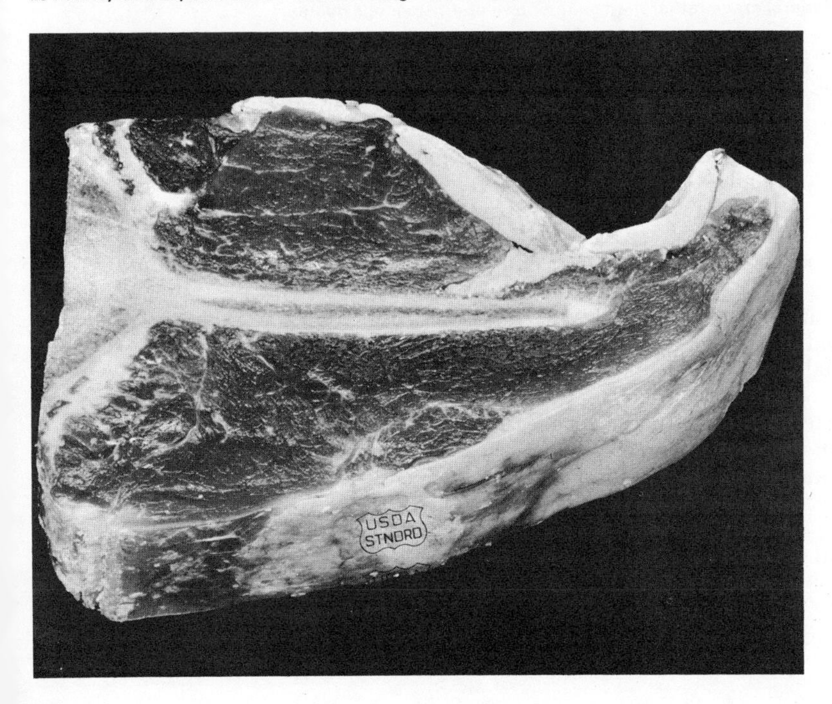

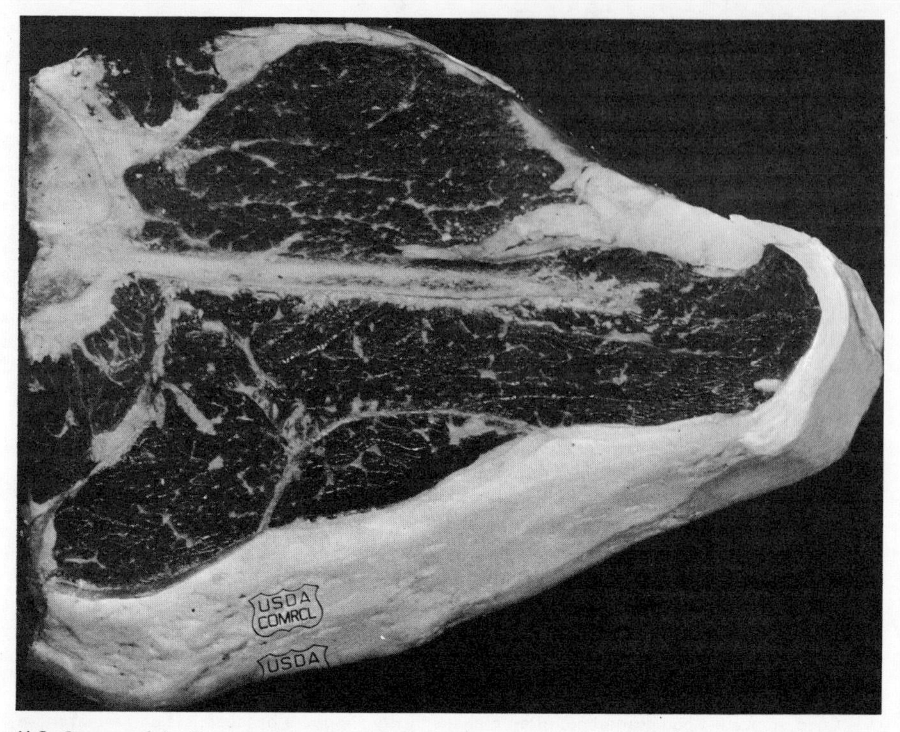

U.S. Commercial.—Commercial grade beef is produced only from mature animals. It has a very good flavor, but most cuts require long, slow cooking with moist heat to make them tender. In some respects, Commercial beef resembles Prime and Choice. For example, notice that it is similar to those grades in the amount of marbling. This is a good reason consumers should rely on the Federal grade rather than on their own ability to judge quality.

quality are the age of the animal from which it came, the color and texture of the lean, and the amount of marbling—small deposits of fat within the lean. Fortunately, today's consumers need not be experts in judging the quality of beef, veal, calf, and lamb since about 80 percent of the beef, 60 percent of the lamb, and smaller but significant amounts of the veal and calf sold at retail have been identified for quality by USDA meat graders. This is a voluntary service which is supported entirely by fees collected from those who use the service.

Standards used for grading include the best information available for reflecting differences in quality, and Federal meat graders are highly skilled in applying them. They grade only carcasses or wholesale cuts because quality differences cannot be appraised accurately in retail cuts.

When meat is graded, a shield-shaped grademark enclosing the letters "USDA" and the appropriate grade name—such as Prime, Choice, or Good—is applied to the meat as a long, ribbonlike imprint. Thus, one or more grademarks will appear on most retail cuts. This stamping is done with harmless, purple, vegetable coloring. When the grademark is applied to

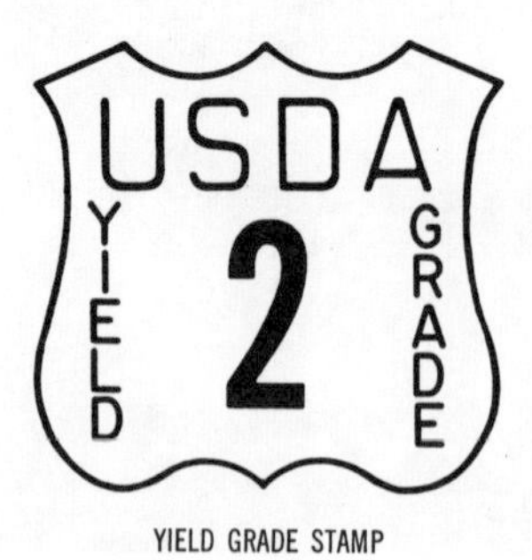

YIELD GRADE STAMP

veal, calf, yearling mutton, or mutton, the class name (veal, calf, etc.) is also included with the grade name.

USDA meat grades are applied uniformly in all parts of the country and at all times of the year—regardless of the supply. Therefore, a USDA Choice rib roast, for instance, will be equally delicious no matter where or when you buy it.

There are eight USDA quality grades for beef, six for veal and calf, and five for lamb and yearling mutton. The top three grades—Prime, Choice, and Good—are the same for all. The remaining grades for beef are Standard, Commercial, Utility, Cutter, and Canner. For veal and calf they are Standard, Utility, and Cull, and for lamb, yearling mutton, and mutton they are Utility and Cull. The Utility, Cutter, Canner, and Cull grades are generally used in processed meat items such as frankfurters.

Yield Grades. Beef carcasses of the same quality grade—Choice, for instance, can differ greatly in value due to differences in their yields of usable meat. These result mostly from differences in the amount of fat trimmed off in making retail cuts, but they are also affected by the thickness and plumpness of the muscles.

To identify carcasses for these differences, USDA developed a system of five yield grades which are designated by numbers—1 to 5. Yield Grade 1 identifies carcasses with the highest yields of cuts and Yield Grade 5 those with the lowest.

Yield grades are determined separately from quality grades, and carcasses can be graded for quality or yield or both. Yield grades are of no particular concern to consumers who buy only retail cuts which are trimmed of excess fat before being placed in the meat counter. But they can be very helpful to the person who buys beef in carcass form—a side or a quarter—for his home freezer.

The following tabulation shows the expected yields of retail cuts from typical carcasses—or sides—for each of the yield grades.

Expected Yield of Cuts From Typical Carcasses

Yield grade	Percentage of carcass weight
1	82.0 or more
2	77.4
3	72.8
4	68.2
5	63.6 or less

On a 600-pound carcass the 4.6 percent difference in yields of cuts between yield grades means a difference of nearly 28 pounds of meat. At 1968 retail prices this reflected a value difference of about $3.60 per hundredweight (cwt.)—or $21.60 on a 600-pound carcass or a 1,000-pound live animal. A difference of two yield grades, such as between Yield Grade 2 and Yield Grade 4, would mean a value difference of $7.20 per cwt., or $43.20 on a 600-pound carcass. The beef ribs from Yield Grade 2 and Yield Grade 4 carcasses show obvious differences in the amount of external fat and in the size of the ribeye muscle.

Consumers should not confuse the shield-shaped grade stamps which identify the quality of the meat or its cutability (yield grade) with the round inspection stamp which certifies its wholesomeness. Since Federal grading is voluntary, there is no assurance that meat advertised as "federally inspected" is of any particular grade. On the other hand, all meat that is federally graded has passed an inspection for wholesomeness.

Many packers and retailers use their own brand names to identify or advertise the various kinds of meat that they merchandise. Some of these brands may reflect levels of quality similar to the USDA grades, but there is no assurance or requirement that they do so. The basis for these brands and the uniformity with which they are applied are governed entirely by the company which uses them.

Buying Pork. In contrast with other meats, USDA pork carcass grades are not intended to identify differences in quality to consumers. They are similar to the yield grades for beef in that they identify carcasses for differences in yields of trimmed wholesale cuts.

PORK CHART

Wholesale Cuts of Pork and Their Bone Structure

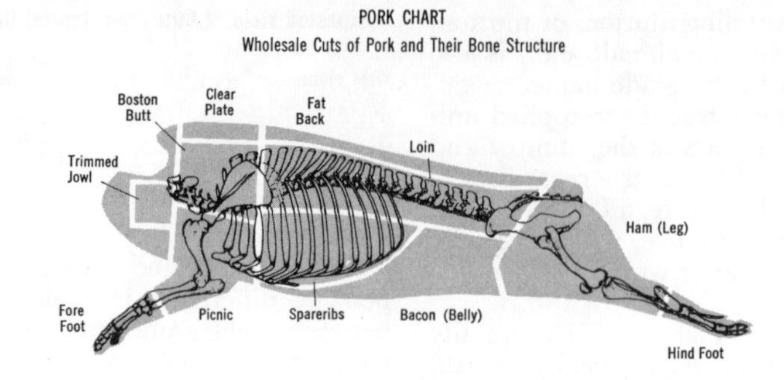

Retail Cuts of Pork and Where They Come From

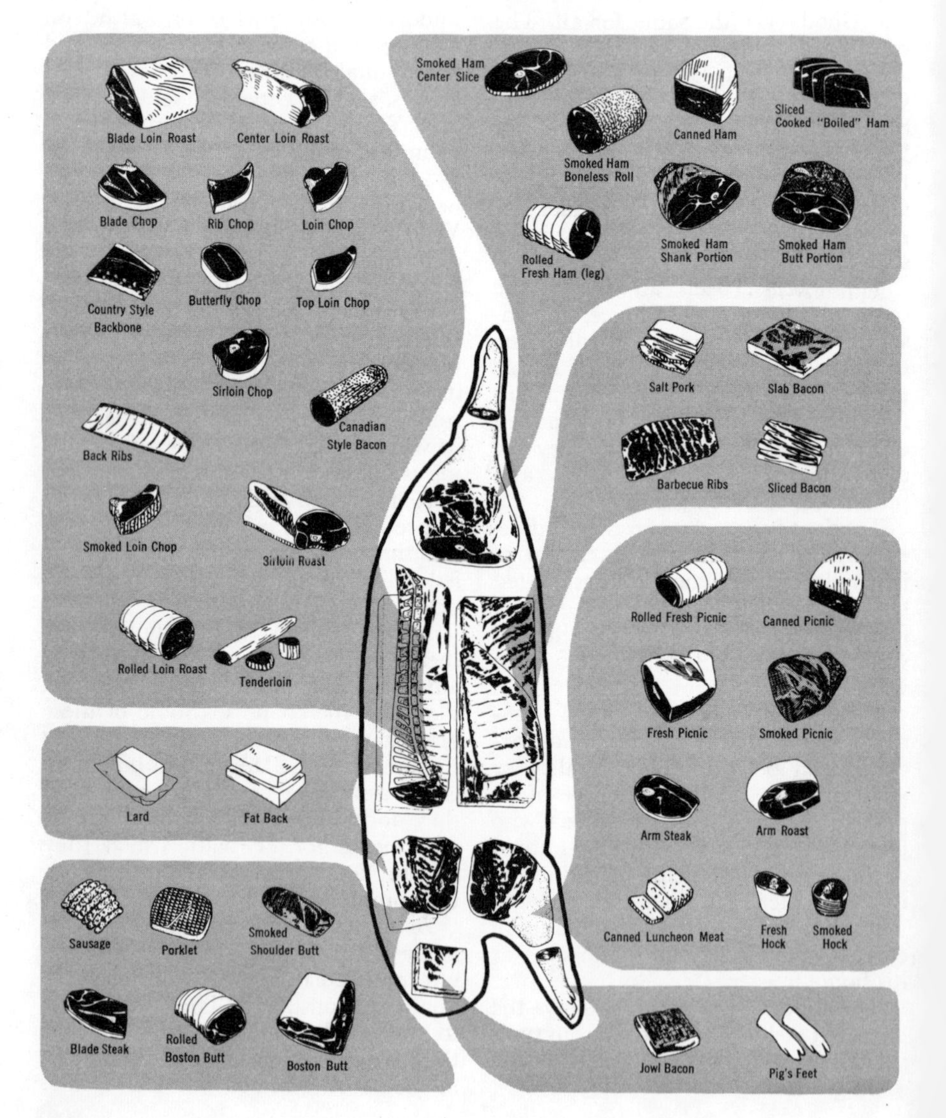

Although there is less difference in the tenderness, juiciness, and flavor of pork than of beef, there are wide differences in other factors that are important to consumers. Therefore, consumers need to pay close attention to what they select. A high proportion of lean is probably the most important factor. This can be assured by selecting cuts which carry little fat and which have plump, full muscles.

Cuts which contain several muscles, like rib end loin roasts and Boston butts, also can vary greatly in the amount of fat between the muscles. Picnic shoulders likewise vary in the amount of fat over the outside, that is, under the skin. Hams and picnic shoulders with short shanks are preferable. In high quality fresh pork the lean will be firm, grayish pink or darker in color, and it will have at least a slight amount of marbling—more is better. Soft, pale, watery lean is definitely less desirable.

A high percentage of pork is sold as processed products. This processing may include curing, smoking, cooking, and canning.

Pork occasionally contains trichinae (tiny parasites), which can be transmitted to humans producing a disease known as trichinosis. Therefore, in federally inspected plants, processed pork products that might be eaten without any further cooking must be heated to an internal temperature of at least 137° F. That temperature kills any trichinae that may be present.

This requirement makes the possibility of anyone contracting trichinosis extremely remote.

Because pork is processed in so many different ways, consumers should read the labels very carefully. This will permit them to better compare prices and also guide them in using it properly.

"Cured" pork has been treated with curing ingredients—primarily salt, sodium or potassium nitrate and/or nitrite, and sugar. Salt is used for flavor and as a preservative, the nitrate and nitrite combine with the meat pigments to develop the typical red color of cured meat, and the sugar is added for flavor. These ingredients usually are applied to the meat in a brine solution. In hams, the brine usually is distributed by pumping it into the arteries. This permits the curing to be done very quickly. But it also produces a very mild flavor. Pork that is "cured" only may also be called "corned."

In federally inspected plants, if the curing results in an increase in weight of up to 10 percent, the pork must be labeled with the words "water added." If the weight is increased by more than 10 percent, it is labeled as "imitation." "Smoked" means that the pork has been subjected to actual smoke. Artificial or natural smoke flavorings also are permissible, but these must be indicated on the label.

Cured pork is frequently labeled as "cooked," "fully cooked," "ready-to-eat," or "ready-to-serve," etc. These terms mean that the pork has been heated to develop the typical color, flavor, and texture associated with thorough cooking. Cuts that are not identified with a "fully cooked" or a similar label require cooking before serving.

Hams that have been long-cured and aged also are produced in many parts of the country. After curing, these hams usually are heavily smoked and then aged to develop a very distinctive flavor. During aging, the hams also shrink in weight. Meat packers in Smithfield, Va., produce such a specialty ham which is commonly referred to as "Smithfield ham." These hams are "long-cut"—that is, they include part of the sirloin region normally left on the loin. They also have long shanks and very little of the skin and fat are removed from the outside.

Normally cured and smoked hams are also available with none, some, or all of the bones removed and with part or all of the skin and part or nearly all of the fat removed.

During recent years, packers have produced an entirely boneless, skinless, cured and smoked ham from which substantially all of the fat has been removed. This has become a very popular item because of its convenient size, its ease of preparation and serving, and its almost complete freedom from waste.

The canned cured hams and picnic shoulders are boneless and skinless and usually have had a substantial amount of the fat removed. They may be smoked or unsmoked and may contain added materials such as champagne or honey. These items are also very popular because of their convenience of serving and lack of waste. At the time of canning, these meats may have an increase in weight of up to 8 percent over their weight before curing. The label on the can will indicate whether refrigeration is necessary.

Most cured hams and sliced bacon are sold under packer brands. By careful comparison of brands over an extended period of time, a family may find one or more which suit them best.

Sausages. A mealtime and snacktime favorite of millions of Americans, sausages include a wide assortment of seasoned and processed meat products. Probably the best known of these items are fresh pork sausage and the ever popular frankfurter and bologna. Sausage products have little or no waste, can be prepared quickly and easily, and served in a variety of ways—as sandwiches, snacks, salads, main dishes, and hors d'oeuvres.

Sausage making originated as a means of preserving meat and goes back as far as recorded history. Many of our present-day sausages are named for the place of their origin. For example, the frankfurter originated in Frankfurt, Germany, and bologna originated in Bologna, Italy. Lebanon bologna, however, is an American product, originating in Lebanon, Pa.

Sausage products are processed in several ways—fresh, cured and dried, and cured and cooked. Most sausages are made from varying combinations of beef, pork, and veal, although meat byproducts like heart meat, tongue meat, and tripe also are used. In addition, some items include cereal or nonfat dry milk as extenders. Most sausage products processed in federally inspected plants cannot contain more than 3½ percent of these extenders without being labeled as imitation. However, some loaf items may contain more than 3½ percent extenders—including such other ingredients as pickles, olives, or macaroni. Addition of byproducts and cereals generally tend to lower the quality of sausages, but many people feel that the addition of small amounts of nonfat dry milk makes the quality of some sausages more desirable.

Federal meat inspection regulations require that the ingredients used in a sausage product be listed on the label in descending order of predominance.

Loaf items are cooked in molds or loaf pans and then sliced and packaged for sale. Practically all other sausage products are stuffed into casings or canned.

Some sausages are dried during processing. Dried sausages like pepperoni, thuringer, and dry salami are quite firm, very flavorful, and normally do not need to be refrigerated.

Many seasonings are used in making sausages. Salt is always used and serves as a flavoring ingredient and a preservative. Other common seasonings are sugar, pepper, sage, mace, ginger, nutmeg, and garlic. Some sausages are characterized by a particular seasoning ingredient. For example, cooked salami contains whole pepper corns.

Variety meats—sometimes referred to as byproducts—include items like hearts, livers, tongues, tails, sweetbreads, kidneys, brains, tripe, and chitterlings. In general, these items are in much greater demand in other countries—Europe, in particular—and so a rather substantial proportion of many of these items is exported. This is somewhat difficult to understand because livers, tongues, hearts, and kidneys, in particular, are all highly nutritious and, except for calf liver, usually are quite reasonable in price.

Buying for the Freezer. Freezing is an excellent way to preserve most kinds of meat, and families which raise their own livestock and other produce may obtain substantial savings by renting one or more lockers in a freezer locker plant or from having a locker plant process their meat for storage in a home freezer.

However, the great majority of consumers must purchase all of their meat. For these families, there may be less monetary advantage in owning a freezer but this may be offset by other factors such as the convenience of having a ready supply of meat on hand at all times.

Families having limited freezer space—such as in a combination refrigerator-freezer—usually will be limited to retail stores as a source of supply but by careful management they can generally arrange to have a reasonable assortment of different kinds of meat on hand most of the time. And, by buying "on special," they can also make considerable savings. However, this approach may require rewrapping meats in a stronger material and taking care that only relatively small amounts of meat are frozen at any one time. If they desire to do so, families with larger freezers usually will be able to purchase their meat from specialized dealers such as locker plants or freezer provisioners.

Buying from a freezer provisioner or locker plant usually involves purchasing a side, quarter, or wholesale cut. This will require less effort on your part than buying retail cuts and freezing them yourself, since all of the wrapping and freezing will be done by the dealer. Other advantages of buying from a locker plant or freezer provisioner are that the meat can be frozen more rapidly and you can indicate how long you want the meat aged and how it is to be cut. However, buying meat as a side, quarter, or wholesale cut may result in your getting more of some cuts than you would like—or even some cuts that you might prefer not to have at all. Buying retail cuts for freezing permits you to buy only the cuts you actually want.

Making a valid comparison of the cost of buying meat in the form of retail cuts or as a side, quarter, or wholesale cut can be very frustrating to most consumers. This is because the average family has little or no knowledge about the actual proportion of the different cuts—as well as the amount of fat and bone—that they will get from a side of beef. However, the following example shows how such a comparison can be made. Let's assume that you can buy a 300-pound side of beef (USDA Choice, Yield Grade 3) for 65 cents per pound—cut, wrapped, and frozen. The total cost would be \$195 (300 pounds x 65¢=\$195).

But, as indicated in the table below,

Retail Cuts	Approximate Percent of Side Weight (Yield Grade 3)	Weight, Pounds (from 300 lb. side)		Local Prices per lb.		Retail Value
Round Steak	11	33	×	________	=	________
Rump Roast (boneless)	3	9	×	________	=	________
Porterhouse, T-bone, club steaks	5	15	×	________	=	________
Sirloin Steak	8	24	×	________	=	________
Rib Roast	6	18	×	________	=	________
Chuck Blade Roast	9	27	×	________	=	________
Chuck Arm Roast	6	18	×	________	=	________
Ground beef	11	33	×	________	=	________
Stew Meat	11	33	×	________	=	________
Brisket (boneless)	3	9	×	________	=	________
Total Retail Cuts	73	219				
Waste (fat, bone, shrinkage)	27	81				
TOTAL	100	300		TOTAL RETAIL VALUE		________
				AVERAGE RETAIL PRICE PER LB.		________

such beef normally will yield only about 73 percent of its weight in trimmed cuts (when the cutting and trimming are done as usual in retail operations). Therefore, 300 pounds x 73 percent=219 actual pounds of cuts. And the actual average cost of the cuts would be 89 cents per pound ($195÷219 pounds=89¢ per pound).

Now, using the table below, let's see how you could compare this cost with that of buying an equivalent amount of retail cuts. To determine the total cost of such an assortment of retail cuts simply insert retail prices per pound for each cut in the column headed "Local prices," multiply each price by the weight shown in the second column, and enter the answer in the last column headed "Retail value." The total of this column will be the total cost of 219 pounds of retail cuts in the same proportion as would be obtained from a 300-pound side. (In the example, this would compare with the $195 total cost of the 300-pound side.) The average cost of the cuts per pound would be determined by dividing the total cost by 219 pounds. (In the example, this would compare with the 89 cents per pound.) For additional information on this subject, the reader is referred to U.S. Department of Agriculture Home and Garden Bulletin No. 166, "How to Buy Meat for Your Freezer."

Families purchasing meat from a locker plant or a freezer provisioner should make sure that the supplier has a well-established reputation for honesty and for fairness. Although most businessmen are honest, there are always a few who will take advantage of the uninformed. In this connection, one of the practices that consumers should beware of is known as "bait and switch."

This takes the form of offering beef, for instance, at very low prices and sometimes advertising this as "U.S. Choice" or as "U.S. Prime." Having attracted a potential customer to his plant with this "bait," the dealer will show him the advertised beef. Although it may be of the quality grade advertised, this "bait" carcass will usually be a specially selected specimen that is very fat and wasty.

However, hanging alongside will be another obviously leaner carcass which the dealer then persuades the customer is what he really should buy. But, the price of the leaner beef will be much higher even though it really may be lower in quality and actually have cost the dealer less than the normal wholesale price for the advertised grade. That is the "switch."

In most cases, the leaner carcass will not carry a USDA grade but the dealer will assure the customer that it has been inspected by USDA (hoping that this may make him think that it also has been graded) or that it rates a "Fancy," "Supreme" or some other likely sounding "grade" name.

Since the customer usually is not present to make an inventory of the various cuts at the time his meat is being cut, it also is quite easy, for instance, for such a plant to fail to deliver a portion of an order, to substitute a lower grade of meat than ordered, or to charge for excess weight.

Customers should remember that the only official USDA grades for meat are those listed previously. Consumers also should remember that a very high percentage of the beef and lamb that qualifies for Choice or Prime is actually graded and is readily available at all times. So, if they want this quality of beef or lamb they should insist the grade stamp be left on the cuts.

Some dealers also advertise a "beef bundle" or a "steak package." Unless these advertisements indicate specifically the grade of the meat and the kind and amount of the various cuts included, the average family would be well advised to steer clear of such "deals." They should also beware of advertisements which offer "something for nothing"—bargains which are too sensational to be realistic. No dealer can really afford to give meat away or to sell it at a loss, and reputable ones will not pretend to do so.

As pointed out earlier, there has been a retail sales value difference of

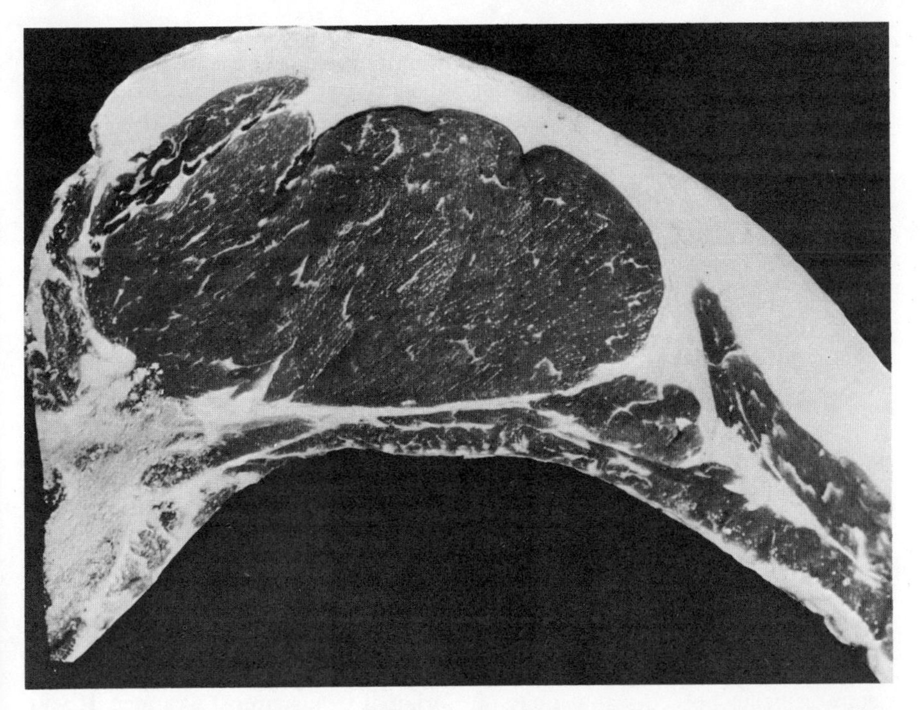

These rib cuts from beef carcasses represent two yield grades—the rib above comes from a Yield Grade 2 carcass. The rib below obviously has more fat; it is from a Yield Grade 4 carcass.

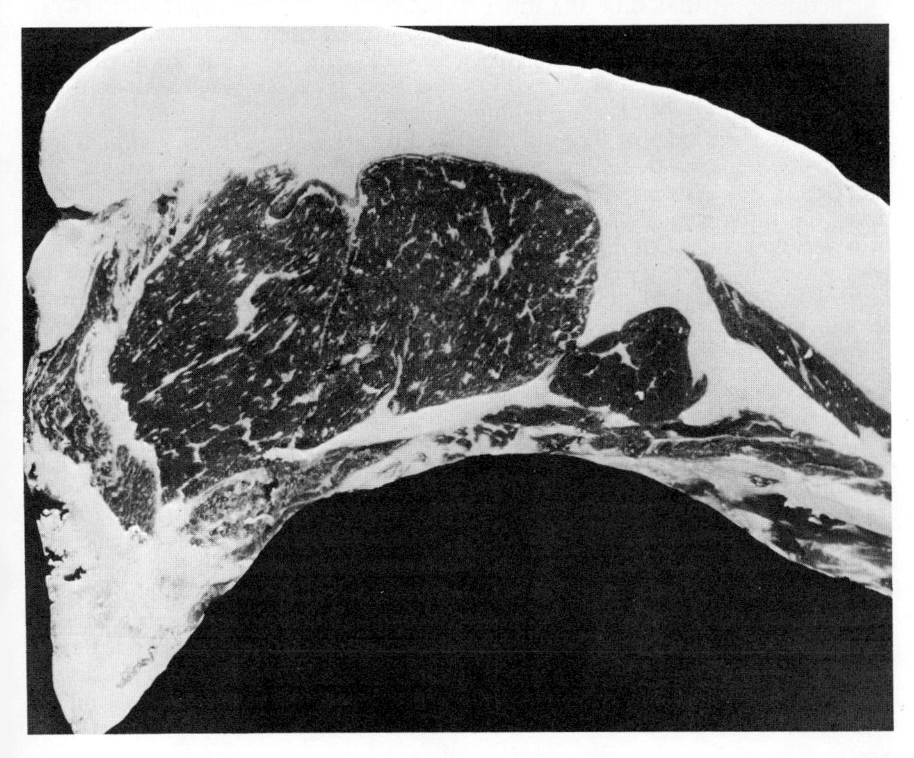

about $3.60 per cwt. between typical carcasses—or sides—of adjacent yield grades. However, in wholesale trading up to this time, the price differences between yield grades have been substantially less than this. Therefore, in purchasing a side of beef, for instance, it *should* be best to purchase as high a yield grade as possible since the prices charged should be in line with current wholesale prices. However, this may not be the case.

For example, in mid-1968 a freezer provisioner in the Washington, D.C., area quoted U.S. Choice heifer sides at 53 cents per pound and U.S. Choice steer sides at 69 cents per pound. When asked about this difference in price for the same quality grade, the salesman explained that the steer sides were Yield Grade 1, 2, or 3 and that the heifer sides were Yield Grade 4 or 5.

Subsequent examination revealed there was a substantial difference in cutability (yield of cuts) between the steer and heifer beef, but that none of it had actually been yield graded. Furthermore, at that time the difference in the wholesale price of these two kinds of carcasses was much less than 16 cents per pound.

This same company also was selling U.S. Prime steer sides at 99 cents per pound—30 cents per pound more than the U.S. Choice steer sides. At that time, the difference in the wholesale price between such Prime and Choice beef was only 2 cents per pound. In beef of the same yield grade there is seldom more than 2 cents per pound difference between the wholesale prices for Prime and Choice or Choice and Good.

The foregoing discussion is not intended to discourage consumers from freezing meat or from owning home freezers. Rather, it is intended to show consumers how they can make realistic comparisons of different methods of buying meat and also to caution them about the practices of some unscrupulous suppliers. Freezing is an excellent means of preserving meat and other foods, and freezers are a very convenient method of storage.

Care, Storing, and Freezing. Meat is usually the most expensive item in the food budget and it is perishable, so it is important to use care not only in selection at the market but also in use down to the last bit of leftover.

Keep meat clean and cold—in the refrigerator (35° to 40° F.) or in the freezer (at 0° F. or below) until it is cooked. The cold temperature slows down changes that affect eating quality and cause food spoilage. Generally, the lower the temperature, the slower the change. A few meat items may be held at room temperature—canned luncheon meats, certain sausages, some small canned hams, and some dry-cured hams.

For short-time refrigerator storage, place fresh meat in the special meat compartment, or in the coldest part of your refrigerator (not the ice cube maker) as soon as possible after purchase. Prepackaged meat may usually be refrigerated for 1 to 2 days in its original (transparent) wrapper. If you plan to keep the meat refrigerated for longer than 2 days, you should rewrap the meat loosely so air will circulate and dry the meat surface slightly, as bacteria grow less quickly upon a dry surface.

Fresh beef, veal, lamb, and pork—in the form of roasts, chops, cutlets, and steaks—may usually be held 3 to 5 days in the refrigerator before there is evident loss of palatability or flavor. Cured and smoked meats, like bacon, bologna, hams, sausage, and frankfurters, usually may be stored for 7 days in the refrigerator. Fresh sausage, ground meats, variety meats, and stew meats should be used within 1 to 2 days because they are especially perishable.

To prepare fresh meat for freezing, remove excess fat and divide the meat into individual or meal-size portions. Boneless cuts save storage space and are not likely to puncture the wrapping material. Wrap meat tightly in a moisture and vapor resistant packaging material like foil or plastic. Proper packaging prevents foods from drying out and prevents air from entering the package. Separate individual portions, like chops and hamburger patties, with double layers of waxed paper or foil to prevent them from freezing together. Label and date packages.

Place your meat promptly in a freezer, or in a refrigerator's freezer section where a temperature of 0° F. or lower is maintained. Turn your freezer control to the coldest position to speed freezing and help prevent warming of any other stored frozen food. Limit the amount of food to be frozen at one time to 2 pounds per cubic foot of the total freezer space. If your freezer will not maintain a temperature as low as 0° F., the meat held there must be used considerably sooner than the freezer times that are given below.

Frozen meat, if properly packaged, frozen, and stored, may be kept for long periods with little change in its eating quality. For best eating, use beef and lamb roasts and steaks within 12 months; pork, calf, and veal roasts within 8 months; lamb, pork, and veal chops or cutlets, and variety meats within 4 months; ground and stew meats within 3 months; and use fresh sausage within 2 months.

Freezing of cured meats is not recommended because seasonings added during curing accelerate the development of rancidity. If cured meats are frozen, they should be used within a month or two.

Frozen meat may be cooked with or without thawing. Frozen meat takes about 1⅓ to 1½ times as long to cook as thawed or fresh meat. Whenever possible, frozen meat should be thawed in its wrappings in the refrigerator and cooked soon after thawing. However, thawed meat is no more perishable than unfrozen meat. Thawed meat may be refrozen, if necessary, but it may be less tender and juicy.

Cooked meats should be covered or wrapped and refrigerated promptly. A rapid cooling in the refrigerator helps prevent bacterial growth and spoilage. Gravy and meat broth are highly perishable and so should be refrigerated quickly and stored only for 1 or 2 days.

When refrigerated, cooked meat is best if used within 2 days. To keep cooked meat longer, remove meat from bones (to save storage space), wrap tightly in moisture and vapor resistant material, and freeze quickly. Cooked meat, as well as many cooked combination dishes containing beef or veal, can be stored in the freezer at 0° F. for 2 or 3 months. When you want to use frozen cooked casseroles or stews, you can heat them from the frozen state without thawing first.

Guidelines for Cooking Meat. The key to success in cooking meat is to use medium to low temperatures and to cook it for as short a time as possible. When prepared in this manner, beef, veal, lamb, and pork are juicy with maximum tenderness. The aroma from meat cooked at low temperatures is more pleasant and the color is more even than that of meat cooked at high temperatures. Another advantage of low to moderate cooking temperatures is that there is more meat to serve because of the smaller losses through evaporation, shrinkage, and drippings.

The degree of doneness of meat is a matter of individual preference. Cook beef as you like it—rare, medium, or well done.

Rare beef has a puffy, full appearance, a brown exterior, reddish-pink interior, and lots of clear red juice. The internal temperature of rare roast is 140° F. Beef cooked to a medium degree, with an internal temperature of 155° to 160° F., has a light pink interior and less juice of a lighter color than rare beef. Well-done beef is light brown throughout and the internal temperature will be 170° to 180° F.

The temperatures cited above are those associated with roasts; but small roasts and steaks may reach a given stage of doneness at a lower internal meat temperature. To check the doneness of a steak or chop, cut along the bone and observe the interior color of the meat.

Veal should be cooked well done (to 170° F. internal temperature) to make it tender and palatable. Well-done veal has a red-brown exterior and a gray interior color. Lamb is usually preferred medium (170° F. internal temperature), or as well done (180° F.). Medium lamb chops have a grayish-tan interior with a tinge of pink. Well-done lamb is grayish-tan with no trace of pink.

Variety meats are usually cooked to the well-done stage.

Fresh pork should be cooked thoroughly. The recommended internal temperature for pork loin is 170° F. Research has proved that the 185° F. recommended for many years is not necessary—and cooking pork to only 170° F. makes for juicier meat and fewer cooking losses than the higher temperature. A good test for "doneness" of fresh pork is to make small cuts next to the bone and into the thicker part of the meat. If the juice is still pink, the pork is not done. Heat "cook-before-eating" cured hams to 160° F. and picnic shoulders to 170° F. "Fully cooked" cured shoulders and hams may be served unheated, but heating them to 130° F. brings out a better flavor.

Roasting. In roasting, the meat is surrounded and cooked by heated air in an oven. The meat is not covered and no water is added.

Specific cuts of beef in the Prime, Choice, and Good grades which are suggested for roasting include rib, loin, sirloin, tenderloin, and sirloin tip. In the Prime and Choice grades, the top round, eye of round, and blade chuck cuts are recommended for roasting.

Large blocky cuts of veal—from the leg, loin, rib, and shoulder—are generally roasted. Nearly all lamb cuts are tender enough for roasting, particularly those from the leg, loin, rib, and shoulder. Besides fresh and cured ham and shoulder, those pork cuts which are roasted successfully include loin or rib roasts and spareribs.

Place any meat to be roasted fat side up in a shallow pan so that the fat may baste the meat as it cooks. Insert a meat thermometer into the center of thick cuts, being careful that the tip touches neither fat nor bone. Roast the meat uncovered in a 325° F. oven until the thermometer registers the desired internal temperature. Remove meat from the oven and allow it to stand for a few minutes to make carving easier.

As a guide, approximate roasting times are given in timetable below; they are based on meat at refrigerator temperatures as the cooking begins.

Allow for extra time to roast thick, chunky cuts, boneless or rolled cuts, meat with an outside fat layer, and stuffed roasts. Unthawed roasts may take one and a half times as long to cook as fresh or thawed roasts of the same weight and shape. The amount of the additional cooking time needed depends upon the size and shape of the meat cut, as well as on its initial temperature.

Broiling, Pan Broiling, or Pan Frying. Broiling is cooking meat one side at a time by heat from a flame, electric unit, or glowing coals. In pan broiling, the meat is cooked in an uncovered pan over direct heat, and the fat that cooks out of the meat is drained off and not allowed to accumulate. When fat is added to the pan or allowed to

Estimated Times for Roasting Meat at 325° F.

Kind of meat and cut	Ready-to-cook weight Pounds	Time required for center of meat to reach a given temperature					
		° F.	Hours	° F.	Hours	° F.	Hours
Beef roasts	5	140	2 to 3	160	2½	170	3 to 3¾
Veal roasts	3 to 5					170	2½ to 3½
Lamb roasts	5			150	2½ to 3	180	2¾ to 3¼
Fresh pork roasts	5			170	2¾ to 3½	185	3½ to 4
Spareribs	3						1½
Stuffed pork chops							¾
Mild cured ham	6	130	1½ to 2	160	2½		
Mild cured pork shoulder	6					170	3½

accumulate, the method is pan frying.

Beef steaks especially suitable for broiling, pan broiling, or pan frying include tenderloin (filet mignon) in all grades, and porterhouse, T-bone, club, strip loin, sirloin, rib, ribeye in the Prime, Choice, and Good grades. The same three cooking methods also may be successfully used for sirloin tip, top round, and blade chuck steaks—but only in the Prime and Choice grades.

Many cuts of lamb in the Prime and Choice grades are recommended for broiling, pan broiling, or frying, including leg steaks and loin, sirloin, rib, and shoulder chops. Ground lamb or beef is also broiled or pan broiled frequently. Pork chops may be broiled or pan broiled, as well as cured ham slices, bacon, and Canadian bacon. Veal and pork steaks, cutlets, and chops may be pan fried.

Steaks, chops, or meat patties at least an inch thick, and cured ham slices ½ inch thick, are best for broiling. Thinner pieces of meat are usually more satisfactory when pan broiled or pan fried.

To broil, pan broil, or pan fry, trim the outer edge of fat from the meat to within ½ inch—this reduces spattering and, when broiling, lessens the danger of a steak or drippings catching on fire. Slash the remaining fat at intervals to prevent curling of the meat while it cooks.

Place the meat on a broiler rack and slowly broil one side. When browned on one side, season the meat and turn it over. Broil the other side to desired doneness and season it. Very thick steaks or chops should be cooked more slowly than thin cuts. Otherwise, the outside may char before the inside cooks. Also, large steaks take longer to reach a given doneness than small steaks with the same thickness. Very thick steaks or chops may be warmed or partially cooked in a 350° F. oven and then browned under the broiler.

To pan broil, cook the meat slowly in a preheated, heavy, uncovered frying pan over medium heat. To pan fry, add a small amount of fat to preheated pan. Turn the meat occasionally. Enough heat must be applied or the meat will stew in the juice rather than brown. To increase browning, dredge meat in seasoned flour or crumbs before pan frying.

Allow 10 to 25 minutes for broiling 1-inch-thick steaks. Lamb chops and cured ham slices require 12 to 20 minutes. Bacon needs about 4 to 5 minutes, Canadian bacon about 10 minutes, liver about 12 minutes, and kabobs around 20 minutes. Ground meat patties take 8 to 15 minutes, depending on their thickness and degree of doneness desired. Cooking time for pan broiled meat is about the same as that for broiled meat of similar thickness and size. Frying usually takes a little less time than the times given for broiling.

To test broiled meat for doneness, cut a small slit in the lean and note the color and texture. Or, press the meat lightly with a fork; very rare meat is soft and pulpy; medium rare is slightly resistant, and well-done meat is quite firm.

When meat is broiled, pan broiled, or fried, it will be more tender and juicy if cooked only to the rare stage, rather than well done.

Braising. Braising, cooking by steam trapped and held in a covered container or foil wrap, is recommended for less tender cuts of meat. The source of steam may be water or other liquid added to meat, or it may be meat juices. Braising may be done in a heavy pan on top of the range, in a moderate oven, or in a pressure saucepan.

Pot roasting is braising large cuts of meat. Stewing or simmering is a form of braising and refers to cooking meat in liquid just below the boiling point. For stews, meat is cut into small 1- to 2-inch cubes.

Many beef cuts, particularly in the lower grades—Standard or Commercial—are best prepared by braising them. These include sirloin, sirloin tip, round, flank, chuck, shoulder, rump, and short ribs.

Braising is good for many cuts of veal because the combination of browning and steaming tenderizes the meat and develops its flavor. Best veal cuts for braising include arm or blade steaks or chops, breast, cutlets or round steaks, loin or rib chops, and riblets. In lamb, the cuts most suited to braising are breast, leg steaks, riblets, shanks, shoulder chops, and roasts. All pork chops or steaks are very satisfactory when braised, as are spareribs and cured ham shanks.

In braising meat, brown the meat slowly on all sides in enough fat to keep the meat from sticking. Meats which have a considerable amount of fat (and have not been breaded or floured) can be browned without added fat—brown first the sides with the greatest amount of fat. Add fat to brown breaded, floured, or low-fat meats like veal. Browning is optional; some cuts like corned beef are never browned.

After browning the meat, you may need to add a small amount of liquid (around ½ cup for a roast)—water, broth, cider, tomato or vegetable juice, wine, meat stock, or diluted soy sauce may be used. Some cuts have enough juices to provide steam without requiring added moisture.

Add liquid in small amounts as needed rather than all at once, to retain flavors developed during browning. For soups and large cuts like corned beef, cover meat with water. Cover pan tightly and simmer meat in a 350° F. oven or over low to medium heat until the meat is fork tender.

Braising and simmering times depend on kind, size, and thickness of the meat. Allow ½ to 1 hour to braise chops and cutlets (½ to 1 inch thick); the longer time for pork or larger, thicker cuts. Flank steak, lamb breast or shank, and boneless cured pork shoulder butt require 1½ to 2 hours. Chuck and round steak (1 to 1½ inches thick) generally need 2 to 2½ hours as do short ribs, and lamb and veal shoulder roasts. Beef roasts and shanks (3 to 5 pounds) require 3 to 4 hours. Allow 2½ to 3 hours for 1½-inch cubes of beef to become tender in stews, and 1½ to 2 hours for cubes of lamb, pork, or veal. Fresh or corned beef brisket (8 pounds) and whole cured hams (12 to 16 pounds) require 4 to 5 hours of simmering time.

Country-cured hams should be scrubbed, soaked overnight in water, and then simmered (15 to 20 minutes per pound) to remove excess salt before they are roasted or braised.

Braising in a pressure saucepan shortens the cooking time, but the meat may shrink more (leaving fewer servings) and be less juicy than meat braised in the oven or over direct heat. Meat braised at 10 pounds of pressure is fork tender in about a quarter of the time required for a conventional braising.

If you add vegetables to braised meat, do this during the last 30 to 45 minutes of cooking. Be cautious about using strongly flavored vegetables, such as turnips and parsnips. Green or partially ripe fruits—peaches, pears, gage plums—give beef stew a tart and unusual flavor.

A famous dish prepared by simmering is the New England boiled dinner. Simmer corned beef with bay leaf, pepper corns, onion, carrot, and parsley until tender. Slice meat evenly and serve with carrots, cabbage, and potatoes which have been simmered separately or with the meat for the last half hour of cooking time.

Cooking Variety Meats. Variety meats, considered a gourmet item by many people, are often more economical than regular meat cuts and offer an interesting change of menu. The choice of a cooking method for variety meats depends on how tender the particular meat is. Variety meats are usually cooked well done regardless of the cooking method.

Brains, sweetbreads, and veal (calf) liver and kidneys are tender and can be pan fried or broiled. For variation, they can be braised or simmered. Less tender variety meats—heart, tongue, tripe, and beef liver and kidneys—need braising or simmering.

To prepare a variety meat for cooking, you should remove any large blood vessels and wash the meat in water (warm water for heart, but cold water for kidneys, sweetbreads, and brains).

For kidneys, remove the outer membrane, split the kidneys lengthwise through the center, and remove inner fat and tubes. To broil kidneys, dip them in melted butter or margarine, and place them on a cold broiler grid. Broil them until they are brown on each side. To simmer kidneys, place them in a deep pot and add water to cover them. Then simmer till tender, which takes about 1 to 1½ hours for beef kidneys, ¾ to 1 hour for veal kidneys. Change water once during the simmering time to eliminate any strong odor.

To broil liver, dip the sliced liver in melted butter or margarine, place on cold broiler grid, and broil just long enough for the liver to lose its red color—about 3 minutes on each side.

Heart may be stuffed with dressing and braised until tender. Or you may wish to simmer beef heart 3 to 4 hours (2½ to 3 hours cooking time for lamb, pork, and veal hearts) in salted water until tender.

Sweetbreads and brains may be simmered for 20 minutes in water containing a teaspoon of salt and 1 tablespoon vinegar or lemon juice per quart (this liquid firms and whitens the meats). Then, dip the meat in salted fat and broil lightly 10 to 15 minutes; or heat in cream or tomato sauce; or coat with crumbs or flour and fry about 20 minutes until tender and lightly browned.

Cooking Ground Meat. Homemakers serve ground meat frequently—it can be formed into meat patties (which are broiled or fried), meat loaves, meatballs, or used in meat sauces.

To prepare juicy ground meat, handle the meat as little as possible. Excessive mixing results in a more compact, less tender product. Be careful not to overcook the meat or it will be too dry.

Meatballs may contain ground meat mixed with seasonings, breadcrumbs, mashed potatoes, rice, and liquid. The meat mixture is often shaped, browned, and simmered in a sauce for 30 to 45 minutes over low heat or in a 350° F. oven. During cooking the meat is basted with the sauce occasionally. Meatballs also may be fried in a pan or in deep fat.

A meat loaf mixture—possibly containing onions, green peppers, mushrooms, and celery—may be packed in a loaf pan or mold and baked uncovered at 350° F. The cooking time depends on size and shape of loaf.

Leftover cooked meat may be cubed or ground and included in many recipes calling for braised or simmered meat. Just eliminate the browning step and reduce the braising or simmering time. Ground cooked meat can be used in croquettes, salads, souffles, omelets, and casseroles.

To make a meat roll, spread biscuit or pie dough with chopped or cubed cooked meat moistened with gravy. Roll like a jelly roll; slice 1 inch thick; and bake it on a greased pan until browned.

A good hash is made up of finely chopped leftover meat, cubed potatoes, onions, and well-seasoned gravy. All these are fried together until firm enough to dip. Fry slowly to allow potatoes to absorb flavor of the meat.

Seasoning. A high-quality piece of meat really requires only salt and pepper for seasoning. However, to give variety you may season it with spices and herbs, marinate it, baste it with a glaze or sauce, or fill it with a stuffing.

Seasonings sprinkled on raw meat surfaces penetrate only slightly. Spices and herbs are often added to the cooked meat or its sauce. But a word of caution: Limit the number and amount of spices and herbs used at any one time with meat. Heat may produce a stronger aromatic flavor than is desired. Omit or reduce salt when seasoned salt (salt combined with a spice or herb) or soy sauce is used—otherwise the meat may turn too salty.

Remember, it is so easy to add flavor with seasoning—but impossible to remove it when too much is added.

Commercial tenderizers may be applied to the surface of raw meat to increase its tenderness. Like seasonings, they penetrate for only a short distance, so they are more effective in tenderizing steaks than roasts. Papain, the enzyme used in most commercially prepared tenderizers, tenderizes meat proteins primarily during cooking at the temperatures between 140° and 176° F. Over tenderization may occur if enzyme-treated meat is cooked at too low a temperature, if it is held at serving temperatures for a long time, or if it is reheated. Some commercial tenderizers contain added seasonings.

Marinating is used to introduce flavor into a meat dish. At one time, marinades were used for tenderizing purposes, but most cooks today use them for flavor. Marinades usually include an acid (lemon juice, cider, or vinegar), seasonings (salt, pepper, onion, garlic, spices or herbs), and sometimes a fat (olive, vegetable oil).

To marinate, soak small cuts (cubes or chops) for a few hours in enough liquid to entirely cover them. Marinate large cuts overnight to 24 hours in the refrigerator. The acid penetrates meat slowly, so you should allow time for the flavor to reach the center. To reduce the amount of marinade required, use a container (not aluminum as the acid may pit it) only slightly larger than the meat, or encase the meat with marinade in a plastic freezer bag. Turn the meat several times.

Moderately low roasting temperatures have made it not necessary to baste meat to combat excessive dryness. However, basting or glazing a baked ham continues as a traditional cooking method, and other meat cuts may be basted with a glaze, sauce, or wine to add flavor. Try basting meat during the last 30 minutes of roasting, using grape juice, apple cider, cranberry sauce, maple sirup, or sweet-sour sauce. Remove the skin of cured and smoked pork shoulders and hams and score the fat just before basting. Other meat cuts require no special treatment before basting.

Stuffing may also add distinction to many meats. You can stuff breast of lamb or veal; pork chops; shoulder of veal, lamb, or pork; lamb or pork crown roasts, spareribs, and tenderloins. Also, before roasting or braising, you can roll thin slices of boneless meat (slices should be pounded flat) around stuffing and fasten with toothpicks or a small skewer, or tie with a string.

The stuffing base can be bread, rice, cornbread, potatoes, corn, ground meat, macaroni, or fruit. For variety and flavor, add anchovies, ripe olives, mushrooms, green peppers, nuts, or pickles. Many people prefer a rich, flavorful stuffing for veal and a fruit stuffing for pork. Stuff veal with a sausage or ham mixture, or with your favorite poultry stuffing. Stuff pork with a cooked mixture of dried apricots, prunes, rice, celery, onion, and almonds, or with prunes and apples.

Ground meat combines readily with numerous flavors or seasonings to make it subtle, spicy, hot, or pungent, as you prefer.

When you are pan broiling meat patties, use a teaspoon of salt per pound of meat, and add a little barbecue or Worcestershire sauce to the pan just before the cooking is completed—this gives a tangy flavor.

Meat loaves may be distinctively yours. Add sage, garlic, or dry mustard for a new flavor. For a surprise, pack the meat around whole peeled carrots, or around rectangles of sharp processed cheese, or around a row of hard-cooked eggs. Alternate layers of seasoned ground meat with layers of sliced onions, sliced fresh tomatoes, and cooked bacon.

Cooking meat is not difficult—you actually have more freedom in preparing meat than you do in making a cake, which requires precise measurements. Just follow the basic recommendations in this section: Select the grade and cuts of meat best suited to the method of cooking you plan to use, store it properly, and cook it at a low temperature.

Violet B. Crosby
Ashley R. Gulich

Poultry: A Tasty, Anytime Delight That's Popular Dozens of Ways

Poultry is high on the list of popularity in American meals—and that's no accident. With today's modern production, processing, and marketing methods, chicken, turkey, duck, and geese are available the year around—for roasting, broiling, frying, stewing, or making soups, salads, or practically whatever you can think of.

Packaged, cut-up chicken and turkey, heat-and-serve fried chicken, and the newer turkey and chicken rolls, roasts, or bars make poultry among the most versatile and easy-to-prepare dishes you can find. Roasts and rolls, all meat and boneless, make a wonderful dish for buffet dinners, late parties, or any time.

Because of seasonal production and limited supplies, "chicken on Sunday" and "turkey on Thanksgiving" were meals looked forward to with mouth-watering anticipation in the 1930's. But those days are in the past—today's consumers have a delectable variety of poultry products to serve any day of the week, any week of the year.

How well our American palates are satisfied by poultry is reflected by its frequent appearance on the family menu. Per capita consumption of poultry has jumped spectacularly in the past 30 years—we now eat more than twice as much chicken as we did back in 1940, and three times as much turkey.

The terms for "poultry" include chickens, turkeys, geese, guineas, and duck. Broiler-fryer chickens are produced most heavily in the Del-Mar-Va Peninsula, where Delaware, Maryland, and Virginia converge, and in the Southeast, notably in Georgia, Mississippi, Alabama, Arkansas, and the Carolinas.

Stewing hens, a byproduct of the egg industry, are produced in the Southeast, Midwest, parts of the Northeast, and in California.

Major production areas for turkeys are the Midwest and California.

Ducks are produced mostly on Long Island, N.Y., and to a lesser degree in the Midwest, Massachusetts, and Virginia.

Today's poultry is pampered—mass produced in well-designed housing with automated feed and water supplies, so the birds don't have to forage for part of their meals as they did in the past.

Young poultry is marketed at a very tender age. Broiler-fryers are ready for market in about 9 weeks, and 20-pound tom turkeys usually in about 5 months.

Poultry is an excellent source of high-quality protein, with the amino acids essential to growth and health. Weight watchers are partial to chicken and turkey because an average serving contains fewer calories than an average serving of most other meats. Poultry also provides many other essential nutrients including iron, thiamine (vitamin B_1), riboflavin (vitamin B_2), and niacin.

As a protection to the American

Violet B. Crosby is a Home Economist in the Labels, Standards, and Packaging Branch, Technical Services Division, Consumer and Marketing Service.

Ashley R. Gulich is Chief of the Standardization Branch, Poultry Division, Consumer and Marketing Service.

people, Congress has enacted two laws requiring that poultry products be safe for your family.

The Poultry Products Inspection Act—passed in 1957—required Federal inspection of all poultry moving in interstate commerce.

The newer law, the Wholesome Poultry Products Act, enacted in 1968 and amending the previous act, goes even further. It requires inspection—at least as good as Federal inspection—of all poultry regardless of whether it moves in interstate commerce. Under this new law, the U.S. Department of Agriculture provides cash assistance and technical advice to help States develop inspection programs equal to the Federal program. If a State does not develop an adequate inspection program, all poultry processing plants within that State will then come under mandatory Federal inspection.

In these ways, you are protected wherever you might buy your poultry.

Poultry inspection involves many aspects. Processing plants must meet strictest requirements for cleanliness; they must have adequate equipment and procedures to do a good job. Inspectors—who are either doctors of veterinary medicine or are trained specialists under a veterinarian's supervision—keep constant watch over the plant, over the processing operation, over every bird that comes through the plant.

Any birds found to be unhealthy or not fit for eating are removed immediately from the processing line and condemned for use as human food. Inspectors also make sure that the products are not adulterated and are truthfully labeled—all labels must be federally approved before they can be used.

INSPECTION LEGEND—SYMBOL OF WHOLESOMENESS

In addition, official laboratories run continuous tests on poultry products to guard against bacterial or chemical contamination.

USDA also has specified minimum meat requirements for many processed poultry products. For example, if a product is labeled "Turkey Pie" it must contain at least 14 percent cooked, deboned turkey meat. Chicken dinners must contain at least 18 percent cooked, deboned chicken meat; chicken a la king, at least 20 percent meat; and chicken noodles or dumplings, at least 15 percent meat.

When you see the round USDA inspection mark on poultry—and on poultry products like pot pies and prepared dinners—you can be sure they have passed strict standards for wholesomeness, proper preparation, and labeling.

Another valuable USDA service is grading poultry for quality. This is a voluntary program—paid for by processors at no cost to the taxpayer. The official USDA grade shield is your assurance of quality.

Before poultry can be graded, it must first be federally inspected for wholesomeness.

The poultry grader—a Federal or Federal-State quality expert—examines each bird for conformation (overall shape and appearance), meatiness, amount of fat, and the presence or absence of defects (torn skin, discolorations, or bruises).

Grades are based on nationally uniform standards of quality, so that U.S. Grade A, for example, in New York means the same as U.S. Grade A in San Francisco. USDA standardization specialists constantly work to keep the standards up to date with current marketing practices and consumer desires.

The top grade for poultry, and the only one commonly found in stores, is U.S. Grade A. Grade A birds have good overall shape and appearance.

They are meaty, have a well-developed layer of fat in the skin, and are practically free from defects such as cuts and bruises.

Official standards also provide for U.S. Grade B and U.S. Grade C poultry. These birds are not as attractive as Grade A. They may have defects and faulty conformation, and could be lacking in fleshing and fat cover.

Because our poultry today is quite uniform in quality, most birds are U.S. Grade A. Birds graded below U.S. Grade A are usually sold without the grademark in supermarkets, or are used in processed foods where appearance is not important.

Until recently, the grademark was found only on poultry or poultry parts. In 1965, grade standards were developed for raw, ready-to-cook poultry rolls, roasts, or bars which can now be graded U.S. Grade A if they meet USDA standards.

In addition to making sure the poultry you buy has been inspected and graded, you will also want to know the age of the bird. Age indicates tenderness and suggests ways to cook the poultry.

Poultry is usually labeled according to age with the following terms:

- Mature chickens may be labeled—mature chicken, old chicken, hen, stewing chicken, or fowl.
- Mature turkeys may be labeled—mature turkey, yearling turkey, or old turkey.
- Mature ducks, geese, and guineas may be labeled—mature or old.
- Young chickens may be labeled—young chicken, Rock Cornish game hen, broiler, fryer, roaster, or capon.
- Young turkeys may be labeled—as young turkey, fryer-roaster, young hen, or young tom.
- Young ducks may be labeled—as duckling, young duckling, broiler duckling, fryer duckling, or as roaster duckling.

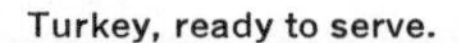

Turkey, ready to serve.

You can usually save money if you buy whole poultry and cut it into serving pieces yourself. Whole poultry usually is a few cents less per pound than cut-up poultry.

It is also more economical to buy large turkeys rather than small ones. Not only do the larger birds usually sell for a few cents less per pound, but they also have a larger proportion of meat to bone, so you get a bargain two ways. Smaller turkeys, however, do offer more varieties of cooking than large ones.

How often have you asked yourself, "How much poultry should I buy for my family?" Naturally, the amount depends not only upon the kind of poultry you choose, but also on the cooking method, the number and size of the servings, and whether or not leftovers are desired.

For whole broiler-fryers, stewing chicken, turkey, duckling, or goose, the average serving per person is about 3 ounces of cooked meat (without bone), and you will need to buy ½ pound for each serving. For a boneless turkey roast, count on only ⅓ pound per serving. If you are buying cut-up chicken, these are the serving sizes often used: one breast half, one leg, two drumsticks, two thighs, or four wings.

Remember that poultry, like all meats, is perishable; therefore, proper storage is important. So buy frozen, chilled, or smoked poultry only from freezer or refrigerator cases in order to obtain a top-quality product. It is wise to examine packages to be sure the wrappers are neither torn nor broken. Any frozen poultry should be solidly frozen when purchased.

Chilled raw poultry should be stored promptly in the coldest part of the refrigerator and used within 1 to 2 days. The transparent wrap on packaged poultry is designed to control moisture loss, and is suitable for short term home refrigerator or freezer storage, as well as storage in the retail case.

If poultry is purchased in market paper, unwrap it and remove the giblets. Place the poultry on a platter or tray, cover with wax paper or plastic wrap, cover giblets, and refrigerate separately.

Frozen raw poultry should be kept in the freezer at 0° F. or lower. It is important that all poultry be packaged in moisture and vapor resistant wrapping or bag, or in suitable rigid containers, and kept solidly frozen until ready to use. Be sure to label all the packages with the date and kind of poultry.

The maximum length of time that frozen poultry will maintain quality in the home freezer depends on the quality of the poultry at the time that it's frozen, the kind of packaging or container used, and the storage temperature.

Suggested maximum storage times to maintain quality in frozen poultry in the home freezer at 0° F. are:

	Months
Uncooked poultry:	
Chicken and turkey	12
Duck and goose	6
Giblets	3
Cooked poultry (slices or pieces):	
Covered with broth or gravy	6
Not covered with broth or gravy	1
Poultry meat sandwiches	1
Cooked poultry dishes	6
Fried chicken	4

Smoked poultry should be stored in the refrigerator. If it is to be held longer than 2 weeks, be certain it is wrapped in moisture- and vapor-proof paper or aluminum foil, or placed in plastic bags and frozen.

Freeze-dried poultry may be held at room temperature up to 2 years if the container has a good, solid seal. Of course, quality of the product will depend on condition of the raw poultry, care with which it was freeze-dried, and the seal of the container.

Canned poultry should be kept in a dry place at room temperature (not above 70° F.). It may be stored for a year.

Ready-to-cook, chilled poultry is indeed ready to cook—merely rinse in cool water, drain, and pat dry; then prepare, using your favorite cooking method. If the poultry is to be fried, broiled, or oven-browned, make sure it is dry to prevent spattering.

Frozen poultry usually is thawed before cooking. Whole poultry (frozen without giblets) or frozen poultry parts may be cooked without thawing. Cooking time will be longer than for unfrozen poultry. Do not thaw commercially frozen stuffed poultry before cooking. Do follow the manufacturer's instructions printed on the label.

As soon as possible after serving, separate any leftover poultry and stuffing. Place each in a covered container, or loosely wrap each in a moisture- and vapor-proof wrapping or container and store in the coldest part of the refrigerator. If you plan to hold them longer than 1 or 2 days, they may be frozen if they are properly packaged in airtight containers.

Promptly refrigerate any leftover broth or gravy, and use within 1 or 2 days. Reheat gravy and broth to boiling before eating.

There are three recommended methods of thawing poultry. The method used will depend on the length of time and the amount of space which is available for thawing.

- Thawing in the Refrigerator—Place poultry, still in its original wrap, on tray or platter. Thaw in refrigerator for 1 or 2 days until pliable. Turkeys weighing 18 pounds or over may take 3 days to thaw.
- Thawing in Cold Water—If it needs to be thawed on short notice, the poultry should be placed, in its watertight wrapper, in cold water. Change the water often to hasten thawing. Time required will be about 1 hour for small birds and up to 6 or 8 hours for large turkeys. Thaw until pliable.

Or you can use a combination method—partially thaw poultry in the refrigerator and complete the thawing in cold water.

- Thawing at Room Temperature—If it is not practical to use the thawing methods mentioned, you may safely thaw poultry in a cool room away from heat. To keep the surface temperature of the bird cool during thawing, the following precautions are recommended: Leave poultry in its original plastic wrapping, and place it in a closed, double wall paper bag or wrap the poultry in newspaper and set in a corrugated box. Thaw until poultry becomes pliable.

As with all foods, use care and cleanliness in handling fresh-chilled, frozen, or cooked poultry to guard against food poisoning bacteria.

Before cooking poultry, the main concern in handling is avoiding possible cross-contamination to other foods or surfaces in the kitchen. For this reason, after touching raw poultry you should wash your hands before working with other foods. Always clean and sanitize any food handling equipment, such as knives and cutting boards, after they have contacted raw meat or poultry prior to using them again.

Do *not* partially cook poultry 1 day and complete the cooking the following day. This is not considered a good procedure, as it would give bacteria an additional opportunity to grow. If staphylococci are present, a toxin is produced which can cause food poisoning. To avoid this danger, completely cook the bird at one time.

How can you cook poultry? How *can't* you cook it would be a better question. It can be baked, broiled, roasted, fried, braised, barbecued, stuffed, stewed, or cooked with other foods such as vegetables, rice, and special seasonings for delicious gourmet dishes.

Young, tender-meated poultry is most suitable for barbecuing, frying, broiling, or roasting. Mature, less tender-meated poultry may be preferred for stewing and baking, for use in casseroles, soups, and salads. No matter how you choose to serve it, you are sure to please your family because poultry is one of the most popular foods—for young and old alike.

Roast Whole Poultry—All kinds of poultry—chicken, turkey, duck, goose, and guinea—are delicious roasted. Whole poultry may be roasted stuffed or unstuffed.

To prepare it for roasting, rinse the

poultry, drain, and pat dry. Rub cavity lightly with salt, if desired. It is not necessary to salt poultry which is to be stuffed.

Fill wishbone (neck) area lightly with stuffing. Fasten neck skin to back of bird with skewer. Stuff body cavity lightly. Tuck legs under bird, using skewers or string, and shape wings akimbo-style—that is, bring wing tips onto back. Insert a meat thermometer in the inner thigh muscle.

Place poultry, breast-side up, in a shallow pan. If desired, brush skin with oil or melted fat. To roast poultry halves, quarters, pieces, or roasts, place skin-side up in a shallow pan. If poultry browns early in the roasting period, cover the breast and drumstick lightly with aluminum foil or moisten a thin cloth with fat and place it over the breast and legs to prevent overbrowning. Baste with drippings, if desired. Ducks, geese, and guineas have sufficient fat so that they need no basting.

At the half or two-thirds point of roasting, cut the string or skin to release the bird's legs. The meat is done when the temperature reaches 180° to 185° F. Also check the stuffing temperature; this should be at least 165° F.

A second way to test for doneness is to press thc flcshy part of the drumstick with protected fingers.

When done the meat will feel soft, the drumstick will move easily, and the leg joint will give readily.

Braising Poultry—To change oven roasting to braising, just cover the poultry while it is cooking. A small amount of water may be added, if desired. Braising is suitable for all poultry, but it is excellent for mature, less tender birds. Cooking the poultry covered and with a small amount of moisture tenderizes the meat and also brings out its rich flavor.

Broiling Poultry—In these low-fat, low-calorie times, nothing beats broiled poultry. Young chickens, Cornish game hens, small broiler-fryer turkeys, ducklings, and guineas can be broiled satisfactorily. Pieces are seasoned, placed in a broiler pan, and brushed with melted fat or cooking oil. Follow manufacturer's direction for the correct distance to place the broiler pan from the heating element. Broil 20 to 30 minutes on one side or until it's browned. Then turn, brush with fat or oil and broil until done, about 15 to 25 minutes longer. Since turkey and duck pieces are thicker, they require a longer broiling time, about 30 minutes on each side.

Rotisserie Cooking—Great for the family table is young poultry cooked on special rotisserie equipment that turns the bird slowly on a rotary spit over or under direct heat.

To mount a whole bird, attach the neck skin with a skewer to the back

Roasting Guide for Poultry

Kind	Weight, ready to cook (pounds)	Approximate roasting time at 325° F. (hours)	Internal temperature when done
Chickens, whole, stuffed:			
Broilers or fryers	1½ to 2½	1 to 2	
Roasters	2½ to 4½	2 to 3½	
Capons	5 to 8	2½ to 3½	
Ducks	4 to 6	2 to 3	
Geese	6 to 8	3 to 3½	
	8 to 12	3½ to 4½	
Turkeys:			
Whole, stuffed	6 to 8	3 to 3½	180 to 185 in thigh
	8 to 12	3½ to 4½	180 to 185 in thigh
	12 to 16	4½ to 5½	180 to 185 in thigh
	16 to 20	5½ to 6½	180 to 185 in thigh
	20 to 24	6½ to 7	180 to 185 in thigh
Halves, quarters, and pieces	3 to 8	2½ to 3	
	8 to 12	3 to 4	
Boneless roasts	3 to 10	3 to 4	170 to 175 in center

When meat thermometer is used in roasting poultry, it should be inserted into center of inner thigh muscle.

of the body. Tie or skewer wings close to the body. Insert the spit through the length of the body and tighten holding prongs. Tie tail and drumsticks firmly to the rod. When properly balanced, the bird will rotate evenly as the spit is turned.

More than one bird can usually be cooked at a time if the spit is long enough. Mount the birds in opposite directions (neck to neck) to maintain good balance on the spit. Brush skin with oil or melted fat. Follow manufacturer's directions for rotisserie temperature setting and time. Test for doneness as you would for roast poultry.

Frying Poultry—Frying is America's favorite method of cooking poultry. Crisp fried poultry is always a treat, whether it's young broiler-fryer chickens, capons, Cornish game hens, fryer-roaster turkeys, ducklings, or guineas.

You can fry poultry without a coating if pieces are thoroughly dried. However, coatings give a crisp surface and help to retain moisture in the meat.

Suitable coatings to use with poultry

are quick and easy to make: Flour—combine ½ cup flour, 1 teaspoon salt, and ⅛ teaspoon of pepper; batter—combine 1 egg, ¾ cup milk, 1 cup flour, and 1 teaspoon salt; crumb or cereal—use fine dry breadcrumbs or crushed cereal flakes on batter-dipped poultry pieces.

Perhaps the easiest way to fry chicken is to ovenfry the pieces. This is the reliable "put it in the oven and forget it for a half hour method." Place poultry pieces in a shallow pan containing ⅛ inch melted fat; turn pieces to coat both sides with fat. Cook at 400° F. for 30 minutes, turn and cook 20 to 30 minutes longer until crisp and tender.

When the hostess wants to shine, serving crisp french-fried (deep fat fried) poultry always makes a hit. Place coated poultry in enough hot fat (365° F.) to cover. Fry only a few pieces at a time. Serving-size pieces take about 10 to 15 minutes.

Another great crisp way with poultry is to panfry the pieces. Place poultry skin-side down in about ⅛ inch of fat preheated in a heavy frying pan. Cook uncovered 15 to 25 minutes on each side or until poultry is tender and crisp. For turkey or duckling, cover tightly after browning and cook slowly 45 to 60 minutes until tender—turn occasionally.

Simmering or Stewing Poultry—An excellent cooking method for mature, less tender poultry is simmering (or stewing). Young poultry may be cooked by this method, but will lack the full rich flavor of mature poultry. Cover poultry with water and simmer until meat is tender. If you desire, brown the pieces in a little hot fat in a frying pan before serving. Tender meat from cooked poultry adds elegance to many easy-to-prepare dishes, such as casseroles, souffles, pies, a la kings, sandwiches, salads, etc.

In the recipes, the kinds of poultry (turkey, chicken, duck, guinea, or goose) can be used interchangeably, or you may substitute rabbit for poultry. Some recipes contain shortcut methods of preparation.

STUFFING FOR POULTRY

About 1 quart stuffing

¾ cup chopped celery
2 tablespoons chopped onion
3 tablespoons poultry fat, butter, or margarine
3 tablespoons chopped parsley
½ teaspoon poultry seasoning
½ teaspoon salt
⅛ teaspoon pepper
¼ cup poultry broth or milk (optional)
1 quart soft bread cubes

Slowly cook the celery and onions in fat until tender.

Blend in parsley, poultry seasoning, salt, pepper, and broth or milk.

Pour mixture over bread and toss lightly until well blended.

See earlier instructions for stuffing poultry, or bake in a separate pan. If stuffing is baked in a separate pan, baste with drippings for added flavor.

Allow about ½ cup stuffing for each pound of ready-to-cook poultry.

Oyster Stuffing: Omit the celery and reduce parsley and onion to 1 tablespoon each. Add ½ pint oysters, heated in their own liquid and drained.

Nut Stuffing: Omit the parsley and poultry seasonings and add ½ cup of chopped nut meats—pecans, roasted almonds, filberts, or cooked chestnuts.

Cornbread Stuffing: Use cornbread crumbs in place of bread cubes.

BROWN POULTRY GRAVY

(moderately thick)

About 2 cups gravy

¼ cup flour
2 to 4 tablespoons poultry fat from drippings
2 cups poultry broth, milk, or water

Blend flour into fat. Brown over low heat. (If brown drippings are used, it is not necessary to brown the flour.)

Add liquid slowly, while stirring constantly.

Cook until gravy thickens, stirring constantly.

Season to taste.

For variety: Giblet gravy—Add ½ cup chopped, cooked giblets.

HOT TURKEY STUFFING SANDWICH

6 servings

6 slices hot turkey
12 slices hot baked stuffing
2 cups hot poultry gravy

Place the turkey between 2 slices of stuffing.

Cover with gravy.

Serve immediately.

STUFFING

(*For Hot Turkey Sandwich*)

¼ cup chopped onion
⅓ cup chopped celery
⅓ cup turkey fat, butter, or margarine
1 cup turkey broth (unsalted)
1 teaspoon salt*
1 teaspoon poultry seasoning
2 eggs
2 quarts cubed bread

Slowly cook the onion and celery in fat until tender.

Add broth, salt, poultry seasoning, and egg. Mix well.

Pour mixture over bread and toss lightly until well blended.

Pack lightly into greased loaf pans.

Bake in a preheated 350° F. oven (moderate) for 45 minutes.

Cool slightly. Remove from pan and slice into 12 slices.

CHICKEN SALAD

6 servings, about ⅔ cup each

3 cups diced cooked chicken
½ cup chopped sweet pickles
1 cup diced celery
1 teaspoon chopped onion
1 tablespoon sweet pickle liquid
¾ cup mayonnaise
1 teaspoon salt
¼ teaspoon prepared mustard

Combine all ingredients, toss lightly.

Chill.

Serve on crisp salad greens.

For variety, Hawaiian salad: Use pineapple tidbits in place of pickle and onion. Use 1 teaspoon soy sauce in place of pickle juice. Top salad with toasted almond slivers.

---

*If seasoned broth is used, reduce salt in recipe.

TURKEY-AVOCADO CUTLET

10 cutlets, ½ cup each

1¼ cups milk
½ cup flour
3 tablespoons butter or margarine
2 cups diced, cooked turkey
2 cups diced avocado
1 egg
¾ cup fine, dry breadcrumbs
1¼ teaspoons salt
¼ teaspoon pepper
1 teaspoon finely chopped onion
¼ teaspoon Worcestershire sauce
Fat for frying

Coating

½ cup flour
2 beaten eggs
3 cups fine, dry breadcrumbs

Gradually stir milk into flour.

Add butter or margarine. Slowly cook over low heat (or hot water) until very thick, stirring constantly.

Combine sauce, turkey, avocado, egg, ¾ cup of crumbs, salt, pepper, onion, and the Worcestershire sauce. Chill. (Do not hold mixture more than a few hours.)

Shape into cutlets.

Roll cutlets in flour, gently dip into beaten egg, and then in crumbs.

Fry in deep fat at 375° F. until golden brown. Drain and serve immediately.

CHICKEN CORN CASSEROLE

6 servings, about ½ cup each

1¼ cups chicken broth (unsalted)
¼ cup flour
¼ cup chicken fat, butter, or margarine
1 teaspoon salt*
¼ teaspoon pepper
2 tablespoons chopped onion
1½ cups chopped cooked chicken
1 cup drained, canned, whole kernel corn
¼ cup shredded cheese (or finely chopped)
2 tablespoons chopped pimiento
¼ cup fine, dry breadcrumbs
1 tablespoon melted butter or margarine

Gradually stir broth into flour.

Add fat, salt, pepper, and onion. Cook slowly until thickened, stir often.

Blend chicken, corn, cheese, and pimiento into the sauce.

---

*If seasoned broth is used, reduce salt in recipe.

USDA inspectors check a chicken at poultry processing plant in Delaware.

Place in a 1-quart baking pan or casserole.

Top with breadcrumbs mixed with butter or margarine.

Bake in a preheated 350° F. oven (moderate) for about 45 minutes or until the crumbs are brown and the mixture is hot.

SCALLOPED TURKEY AND VEGETABLE

6 servings, about ½ cup each

3 tablespoons chopped onion
1 cup diced celery
½ cup diced carrots
½ cup frozen or fresh green peas
1 cup turkey gravy, moderately thick
2 cups chopped, cooked turkey
½ cup sour cream
½ teaspoon salt*
1 tablespoon parsley flakes
¼ cup fine, dry breadcrumbs
1 tablespoon melted butter or margarine

Cook onion, celery, carrots, and peas in small amount of water until tender, about 15 minutes. Drain.

Combine vegetables with gravy, turkey, sour cream, salt, and parsley flakes.

Place in a 1-quart baking pan or casserole.

Top with crumbs mixed with butter or margarine.

*If seasoned vegetables and gravy are used, reduce salt in recipe.

Bake in a preheated 350° F. oven (moderate) for 30 minutes or until crumbs are brown and mixture is hot.

(This is an excellent way for using leftover cooked vegetables, gravy, and cooked turkey.)

ZESTY CREAMED TURKEY

6 servings, about ½ cup each

¼ cup chopped onion
¼ cup turkey fat, butter, or margarine
3 tablespoons flour
1½ cups turkey broth (unsalted)
½ cup light cream or milk
½ teaspoon salt*
2 teaspoons curry powder
¼ teaspoon ginger
3½ cups chopped, cooked turkey

Slowly cook the onion in fat until it is tender.

Blend in the flour.

Stir in broth and cream or milk Cook mixture until it is thickened stirring often.

Add salt, curry powder, ginger, and turkey.

Cook over low heat (or hot water until hot—about 15 minutes.

Serve over rice, chow mein noodles or toast.

*If seasoned broth is used, reduce salt i recipe.

Rose G. Kerr

Savvy With Seafood in the Store and Kitchen for That Tang of the Deep

Did you know there are more than 240 species of fish and shellfish sold in the United States? When you are looking for variety, they give you more choice than any other food group. You can buy fish and shellfish fresh, frozen, canned, cured, and in a wide variety of convenience and specialty products.

Most varieties of fresh fish and shellfish, like many other foods, are at their best at the peak of the season. Your local dealer can advise you about seasonal offerings and help you select the species best suited to your needs. The less known types are often as satisfactory as the better known ones and are usually less expensive.

Fresh whole or dressed fish should have these characteristics: odor—fresh and mild; eyes—bright, clear, and full; gills—red and free from slime; skin—iridescent; and flesh—firm and elastic, not separating from the bones. Fresh fillets, steaks, and chunks should also have a mild, fresh odor, and fresh-cut appearing flesh without any traces of browning or drying.

Frozen fish and shellfish are available the year round. Their packages should be solidly frozen and have little or no odor. The wrapping should be of a moisture-vapor-proof material with little or no air space between the seafood and the wrapping. An ice glaze is sometimes utilized to protect dressed fish, shrimp, and steaks from drying out. A white cottony appearance, a brownish tinge, or any discoloration in the frozen flesh indicate poor quality.

Canned and cured fish and shellfish also are usually available the year round. A wide variety of canned, pickled, salted, smoked, and spiced fish and shellfish is available on the market today.

Fish and shellfish are sold in many different forms or cuts. Learning to recognize these forms, and how best to use them, is very important in buying and serving fish and shellfish. Unless otherwise stated, most market forms of fish and shellfish are available both fresh and frozen, are usually sold by weight, and are ready to cook, heat, or serve as purchased.

Market Forms of Fish: In this country "fish" means fin fish. The different market forms of fish are:

Whole fish are sold just as they come from the water. Before cooking, the fish must be scaled, eviscerated, and usually the head, tail, and fins removed. Some small fish, like smelt, are often cooked with only their entrails removed.

Dressed fish are scaled, eviscerated, and sometimes the head, tail, and fins removed. The smaller size fish are called pan-dressed.

Steaks are cross section slices from a large dressed fish cut ⅝ to 1 inch thick. A cross section of the backbone is usually the only bone in a steak. Chunks are cross sections of a large dressed fish. A cross section of the backbone is usually the only bone in a chunk.

Single fillets, the most common type, are the sides of the fish cut lengthwise away from the backbone. They are

Rose G. Kerr is Chief of the National Home Economics Research Center, Bureau of Commercial Fisheries, U.S. Department of the Interior.

practically boneless and may or may not be skinned. Butterfly fillets are the two sides of the fish cut lengthwise away from the backbone and held together by the uncut flesh and skin of the belly. These fillets are practically boneless.

Frozen raw or fried breaded fish portions are cut from frozen fish blocks, coated with a batter, breaded, packaged, and frozen. Portions weigh more than 1½ ounces and are at least ⅜ inch thick. Raw portions must contain not less than 75 percent and fried portions not less than 65 percent fish flesh, according to U.S. Department of the Interior (USDI) standards. They may be purchased raw or partially cooked.

Frozen fried sticks are cut from frozen fish blocks, coated with a batter, breaded, partially cooked, packaged, and frozen. Fried fish sticks weigh up to 1½ ounces, must be at least ⅜ inch thick, and contain not less than 60 percent fish flesh, according to USDI standards.

Canned fish are packed in a great variety of convenience and specialty items, as well as the ever popular tuna, salmon, and Maine sardines.

MARKET FORMS OF FISH

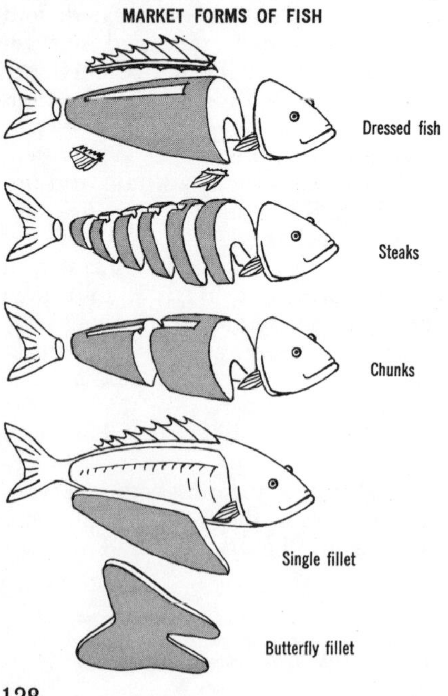

Tuna is packed from six species. The catch includes albacore, blackfin, bluefin, skipjack, yellowfin, and little tuna. Albacore has lighter meat than the others and is the only tuna permitted to be labeled "white meat" tuna. The other species are labeled "light meat" tuna. Canned tuna is packed in oil or water. In descending order of price, the packs of tuna are: solid, chunk, and flaked or grated.

Salmon is packed from five species. Canned salmon is usually sold by the name of the fish, since there is a difference in the color, texture, and flavor of the salmon. Higher priced varieties are deeper red in color and have a higher oil content. In descending order of price, the packs of salmon are: red or sockeye; chinook or king; medium red, silver, or coho; pink; chum or keta.

Cured fish are processed from many different species. Some of the more common cured fish on the market are pickled and spiced herring; salt cod and salmon; smoked chubs, salmon, and whitefish; as well as many convenience and specialty items.

Market Forms of Shellfish: In this country "shellfish" means crustaceans and mollusks. The crustaceans include crabs, lobsters, and shrimp. Clams, oysters, and scallops are mollusks.

Several species of clams are widely used for food. On the Atlantic coast, they are the hard, soft, and surf clams. On the Pacific coast, the most common species are the butter, littleneck, razor, and pismo clams. The hard clams, or hard-shell clams, are commonly called "quahog" in New England, where "clam" generally means the soft-shell variety. Littlenecks and cherrystones are the trade names for the smaller sized hard clams generally served raw on the half shell. The larger sizes of hard, soft, and surf clams are called "chowders" and are used mainly for chowders and soups. Clams are sold by the dozen or by weight.

Clams in the shell are just as they come from the water. Fresh clams should be alive when purchased and the shells should close tightly when tapped. Shucked clams are the meat removed from the shells. The meat is pale to deep orange in color and has a fresh, mild odor. Fresh shucked clams are packed in little or no liquid.

Frozen raw or fried breaded clams are shucked clams coated with a batter, breaded, packaged, and frozen. They may be purchased raw or partially cooked. Canned clams are available whole, minced, or in chowder, bouillon, broth, and nectar.

The three principal species of crabs are the blue, Dungeness, and king. Blue crabs come from the Atlantic and Gulf coasts and weigh from ¼ to 1 pound. Dungeness crabs are from the Pacific coast and weigh from 1¼ to 2½ pounds. King crabs come from the coast of Alaska and weigh from 6 to 20 pounds. A big king crab can easily measure 6 feet across from the tip of one leg to the tip of the opposite leg. Growing in popularity are the stone crabs from Florida and the tanner crabs from Alaska.

Crabs in the shell are sold fresh, frozen, or cooked. Fresh crabs should be alive and active when purchased. Cooked crabs are bright red and have a mild odor. Blue crabs are sold by the dozen, and Dungeness crabs are sold individually.

Soft-shell crabs are molting blue crabs just after they have shed their shells and before the new shells have hardened. They are sold just as they come from the water. They should be alive and active when purchased.

Frozen crab legs are the legs of cooked king and tanner crabs which have been frozen and split or cut into sections. The meat is white with an attractive red tint on the outside.

Crab meat is the meat removed from cooked crabs. The meat is packed and chilled, frozen, pasteurized, or canned. The body meat from Dungeness crab is white and the claw meat has a brownish-red tint on the outside. King crab meat is primarily leg meat. It is white with an attractive reddish tint on the outside.

In descending order of price, the packs of blue crab are: Lump meat—whole lumps of white meat from the two body muscles which operate the swimming legs; flake meat—small pieces of white meat from the body; flake and lump—a combination of the first two kinds; claw meat—brownish tinted meat from the claws.

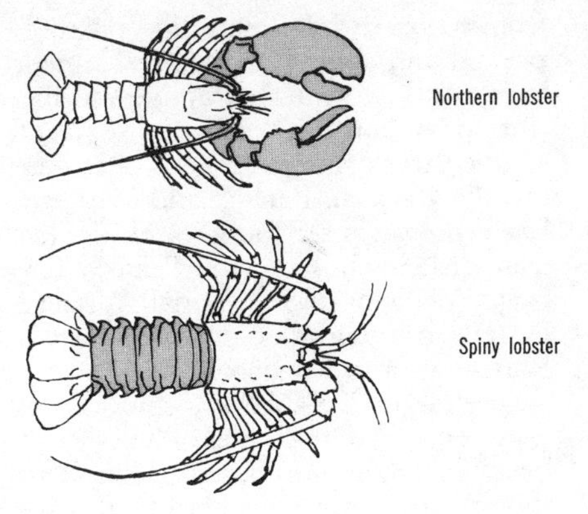
Northern lobster

Spiny lobster

Northern lobsters are caught in the cold waters off the coast of Maine and Massachusetts. Off the coasts of California and Florida another shellfish is caught which is known locally as "lobster." More properly, it is a spiny or rock lobster. The large, heavy claws of the northern lobsters distinguish them from the spiny lobsters, which have no claws. Lobsters usually weigh from ¾ to 4 pounds.

Lobster Market Sizes

Trade name	Weight
Chicken	¾ to 1 pound
Quarters	1¼ to 1½ pounds
Large	1½ to 2½ pounds
Jumbo	Over 3 pounds

Lobsters in the shell are sold fresh, frozen, or cooked. The fresh lobster should be alive and active when purchased. The "tail" of a live lobster curls under the body and does not hang down when the lobster is picked up. Cooked lobsters should be bright red and have a fresh, mild odor.

Frozen spiny lobster tails are spiny lobsters with their heads removed, graded according to size, and frozen. Spiny lobster tails should have clean, white meat and no odor. The average market size of spiny lobster tails is 2 to 8 ounces.

Lobster meat is the meat removed

from cooked lobsters. The meat is packed and chilled, frozen, or canned. It is white with an attractive reddish tint on the outside.

The three principal species of oysters are the Eastern, Pacific, and Western. Eastern oysters are found or cultivated from Massachusetts to Texas. The large Pacific oysters and small Western oysters are found or cultivated from Washington to Mexico.

Oysters in the shell are sold just as they come from the water. They should be alive when purchased. The shells should close tightly when tapped. Live oysters are sold by the dozen.

Shucked oysters are oysters removed from the shells; they should be plump and have a natural creamy color and clear liquid. Shucked oysters have a fresh, mild odor and are packed in little or no liquid. Avoid oysters with an excess amount of liquid because this indicates poor quality and careless handling. Shucked oysters are graded according to their size.

Frozen raw or fried breaded oysters are shucked oysters coated with a batter, breaded, packaged, and frozen. They are available raw or partially cooked. Canned oysters are available on the market whole and as stew.

Many people are not aware that scallops are a shellfish—a mollusk with two shells, similar to the clams and oysters. But in at least one respect scallops differ from clams and oysters because they are active swimmers, moving freely through the water and over the ocean floor. Actively snapping its shells together provides locomotion for the scallop and results in development of an oversized muscle that's called the adductor muscle. This excellently flavored muscle is the only part eaten by Americans.

The two principal species of scallops on the market are bay and sea. Large sea scallops are taken from the deep waters of the North and Middle Atlantic. The sea scallop's shell is saucer shaped and sometimes grows as large as 8 inches across. The adductor muscle may be as large as 2 inches across. Small bay scallops are taken from inshore bays and estuaries from New England to the Gulf of Mexico. The shell of the bay scallop is much smaller than the sea scallop. Its maximum width is about 4 inches. In shape it resembles the sea scallop except that the shell is grooved and has serrated or scalloped edges. The adductor muscle of the bay scallop is about a half inch across. Increasing in popularity are calico scallops from Florida and sea scallops from Alaska.

Shucked scallops are the adductor muscles removed from the shells. The meat is a creamy white, light tan, orange, or pinkish. Fresh scallops should have a sweetish odor and be packed in little or no liquid. Frozen raw or fried breaded scallops are shucked scallops coated with a batter, breaded, packaged, and frozen. Fried scallops must contain not less than 60 percent scallop meat, according to USDI standards. They are available raw or partially cooked.

Kinds of shrimp in the United States are common or white shrimp, which is greenish-gray; brown or Brazilian shrimp, which is brownish-red; pink or coral shrimp; and Alaska, California, and Maine varieties, which vary in color and are relatively small. Although raw shrimp range in color from greenish-gray to brownish-red, when cooked they all take on an attractive reddish tint. There is very little difference in the appearance and flavor of the cooked shrimp. Shrimp

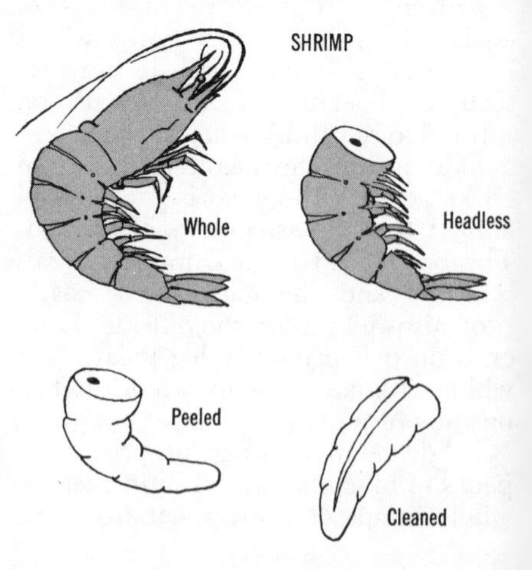

INSPECTIÓN SHIELD

U.S. GRADE A SHIELD

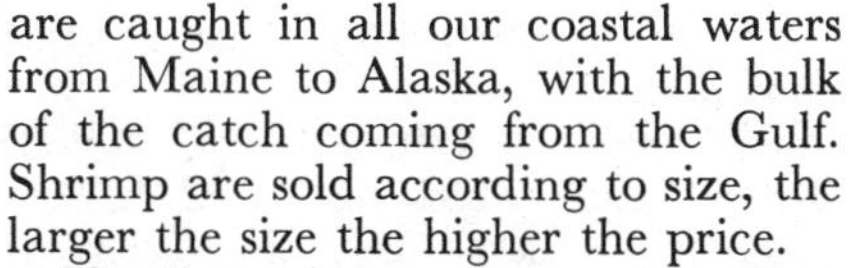

are caught in all our coastal waters from Maine to Alaska, with the bulk of the catch coming from the Gulf. Shrimp are sold according to size, the larger the size the higher the price.

Headless shrimp are, of course, shrimp with the heads removed and are graded according to size. Fresh shrimp have a fresh, mild odor and firm meat. "Green shrimp" does not refer to the color of the shrimp but is the term used by the trade to describe raw shrimp.

Peeled and cleaned shrimp are headless shrimp with the shell and intestinal tract removed. They may be sold raw or cooked. The cooked shrimp should have an attractive reddish tint and a mild odor. They may be purchased fresh, frozen, and canned.

Frozen raw or fried breaded shrimp are peeled and cleaned shrimp coated with a batter, breaded, packaged, and frozen. Breaded raw shrimp must contain not less than 50 percent shrimp meat, according to USDI standards. They are available raw or partially cooked.

Inspection, Standards, Grades: The U.S. Department of the Interior, through the Bureau of Commercial Fisheries, makes available an official inspection service for all the types of the processed fishery products—fresh, frozen, canned, and cured. The service is voluntary, offered upon a fee-for-service basis.

Under continuous inspection, one or more inspectors are assigned to a processing plant whenever it is operating. They make continuous checks on quality of the raw product, as well as plant conditions under which the product is being prepared, processed, and packed. This service is made available only if the plant meets rigid sanitary requirements for facilities, equipment, and raw material.

Products packed in any plant operated under the continuous inspection program, and in compliance with USDI inspection regulations, may be labeled with the official USDI inspection shield which carries the statement "Packed Under Continuous Inspection of the U.S. Department of the Interior."

Grade standards have been established by the Bureau of Commercial Fisheries, U.S. Department of the Interior, for a total of 15 processed fishery products.

Quality grades for fishery products are Grade A, B, C, and substandard. The grade most widely sold in the stores is Grade A. It is produced in the greatest volume and retailers have found that this high quality product pleases their customers.

- Grade A means top or best quality. Grade A products are uniform in size, practically free from blemishes and defects, and possess a good flavor.
- Grade B means good quality. Grade B products may not be as uniform in size or as free from blemishes or defects as Grade A products. This grade may be termed a general commercial grade, and is quite suitable for most purposes.
- Grade C means fairly good quality. Grade C products are just as wholesome and may be as nutritious as the higher grades. They have a definite

value as a thrifty buy for use in dishes where appearance may not be quite so important.

If a product carries a grade label A, B, or C, it must meet quality requirements of the USDI Grade Standards.

Any fishery products packed under continuous inplant inspection of the U.S. Department of the Interior are permitted to use the prefix "U.S." with the grade designation, such as U.S. Grade A.

The brand name on processed fishery products—fresh, frozen, canned, and cured—is also an indication of quality. Processors of nationally advertised products make every effort to maintain the same quality year after year. Many stores, particularly chainstores, pack under their own name or private label.

Buying Tips: The amount of fish or shellfish to buy per serving varies with the recipe to be used, size of serving, and amount of bone or shell in the product. Allow approximately 3 ounces of cooked, boneless fish or shellfish per serving—a little less for small children and a little more for adolescent boys and for men.

In Washington, D.C., early in 1969 a shrimp price comparison was made that should be of interest to you as a buyer. Raw, headless shrimp in the shell was selling for $1.38 a pound. It yields about 8 ounces of cooked, peeled, and cleaned shrimp. Therefore, it would require 2 pounds costing $2.76 ($1.38 x 2) to yield a pound of cooked, peeled, and cleaned shrimp of the same size which was selling in the same market for 69 cents for 4 ounces or a total of $2.76 ($0.69 x 4)—and you do not have to peel, clean, and cook this shrimp. This cost comparison illustrates how some convenience foods can save you time without increasing your food budget.

Be sure to check the labels on canned, frozen, and cured packaged fishery products. Besides describing contents and weight of the package, the label may tell the grade, size, and species; other ingredients added; number of servings; cooking or heating directions; and recipes or serving ideas.

Home Care and Storage: Use fish and shellfish as soon as you can. If storage is necessary, a rule of thumb to remember is the lower the temperature the slower the deterioration.

Fresh fishery products should be placed in the coldest part of the refrigerator as soon as possible after pur-

Approximate Yield and Approximate Amount to Purchase Per Serving

	Fish and shellfish as purchased	Yield (percent)	Amount to purchase (ounces)
Fish	Whole	27	11
	Dressed or pan-dressed	38	8
	Fillets, steaks, and chunks	61	5
	Portions and sticks	90	3½
	Pickled and spiced	100	3
	Salted	72	4¼
	Smoked	66	4½
	Canned tuna	100	3
	Canned salmon	81	3¾
Clams	In the shell:		
	Hard	14	21½
	Soft	29	10½
	Shucked	48	6½
	Breaded, raw or fried	84	3¾
	Canned minced clams	100	3
Crabs	In the shell:		
	Blue	14	21½
	Dungeness	24	12¼
	Soft-shell	66	4½
	King crab legs	52	6
	Cooked meat	97	3¼
	Canned meat	85	3½
Lobsters	In the shell	25	12
	Spiny lobster tails	51	6
	Cooked meat	91	3½
Oysters	In the shell	12	25
	Shucked	48	6½
	Breaded, raw or fried	88	3½
	Canned whole	100	3
Scallops	Shucked	63	5
	Breaded, raw or fried	87	3½
Shrimp	Headless	50	6
	Peeled and cleaned	62	5
	Cooked, peeled, and cleaned	100	3½
	Breaded, raw or fried	86	3½
	Canned whole	100	3

chase. A refrigerator temperature of 35° to 40° F. is needed to maintain a quality product. It is a good idea to have a refrigerator thermometer so you can check the temperature periodically.

Prepackaged fish and shellfish may be stored in the refrigerator in the original packaging. These wrappings or containers are designed for short time refrigeration. Fresh fish and shellfish wrapped in butcher paper should be unwrapped, placed on a plate or tray, and covered with aluminum foil or plastic wrap before refrigerating. Do not hold fresh fish or shellfish in the refrigerator longer than 1 or 2 days before cooking.

Frozen fishery products should be placed in the freezer or frozen food compartment of the refrigerator immediately after purchase, unless they are to be thawed for cooking. A freezer temperature of 0° F. or below is needed to maintain quality products. Since frozen food compartments of some home refrigerators are not designed to maintain a temperature of 0° F. or below, fishery products held there will maintain their high quality for only a few days.

Freezing is an excellent method of preserving fish and shellfish. It can be done simply and effectively at home. Freezing does not improve quality, so freeze only high quality fresh fish and shellfish. Keep clean all fish and shellfish to be frozen, and anything that touches it, because freezing does not sterilize the fish and shellfish. The extreme cold simply slows down the changes which affect the quality or cause spoilage.

Usually it is best to prepare fish and shellfish for cooking before freezing. Less freezer space is required when all the waste has been removed, and the packages can be sized according to your family's needs.

Protect any seafood to be frozen by wrapping or packaging it carefully in moisture-vapor-proof packaging material. Suit the packaging, such as bags, cartons, containers, and wrappings, to the kind, shape, size, and consistency of the product. Proper packaging prevents air from entering the package and causing dehydration, oxidation, and freezer burn. Label each package with the date, kind, and type of product, and the weight or number of servings.

Freeze at 0° F. or below, following directions that came with your freezer. Store frozen seafood at 0° F. or below. For maximum quality do not hold raw, frozen fishery products in the freezer longer than 4 to 6 months.

Cooked fishery products may be stored either in the refrigerator or freezer. If stored in the refrigerator, cooked fish or shellfish should be placed in a covered container. Do not hold cooked seafood in the refrigerator longer than 3 or 4 days. It may also be stored in the freezer if packaged in a moisture-vapor-proof material. For best quality, do not hold cooked fish or shellfish in the freezer longer than 2 or 3 months.

Canned fish should be stored in a cool, dry place. It should not be stored longer than a year.

Pickled, salted, smoked, and spiced fishery products should be stored in the refrigerator. Cured fishery products will keep for several weeks in the refrigerator.

Thaw fish and shellfish just before cooking. Refrigerator thawing is best. Allow 24 hours for thawing a 1-pound package. If quicker thawing is necessary, place the wrapped package under cold running water to thaw. Allow about an hour for thawing a 1-pound package. Do not thaw fish or shellfish at room temperature or in warm water.

Frozen breaded fishery products should not be thawed before cooking. Frozen fillets, steaks, and shrimp may be cooked without thawing if additional cooking time is allowed. Fillets, steaks, or shrimp to be breaded or stuffed should be thawed.

Tips on Cooking: Fish and shellfish are an excellent source of high quality protein and also provide minerals and vitamins so necessary for good nutrition. You can prepare fishery products in an amazing variety of ways—such as baked, broiled, fried, poached, grilled, and steamed. In planning menus, seafood can be the star in any course—appetizer, cocktail, soup, or salad, as well as the main dish.

Although raw fish is enjoyed in various countries of the world, cooking fish and shellfish is necessary to make it acceptable for most Americans. You can easily learn to cook any seafood so it will be tender, flavorful, moist, and appetizing in appearance. Just use a moderate temperature and short cooking time—and you have won the battle.

Fish and shellfish are cooked to develop flavor and to soften the small amount of connective tissue present. Seafood is naturally tender. Cooking it at too high a temperature or for too long a time toughens it, dries it out, and destroys the fine natural flavor.

How can you tell when seafood is cooked? Raw fishery products have a watery, translucent look. During cooking the watery juices become milky colored, giving the flesh an opaque, whitish tint. This change in color is quite unmistakable. When the flesh is opaque in the center of the thickest part, the fish is cooked. At this point the flesh will flake easily when tested with a fork and will separate readily from the bones.

Cooked fish is tender and delicate; handle it as little and as gently as possible during and after cooking to preserve its appearance. Also, serve it as soon as possible after cooking. Holding cooked seafood at serving temperature is the same thing as overcooking.

Any of the basic cooking methods may be used. You may vary these methods by using different seasonings, marinades, sauces, and stuffings.

Baking is one of the simplest ways to cook fish and shellfish. Once in the oven, the seafood needs little attention. "Bake it easy" is the most important guide to follow.

Fish and shellfish will be at their finest when cooked in a preheated, moderate oven, at 350° F. for a relatively short time. This keeps the moisture and flavor in the seafood. Fishery products not baked in a sauce or with a topping are basted with melted butter or margarine to keep them moist and tender. All market forms of fish and shellfish can be baked.

HALIBUT HAWAIIAN

6 servings

2 halibut steaks (1 pound each), fresh or frozen
1 teaspoon salt
1 cup soft bread cubes
1 cup drained crushed pineapple
1 cup cooked rice
2 tablespoons lemon juice
¾ teaspoon salt
½ teaspoon curry powder
2 tablespoons butter or margarine, melted

Thaw frozen steaks. Sprinkle them with salt.

Combine remaining ingredients except butter or margarine.

Place one steak in a well-greased baking pan, 12 by 8 by 2 inches. Place stuffing on steak and cover with the remaining steak. Secure with toothpicks or skewers. Brush top steak with butter or margarine.

Bake in moderate oven, 350° F., for 30 to 40 minutes or until fish flake easily when tested with a fork.

Broiling, like baking, is a dry heat cooking method; but in broiling the heat is direct, intense, and comes from only one source. Thin pieces of food tend to dry out under the broiler so when planning to broil, choose pan-dressed fish, fillets, or steaks that are around 1 inch thick in preference to thinner ones. For more satisfactory results in broiling, any frozen fishery products should be thawed. Baste the seafood well with melted butter or margarine, or a sauce, before placing it under broiler. Baste once in broiling to keep moist and tender.

Follow your range manufacturer's directions for preheating and operating the broiler. Length of time it takes to broil depends on thickness and size of the seafood and the distance that it is placed from the heat. As a general guide have the surface of the fish or shellfish about 3 to 4 inches from the source of heat, and place thicker cuts farther from the heat than thin ones.

As a rule, fish or shellfish does not need to be turned—because the heat of the pan will cook the underside adequately. Turn the thicker pieces, such as pan-dressed fish, when half the allotted cooking time is up. Baste again with butter, margarine, or a sauce. Always serve any broiled fish sizzling hot.

Charcoal cooking is a natural for fishery products because they cook so quickly. Most of the basic cooking methods can be used on a charcoal grill—baking, broiling, frying, grilling, boiling, steaming, and smoking.

Pan-dressed fish, fillets, steaks, crabs, lobsters, scallops, and shrimp are all excellent for charcoal cooking. When frozen, they should be thawed before cooking. Because fish flake easily as their cooking nears completion, use of a well-greased, long-handled, hinged wire grill is recommended.

Thicker cuts of fish and shellfish are preferable for charcoal broiling and grilling as they tend to dry out less. Also, to be sure of serving juicy and flavorful seafood, use a sauce which contains some butter or oil and baste generously before and during cooking. Fish and shellfish are usually cooked around 4 inches from moderately hot coals.

ALASKAN KING CRAB LEGS

6 servings

3 packages (12 ounces each) precooked, frozen king crab legs
½ cup butter or margarine, melted
2 tablespoons lemon or lime juice
½ teaspoon paprika
Melted butter or margarine

Thaw crab legs.

Place crab legs in a single layer, flesh side up, on a baking pan, 15 by 10 by 1 inches.

Combine ½ cup melted butter or margarine and lemon or lime juice. Pour sauce over crab legs.

Broil about 4 inches from source of heat for 8 to 10 minutes or until heated through.

Sprinkle with paprika.

Serve with melted butter or with margarine.

CHESAPEAKE BAY SEAFOOD BAKE

6 servings

6 dozen soft-shell clams
12 small onions
6 medium baking potatoes
6 ears of corn in the husks
12 live, hard-shell blue crabs
Lemon wedges
Melted butter or margarine

Wash clam shells thoroughly.

Peel onions and wash potatoes. Boil onions and potatoes for 15 minutes. Drain.

Remove corn silk from corn and replace husks.

Cut 12 pieces of cheesecloth and 12 pieces of heavy-duty aluminum foil, 18 by 36 inches each. Place 2 pieces of cheesecloth on top of 2 pieces of foil. Place 2 onions, a potato, ear of corn, 1 dozen clams, and 2 crabs on cheesecloth.

Tie opposite corners of the cheesecloth together. Pour 1 cup of water over the package. Bring foil up over the food and close all edges with tight double folds. Make 6 packages.

Place packages on a grill about 4 inches from hot coals. Cover with hood or aluminum foil.

Cook for 45 to 60 minutes or until onions and potatoes are cooked.

Serve with lemon wedges and melted butter or margarine.

Frying, one way of cooking food in fat, is probably the most widely used method of preparing fishery products. Choose a fat that may be heated to a high temperature without danger of smoking—a smoking fat begins to decompose and will give to seafood an unpleasant flavor and odor. Because they begin smoking at a higher temperature, vegetable oils and fats are preferable to fats of animal origin.

Temperature of the fat is extremely important. Too high heat will brown the outside of the seafood before the center is cooked. Too low heat will give a pale, greasy, fat-soaked product. The most satisfactory frying temperature for fish and shellfish is 350° F.

Frozen seafood that is to be breaded must be thawed before frying. Separate the pieces, cut into portions, dip in liquid, and roll in crumbs. Frozen raw breaded portions, clams, oysters, and shrimp should not be thawed prior to cooking.

After frying, drain the seafood immediately on absorbent paper so as to remove excess fat. Keep the fish and shellfish warm in a slow oven until all the pieces are cooked, and then serve immediately.

Deep-fat frying, cooking in fat or oil deep enough to completely immerse the food, is a quick method of cooking and an excellent way to cook tender foods like seafood.

You need a heavy, deep saucepan or french fryer with straight sides, a fry basket to fit the fryer, a deep-fat frying thermometer, or an electric fryer with automatic temperature control. Use enough fat to float the seafood, but do not fill the fryer more than half full. You must allow room for the seafood and for the bubbling fat.

The seafood may be dipped in a liquid and coated with a breading or dipped in batter. The coating will keep the seafood moist during frying and give it a delicious crispness.

Place only one layer of seafood at a time in the fry basket and allow enough room so the pieces don't touch. This prevents the temperature of the fat from dropping suddenly, and assures thorough cooking and even browning. When the fat has heated to 350° F., lower the basket into the fryer slowly.

FLOUNDER KIEV

6 servings

2 pounds flounder fillets, fresh or frozen
½ cup butter or margarine, softened
2 tablespoons chopped parsley
1 tablespoon lemon juice
¾ teaspoon Worcestershire sauce
¼ teaspoon liquid hot pepper sauce
1 clove garlic, finely chopped
½ teaspoon salt
Dash pepper
2 eggs, beaten
2 tablespoons water
½ cup flour
3 cups soft breadcrumbs
Fat for frying

If flounder fillets are frozen, thaw them out.

Combine butter or margarine, parsley, lemon juice, Worcestershire sauce, liquid hot pepper sauce, and garlic. Place mixture on waxed paper and form into a roll. Chill sauce until hard.

Skin fillets. Cut fillets into 12 strips, about 6 by 2 inches. Sprinkle fish with salt and pepper.

Cut hardened sauce into 12 pieces. Place a piece at one end of each strip of fish. Roll fish around sauce and secure with a toothpick.

Combine egg and water.

Roll fish in flour. Dip fish in egg and roll in crumbs. Chill for 1 hour.

Fry in deep fat, 350° F., for 3 to 5 minutes or until brown and fish flake easily when tested with a fork.

Drain on absorbent paper. Remove the toothpicks.

Pan-frying, cooking in a small amount of fat in a frying pan, is an excellent way of cooking fish and shellfish.

The general procedure is to dip the seafood in a liquid and then coat it with a breading or batter. Heat about ⅛ inch of fat in a heavy frying pan. For pans with a temperature control, the right heat is 350° F.

Place one layer of breaded fish in the hot fat, taking care not to overload the pan and thus cool the fat. Fry until brown on one side, turn carefully and brown the other side.

WESTERN FRIED RAINBOW TROUT

6 servings

6 pan-dressed rainbow trout, fresh or frozen
¼ cup evaporated milk
1 teaspoon salt
Dash pepper
½ cup flour
¼ cup cornmeal
1 teaspoon paprika
Fat for frying

Thaw frozen fish. Clean, wash, and dry fish.

Combine milk, salt, and pepper. Combine flour, cornmeal, and paprika. Dip fish in the milk and then roll it in the flour mixture.

Place fish in a single layer in hot fat in a 12-inch frying pan. Fry at a moderate heat for 4 to 5 minutes or until brown. Turn carefully.

Fry 4 to 5 minutes longer or until fish are brown and flake easily when tested with a fork.

Drain on absorbent paper.

Oven-frying, which is not true frying, is a hot oven method. Fish or shellfish are cut into serving-size portions, dipped in salted milk, and rolled in toasted, fine, dry crumbs. The seafood is then placed on a shallow, well-greased baking pan.

A little melted butter or margarine is poured over the seafood and it is baked in an extremely hot oven, 500° F.

Nice features of oven-frying are that the seafood does not require turning, basting, or careful watching, and cooking time is short. The crumb coating and high temperature prevent escape of flavorful juices and give an attractive, brown crust.

FISH A LA STROGANOFF

6 servings

6 frozen raw breaded fish portions (2½ or 3 ounces each)
2 tablespoons butter or margarine, melted
Paprika
2 cups cooked egg noodles
2 tablespoons butter or margarine
1 teaspoon poppy seeds
Stroganoff sauce
Chopped parsley

Place frozen fish portions in a single layer on a well-greased baking pan, 15 by 10 by 1 inches.

Pour butter or margarine over portions.

Sprinkle with paprika.

Bake in an extremely hot oven, 500° F., for 15 to 20 minutes or until brown and fish flake easily when tested with a fork.

Combine noodles, butter or margarine, and poppy seeds. Arrange noodles on a warm serving platter and place fish portions on top.

Pour the Stroganoff sauce over the portions. Sprinkle with parsley.

STROGANOFF SAUCE

About 2⅔ cups sauce

1 can (4 ounces) sliced mushrooms, drained
½ cup chopped onion
1 clove garlic, finely chopped
2 tablespoons butter or margarine, melted
1 can (10½ ounces) condensed cream of chicken soup
¼ teaspoon paprika
¼ teaspoon salt
Dash pepper
1 cup sour cream

Cook mushrooms, onion, and garlic in butter or margarine until tender.

Add soup and seasonings. Cook over low heat for about 10 minutes, stirring occasionally.

Add sour cream. Heat.

Boiling. Cooking seafood directly in water, or boiling, is commonly used for cooking crabs, lobsters, and shrimp but may be used for any fish or shellfish. The water may be seasoned with salt, spices, herbs, lemon, vinegar, or wine, or some combination of these seasonings.

Place the seafood in gently boiling, seasoned water, cover, and simmer until tender. Cooking time will vary with the size and quantity of fish or shellfish being cooked.

SOUTHERN PICKLED SHRIMP

6 servings

1½ pounds frozen raw, peeled, cleaned shrimp
½ cup chopped celery leaves
¼ cup whole mixed pickling spice
2 quarts boiling water
2 cups sliced onions
5 bay leaves
1½ cups salad oil
1½ cups white vinegar
¼ cup chopped pimiento
2 tablespoons capers and liquid
1½ teaspoons celery seed
1½ teaspoons salt
¼ teaspoon liquid hot pepper sauce
Salad greens

Thaw frozen shrimp. Rinse it with cold water.

Tie celery and pickling spice loosely in a piece of cheesecloth. Place in boiling water and simmer about 10 minutes. Add shrimp.

Cover and simmer 3 to 5 minutes depending on the size. Drain.

Arrange sliced onions and shrimp in alternate layers in a bowl. Add bay leaves.

Combine remaining ingredients except salad greens. Pour sauce over onions and shrimp. Cover and chill for about 6 hours, stirring occasionally.

Drain. Serve on salad greens.

Poaching is cooking in a simmering liquid—milk, lightly salted water, water seasoned with spices and herbs, or a mixture of white wine and water, to name just a few liquids.

Place seafood in a single layer in a shallow, wide pan, such as a large frying pan, and barely cover it with liquid. Cover the pan and simmer the fish just until it flakes easily when tested with a fork. Because the poaching liquid contains flavorful juices, the liquid is often partly evaporated by boiling and thickened so as to make a sauce for the fish.

As an entree, poached seafood can be simply served with a sauce or used as the main ingredient of a casserole or other combination dish. Chilled poached seafood makes delicious cocktails and salads.

SHANNON SALMON STEAKS

6 servings

2 pounds salmon steaks, fresh or frozen
2 tablespoons butter or margarine
½ cup cider or apple juice
1 teaspoon salt
½ cup coffee cream
1 tablespoon flour
1 can (4 ounces) of sliced mushrooms, drained
2 tablespoons chopped parsley

Thaw frozen steaks. Cut steaks into 6 portions.

Melt butter or margarine in a 12-inch frying pan. Place fish in pan. Add cider and salt. Cover and simmer for 5 to 7 minutes or until fish flake easily when tested with a fork. Remove fish to a warm serving platter, and keep warm.

Blend cream and flour to make a smooth paste. Add mushrooms, parsley, and cream mixture to liquid in frying pan. Cook until thick and smooth, stirring constantly.

Pour sauce over the fish.

Steaming is cooking fish and shellfish by means of the steam generated from boiling water. When cooked in steam in a tightly covered pan, the seafood retains natural juices and flavors.

A steam cooker is ideal, but any deep pan with a tight cover is satisfactory. If a steaming rack is not available, anything may be used which prevents the seafood from touching the water.

Water used for steaming may be plain, or seasoned with various spices, herbs, or wine. When the water boils rapidly, the seafood is placed on the rack, the pan covered tightly, and the seafood steamed.

NEW ENGLAND STEAMED CLAMS

2 servings

4 dozen small soft-shell clams
½ cup boiling water
Melted butter or margarine

Wash clams thoroughly. Place in a large saucepan. Add water. Cover and bring to the boiling point.

Reduce heat and steam for 7 to 10 minutes or until clams open. Drain clams, reserving liquid. Strain liquid.

Serve clams hot in the shells with separate containers of clam liquid and melted butter or margarine.

For further reading:

The following publications on fish cookery published by the Bureau of Commercial Fisheries, Fish and Wildlife Service, U.S. Department of the Interior, may be obtained from the Superintendent of Documents, Government Printing Office, Washington, D.C. 20402, at the prices indicated.

Fishery Market Development Series

No. 1 Florida Fish Recipes (35 cents)
No. 2 Can-Venient Ways with Shrimp (35 cents)
No. 3 Heirloom Seafood Recipes (20 cents)
No. 4 The Letters from the Captain's Wife (70 cents)
No. 6 Fancy Catfish (25 cents)
No. 7 Seafood Slimmers (25 cents)
No. 8 Let's Cook Fish (60 cents)
No. 9 Fish for Compliments on a Budget (15 cents)
No. 11 Flavor of Maine (35 cents)

A. Elizabeth Handy

Eggs—Nature's Prepackaged Masterpiece of Nutrition

The egg is truly nature's masterpiece! It is a prepackaged container of many important nutrients needed by every member of the family for good health.

Eggs are especially valued for the amount and high quality of the protein they contain. When you serve eggs to your family, you can be confident you are giving them the kind of protein needed to build and repair body tissues. In fact, egg protein is so near perfection that scientists often use it as a standard to measure the value of protein in other foods.

Eggs also provide your family with significant amounts of vitamin A, iron, and riboflavin (vitamin B_2), and they are one of the few foods that contain natural vitamin D. In addition, eggs contribute smaller amounts of many other nutrients, including calcium, phosphorus, and thiamine (vitamin B_1).

Eggs—the remarkable storehouse of needed nutrients—are one of the first solid foods given to babies. They provide the nutrients needed by children and teenagers for rapid growth. They continue to be important for adults because of their excellent nutritive value, taste appeal, convenience, and economy. And eggs are often included in the first semisolid diet for convalescents.

Since eggs are relatively low in calories, yet high in essential nutrients, they also merit a place in the weight watcher's diet, supplying only about 80 calories per large egg.

When you buy eggs, look for the U.S. Department of Agriculture grade shield on the carton or on the tape that seals the carton. It is your best assurance of both quality and size. The grade will be shown within the shield. The size will be found either within the shield or elsewhere on the carton.

The three consumer grades are U.S. Grade AA (or Fresh Fancy), U.S. Grade A, and U.S. Grade B.

The grade you will find most often is U.S. Grade A. Often, AA quality eggs are included in the cartons with A quality eggs.

SHIELD GIVING QUALITY AND SIZE OF FRESH EGGS

U.S. Grade AA (or Fresh Fancy) and U.S. Grade A eggs have a round, firm yolk, and a high, thick white when broken out. They are ideal for all purposes, but especially for frying and poaching where their up-standing appearance is important.

Grade B eggs have less thick white and the yolk may be somewhat flattened. They are good for general cooking and baking.

Fresh Fancy Quality (or U.S. Grade AA) eggs are produced under USDA's Quality Control program. These eggs

A. Elizabeth Handy is the Home Economist in the Standardization Branch, Poultry Division, Consumer and Marketing Service.

Eggs: Minimum Weight Per Dozen

USDA sizes (or weight classes)	Weight (in ounces)
Jumbo	30
Extra Large	27
Large	24
Medium	21
Small	18
Peewee	15

reach the market quickly under strictly controlled conditions, guaranteeing to the consumer a fresh and top quality product.

The six USDA sizes or weight classes are based on the minimum weight of eggs per dozen.

Although the weight of individual eggs within a carton may vary slightly, the minimum weight per dozen must meet USDA standards.

Retail stores usually carry only two or three sizes in one or two grades. The sizes that you will find most often are Extra Large, Large, and Medium, since most of the eggs produced come in these sizes.

Size and quality are not related—they are entirely different. Large eggs may be high or low quality; high-quality eggs may be either large or small. In other words, any size egg could be Grade AA (or Fresh Fancy), Grade A, or Grade B. The grade depends on quality, not size.

The official USDA grade shield on a carton of eggs means that experienced Federal-State egg graders have supervised every step of the grading and packing operations. It certifies the eggs were a specific quality and size at the time of grading.

USDA's grading program for shell eggs is a voluntary service paid for by the user. Individuals, firms, or governmental agencies that desire the service must request it and pay a fee.

Grading, sizing, labeling, and packaging of shell eggs are controlled on a State-by-State basis in accordance with State egg laws. These laws and regulations are enforced by State regulatory agencies.

The Federal-State service is conducted under cooperative agreements between USDA and State departments of agriculture. It is performed by USDA licensed graders who may be either State or Federal employees.

Under the USDA grading program, each carton of eggs must be clearly marked to identify the grade, the size, the packer or distributor, and the date or code to indicate when packed. Since the program is voluntary, remember that only cartons bearing the official USDA grade shield have been U.S. Government-graded.

Although the handling of shell eggs may vary by State and region, eggs pass through a number of important processes on their way to you—the consumer. Some of the steps involved are frequent gathering, careful handling, proper cleaning, rapid cooling, controlled temperature and humidity, proper grading, sizing, labeling, and packaging, and a prompt movement through marketing channels.

With today's large-scale commercial egg production and technical management and marketing operations, it is now possible to move eggs from the farm to the retail markets within 1 or 2 days.

Through the Federal-State grading program, shell eggs are classified according to the U.S. standards for quality of individual shell eggs. These standards are the yardstick used to measure the quality of the white and yolk and the cleanliness and soundness of the shell.

Interior egg quality is determined by "candling," which is a process of examining the interior of the egg without breaking the shell. The eggs are twirled in front of a light so the inside can be observed. Years ago a candle was actually used, hence the term "candling." Later, a "hand-candling" instrument was used exclusively.

Today, large commercial operations use electronic equipment for "mass scanning" or "flash candling," and thousands of eggs can be examined per hour. The eggs are placed in from one to 12 rows on a continuous conveyor system and mechanically rotated. During this process, skilled personnel observe the condition of the yolk and the white and the cleanliness and soundness of the shell, and remove any eggs that don't meet prescribed standards.

To further assure that consumers are getting high-quality eggs, another quality-control device—the breakout test—is used by USDA and by industry graders. This test is performed by breaking out a random sampling of eggs from each shipment onto a flat surface. Yolks are carefully observed, and the height of the thick white is measured with a special instrument called a micrometer.

USDA also provides other voluntary services to furnish an even closer check on egg quality. These include on-the-farm inspection of eggs and retail store quality audits in which samples are purchased from store display cases and checked again for quality.

Egg prices vary by size for the same grade. The amount of price variation depends on the supply of the various sizes. Consumers often ask for a "rule of thumb" to determine which size is the most economical. Generally speaking, if there is less than a 7-cent price spread per dozen eggs between one size and the next smaller size in the same grade, you will get more for your money by buying the larger size.

When considering cost, remember that 1 dozen large eggs represents 1½ pounds (24 ounces) in the shell. If the large eggs are selling for 60 cents per dozen, that's the equivalent of 40 cents per pound—and very reasonable for a pound of protein-rich food. At this price, a serving of two large eggs (weighing ¼ pound) would cost only 10 cents.

Buy only fresh, clean, sound-shelled eggs. Do not buy eggs that are cracked or dirty. An increasing number of States prohibit the sale of cracked eggs because they may contain bacteria that might cause food poisoning. If, by chance, you should find either cracked or dirty eggs in a carton, they will be safe to eat if used in thoroughly cooked dishes. Wash soiled eggs in hot water immediately prior to using.

Be sure to purchase eggs from a refrigerated display case and refrigerate them promptly at home large end up to help maintain quality. Shell eggs kept at temperatures between 70° and 80° F. will lose more quality in 1 day than in 1 week under refrigeration. At refrigerator temperatures, shell eggs will maintain their inherently high quality for several weeks, but for best flavor and cooking performance, use them within a week.

Purchase either brown or white shelled eggs. The color does not affect the nutritive value, quality, flavor, or cooking performance of the eggs. The only difference is in the shell itself. Consumer preference has traditionally varied in different parts of the country—some people prefer white eggs, and others prefer brown. The color is determined by the breed of the hen laying the egg and it may vary from white to deep brown. In other words, shell color is a breed characteristic.

To replace the natural "bloom" or coating which covers the pores of the eggshell, washed eggs are frequently shell-treated or protected by being dipped in or sprayed with a fine mist of a harmless, tasteless, odorless oil. The oil covers the pores and retards the loss of natural carbon dioxide and moisture from the egg, thus helping to preserve quality.

Consumers sometimes say that eggs taste different today. One reason for the flavor change is the hen's different diet and environment. Today's commercial laying flocks do not have access to feeds which cause strong flavors, and the eggs are gathered so frequently that their porous shells do not absorb odors from the environment. Great care is also taken in marketing to keep the eggs away from foods with strong odors that might be absorbed—this is also a very good practice to follow in your home.

Some people wonder why the broken-out eggs seem smaller these days. They say the eggs don't cover as large an area in the frying pan as they once did. This is because of the freshness of today's eggs. Fresh, high-quality eggs cover only a small area when broken out. They have a large amount of thick white which stands high and firm around the yolk. As the eggs age, the amount of the thick white decreases and the white becomes thinner, causing the eggs to spread out and cover more area, thus making them appear to be larger.

Yolks with colors of various shades are equally good. Yolk color is also a matter of preference. The color may vary, depending on the hen's diet. Eggs produced by today's commercial laying flocks tend to have yolks that are more uniform in color and also lighter in color because the hens are fed a controlled ration.

Leftover yolks should be refrigerated promptly in tightly closed containers. Cover the yolks with cold water before storing. Use within a day or two.

Occasionally, a small blood or meat spot is found in an egg. Although these eggs rarely reach consumers, the spot can be easily removed. The eggs are perfectly wholesome and just as good as other eggs. These spots are not a sign the eggs are fertile. The chances of consumers receiving a fertile egg in today's market are extremely rare.

With modern production and marketing practices, it is also very seldom, indeed, that consumers find storage eggs in the retail market. Most of the shell eggs are marketed promptly.

The white, twisted, ropelike strands of material found in raw eggs often raise questions. Known as "chalazas," these strands are highly concentrated white appearing on each side of the yolk. They are a perfectly natural, wholesome part of the egg and serve to anchor the yolk in place. Chalazas are found in all eggs, with varying degrees of prominence.

A cloudy or slightly milky white occasionally found does not affect use of the eggs. It is a normal characteristic of fresh eggs. Cloudiness or milkiness merely indicates that carbon dioxide which is naturally present in a fresh shell egg has not yet escaped through the shell. The white becomes clearer as the egg ages.

Egg white sometimes sticks to the inside of the shell of raw eggs, making it difficult to remove. Basically this too is because the eggs are fresher and the white is thicker.

Leftover egg whites should be refrigerated promptly in tightly covered containers and used within a day or two.

Hard-cooked eggs should also be refrigerated promptly—either in the shell or out. If the shell is removed, put the eggs in a tightly closed container or wrap them with moisture-proof, vaporproof material. Use within a few days.

Difficulty in peeling some hard-cooked eggs is associated with the freshness of the eggs reaching today's consumers. Since older eggs are usually easier to peel, use your oldest eggs for hard cooking.

The green discoloration that sometimes appears between the white and the yolk of hard-cooked eggs is harmless. This greenish color results from a chemical reaction between the sulfur in the white and the iron in the yolk. Sulfur and iron are natural wholesome components of the egg. To help prevent discoloration, hard-cook the eggs at low temperature, avoid overcooking, and cool them promptly.

About one out of 10 shell eggs produced in the United States today is processed into liquid, dried, or frozen form. For large quantity food buyers and the commercial manufacturers of food products, these convenience items are time, labor, and space savers which provide uniformity of the end product. Yet these products contain the natural goodness and the cooking functions of the shell egg.

In 1968, around 72 percent of all egg products were processed under the USDA voluntary egg products inspection program. The service is available to processors who request it and pay a fee. Under this program, egg products must be processed under continuous USDA supervision in a sanitary manner, in an approved plant with proper facilities, and pasteurized in accordance with USDA's requirements to assure wholesomeness of the products. Only officially inspected and passed products may carry the USDA inspection mark.

Generally, liquid, dried, and frozen egg products as such are not available at the retail level, but a few specialty stores may stock dried-egg solids for use by campers and hunters. Some companies also sell them directly to interested persons.

Each of us benefits—probably more than we realize—from the egg products industry. Most of these egg products are used by quantity buyers and in the commercial manufacturing of bakery products, noodles, macaroni, mayonnaise, confections, ice cream, and in the growing variety of ready-prepared quick bread, cake, frosting, and pudding mixes now on the market. Advances in the egg products industry have played a large part in making these convenience or ready foods available to you and your family.

EGG PRODUCTS INSPECTION MARK

Since the food processors are now looking upon eggs as a new product challenge, you will probably be seeing more new egg items in the stores.

Canned eggnogs which require no refrigeration until opening, egg salads, packaged omelets, egg custards, hard-cooked egg rolls, and instant scrambled eggs are already available in certain sections of the country. Other fascinating new products are still in the testing stages and may appear soon—frozen fried eggs, packaged chiffon pies, and many others.

For breakfast, lunch, or dinner—in plain or party fare—eggs are a family favorite with U.S. consumers. During 1968, we ate enough eggs to account for 318 eggs for each man, woman, and child in the civilian population.

Eggs can be used in literally hundreds of different ways. Cooked alone, they may be scrambled, fried, poached, cooked in the shell, baked or shirred, or made into omelets. They also combine easily and well with practically all foods including cereals, breads, milk, cheese, fruits, vegetables, meats, seafood, and poultry. They add color, nutritive value, and flavor to foods.

Suggested Ways to Use Eggs

Appetizers:
Egg dips, canapes
Soups:
Bisques, consommes
Entrees:
Poached, scrambled, fried, hard and soft cooked, baked, omelets, souffles, fondues, loaves
Sandwiches:
Club, fried, hard cooked, egg salad
Salads:
Caesar salad, mousses, aspics, poultry, and fish salads
Dressings:
Thousand Island, cooked salad dressings, mayonnaise
Breads:
Muffins, waffles, cornbread, french toast, dumplings
Beverages:
Eggnogs—plain or fancy
Desserts:
Meringues, pies, puddings, custards, souffles, cream puffs, cakes

Moderate to low temperatures with proper timing are the general rules to follow in cooking to assure uniformly tender, attractive egg dishes. High temperatures and long cooking cause egg protein to shrink with an accompanying loss of moisture, making the protein in the egg "rubbery" or tough.

From an early morning eye-opener to a late-at-night snack, eggs are not only versatile and delicious, but also economical and easy to prepare.

You may not realize how many important functions eggs serve in cooking. We use them for leavening as in cakes, breads, souffles, and omelets; thickening custards, sauces, and puddings; emulsifying mayonnaise and salad dressings; coating for breaded poultry, meat, and fish; binding together croquettes, meat loaves, and egg loaves; retarding of crystallization in candies and in icings; garnishing canapes, salads, and main dishes; and for clarifying soup stock.

A quick search of any cookbook will give you unlimited ideas as to how you can make eggs work for you.

Use all the traditional methods of scrambling, frying, poaching, and cooking in the shell, but also be sure to try some of the new and different recipes you'll find. A few suggested recipes and uses are included here.

CHEESE FONDUE

8 servings

2 cups hot milk
2 cups shredded mild or sharp cheese
2 cups soft breadcrumbs
2 tablespoons butter or margarine
¼ teaspoon salt
6 egg yolks, beaten
6 egg whites, stiffly beaten

Preheat oven to 350° F. (moderate).

Combine milk, cheese, breadcrumbs, fat, and salt.

Stir a little of the hot mixture into egg yolks; then stir egg yolks into rest of hot mixture.

Gently fold in egg whites.

Pour into buttered 2-quart baking dish. Bake about 30 to 40 minutes, or until knife inserted in center comes out clean. Serve immediately.

Variation: Add ¼ cup finely chopped and crisply cooked bacon to mixture before folding in egg whites.

MOLDED EGG SALAD

6 servings

1 tablespoon unflavored gelatin
½ cup cold water
½ cup boiling water
⅔ cup mayonnaise
2 tablespoons lemon juice
¼ teaspoon salt
6 chopped hard-cooked eggs
⅓ cup sliced olives
¼ cup chopped pickles
¼ cup chopped celery
½ teaspoon minced onion
2 tablespoons chopped parsley

Soften gelatin in cold water, then dissolve in boiling water.

Stir gelatin mixture gradually into mayonnaise. Add lemon juice and salt and mix well.

Chill until thick but not set.

Blend in eggs, olives, pickles, celery, onion, and parsley. Mix well.

Pour into 1-quart mold. Chill until set. Unmold on salad greens.

Variation: Reserve one hard-cooked egg, cut in slices, and several olive slices. Soften 1½ teaspoons unflavored gelatin in ¼ cup cold water; dissolve in ½ cup boiling water. Add 2 tablespoons lemon juice. Chill until thick but not set. Pour into chilled ring mold. Arrange egg and olive slices in clear gelatin. Allow to set before adding above mixture.

EGG SALAD SANDWICH FILLING

6 sandwiches

6 finely chopped hard-cooked eggs
¼ cup finely chopped sweet pickles
¾ cup finely chopped celery
2 tablespoons chopped parsley
½ cup mayonnaise
½ teaspoon salt
¾ teaspoon dry mustard
⅛ teaspoon pepper

Combine all ingredients. Mix well. Spread on bread.

Note: May be served as a salad on greens.

CHOCOLATE SOUFFLE

6 servings

2 ounces (2 squares) semisweet or unsweetened chocolate
3 tablespoons butter or margarine
3 tablespoons flour
1 cup milk
¾ cup sugar
¼ teaspoon salt
5 egg yolks, beaten until foamy
1 teaspoon vanilla
5 egg whites

Preheat oven to 350° F. (moderate).

Melt chocolate and fat in top part of double boiler. Stir in flour. Add milk, sugar, and salt, and cook over hot water until thick and smooth.

Add egg yolks and cook over hot water for 2 or 3 minutes, while stirring constantly.

Remove from heat, add vanilla, and cool slightly.

Beat egg whites until shiny and stiff enough to hold a good peak. Gently fold half of the whites into chocolate mixture; add remaining egg whites, cutting them in lightly.

Pour into 1½-quart straight-sided baking dish, set in a pan of hot water. Bake for 50 to 60 minutes.

CHOCOLATE PEPPERMINT PUFFS

5 to 6 dozen

4 egg whites
¼ teaspoon salt
¼ teaspoon cream of tartar
1½ cups sugar
12-ounce package chocolate bits
½ teaspoon peppermint extract

Preheat oven to 300° F. (very slow oven).

Beat egg whites until foamy. Add salt and cream of tartar, beating until stiff but not dry.

Add sugar gradually, beating constantly until very stiff peaks form. Fold in chocolate bits and peppermint.

Drop from a teaspoon onto foil or ungreased heavy paper on a cookie sheet. Bake for 25 minutes. Remove from paper while slightly warm.

Variations:

Chocolate-Coconut Puffs—Omit peppermint. Add ½ cup flaked coconut and 1 teaspoon vanilla.

Chocolate-Nut Puffs—Omit peppermint. Add ½ cup chopped nuts and 1 teaspoon vanilla.

Butterscotch Nut Puffs—Omit peppermint and the chocolate bits. Add 12 ounces (2 cups) butterscotch bits, ½ cup of chopped nuts, and 1 teaspoon of vanilla.

LEMON DATE BARS

18 bars

Crust:
½ cup butter or margarine
¼ cup confectioner's sugar
1 cup sifted flour
1 teaspoon grated lemon rind

Preheat oven to 350° F. (moderate).

Beat fat and sugar until creamy. Blend in flour and lemon rind.

Press crust into bottom of greased 8-inch-square baking pan. Bake for 20 minutes.

Topping:
3 eggs
1 cup granulated sugar
2 tablespoons flour
½ teaspoon baking powder
½ teaspoon salt
1 cup flaked coconut
¾ cup chopped pitted dates
2 tablespoons lemon juice

Beat eggs until foamy. Add sugar gradually, beating until thick.

Blend in flour, baking powder, salt, coconut, dates, and lemon juice.

Spoon topping over crust.

Bake about 30 minutes or until top is firm and golden brown. Cool and cut into bars.

BAKED CUSTARD

6 servings

4 eggs, slightly beaten
⅓ cup sugar
¼ teaspoon salt
3 cups hot milk
1 teaspoon vanilla
Nutmeg, as desired

Preheat oven to 325° F. (slow).

Combine eggs, sugar, and salt. Stir in the milk gradually. Add vanilla.

Pour into custard cups. Sprinkle with nutmeg. Set the cups in a pan of hot water.

Bake for 30 to 40 minutes, or until a knife inserted in center comes out clean.

Variations:

Coconut Custard—sprinkle 2 tablespoons of coconut into cups and add custard mixture.

Almond Custard—brown a cup of chopped almonds in 2 tablespoons of butter or margarine. Sprinkle into cups and add custard mixture.

Harold E. Meister
Jennie L. Brogdon

Versatility, Inc., With Milk and Our Other Dairy Foods

You have probably never gone a whole day without having milk and other dairy products. From the first meal in the morning to the last evening snack, these versatile foods add flavor, wholesomeness, and variety to our diets.

What are the dairy foods that are so prevalent in our daily meals? Milk, cream, butter, cheeses, and all the good dishes containing these foods.

Milk may be processed in a number of ways. These products include whole, skimmed, and flavored fresh milk; cultured, canned, and dried milk; fresh and cultured cream; and frozen desserts.

Most of the milk sold in the United States is cow's milk. Some goat's milk is available as a specialty product. It is used mainly by people who are allergic to cow's milk or who are on other special diets. Goat's milk is sold fresh and canned.

Almost all fresh milk and cream on the market is pasteurized to protect the consumer. In pasteurizing, milk is heated briefly to kill harmful bacteria. Then it is chilled rapidly. Most fresh whole pasteurized milk is homogenized. The homogenizing process disperses the fat evenly through the milk.

The U.S. Public Health Service has set standards for Grade A pasteurized milk and milk products. To earn this grade, milk must be produced under sanitary conditions and be handled carefully. Fresh whole milk must contain not less than 3.25 percent milkfat (sometimes called butterfat) and not less than 8.25 percent nonfat milk solids (protein, milk sugar, and minerals).

Many cities, counties, and States have adopted the U.S. Public Health Service standards for milk. Others have established their own standards.

Movement of ample supplies of safe, wholesome milk between producing and consuming markets is assured by local, State, and Federal cooperation.

The U.S. Department of Agriculture has established grades for nonfat dry milk. The USDA grade shield signifies that the product has been packaged in a clean, sanitary plant and that it meets exacting quality requirements. The highest quality of instant nonfat dry milk is designated U.S. Extra Grade.

U.S. Government regulations provide that nonfat dry milk and fresh skim milk may be fortified with vitamins A and D. Fresh whole milk may be fortified with vitamins and minerals.

In some States, you will find filled milk and imitation milk in the stores. Filled milk is a combination of skim milk and vegetable fat; or of nonfat dry milk, water, and vegetable fat. Imitation milk is a combination of several nondairy ingredients made in the semblance of milk. The ingredients include vegetable fat which is often coconut oil, protein such as sodium caseinate or soya solids, corn sirup solids, flavoring agents, stabilizers, emulsifiers, and water. Minimum standards have not been set to assure nutritional qualities comparable to fresh fluid milk.

Coffee whiteners, dry whipped topping mixes, and most of the whipped

Harold E. Meister is Deputy Director, Dairy Division, Consumer and Marketing Service.

Jennie L. Brogdon was a Food Technologist, Human Nutrition Research Division, Agricultural Research Service. She is now doing graduate work at the University of Maryland.

toppings in pressurized cans are made from nondairy products.

When buying milk, remember that fresh milk and cultured milk cost more than dried and canned forms. Milk that is fortified with multiple vitamins and minerals is generally the most expensive.

If you want to cut food costs and still provide the milk which your family needs, you might try changing your patterns for buying and using milk. Here are some suggestions:

- Buy fresh fluid milk at a food or dairy retail store. Milk often costs more when delivered to the home.
- Buy fresh milk in multiquart containers if you can use this amount without waste. Usually, milk in ½- or 1-gallon containers costs less per quart than in single quarts.
- Use evaporated milk in cooking.

Unless you rely on fortified milk as a principal source of vitamin D, you can—

- Buy fresh milk without added vitamins and minerals, if there is a difference in price between nonfortified and fortified milk.
- Use nonfat dry milk in cooking or as a beverage. Some families mix equal amounts of reconstituted nonfat dry milk and fresh whole milk to make a beverage.

Fluid milk, cream, and cultured milk products are at their best in flavor and nutritive value when they are kept clean, cold, and tightly covered. Rinse off the bottle or carton, and dry with a clean cloth before placing it in the coldest part of your refrigerator (40°F.). Keeping these dairy products tightly covered will prevent absorption of odors and flavors from other foods in the refrigerator.

Don't let milk and cream stand in the light because it destroys riboflavin and may cause an off-flavor. Put these products in the refrigerator as soon as possible after they are purchased or delivered to your home, and take them out only long enough to measure the amount needed for immediate use.

Don't mix new milk with old unless you are going to use it immediately. And don't put unused milk back in the original container once it has been removed from it; store this milk in a separate container.

Canned milk can be stored at room temperature until opened. Then refrigerate like fresh milk.

Keep dry milk at 75° F. or lower, if possible, until reconstituted; then treat it like fresh milk. Close the packages immediately after using. If the milk powder is exposed to moisture in the air during storage, it may become lumpy and stale.

For best flavor, use fluid milk and cream within 3 to 5 days and cultured products within 2 or 3 days. Unopened jars of sterilized cream can be kept for several months in the refrigerator. After opening, use within 10 days. Pressurized cans of whipped cream may be kept for several weeks.

Milk that has been frozen for a month or less can be used although the flavor and appearance may be changed. Do not freeze sour cream, yogurt, evaporated milk, or cream.

Most forms of milk can be used interchangeably. Reconstituted nonfat dry milk or evaporated milk diluted with an equal amount of water may be used in place of whole milk in some recipes. You might want to add 2½ teaspoons of butter or margarine to 1 cup of reconstituted nonfat dry milk whenever you are using this in place of whole milk.

Due to the tangy flavor, buttermilk

SHIELD ON U.S. GRADED NONFAT DRY MILK

Fresh milk is a key part of a school lunch.

cannot replace the other forms of milk in some recipes. If buttermilk is used in place of sweet milk in cakes and quick breads, use ¼ teaspoon of baking soda and ½ cup of buttermilk in the place of 1 teaspoon of baking powder and ½ cup of sweet milk.

If you do not have any buttermilk available, you can use home-soured milk. Add 1 tablespoon of vinegar or lemon juice to 1 cup fresh milk or to ½ cup evaporated milk plus ½ cup water. Let stand 5 minutes. Use 2 teaspoons of vinegar or lemon juice to 1 cup of reconstituted nonfat dry milk. Let stand 10 minutes.

Sweetened condensed milk is used primarily in desserts, candies, frostings, and special recipes because of the added sugar.

Homogenized milk can be used interchangeably with nonhomogenized, but you may notice slight differences in texture. Sauces made with homogenized milk will be stiffer and show more fat separation. Commercial and cornstarch puddings also will become thicker when made with homogenized milk. Soups, gravies, and scalloped potatoes will curdle more readily.

Either undiluted evaporated milk or unreconstituted nonfat dry milk may be added to sauces, custards, mashed vegetables, ground meat and poultry dishes, or baked goods to increase nutritive value.

When you reconstitute nonfat dry milk, follow the mixing directions on the package; for ease in measuring, use 1 cup of dry milk to 3 cups of water. In many recipes, the nonfat dry milk can be added with the dry ingredients. Add the water for reconstituting the milk along with the other liquid ingredients in the recipe.

Both evaporated milk and nonfat dry milk can be reconstituted with liquids from cooked vegetables and meats for creamed or scalloped dishes or with some fruit juices to use in puddings and in other desserts.

Lowered temperatures are recommended when cooking dishes in which milk is the main ingredient. If milk is cooked at too high a temperature or for too long a time, some of the protein coagulates into a surface film or a coating on the sides of the pan. Also, off-flavors develop and the milk may scorch.

Heat milk over low heat or in a double boiler, being careful not to let it boil. Casseroles cooked in the oven should be baked at low temperatures, and custards set in a pan of hot water.

Fluid milk is the major ingredient of white sauce. Learn to make a smooth, well-seasoned white sauce and you have the basis for many dishes. White sauce is prepared in thin, medium, or thick consistency, depending upon the amount of flour which is used to thicken the milk.

Thin or medium white sauce is used in gravies and in creamed and scalloped vegetables, egg, fish, and meat dishes. Thin white sauce is also used in cream soups. Thick white sauce is used in hollandaise sauce and as a binder for croquettes and souffles.

The sauce can take on a new identity with added ingredients such as mushrooms, onions, eggs, pimiento; or when seasoned with curry powder, dry mustard, chives, parsley, or other herbs.

Have you ever prepared a cream soup or other creamed dish that curdled? Curdling results when casein, a protein of milk, coagulates or clumps together. Such a coagulation can be caused by acids in foods. A high salt content or tannins in foods can also cause milk protein to coagulate. Tomatoes, peas, carrots, and asparagus are some of the vegetables which might cause curdling.

Any procedure which will keep the protein from clumping together will keep the mixture smooth. There are several ways to accomplish this: Prepare the milk in a white sauce; stir it constantly when the vegetable is added; add the vegetable shortly before serving, and heat briefly. This *golden squash soup* is made using some of these procedures.

GOLDEN SQUASH SOUP

6 servings, 1 cup each

1 small onion, sliced
2 tablespoons butter or margarine
¼ cup flour
5 cups milk
1½ cups cooked, pureed Hubbard squash (fresh or frozen)
1½ teaspoons salt
¼ teaspoon celery salt
⅛ teaspoon curry powder
Pepper as desired
2 tablespoons chopped parsley

Cook onion in fat in a large saucepan for a few minutes. Blend flour with onion; add milk. Cook over low heat, stirring constantly, until thickened. Remove from heat; gently blend in squash and seasoning. Heat to serving temperature, but do not boil. Sprinkle each serving of soup with parsley.

There are times when you want the milk to coagulate; for example, when you use rennin to make a junket dessert. A firmer clot will be formed if you do not boil the milk and if you do not stir the mixture too much after adding the rennin. Evaporated milk should not be used for this dessert because a very soft curd is formed.

Yogurt, which is custardlike in texture and acid in flavor, can be eaten "as is" or used in desserts, dips, salad dressings, or for cooking. When yogurt is used in cooking, fold or stir gently into the other ingredients so that the texture is not changed.

The velvety, thick consistency and tangy flavor of dairy sour cream adds a gourmet touch to foods from appetizers to desserts. As an appetizer, try this dip.

SOUR CREAM-HAM DIP

About 1 cup

1 cup dairy sour cream
1 can (4½ ounces) deviled ham
1 teaspoon prepared mustard
1 tablespoon grated onion

Whip dairy sour cream until fluffy. Mix ham, mustard, and onion.

Blend into sour cream.

Serve with crackers, potato chips, or raw vegetables.

As it comes from the carton, dairy sour cream is a ready-to-use salad dressing or an instant sauce for raw or cooked vegetables or baked potatoes. You can also purchase a dry mix for sour cream sauce that can be used for these same purposes. You can make a fancier sauce by adding ingredients like chives, horseradish, dill seed, onions, or nuts.

When used in dressings or sauces which contain acid foods such as vinegar or lemon juice, the sour cream may become thin when it is mixed. However, it will return to its original consistency after the product is chilled.

Remember when heating sour cream that it reacts as milk does to high temperatures, and may curdle. This may also happen if it is heated at low temperatures for a long time. It is best to add the sour cream near the end of cooking and to keep the temperature low. If the mixture should curdle, the appearance will be unattractive but the flavor will still be good.

Sour half-and-half may be substituted in many foods for sour cream. However, because of the lower fat content, do not substitute sour half-and-half in cakes and cookies unless these contain fat in addition to the sour cream.

Rich, smooth cream is an essential ingredient in fine cooking. Light or table cream is used "as is" for beverages, cereals, or desserts as well as for cooking. Heavy cream, in addition to being used for cooking, is used for whipping.

Thick, luscious mounds of whipped cream naturally team up with desserts—as a garnish, as part of the dessert, or even as a dessert by itself. Whipped cream also can be included in salads or party sandwiches.

Heavy cream should whip to twice its volume. That is, 1 cup (½ pint) of cream yields about 2 cups of whipped cream. This volume is best obtained with cream that is 30 to 35 percent fat, is at least 24 hours old, and is thoroughly chilled to between 35° and 40° F. It helps to chill the bowl and beater, too. Use a deep, narrow bowl with straight sides rather than a wide and shallow one.

Beat the cream until it is fairly stiff. Be careful not to overbeat or you will have butter.

When the cream is stiff, fold in a tablespoon of sugar per cup of unwhipped cream and ½ teaspoon vanilla or other flavoring. More sugar can be added, if you wish. Do not add the sugar too soon or it will take longer to whip the cream and the volume will not be as great. Sweetened whipped cream will not be as stiff or as stable as unsweetened. You might prefer to use unsweetened whipped cream when it is a topping for some desserts.

Whipped cream can be frozen in individual portions and used as a garnish. This is particularly good on warm fruit pies.

Whipped instant nonfat dry milk or whipped evaporated milk can be substituted in many recipes in which whipped cream is used. For the best results, whip instant nonfat dry milk according to package instructions. Evaporated milk should not be diluted when it is to be whipped. Place the evaporated milk in the freezer until it is icy around the edges and partially frozen. Then whip until stiff. Unlike cream, evaporated milk triples in volume so that ⅔ cup of milk will yield 2 cups after whipping.

If you wish to serve whipped cream

as a dessert, fold in rum, sherry, or brandy to taste in place of the vanilla flavoring. Or fold in 1 cup of applesauce or other fruit puree to 2 cups of whipped cream.

Ice Cream, America's favorite dessert, was also popular during our colonial days. There are many flavors on the market, but vanilla, chocolate, and strawberry are still the bestsellers. Frozen custard, fruit sherbet, and ice milk are other popular desserts.

Frozen desserts should be stored in the tightly closed carton at 0° F. or colder. If you store ice cream in a refrigerator frozen-food compartment, use it within a week. When the ice cream is partially used up, cover the surface with a protective wrap so as to avoid the loss of moisture.

Commercial frozen desserts are excellent. But homemade ice cream or sherbet is a treat worth your effort. There are prepared mixes on the market, or you can find a recipe in almost any cookbook. Quality of ice cream is improved if the dairy products used are homogenized or in concentrated form, such as evaporated milk. Adding gelatin or egg also improves quality.

There are two methods of preparing these desserts—stirred and unstirred or still -frozen.

Versatile dairy products can be served as ice cream, above; as an ingredient in soup, left; and as cheese and milk with a meal, right.

The stirred method requires either hand or electric power to turn the dasher crank. When you first begin, turn the dasher slowly and steadily to insure a smooth cream. Do not turn the dasher too fast or your mixture may be churned to butter. When the ice cream is frozen to a mush (about 5 to 10 minutes), turn the dasher more rapidly to whip air into the cream. To harden the ice cream to serving consistency and also to insure a well-blended flavor, freeze the cream at least 1 hour after mixing is completed.

Continuous stirring in the freezer keeps ice crystals small and incorporates air. When the dessert is still-frozen, as in refrigerator trays, some other means must be used to keep the ice crystals small and prevent formation of a solid ice mass. This is done by rapid freezing; by folding in a fluffy beaten product such as whipped cream or beaten egg white; and by removing the mushy mixture from the refrigerator freezer, beating it until well-blended, and returning it to the freezer until firm. Even when these procedures are used, texture of a still-frozen dessert is less smooth than that of a stirred one because the ice crystals are larger. These ice crystals will continue to form during storage so that still-frozen dessert is best eaten soon after preparation.

Ice cream is easier to scoop or slice if it is at refrigerator temperature for a short time—about 10 minutes for a pint and 20 minutes for a half gallon.

Butter is one of our oldest staple foods. Recorded history shows it was used in India as long ago as 2000 B.C. In the United States, the buttermaking industry has developed in stages starting as a farm operation; then moving into small plants receiving cream delivered by horse and wagon; then to larger central plants to take advantage of the savings in volume operations. Plants are continuing to consolidate into larger units. Consumers benefit because these plants are taking advantage of the newest milk and cream processing equipment and churns, automated packaging equipment, and sanitary controls. All of these things play a part in giving us wholesome butter with a fine flavor and good spreadability.

Butter is made by churning pasteurized cream. By law, butter must contain not less than 80 percent milkfat. It may or may not contain salt. If no salt is added the package is usually labelled "unsalted butter." However, in some markets it is known as "sweet" butter.

The highest quality butter is made from sweet cream, or sweet cream to which a culture similar to that used in cultured milk products has been added. Cultured butter has a mildly acid flavor and aroma. Unsalted butter packed for sale to consumers generally has this pleasing acid flavor.

Whipped butter is made by whipping air or inert gas into butter. This increases volume and makes the butter easier to spread. Most of the whipped butter sold in this country is unsalted.

Most of the butter offered to consumers has the U.S. Department of Agriculture shield with a letter grade indicating the butter's quality at time of grading. The assigned grade is based on official standards and specifications. Tests are run on the butter's "keeping quality" as a check for wholesomeness. Only butter manufactured in a plant inspected and approved by USDA for sanitation and good operating practices can be officially graded.

U.S. Grade AA butter has delicate, sweet flavor, with a fine, highly pleasing aroma. It has a smooth texture with good spreadability. U.S. Grade A butter is made from fresh cream. Its flavor and aroma are pleasing but not quite as fine as for the top grade.

To maintain the delicate flavor, store butter in the original wrappings until ready for use. Keep in the coldest part of the refrigerator and only remove as much as you will use at one time. If butter is exposed at room temperature for long periods, light and heat may hasten rancidity. Always keep butter covered so it will not absorb flavors from other foods. The butter compartment on the refrigerator door keeps

SHIELD ON U.S. GRADED BUTTER AND CHEDDAR CHEESE

butter at spreading consistency. If you do not plan to use the butter within a short period of time, keep it in the freezer. It can be frozen in the original container unless you plan to keep it for several months; then it should be overwrapped with moisture-proof material.

Butter adds a pleasing, distinctive flavor to vegetables, creamed dishes, desserts, icings, and of course, to hot breads and rolls. Sauces that combine butter with many different kinds of seasonings are also good and very easy to make. Melt or whip the butter with parsley, lemon, dill, basil, or other herbs. Start with ¼ teaspoon seasoning to ¼ cup (½ stick) butter and increase according to your taste.

Try out your own combinations; you might even become noted for your own special sauce.

A dessert hard sauce is made by creaming butter with confectioner's sugar and flavoring it with extracts or spices or with wine, brandy, whiskey, or rum. This is the traditional sauce for English plum pudding.

For any flour mixture that contains a considerable amount of fat, butter is a good choice since it adds fine flavor as well as shortening. It has long been a favorite for cakes, puff pastry, and butter cookies.

Butter can also be used as the shortening in plain pastry, but because butter is only 80 percent fat the crust will not be as tender as one made with another shortening, unless you use more of it. Use 1 cup plus 2 tablespoons of butter in place of 1 cup of vegetable or other shortening.

Do not use whipped butter as a substitute for butter in a recipe since the shortening power is not the same as for unwhipped butter.

Butter can be used for pan frying. Don't let the temperature get too high or the butter will smoke and brown.

Because butter has a low smoking point, it is not suitable for deep-fat frying.

Cheese is available in many styles, flavors, and textures to suit just about every taste and occasion. The refrigerated showcase in any modern food market is most enticing with its display of various shapes and sizes of cheese packages—wedges, oblongs, segments, cubes, slices, blocks, and cut portions. For many people, their adventuresome spirit takes over when they see the attractive cheese display, and they buy unfamiliar varieties for the pure enjoyment of getting acquainted with new cheese flavors and textures. Others like to choose with more certainty the type of cheese that will be just right for a particular dish, a particular occasion, or to suit their taste.

With more than 400 varieties of natural cheese alone, there are bound to be several cheeses for every taste. You may not like some kinds, others may become favorites. If you are used to a mild Cheddar, try other mild cheeses first, and then stronger flavored ones. For still more variety, the market offers pasteurized process cheese and related products.

The following information on the various forms of cheese available in retail markets may enlarge your own acquaintance with the cheese family.

Natural Cheese is made by coagulating milk and then separating the curd or solid part from the whey or watery part. Most natural cheeses are made from whole cow's milk, although some are made from skim milk, whey, or mixtures of all three.

Many of the popular varieties of natural cheese, although originating in Europe, are now produced in the United States, and are available in most food stores, delicatessens, and specialty cheese stores.

Many persons prefer natural cheeses

to other forms of cheese because each has its own characteristic flavor and texture. Flavors range from bland cottage cheese to tangy Blue (or bleu) or pungent Limburger. Textures vary, too—from the smooth creaminess of cream cheese to the firm elasticity of Swiss cheese. Flavor and body and texture of cheeses are closely related to degree of ripening or aging. Some natural cheeses are used unripened.

Soft unripened varieties such as cottage, cream, Neufchâtel, and ricotta cheese contain relatively high moisture and do not undergo any curing or ripening. Examples of firm, unripened cheeses are Gjetost and Mysost.

In the soft, ripened cheeses, curing progresses from the outside or rind of the cheese toward the center. Particular molds or culture of bacteria or both, which grow on the surface of the cheese, aid in developing the characteristic flavor and body and texture during the process of curing. Curing continues as long as the temperature is favorable. These cheeses include such varieties as Brie, Camembert, and Limburger. They usually contain more moisture than semisoft, ripened varieties.

Semisoft, ripened cheeses ripen from the interior as well as from the surface. This ripening process begins soon after the cheese is formed, with the aid of a characteristic bacterial or mold culture or both. Curing continues as long as the temperature is favorable. Examples of these cheeses are Bel Paese, Brick, Muenster, and Port du Salut. They contain higher moisture than the firm ripened varieties.

Firm ripened cheeses ripen with the aid of a bacterial culture throughout the entire cheese. Ripening continues as long as the temperature is favorable. The rate and degree of curing is also closely related to moisture content; therefore these cheeses, being lower in moisture than the softer varieties, do usually require a longer curing time. Included are Cheddar, Colby, Edam, Gouda, Provolone, and Swiss.

Very hard ripened cheeses also are cured with the help of a bacterial culture and enzymes. The rate of curing, however, is much slower because of the very low moisture and high salt content. In this category are Parmesan, Romano, and Sap Sago.

Blue-vein, mold-ripened cheese curing is accomplished by the aid of bacteria, but more particularly by the use of a characteristic mold culture that grows throughout the interior of the cheese to produce the familiar appearance and characteristic flavor. The well-known blue-veined cheeses include Blue (or bleu), Gorgonzola, Stilton, and Roquefort.

Pasteurized Process Cheese is a blend of fresh and aged natural cheeses which have been shredded, mixed, and heated (pasteurized), after which no further ripening occurs. It melts easily when reheated. The blend may consist of one or two or more varieties of natural cheese and it may contain pimientos, fruits, vegetables, or meats. Smoked cheese or smoke flavor may also be added.

The flavor of pasteurized process cheese depends largely upon the flavor of the cheese used, which may be modified by flavoring materials added. As an example, pasteurized Gruyere cheese has a nut-sweet flavor, somewhat similar to Swiss.

Process cheese is packaged in slices, ½-, 1-, and 2-pound loaves, and cut portions.

Pasteurized process cheese food is prepared in much the same manner as process cheese except that it contains less cheese, with nonfat dry milk or whey solids and water added. This results in a lower milkfat content and more moisture than in process cheese. Pasteurized process cheese food also may contain pimientos, fruits, vegetables, or meats, or it may have a smoked flavor. The most popular variety is American cheese food.

Cheese food is milder in flavor, has a softer texture, spreads more easily, and melts quicker than process cheese due to a higher moisture content. It is packaged in slices, rolls, links, and loaves.

Pasteurized process cheese spread is

made in much the same manner as pasteurized process cheese food but generally contains higher moisture, and the milkfat content is usually lower. A stabilizer is used in preparing this product to prevent separation of ingredients. It is normally more spreadable than cheese food. Cheese spread may contain pimientos, fruit, vegetables, meat, or have a smoked flavor. It is sold in jars and loaves.

The flavor of pasteurized process cheese spread depends largely upon the flavor of the cheese used, which may be modified by flavoring materials added.

Coldpack Cheese or Club Cheese is a blend of the same or two or more varieties of fresh and aged natural cheese, as in process cheese, except that the cheese is mixed into a uniform product without heating. The flavor is the same as the natural cheese used and usually is aged or sharp. It may have a smoked flavor. The body is softer and spreads easily. Principal varieties are coldpack American cheese and coldpack Swiss cheese. Coldpack cheese is packaged in jars, rolls, or links.

Coldpack cheese food is prepared in the same manner as coldpack cheese, but includes other dairy ingredients as used in process cheese food. In addition, sweetening agents such as sugar and corn sirup may be added. It is packaged in the same way as coldpack cheese.

The flavor resembles the cheese from which it is made but is milder; the cheese food is softer and spreads more easily due to the other ingredients added and the higher moisture content.

The descriptions above show there are significant differences between natural cheeses and different kinds of process cheese and related products. These differences make it very important that you check the labels when buying cheese.

For some purposes you may want natural cheese, for others process cheese or cheese food, and for still others pasteurized process cheese spread or coldpack cheese may best serve your needs. In many cases, they may be packaged alike, but the names on the labels will be different. Do not confuse the brand name with the name of the cheese.

The name of a natural cheese will appear as the variety such as "Cheddar cheese," or "Blue cheese." A very important bit of information on the label of certain varieties of natural cheese pertains to the age or degree of ripening. For instance, Cheddar cheese labeled "mild" usually has been aged 2 to 3 months; "medium" or "mellow" has been aged 4 to 7 months; and "aged" or "sharp," 8 to 12 months.

Pasteurized process cheese labels will always include the name of the variety or varieties of cheese used, for instance, "pasteurized process American cheese" or "pasteurized process Swiss and American cheese." In some cases, pasteurized process cheese may be labeled to indicate a sharp flavor when a much higher proportion of sharp or aged cheese was used in its preparation.

Labels of cheese foods and cheese spreads will include all the ingredients used in preparing these products along with the kinds or varieties of cheese used in the mixture. Also, the milkfat and moisture content may be shown.

Coldpack cheese and coldpack cheese food are labeled in the same manner as other cheese and cheese foods except that "club cheese" or "comminuted cheese" may be substituted for the name "coldpack cheese."

Grades—based on flavor, body, texture, finish, appearance, and color—have been established for some varieties of natural cheese. Grademarks do not usually appear on retail packages, but you may find some packages of Cheddar cheese bearing the U.S. Grade AA mark. Cheeses with this mark are of the highest quality with fine, pleasing flavor. Grade A is very good quality.

Process cheese and cheese foods are not federally graded, but frequently are inspected and bear the USDA "quality approved" inspection shield. Cottage cheese also may have a shield on its container stating that it is "quality approved" by the U.S. Department of Agriculture.

SHIELD ON USDA-INSPECTED PROCESS CHEESE PRODUCTS

To earn the "quality approved" shield, the cheese must have been manufactured in a plant that meets USDA specifications for condition of plant and equipment. A USDA inspector stationed at the plant checks on quality of raw materials and plant sanitation, and inspects the finished products for compliance with Federal specifications.

To find the relative cost of various cheeses, compare the price of equal weights of cheese.

Aged or sharp natural cheeses usually cost more than mild ones; imported cheeses frequently cost more than domestic ones; and prepackaged sliced, cubed, or grated cheeses may cost more than wedges or sticks. Cream or cottage cheese flavored with chives, pimientos, or other ingredients sometimes is more expensive than similar cheese bought plain and seasoned at home. Pasteurized process cheeses often cost less than natural cheeses.

How do you store the cheeses you've selected? Keep them refrigerated. The length of time you can store cheese depends on the kind and the wrapping. Cottage and Ricotta cheeses should be used within a few days. Other soft varieties such as cream and Neufchatel should be used within 2 weeks. Hard cheeses will keep up to several months if protected from drying out and mold contamination.

All cheeses should be kept in their original container or wrappings, if possible. Once a cheese is cut, it tends to dry out rapidly unless it is overwrapped with aluminum foil, plastic wrap, or waxed paper, or stored in a tightly covered container. This is especially needed for cheeses with a strong odor, such as Limburger. Cheese that has become dried out and hard during storage can be grated and kept in a tightly covered jar.

If you want to keep a larger piece of cheese for an extended time, dip the cut surface in melted paraffin.

Jars of process cheese spreads and cheese foods can be kept at room temperature until opened, then refrigerated, tightly covered. These will keep for several weeks.

Freezing is not recommended since the texture of natural cheeses becomes crumbly and mealy, and soft cheeses separate upon thawing. However, certain varieties can be frozen if it is done rapidly, if pieces are less than a pound in weight and an inch in thickness, and if pieces are carefully protected in moisture-proof material. Varieties that can be frozen include Cheddar, Swiss, Edam, Gouda, Brick, Muenster, Port du Salut, Provolone, Mozzarella, and Camembert. If Blue, Roquefort, or gorgonzola cheeses are to be used for salads or salad dressings where a crumbly texture is acceptable, small quantities of these can be frozen. Store the cheeses in the freezer no more than 6 months, thaw in the refrigerator, and use as soon as possible after thawing.

Cheese can be eaten throughout the day in many ways—with crackers, as a toasted sandwich, or with assorted relishes on an appetizer tray. In many European countries, a mild cheese appears at breakfast accompanied by fresh white bread or rolls and jam. Complete the meal with a hot beverage, and you will have a different and delicious way to start the day.

When eating cheese as it is, the important thing to remember is that the characteristic flavor and texture of most cheese is best when served at room temperature. Remove from the refrigerator at least 1 hour before serving. The exceptions are cottage and cream cheese which are served directly from the refrigerator.

Cheese and fruit are natural partners and can become an easy but elegant ending to your next dinner party or buffet. Plan on several varieties with varying flavors and textures. Serve at least one full-flavored variety such as Blue cheese.

You might also include one cheese which is unfamiliar to most of your guests for its conversation value.

Use your prettiest tray or platter. Cut the cheeses in different forms; for example, Swiss into slices, Cheddar into cubes or fingers, and Blue into wedges. Serve a soft cheese in one piece or cut into cubes. The red, wax-coated Edam or Gouda is a colorful addition if served with a slice removed from the top so that the center can be scooped out.

Serve several kinds of fruits. Apples, pears, orange sections, pineapple spears, and seedless grapes are good choices. If apples and pears are served cut, remember that they will darken unless dipped in lemon juice or other citrus juice.

If fresh fruits are not available, you might serve fruit preserves, jam, an especially interesting jelly, or candied and dried fruits.

Finish your tray with crisp crackers or thin slices of pumpernickel or rye bread. Select crackers with flavors that will not compete with the cheeses.

Cheese spreads and dips are popular as snacks and for entertaining. You might prefer making your own, but there are a large number of already prepared snacks and dips available. Whipped cream or Neufchâtel cheese may have clams, chives, mushrooms, onions, bacon, dates and nuts, or other ingredients added.

Cheeses packed in pressurized cans are another convenience. You can use these for canapes and sandwiches. Several different cheeses are available.

The use of cheese in cooking is endless. Cheese makes a delicious combination in casseroles with pasta; with vegetables; and with meats, poultry, and fish.

Attention to two simple rules will insure a successful cheese dish—use low heat and do not overcook. When cheese is melted, it is cooked. Because of its protein nature, cheese that is heated at too high a temperature or for too long a time becomes tough and stringy. The fat separates out from the protein and the flavor may change.

Cheese will melt quicker if it is sliced, cubed, shredded, or grated to use in a recipe. Shred soft cheese on a coarse grater; shred hard cheese on a fine one.

Follow cooking directions carefully in any recipe you use. In general, for best results when you are cooking on top of the stove, use a double boiler. You can cook your cheese dish over direct heat if the heat is low and you stir constantly.

In making cheese sauces, add the cheese last and stir just until melted. Easy cheese sauces can be made from the dry sauce mixes or the condensed Cheddar cheese soups which are on the market.

What cheese should you use for cooking? Your family has certain preferences and many homemakers regard Cheddar or American as the best cooking cheese. However, other varieties such as Blue, cottage, cream, Parmesan, Romano, and Swiss are also excellent for various dishes. With few exceptions, the use of any cheese is not limited.

In general, a sharper, longer aged natural cheese contributes more flavor and better texture to cooked dishes than a milder, less-ripened one. Process cheeses are often preferred for cooking as they melt to a creamy smoothness and blend well with other foods. However, they are often bland in flavor.

CHEESE RAREBIT (WELSH RABBIT)

6 servings, ½ cup rarebit each

1 egg, beaten
1¼ cups milk
3 cups (¾ pound) shredded cheese
1 teaspoon Worcestershire sauce
½ teaspoon dry mustard
2 tablespoons chopped pimiento

Combine all ingredients except pimiento. Cook over low heat, stirring constantly, until cheese is melted and the mixture is slightly thickened. Stir

Cheese rarebit served with a tomato slice on bread.

in pimiento and serve immediately on toast or crackers, as desired.

If the rarebit is made with natural Cheddar cheese it will have a zesty flavor, but must be freshly stirred and served immediately. It may separate and need to be placed over simmering water and stirred until it is again smooth. The texture may be slightly grainy.

If the rarebit is made with process Cheddar cheese it will have an unfailing smoothness and a milder flavor.

GLOSSARY

FRESH FLUID MILK	**Grade A pasteurized milk sold for home use.**
Whole milk	At least 3.25 percent milkfat and 8.25 percent nonfat milk solids.[1]
Homogenized	Fat uniformly distributed through milk.
Cream-line	Layer of cream at top of container.
Vitamin D	Vitamin D increased to at least 400 U.S.P. or International units per quart.
Fortified multiple-vitamin and/or mineral	Added vitamin A, vitamin D, riboflavin, thiamine, niacin, and/or iron, iodine.
Concentrated	Fresh milk with a considerable portion of the water removed.
Skimmed milk	Processed to remove most of the fat, which also removes the vitamin A and vitamin D of fluid whole milk.
Skim (skimmed or nonfat milk)	Less than 0.5 percent milkfat and at least 8 percent nonfat milk solids.
Fortified skim	Added vitamin A and vitamin D, less than 0.5 percent milkfat, and at least 10 percent nonfat milk solids.
Lowfat	Between 0.5 and 2 percent milkfat.
2 percent	2 percent milkfat and—usually—10 percent nonfat milk solids.

[1] Recommended in "Grade 'A' Pasteurized Milk Ordinance," Public Health Service Publication 229 (1965 revision). Minimums of 3 percent milkfat and 8 percent nonfat milk solids have been set by some States for whole milk.

Flavored milk	Flavoring and stabilizer added.
Chocolate milk	Made from whole milk with chocolate and sweetener.
Chocolate-flavored milk	Made from whole milk with cocoa and sweetener.
Chocolate drink (chocolate lowfat milk)	Made from skim or lowfat milk with chocolate and sweetener. Nonfat milk solids may be added.
Chocolate-flavored drink	Made from skim or lowfat milk with cocoa and sweetener. Nonfat milk solids may be added.
Other	Flavored milk: Strawberry, coffee, maple, or other flavoring combined with whole milk. Flavored drink or flavored lowfat milk: Flavoring combined with skim or lowfat milk.
CULTURED MILK	**Made by adding bacterial culture to milk.**
Buttermilk	Thick, smooth liquid. Usually made from skimmed milk; at least 8.25 percent nonfat milk solids.
Yogurt	Semisolid. Made from whole or skim milk. Fruit or other flavorings may be added.
CANNED MILK	**Concentrated by removing water from milk.**
Evaporated milk	Vitamin D usually added. Sterilized.
Whole	At least 7.9 percent milkfat and 25.9 percent total milk solids.
Skim	Low milkfat—often 0.2 or 0.3 percent. At least 18 percent total milk solids. Vitamin A may be added.
Sweetened condensed milk	Sugar added to help preserve milk. At least 8.5 percent milkfat and 28 percent total milk solids.
DRY MILK	**Not more than 5 percent of moisture.**
Nonfat dry or dry skim milk	Made from fluid skim milk. Usually "instantized." Not more than 1.5 percent milkfat in dry product. May be fortified with vitamins A and D.
Whole dry milk	Made from fluid whole milk. At least 26 percent milkfat in the dry product.
FILLED MILK	Combination of skim milk and vegetable fat; or of nonfat milk solids, water, and vegetable fat.
HALF-AND-HALF	Mixture of milk and cream. Pasteurized Grade A.
Half-and-half	At least 10.5 percent milkfat; generally homogenized.
Sour half-and-half	Made by adding bacterial culture to fresh half-and-half; 0.2 percent acidity. Fluid or semifluid.
CREAM	**Pasteurized, Grade A.**
Table cream (coffee or light cream)	At least 18 percent milkfat; generally homogenized.
Sour cream	Made by adding bacterial culture to fresh table cream; 0.2 percent acidity. Fluid or semifluid.
Light whipping cream	At least 30 percent milkfat.
Heavy whipping cream	At least 36 percent milkfat.
Pressurized whipped cream	Liquid containing fresh table or whipping cream, sugar, stabilizer, emulsifier in aerosol can.
FROZEN DESSERTS	**Hard or soft frozen, pasteurized during processing.**
Ice cream	Made from cream, milk, sugar, stabilizers. At least 10 percent milkfat and 20 percent total milk solids.
Frozen custard (French or New York ice cream)	Made from the usual ingredients for ice cream, plus egg yolks. At least 10 percent milkfat and 20 percent total milk solids.
Ice milk	Made from milk, stabilizers, sweeteners. Between 2 and 7 percent milkfat and at least 11 percent total milk solids.
Fruit sherbet	Made from milk, fruit or fruit juice, stabilizers, sweeteners. From 1 to 2 percent milkfat and between 2 and 5 percent total milk solids.

Gladys L. Gilpin
Elinore T. Greeley
Edward W. Ross, Jr.

Fruit—Buy It With Care and Serve It With Flair

Fruit is good just as nature grows it and just as man has learned to process it. Processed fruit—canned, frozen, and dried—is preserved at the peak of its goodness. But the biggest bonus of fruit is that it is ready to serve in any of its forms with little or no preparation.

To make the most of the fine qualities of fruit, learn to select fruits with care, store them properly, and use them with flair.

To help you choose the right quality fruits you want for each specific purpose, the U.S. Department of Agriculture publishes U.S. grade standards for most fresh and processed fruits. The grade standards generally provide for two or more grades for each product, and describe the quality requirements for each grade.

There are several U.S. grades for fresh fruits. U.S. Extra Fancy is an extra-special grade that applies only to apples. This grade shows exceptional quality in appearance, color, shape, and lack of defects. U.S. Fancy is a top grade for most fruits. This grade indicates good color and good shape. The U.S. No. 1 and U.S. Extra No. 1 grades represent the top quality for many fruits and lower grades in the case of some fruits. Fruits of these grades have a good appearance but a few more defects are permitted when these grades represent the second or third highest grade.

Other grades for fresh fruits are U.S. No. 2 or U.S. Combination. You are not likely to see these grades on packages in retail stores.

There are three U.S. grades for processed fruits. U.S. Grade A or U.S. Fancy is the very best, with excellent color; uniform size, weight, and shape; proper ripeness; and few or no blemishes. Use this grade for special purposes where appearance and flavor are important.

U.S. Grade B or U.S. Choice is a very good quality, and a great deal of our processed fruit is packed under this quality. The color, uniformity, and texture are not quite as perfect as Fancy, but the fruit will have a good flavor and will be suitable for any use.

U.S. Grade C or U.S. Standard fruit is useful where appearance and texture are not of great importance. This quality may contain some uneven or broken pieces. Flavor may not be as good as in the higher quality, but the fruit will be wholesome. Grade C is very useful if you chop or puree the fruit, or use it in upside-down cakes, jams, and frozen desserts.

The U.S. Department of Agriculture provides inspection service for certification of the quality of fresh and processed fruits, based on the U.S. grade standards. This is a voluntary service offered to the fruit industry on a fee basis.

Gladys L. Gilpin is a Research Food Technologist, Food Quality and Use Laboratory, Human Nutrition Research Division, Agricultural Research Service.

Elinore T. Greeley is Head of the Standardization Section, Processed Products Standardization and Inspection Branch, Fruit and Vegetable Division, Consumer and Marketing Service.

Edward W. Ross, Jr., is Assistant Chief, Fresh Products Standardization and Inspection Branch, Fruit and Vegetable Division, Consumer and Marketing Service.

Continuous inspection for both fresh and processed fruits is a special service of USDA. Under this program, fruit is inspected by highly trained experts throughout all phases of its processing or packing. When fresh fruits are packed under continuous inspection, the package may show the USDA shield if the product is U.S. No. 1 or better. When processed fruits are packed under continuous inspection, the package may contain a grade name with the prefix, "U.S.", or may show the USDA shield, or both.

Another type of inspection on a lot basis is offered to packers of fruits. Inspection of fresh and processed fruits may be done at shipping points, in warehouses, during the packing operations, and at terminal markets.

Buying Fresh Fruit. Selection of fresh fruit is easy if you follow a few basic pointers.

Buy in season. You get the best quality and prices when you do this. Read the newspapers for information on plentiful foods, a list of foods selected by USDA that are in good supply.

Don't buy just because the price is low. Remember to buy only what you can use and hold without spoilage.

If you don't plan to use fruit for decorative purposes, consider fruit with only superficial blemishes. This kind of fruit suffers no loss of eating quality and may be less expensive. For example, light brown coloration on grapefruit skin and lack of red color on apples or peaches do not detract from the good taste of the fruit.

Select the size of fruit that best meets your needs.

Don't pinch the produce. This causes spoilage, and the consumer pays in the long run. When you do handle fruit to check ripeness, do so carefully to prevent injury.

Look for helpful information on packaged fruit. You may find a grademark, weight or measure, or size of fruit.

Buying Canned Fruit. For canned fruit, the following buying information will be helpful:

Read the label. Federal regulations require that a label have the name of the product, the contents, the name and address of the packer or distributor, and the kind of packing liquid. Sometimes the number of servings is put on the label.

There are three basic can sizes for fruits that are approximately equal to half pint, pint, and quart sizes. These are:

half pint . . . 8 to 8¾ oz. . . . makes 2 servings, ½ cup each
pint . . . 15 to 17 oz. . . . makes 4 servings, ½ cup each
quart . . . 28 to 30 oz. . . . makes 7 to 8 servings, about ½ cup each

AVAILABILITY OF FRESH FRUIT

G=Good Supply F=Fair Supply S=Small Supply

	January	February	March	April	May	June	July	August	September	October	November	December
Apples	G	G	G	G	F	S	S	S	G	G	G	G
Apricots					S	G	G	S				
Avocados	G	G	G	G	G	F	F	F	F	F	G	G
Bananas	G	G	G	G	G	G	G	G	G	G	G	G
Berries (Misc.)					S	G	G	G	S	S	S	
Blueberries					S	G	G	G	S			
Cantaloups		S	S	S	F	G	G	G	G	S	S	
Cherries				S	G	G	S	S				
Cranberries	S								F	F	G	G
Dates	G	F	F	S	S	S	S	S	S	G	G	G
Figs						F	G	G	F			
Grapefruit	G	G	G	G	G	F	S	S	S	G	G	G
Grapes	S	S	S	S	S	F	G	G	G	G	G	F
Honeydews		F	G	F	F	G	G	G	G	G	S	S
Lemons	G	G	G	G	G	G	G	G	G	G	G	G
Limes	S	S	S	S	G	G	G	F	F	F	S	G
Mangoes			S	F	G	G	G	F	S			
Nectarines	S	S				F	G	G	G	S		
Oranges	G	G	G	G	G	F	S	S	S	F	G	G
Papayas	S	S	S	S	F	S	S	S	S	F	S	S
Peaches					S	G	G	G	G	S		
Pears	F	F	F	F	F	S	S	G	G	G	G	F
Pineapple	S	F	G	G	G	G	F	F	S	F	F	F
Plums-Prunes						G	G	G	G	S		
Strawberries	S	S	F	G	G	G	G	S	S	S	S	S
Tangelos	F	S							S	F	G	G
Tangerines	G	S	S	S	S	S				S	G	G
Watermelons	S	S	S	S	F	G	G	G	S	S	S	S

NOTE: Each year's production will vary. This chart is an estimate of probable availability.

Avoid cans that show signs of leakage or that bulge at the ends. Contents will not be harmed by dents in the cans unless the dents have pierced the metal.

Don't undo twist-off lids of glass jars. They are tightly sealed to keep the contents from spoiling.

There is a choice of packing liquids used on canned fruits. Choose from light, heavy, and extra-heavy sirup, but remember, the heavier the sirup, the sweeter the fruit—and the higher the price. Fruit is also packed with juice or water, or is artificially sweetened. The water, juice, and artificially sweetened packs are a boon to diet-conscious people.

Frozen Fruit. The quality of frozen fruit is usually very good. When buying frozen fruit, remember these hints:

Choose frozen fruit packages that are frozen hard. If packages are not firm, it means the fruits may have thawed or partially thawed.

Packages stained by the contents probably have defrosted at some time during marketing, so avoid buying them.

Read the label for important information. Labeling laws require the label to show the product name, the style of cut fruits, information on any sweeteners used, the weight, and the name and address of the packer or distributor. The label may show a quality mark, such as Grade A or Fancy. Look for thawing information and serving directions, too.

Take frozen fruit home in an insulated bag to maintain quality. It's a good idea to pick up frozen foods last on your shopping route.

Dried Fruit. When selecting dried fruit, several pointers may help you get the best value:

Buy well sealed, clean containers.

Good quality dried apples, apricots, peaches, and pears should be bright in color, firm, and pliable.

Try different kinds of packages. Many new transparent bags, plastic containers, or coated cartons are designed to keep dried fruits better and for a longer time.

Note the variety of dried fruit now available. For example, there are many kinds of raisins for different uses: natural seedless, light-colored, seeded (with seeds removed), and clusters of raisins. Don't overlook the pocket-size packages of raisins so handy for lunches and snacks. Dried prunes, both pitted and with pits in, also come in moisturized and low-moisture forms. High-moisture, pitted prunes are ready for quick use, such as for stuffing, and excellent for eating as they are. Dates can be found in pitted or unpitted form as well as in low-moisture nuggets. Low-moisture forms of apples, apricots, and peaches are good for use in sauces and purees.

Read the label. It will show the product name, the weight, and the name and address of the packer or distributor, and any preservative or special treatment. The label may also show the size of the fruit and helpful hints on how to use the fruit.

Storage. Once you have selected your choice of fresh fruits, proper storage and care at home will keep fruits best in quality. Sort fruits before storing them, discarding any that are moldy or decayed.

Set aside any fruit not ripe enough to eat. Pears, bananas, and avocados usually need to be ripened at room temperature before they are stored or used. The optimum temperature for ripening is between 60° and 70° F. Never ripen fruit in direct sunlight. As soon as the fruit is ripe, store according to the direction for each type of fruit given here, unless you plan to use it immediately.

Wash and dry fruits that have smooth, firm skins—apples, pears, and plums—before you store them in the refrigerator. Do not wash berries, cherries, or grapes before storing in the refrigerator. But wash them before using. And do not remove stems or caps because by doing so you could break the skin or injure the tissues of the fruits. It is best to hold soft, juicy fruits in shallow containers so those on the bottom will not be crushed.

Temperature and humidity are very

important when you store fresh fruits. Many refrigerators have closed containers or bins where air does not circulate to dry out fruits. If you store fruits in a plastic bag, make a few small holes in the bag to provide ventilation and let out some of the moisture which accumulates.

The storage times recommended here are short, taking into consideration the time it takes to get fresh fruit into your home. If you are lucky enough to grow your own fruit, you can store fresh fruits for longer periods than are normally recommended.

Canned fruits can be stored at room temperature and will hold their eating quality for extended periods in a cool, dry place. They are safe to eat as long as the can or jar is intact. Color, flavor, and texture may not be top quality if you hold canned fruits for more than a year, or if you keep them in a very warm place. Try to store them in a place no warmer than 75° F.

Frozen fruits must be kept at 0° F. or lower to retain their best eating quality if you hold them longer than a few days. This requires a true freezer. You can keep frozen fruits about a year at this temperature with little or no loss of quality. An ice cube compartment or refrigerator-freezer compartment will not maintain this required temperature.

Dried fruits can be stored at cool room temperature for 6 months or longer. In warm, humid weather, keep them in a refrigerator to best hold their quality. Prunes and raisins are apt to retain their color longer than lighter colored fruits like apples, apricots, and peaches.

Because there is such a variety of fresh fruits available, you should know something about the different buying and storing tips for individual fruits.

Apples. For good eating as fresh fruit, the most common varieties are Delicious, McIntosh, Stayman, Winesap, Golden Delicious, and Jonathan.

For making pies and applesauce, use the tart varieties like Gravenstein, Grimes Golden, Jonathan, and Yellow Newtown (or Albemarle Pippin).

Look for firm, crisp apples that have a fresh appearance. Store fresh apples in the refrigerator to retain crispness. Use ripe apples within a week or two. Firmer apples will keep longer.

Apricots. Plump and juicy-looking apricots showing a uniform, golden orange color are best. Ripe apricots will yield to slight pressure on the skin. Hard, pale yellow or greenish apricots are not very desirable. Store ripe apricots uncovered in the refrigerator and use within 3 to 5 days.

Avocados. Most varieties are pear shaped, but some are oval or round. Skin textures vary from smooth to rough and leathery. Some are green in all stages of ripeness, others turn from green to maroon, brown, or purplish-black as they ripen.

Avocados that yield to gentle pressure are best for immediate use. For use in a few days, select firmer fruit. Light brown, irregular markings sometimes found on the skin have no effect on the flesh of ripe avocados.

Ripen hard or firm avocados at room temperature. If necessary to hold ripe avocados, store them in the warmest part of the refrigerator from 3 to 5 days.

Bananas. Most of our banana supply comes from Central and South America. Bananas harvested green develop better eating quality than those harvested when ripe.

Look for firm, bright bananas, free from any bruises. For immediate use, select solid yellow bananas or yellow bananas with light brown flecks. Choose bananas which are turning yellow or bananas with green tips if you plan to keep them a few days or to cook them.

Bananas will ripen quickly at room temperature. The best temperature is a cool 60° to 70° F. If necessary to hold ripe bananas, store them covered in the warmest part of the refrigerator. Use them within a day or two.

Berries. Strawberries are best when they are firm and have a full red color. They should have the caps and stems attached and should not be wet.

When you purchase blackberries,

raspberries, dewberries, loganberries, and youngberries, look for bright, clean berries. Often a wet or stained container will indicate the berries have poor quality.

Store berries unwashed and uncovered in the refrigerator and use in 1 or 2 days.

Blueberries. Good quality blueberries are dark blue with a silvery bloom. Light purple blueberries usually lack flavor. Store blueberries unwashed and uncovered in the refrigerator and use in a day or two.

Cranberries. Choose cranberries that are plump, firm, lustrous, and red. Store in the refrigerator and use within a week.

Sweet Cherries. The best cherries are dark red or black with fresh-looking stems. Store them unwashed and uncovered in the refrigerator and use them preferably in a day or two. However, they will keep a little longer.

Citrus Fruits. Choose citrus fruits that are heavy for their size. This indicates juiciness. Bright-looking skin and smooth appearance are also important. Slight skin blemishes or surface scars may affect only the appearance and not the eating quality.

Several types of grapefruit are available: Seedless (few or no seeds) white and pink-fleshed varieties, and white and pink-fleshed varieties with seeds.

Lemons should have a glossy skin. A slightly green tint on the skin has no effect on juiciness, but smooth-skinned lemons usually have more juice than rough-skinned types.

The large green limes you see in most stores are the Persian variety, also called Tahitian. The famous Key lime, smaller than the Persian, has yellow flesh when mature.

Oranges are available in many different sizes and varieties. Skin color is not always an index of maturity since some oranges are artificially colored to improve their appearance. Eating quality is not affected by this color.

Good tangerines have a deep orange or yellow color with a bright skin luster. Loose skin is natural.

To hold grapefruit, lemons, limes, and oranges, keep them in a cold room or in the refrigerator, uncovered. They will keep well for a week or two and often longer. Tangerines should be covered and can be held for about a week in the refrigerator.

Dates. Our supply comes from California and Arizona and is also imported. Fully-ripe dates of good quality have a lustrous golden-brown to brown color. Dates can be soft, semidry, or dry depending upon variety and the way they are prepared for packaging.

You will find dates whole with pits and with pits removed. Dates also come diced and in pieces and are often coated to prevent stickiness.

Store dates in a closed container in a refrigerator. They will last for many months if kept cold and fairly dry.

Figs. This fruit may be black, yellow, or green. The black fig is the most popular for eating as fresh fruit. For best flavor, select figs which are fairly soft. Minor healed splits at the stem end and slight scars do not affect the eating quality.

Fresh figs are usually very ripe when you buy them. If you need to hold them for a day or two, keep them in the coldest part of the refrigerator.

Grapes. Common varieties of table grapes are Thompson Seedless, Almeria, Calmeria, and Perlette (green grapes); Tokay, Cardinal, and Red Malaga (bright red grapes); Emperor (red grapes); Ribier (black grapes); and Concord-type grapes (blue-black grapes). Make sure the grapes you buy are well-colored, plump, and firmly attached to the stem. Stems should be green and pliable.

Store grapes unwashed and uncovered in the refrigerator and use them within 3 to 5 days.

Melons. Cantaloups should be mature. On mature cantaloups, the stem is completely gone, leaving a shallow indention, and the skin color between the netting is a light green to yellow. In most common varieties, a thick, coarse, and corky netting covers most of the surface. Mature cantaloups are not necessarily ripe. For immediate eating, select ripe cantaloups. A ripe melon will have a yellowish cast, a pleasant cantaloup odor and the end opposite the stem end will yield to gentle thumb pressure. Mature cantaloups that have not reached the fully ripe stage are best if you plan to hold the melons awhile.

Casaba melons are light green to yellow in color. They are pumpkin-shaped and pointed at the stem end. Casabas have no netting, but have shallow, irregular, lengthwise furrows.

Select firm, golden-yellow casaba melons with a slight softening at the stem end. The casaba melons have no aroma.

Crenshaw melons are large, pointed at the stem end, and round at the other end. The lengthwise furrows are very shallow and the flesh is pale orange and juicy. A ripe crenshaw melon has a golden-yellow rind, will yield slightly to thumb pressure at the rounded end, and it has a pleasant aroma.

Honeydew melons are large, bluntly oval to round, and generally smooth with occasional russeting, a rough, lacy discoloration. The rind is firm and creamy white to yellow in color. A soft, velvety skin indicates maturity in honeydews. For ripe melons, look for a slight softening at the blossom end and a pleasant aroma.

Honey ball melons are very similar to honeydew melons except that they are smaller and have an irregular netting on the rind. Select honey balls in the same manner as honeydew melons.

Store ripe melons in the refrigerator. Place those with a noticeable odor in a plastic bag. If possible, use the melons within a week.

Watermelons are easier to judge for ripeness and quality when sold in halves or quarters so you can see the interior. There are a few factors that help indicate the quality of a whole melon. Look for a smooth surface, a slightly dull rind, fully rounded sides, and a creamy colored underside.

In cut watermelons, look for a good red color and dark brown or black seeds.

Watermelon should be refrigerated. Use cut watermelons in 3 to 5 days. Whole melons will keep longer.

Nectarines. Nectarines are ancient fruits that have characteristics of both the peach and the plum. Most nectarines show a blush red to bright red color over much of the skin surface.

They should have a yellow color between the red areas. Choose plump fruit with a slight softening of the seam.

Russeting or speckling of the skin is characteristic of some varieties of nectarines and does not detract from eating quality.

Store nectarines uncovered in the refrigerator. It is preferable to use nectarines in 3 to 5 days.

Peaches. The two major types of peaches are the freestone, with a pit which easily separates from the flesh, and the clingstone, with a pit which adheres to the flesh. Freestone peaches are more popular for eating as fresh fruit, and clingstones are generally used for canning. Look for peaches that are fairly firm or just beginning to soften. The color between the areas of red on the surface should be yellowish-green or yellow.

Store ripe peaches uncovered in the refrigerator and use within 3 to 5 days.

Pears. There are two general types of pears. Summer pears include Bartletts and winter pears include Anjou, Bosc, Winter Nelis, and Comice.

Look for firm pears with a yellowish-green to yellow color on most varieties. Some pears show an attractive pink blush. Varieties like Bosc are russeted on the skin surface and are best when their skin color is greenish-yellow to brown.

Pineapples. Generally pineapples are picked hard and they may have to be ripened at home.

Look for firm pineapples with a green color turning to yellow or reddish brown. Allow the pineapple to ripen at room temperature.

Refrigerate ripe pineapples and use within a day or two.

Plums and Prunes. Prunes are freestone plums. Plums vary in color from green to red; prunes are purplish black in color. For best eating, look for plums and prunes that are firm, with a bright appearance and a slight glow to the skin. They should yield slightly to a gentle pressure.

Store plums and prunes in the refrigerator and use within 3 to 5 days.

When using fruits, take advantage of the rainbow colors, the fine textures, and variety of flavors. Good color is very important. Fully mature and ripe fruit will have a rich, full, characteristic color.

Browning of light-colored fruits—like apples, pears, and peaches—during preparation is caused by a combination of factors. There are several ways to prevent or delay this effect:

• Keep the air from contact with the fruit by mixing sugar with cut fruit or by covering fruit with sugar sirup. Holding prepared fruit in a solution of salt and vinegar in water will prevent browning.

• Control enzymes, the chemical substances naturally present in fruit. Dipping pared fruits into citrus juice or sprinkling citrus juice on the fruit adds acid which retards the action of enzymes. Freezing also slows down this action. Cooking fruit destroys the enzyme and prevents discoloration.

Texture makes a great difference in the enjoyment that comes from eating fruit. Ripeness is an important factor in the texture of fresh fruit. Fully ripe fruit is best for eating uncooked or for any use that requires fruit to be soft for mashing, sieving, or making into juice. For simmering, broiling, baking, or frying, use firm or slightly underripe fruits which will retain their shape during cooking.

Short cooking periods are best for fruits in most cases. Cook fruits only until tender unless you want a very soft product that will make a smooth sauce or puree. Stir fruits only as necessary to keep them from scorching.

Most fruits can be cooked in a sugar sirup with good results. A few fruits, like Kieffer pears and quince, become hard, tough, and shriveled up when cooked this way. These fruits should be cooked in water to soften them before they are sweetened.

Flavor is an important consideration in preparing fruits. Use only a little sugar with fruits of delicate flavor. Cooking fruit can develop new and interesting flavors, but use low to medium temperatures to prevent caramelization of sugars. To retain best flavor, cook fruits just until tender.

The ways to use fruit are countless.

Uncooked fruits can be used in all parts of a meal, as snacks and as party food.

For Fruit Combinations, mix fresh, frozen, canned, and dried fruit in cups, salads, and fruit plates. Contrast light and dark colors, soft, crisp, and firm textures, and mild and tart flavors. Serve frozen fruit partially thawed for best texture. All canned fruits and many dried fruits may be served just as they are.

When making fruit combinations, chill all fruits.

Fruit cups are favored as an appetizer, but hold their own as a breakfast fruit or dessert. Cut fruit into bite-size pieces and cover with fruit juice.

Fruit salads are appealing as an appetizer or as part of the main course. Vary them by using different combinations of slices, segments, cubes, balls, or whole small fruits.

Fruit plates are often used as the main dish. Larger pieces and whole small fruits are best for fruit plates.

Try out your ingenuity and artistic talent using these combinations as a starter:

Grapefruit and mandarin oranges or combine with avocado, mango, or papaya.

Bananas, oranges, and pineapple.

Blueberries, cantaloup or watermelon, and bananas.

Peaches, bananas, seedless grapes, Tokay grapes.

Strawberries, oranges, apples.

Bing cherries, bananas, oranges, apples.

Raspberries, pears, and cantaloup or honeydew melon.

Fresh and canned fruit makes pleasing salad ensemble to choose from.

Seedless grapes, bananas, strawberries, and pineapple.

For color and flavor accents, garnish with pomegranate seeds, a sprig of mint, a few raisins, cut-up dates, crystallized fruit, maraschino cherries, candied citrus peel, and slivered or chopped nuts.

For a special flair:

Pour a little liqueur on each fruit cup.

Sprinkle shredded coconut on fruit.

Include a few prunes stuffed with cheese on a fruit plate.

Use slices or chunks of cheese for a hearty fruit plate.

Top each fruit plate with a scoop of sherbet.

Fresh Figs Sorrento, a distinctive combination, makes a very flavorful first course. Serve fresh figs and thin slices of prosciutto, an Italian-type, specially flavored ham, on individual plates or from a platter so each person can make his own selection.

Jellied fruit juice makes an ideal hot weather starter for a meal.

JELLIED FRUIT JUICE

6 servings, ¾ cup each

1½ cups cranberry juice
1½ cups orange juice
½ cup pineapple juice
¼ cup lemon juice
¼ cup sugar
2 tablespoons gelatin
½ cup cold water
1 cup boiling water
6 maraschino cherries

Mix the fruit juices and sugar.

Soften gelatin in cold water, stir in boiling water.

Combine mixtures and chill.

Just before serving, break up gelatin mixture slightly with a fork. Garnish with cherries.

Be sure to use canned or reconstituted frozen pineapple juice rather than fresh pineapple juice. One of the enzymes in fresh pineapple will react with the gelatin and destroy its gelling property. This enzyme must be inactivated by heating as is done in processing of canned and frozen concentrated juices.

Fruit accompaniments to the main course can lend distinction to the meal yet are easy to make.

Pickled Prunes require only pitted prunes and any spiced sweet sirup, such as sirup left from watermelon or peach pickles. Heat the sirup to boiling and pour over the prunes. Let stand until cool, then refrigerate until used. These are delicious filled with cottage cheese or cream cheese.

Fruit sherbets combine fruit juice or puree with milk to make an easy mix-and-freeze dessert. This recipe includes gelatin for a smooth texture.

LEMON-LIME SHERBET

6 servings, 3/4 cup each

1 package (3 ounces) lime gelatin
1 cup boiling water
1¼ cups sugar
¼ cup lemon juice
2 tablespoons grated lemon rind
1 quart milk

Mix gelatin, water, and sugar.
Stir in lemon juice and rind.
Chill but do not allow to congeal.
Add the milk and pour into refrigerator trays.
Freeze; stir when the mixture begins to freeze around edges of trays.

For raspberry or strawberry sherbet, replace lemon juice and rind with a package of frozen berries. Color and flavor are best if gelatin and berries are the same flavor.

Avocado Freeze is one way Floridians use avocados. It is smooth and rich, and has a lovely color.

To make 6 servings, about ⅓ cup each, mash 1 large, ripe avocado. Stir in 3 tablespoons lemon juice and ¼ cup sugar; mix until creamy and smooth. Whip 1 cup whipping cream; blend into avocado mixture. Freeze in refrigerator tray.

Party snacks can be made quickly from prepared fruit products available the year around. Punch has long been used to refresh guests and promote good fellowship.

CRANBERRY-APPLE PUNCH

12 servings, about ½ cup each

1 quart apple cider
1 cup sweetened cranberry juice
1 teaspoon lemon juice
2 cups chilled ginger ale

Combine fruit juices and chill.
Just before serving, add ginger ale.

GOLDEN PUNCH

28 servings, about ½ cup each

1 can (6 ounces) frozen pineapple-orange concentrate
1 can (12 ounces) frozen lemonade concentrate
3 cups canned apricot nectar
9 cups water
1 orange, cut into thin slices

Combine all the ingredients except orange slices.
Mix well; chill.
Serve over ice. Garnish punch with orange slices.

A Fruit-Ice Ring will decorate as well as help cool the punch. Half fill a ring mold with water. Arrange a variety of fruits in different colors and shapes in the mold. Good choices of fruit are: whole grapes, cherries, or berries; orange or lemon slices; lengthwise halves of limes; wedges of apples (brushed with lemon juice) and cantaloup; plum halves. Freeze. Unmold and float in punch. Be sure the punch is cold.

Guacamole rates high in border States like Texas. The spicy ingredients used to give this dip its nippy flavor are part of the way of life there.

GUACAMOLE

About 2 cups of dip

3 medium-size ripe avocados
2 teaspoons grated onion
2 tablespoons chili sauce
2 tablespoons lemon juice
½ teaspoon salt
3 or 4 drops Tabasco sauce

Mash the avocados thoroughly.

Mix in other ingredients; chill.

Serve as a dip or spread on crackers, if desired.

"*Instant*" *Fruit Hors d'Oeuvres* can be speared on toothpicks. Use two or more of the following fruit: pineapple cubes or chunks, seedless grapes, whole fresh berries, melon cubes or balls, cubes of seasonal fruits (dipped in lemon juice if necessary to hold their color). A little more work but worth it—banana chunks dipped in lemon juice and then rolled in finely chopped nuts.

Fruit bonbons are similar to confections native to the Mediterranean countries. Bonbons are easy to make and can be prepared ahead of time.

FRUIT BONBONS

4 dozen bonbons

1 package mixed dried fruit
1 cup seedless raisins
⅓ cup candied cherries
1 cup pecans
2 tablespoons cooking sherry
½ cup confectioner's sugar

Remove any pits from dried fruit.

Put mixed fruit and raisins through a food chopper, using the fine blade.

Coarsely chop candied cherries and pecans.

Mix with fruits.

Blend in sherry.

Form into small balls.

Roll the balls in confectioner's sugar before serving.

ORANGE BONBONS

Finely chop 1 cup each of dried figs, raisins, and pitted dates and ½ cup of candied orange peel. Mix together with 1 cup coarsely chopped nuts.

Stir in 2 tablespoons of undiluted orange juice concentrate. Make balls as described above.

Familiar, basic cooking methods can be used for fruits. On top of the range you can make a variety of simmered, boiled, and fried fruit products by these recipes.

Simmered Fruit. To keep fruit pieces whole, make a sirup by heating the water and sugar to boiling. Add the fruit, cover, and bring back to boiling. Then lower heat until sirup just simmers, and cook fruit until tender.

Cook firm varieties of pears in the water to make them tender; add the sugar the last 10 minutes of cooking.

To make apple or rhubarb sauce, cook the fruit in the water until soft, add the sugar, and heat for 1 minute longer.

Cooking Guide for Fresh Fruit

Kind of fruit	Amount[1] of fruit	How to prepare	Amount of water	Amount of sugar	Cooking time after adding fruit
			Cups	Cups	Minutes
Apples	8 medium-size	Pare and slice	½	¼	8 to 10, for slices 12 to 15, for sauce.
Apricots	15	Halve, pit, peel if desired.	½	¾	5.
Cherries	1 quart	Remove pits	1	⅔	5.
Cranberries	1 pound	Sort	1 or 2, as desired[2]	2	5.
Peaches	6 medium-size	Peel, pit, halve, or slice.	¾	¾	5.
Pears	6 medium-size	Pare, core, halve, or slice.	⅔	⅓	10, for soft varieties 20 to 25, for firm varieties.
Plums	8 large	Halve, pit	½	⅔	5.
Rhubarb	1½ pounds	Slice	¾	⅔	2 to 5.

[1] Makes 6 servings, about ½ cup each.
[2] Cranberries make 6 servings with 1 cup water; 8 servings with 2 cups water.

Fruit soup is a favorite Scandinavian dish made with simmered dried fruits. Spices and lemon juice give a tangy flavor. Serve either hot or cold to start the meal or as a dessert. With toasted, slivered almonds used as a garnish, Californians could claim this as their own. Fruit soup made with sour cream can make this a high spot in your meal.

FRUIT SOUP

6 servings, about ¾ cup each

1 package (11 ounces) mixed dried fruit
½ cup light, seedless raisins
1 quart water
1 tablespoon lemon juice
2 tablespoons quick-cooking tapioca
¼ teaspoon salt
¼ cup sugar
1 stick (3-inch) cinnamon
Dash ground cloves
½ cup sour cream, if desired

Remove any pits from dried fruit; cut fruit into large pieces.

Put all ingredients except sour cream into pan, bring to a boil, stirring as needed.

Cover pan, simmer until the fruit is tender, about 20 minutes.

Remove cinnamon stick.

If desired, lightly mix in sour cream just before serving either hot or cold.

Fruit sirups and sauces are often made from berries. In the Blue Ridge Mountains, delectable wild fruit sirups are sold for use on pancakes, waffles, and the like. Fruit sirups are easy to make from the cultivated fruits if you don't have wild ones.

BLUEBERRY SIRUP

About 1 cup sirup

1 cup unsweetened blueberries, fresh, frozen, or canned
¼ cup water or canned blueberry juice
¼ cup sugar

Combine ingredients; bring to boil.
Crush berries with a spoon.
Simmer 2 or 3 minutes.
Strain, if desired.

Year-round grape jelly is delicious and can be made with little work from frozen concentrated grape juice.

GRAPE JELLY

12 glasses (6 ounces each)

3 cans (6 ounces each) frozen grape juice concentrate
6½ cups sugar
2½ cups water
1 bottle liquid pectin

Thaw grape juice concentrate.

Stir sugar into water; heat quickly while stirring constantly, until mixture reaches a full rolling boil that cannot be stirred down.

Boil hard for 1 minute.

Remove from heat; stir in pectin.

Add grape juice and mix well.

Pour immediately into hot home-canning jars or jelly glasses.

Fill jars to ⅛ inch from top, seal immediately with 2-piece metal lids.

Fill jelly glasses to ½ inch from top and cover immediately with a ⅛-inch layer of hot paraffin.

Fruit and nut dessert sauce on cake or ice cream wins praise for the cook.

FRUIT AND NUT DESSERT SAUCE

About 1½ cups sauce

1 package (10 ounces) frozen strawberries, raspberries, or mixed fruits
1 cup liquid from frozen fruits plus water
¼ cup sugar
1 tablespoon cornstarch
1 tablespoon chopped raisins
2 tablespoons lemon juice
¼ teaspoon rum extract, if desired
¼ cup chopped toasted pecans

Thaw and drain frozen fruit.

Use whole berries or cut up large pieces of fruit as desired.

Stir fruit liquid gradually into sugar, cornstarch, and raisins in a saucepan.

Cook over medium heat, stirring constantly, until clear and thickened.

Then add lemon juice, rum extract, pecans, and fruit.

For coconut fruit sauce, omit raisins and pecans. Sprinkle toasted coconut on top of dessert.

Serve party grape punch piping hot.

PARTY GRAPE PUNCH

26 servings, about ½ cup each

- 1 quart grape juice
- 1 can (12 ounces) frozen lemonade, reconstituted
- 1 cup sugar
- 1 teaspoon whole cloves
- 4 sticks cinnamon

Combine all of ingredients; bring to a boil.

Strain and serve punch hot.

Pan-frying adds a delightfully new flavor to fruits.

Pan-Fried Apple Rings are a long-time favorite in Pennsylvania Dutch country. For 6 servings use 3 large apples. Wash, core, and slice the apples ½-inch thick.

Melt 3 tablespoons butter or margarine in a frying pan. Fry the apple rings over moderately low heat until they are tender, turning to brown evenly, about 10 to 12 minutes.

Sprinkle the apples with a mixture of 1 tablespoon sugar and ¼ teaspoon cinnamon before serving.

Pan-Fried Pineapple with coconut garnish can add a Hawaiian touch to your meal. For a quick method, drain a large can (about 30 ounces) of pineapple slices.

Melt 2 tablespoons butter or margarine in a frying pan. Fry the pineapple slices over moderately low heat until lightly browned; turn to brown the other side.

Before serving, sprinkle with toasted coconut.

Glazing is a variation of pan-frying. Sugar is used along with the fat for frying to make a coating on the fruit which adds a new texture and flavor effect.

Glazed Bananas: Cut 4 green-tipped bananas into thirds. Blend together 2 tablespoons butter or margarine, ¼ cup brown sugar, and 1 tablespoon lemon juice in a heavy frying pan.

Add the bananas and cook over low heat, turning bananas several times until the sirup is thick and the bananas well-coated. Keep heat low to prevent scorching. It will take 5 to 10 minutes, depending on size of the bananas and their ripeness.

Or try a West Indies variation, an unusual flavor combination. Prior to serving, sprinkle the bananas with 3 tablespoons grated sharp cheese.

Broiled Fruit is a good complement to meat. Broiling takes only a few minutes, but the fruit should be served immediately; so plan your menu with not too many other last minute tasks.

Peaches, pears, and apricots are all broiled the same way. Provide a whole piece of fruit for each serving. For 6 servings, also have ready 1 tablespoon lemon juice, 2 tablespoons melted butter or margarine, 1 tablespoon brown sugar, and ¼ teaspoon cinnamon.

Peel the fruit, cut into halves, and remove the pits. Arrange fruit halves on broiler pan, hollow side down. Brush top side with lemon juice and butter.

Broil about 8 minutes or until tender and lightly browned. Turn the fruit, brush with lemon juice and butter and sprinkle with the sugar and cinnamon. Broil 2 or 3 minutes longer until the top is golden brown.

Broil canned fruit the same as you would fresh fruit, but reduce cooking time to about 5 minutes on the first side and 2 minutes after turning.

Broiled Bananas are also very tasty. Use green-tipped bananas instead of fully ripe ones. Peel and cut them in half lengthwise. Brush them also with lemon juice and butter.

Since they are thinner than the other fruits, the cooking time is only 4 minutes on the first side, then turn and add the sugar and cinnamon, and broil 2 minutes longer.

To give broiled bananas a tropical flair, sprinkle the tops with flaked coconut and toast a minute longer.

Another easy way to cook fruits is baking. The following method for peaches can also be used for pears or apricots by adjusting the baking time needed to cook the fruit until tender. Serve these fruits either with the main course or as dessert.

For Baked Peaches or Nectarines, peel

and halve 6 pieces of fruit. Arrange the halves hollow side up in a shallow baking dish. Boil ½ cup water.

Combine ⅓ cup of brown sugar, 2 teaspoons lemon juice, and 1 tablespoon of the boiling water.

Pour into hollows of the fruit. Pour remaining water around fruit in baking dish. Bake uncovered at 400° F. until tender, about 30 minutes. Baste with liquid in baking dish if needed during baking.

To prepare East Indian peaches or nectarines, mix ⅛ teaspoon of curry powder into the sugar mixture.

Apricots are baked like peaches but take less time to bake since they are smaller.

For baked pears, pare and halve 6 pears; remove seeds and fibers from center. One-half teaspoon cinnamon may be added with the sugar and lemon juice if desired.

Pears will take about 45 minutes when they are baked at 400° F.

Baked Canned Fruit is easy to prepare and delicious. This usually takes less sugar as most canned fruits are sweetened. Use the drained fruit sirup instead of water.

Start out with 1 large can (about 30 ounces) of peach, pear, or apricot halves, drained. Arrange the fruit in a baking dish hollow side up.

Mix 2 teaspoons lemon juice with 2 tablespoons brown sugar; fill into the fruit hollows. With pears, ¼ teaspoon cinnamon added with the sugar is especially good. Pour ¼ cup of the drained sirup into the baking dish around the fruit. Bake at 400° F. for about 15 minutes until heated through.

Mincemeat-stuffed peaches or pears are simple to make, but will suit a special occasion. Use the mincemeat to fill the fruit. It takes about ½ cup mincemeat for a large can of fruit. Place a marshmallow on top of each piece of the fruit.

Bake as above until the fruit is heated through and the marshmallow browned slightly, about 10 minutes.

Banana bread catches the rich flavor of fully-ripe bananas.

BANANA BREAD

5- by 9-inch loaf

¾ cup sugar
½ cup shortening
2 eggs
1 cup mashed banana
1¾ cups unsifted flour
2 teaspoons baking powder
½ teaspoon baking soda
½ teaspoon salt

Beat the sugar, fat, and eggs together until light and fluffy.

Stir in bananas.

Mix dry ingredients thoroughly.

Add dry ingredients to banana mixture, stirring just until smooth.

Pour into greased 5- by 9-inch loaf pan.

Bake at 350° F. until firmly set when lightly touched on top, or for 50 to 60 minutes.

Cool on rack. Remove from the pan after 10 minutes.

For date-nut banana bread, add ½ cup chopped dates and ½ cup chopped nuts with mashed bananas.

For orange-banana bread, blend 1 tablespoon grated orange rind with the sugar-fat-egg mixture.

Green apple pie will long be remembered if the apples are well selected. They must be past the starchy stage but with a tart flavor and crisp texture.

In some parts of the country, green apple pie means one made from green varieties of apples—but not out in the Midwest. This recipe should be used with slightly under-ripe apples.

DEEP DISH GREEN APPLE PIE

8 servings

6 cups sliced green apples
¾ cup sugar
1 tablespoon cornstarch
¼ teaspoon salt
1 teaspoon cinnamon
½ teaspoon nutmeg
2 tablespoons butter or margarine
Pastry for a 1-crust pie

Put apple slices in an 8-inch square baking pan.

Mix dry ingredients, and sprinkle over apples.

Dot with the fat.

Roll out pastry to an 8-inch square; cut a few slits to allow steam to escape.

Place pastry on top of apples.

Bake at 400° F., 45 to 50 minutes or until apples are tender and crust browned.

For French deep dish apple pie, add ½ cup raisins to the apples. Make a frosting by mixing and beating 1 cup confectioner's sugar and about 5 teaspoons water. When pie has cooled slightly, spread frosting over the top.

Deep dish cheese apple pie is a great choice in Wisconsin where the apples are firm and tart and the cheese is excellent. Just sprinkle shredded cheese over the top of the pie and serve.

Fruit crunch is one countrywide favorite, as it can be made from many fruits starting early in the season with rhubarb and then following the season through to late fall with cranberries. Or you can skip the seasons by using canned or frozen fruit.

PLUM CRUNCH

8 servings

3 cups pitted and quartered fresh plums
⅓ cup granulated sugar
⅓ cup brown sugar, packed
½ cup quick-cooking rolled oats
¼ teaspoon salt
3 tablespoons flour
3 tablespoons butter or margarine, melted

Place the plums in an 8-inch square baking pan.

Sprinkle with granulated sugar.

Combine remaining dry ingredients; mix in the fat until crumbly.

Sprinkle mixture over the fruit.

Bake 1 hour at 350° F. Serve warm.

You can use peaches or nectarines in place of plums. Or use 1 pint of blueberries. Mix ¼ teaspoon cinnamon with the sugar and sprinkle these fruits with 1 tablespoon lemon juice. Or try a combination of 2 cups apple slices and 2 cups rhubarb slices (or a 12-ounce package of frozen rhubarb).

Canned fruit pie fillings make quick fruit crunch desserts. Stir 1 tablespoon lemon juice into 1 can of pie filling.

It is simple to vary the flavors by adding only a few ingredients. For example, use ⅛ teaspoon ginger with blueberries and ½ teaspoon almond extract with cherry. Use ½ teaspoon cinnamon and ¼ teaspoon nutmeg with apple pie filling, then just as you serve the crunch, sprinkle it with ½ cup grated sharp cheese.

You can glamorize peach pie filling in a crunch by adding a few drops of rum extract, ½ teaspoon cinnamon, and ¼ teaspoon nutmeg.

The ultimate satisfaction from the fruits you serve is the result of careful selection, proper storage, and your art and skill in using fruits in many ways.

For further reading:

U.S. Department of Agriculture, *Family Fare: Food Management and Recipes*. Home and Garden Bulletin 1, Washington, D.C. 20250, 1966.

——— *Fruits in Family Meals, A Guide for Consumers*. Home and Garden Bulletin 125, Washington, D.C. 20250, 1968.

——— *Home Canning of Fruits and Vegetables*. Home and Garden Bulletin 8, Washington, D.C. 20250, 1965.

——— *Home Care of Purchased Frozen Foods*. Home and Garden Bulletin 69, Washington, D.C. 20250, 1967.

——— *Home Freezing of Fruits and Vegetables*. Home and Garden Bulletin 10, Washington, D.C. 20250, 1967.

——— *How to Buy Fresh Fruits*. Home and Garden Bulletin 141, Washington, D.C. 20250, 1967.

——— *Official Grade Standards and Inspection for Fresh Fruits and Vegetables*. AMS–520, Washington, D.C. 20250, 1963.

——— *Processed Fruit and Vegetable Inspection . . . at your service*. Program Aid 803, Washington, D.C. 20250, 1967.

——— *Storing Perishable Foods in the Home*. Home and Garden Bulletin 78, Washington, D.C. 20250, 1967.

——— *Storing Vegetables and Fruits in Basements, Cellars, Outbuildings, and Pits*. Home and Garden Bulletin 119, Washington, D.C. 20250, 1966.

Michael A. Castille
Elsie H. Dawson
Edward R. Thompson

The Vegetable Roundup—From Buying to Cooking

Shopping for vegetables can be a delight or a chore. A delight if you know what to look for, a chore if you don't.

The selection ranges from locally grown sweet corn, harvested only hours ago, to the more exotic artichokes or brussels sprouts which may have been transported thousands of miles by fast jet to your city.

Nor is your selection limited to fresh vegetables. Modern technology brings you canned and frozen vegetables that were harvested weeks or months ago at the peak of their goodness, and preserved for your future use and convenience.

But vegetables, whether fresh or processed (canned, frozen, or dried), can vary in quality. These variations in the taste, texture, and appearance of a vegetable usually make a difference in its price.

U.S. grade standards, which define the differences in quality found in vegetables, have been established by the U.S. Department of Agriculture for most fresh and processed vegetables. USDA also administers the Federal-State Inspection Service to provide inspection and certification of the quality of fresh vegetables according to the U.S. grade standards, and maintains a staff of Federal inspectors for processed vegetables. Use of the U.S. grade standards and inspection services by the vegetable industry is voluntary, and users must pay a fee for the inspection service.

The U.S. grade standards and inspection services are used extensively by the packers, processors, buyers, and others in wholesale trading as a basis for establishing the value of a product. You may find an indication of the U.S. grade on some fresh and processed vegetables in your grocery store, although this is not required by Federal law. A few States require that some products be graded and labeled on the basis of either Federal or State grade standards.

Grade designations found on packages of potatoes, onions, carrots, and occasionally other fresh vegetables in retail stores do not mean the product has been officially graded unless the package also bears the official USDA grade shield or the statement "Packed under Continuous Inspection of the U.S. Department of Agriculture" or "USDA Inspected."

U.S. grades for fresh vegetables are:

U.S. Fancy—This is the premium grade for some vegetables. It means the vegetables have outstanding quality and appearance compared to that usually available. Only a very small percentage of a crop qualifies for this grade.

U.S. No. 1—This is the highest grade for most vegetables. In a normal year, about two-thirds of a crop meets U.S. No. 1 grade. These vegetables have good quality and appearance and few defects.

Michael A. Castille is a Marketing Specialist, Fruit and Vegetable Division (Fresh Products), Consumer and Marketing Service.

Elsie H. Dawson is Head of the Consumer Use of Foods Staff, Human Nutrition Research Division, Agricultural Research Service.

Edward R. Thompson is a Marketing Specialist, Fruit and Vegetable Division (Processed Products), Consumer and Marketing Service.

Other grades for fresh vegetables—U.S. No. 2 or U.S. Combination—are not likely to be seen in retail stores.

Like fresh vegetables, most canned and frozen vegetables are packed and priced according to their quality even though a grademark is not on the label. But if a vegetable is packed under continuous USDA inspection, the individual cans and packages may carry the U.S. grademark:

U.S. Grade A or U.S. Fancy—Grade A vegetables are carefully selected for color, tenderness, and freedom from blemishes. They are the most tender, succulent, and flavorful vegetables produced.

U.S. Grade B or U.S. Extra Standard—Grade B vegetables have excellent quality but are not quite so well selected for color and tenderness as Grade A. They are usually a little less tasty.

U.S. Grade C or U.S. Standard—Grade C vegetables are not so uniform in color, tenderness, and flavor as vegetables in the higher grades, and they are usually more mature. They are a thrifty buy when appearance is not too important—for instance, if you are using the vegetables as an ingredient in soup or souffle.

The "Packed under Continuous Inspection of the U.S. Department of Agriculture" shield may be shown along with the grade shield, or it may be shown by itself.

Sometimes the grade name is indicated without the "U.S." in front of it—for example, "Fancy" or "Grade A." A canned or frozen vegetable with this designation must measure up to the quality stated, even though it has not been officially inspected for grade.

INSPECTION SHIELD

The brand name of a frozen or canned vegetable is also an indication of quality. Producers of nationally advertised products spend considerable effort to maintain the same quality year after year. Unadvertised brands may also offer an assurance of quality, often at a slightly lower cost. And many stores, particularly chainstores, carry two or more qualities under their own name labels (private labels). Often the only indication of difference in quality between private-label products is the price.

Other factors that affect the price of canned or frozen vegetables—and how you want to use them—are the form or style of the vegetable—whole, sliced, cut—and whether special seasonings, sauces, or flavorings have been added. Whole vegetables generally cost more than cut styles because it is hard to keep these fragile products whole during processing. Added sauces or special flavorings, of course, also add to the price, but let you serve something different without any extra work.

Experience is the best teacher in any type of buying. But here are a few general rules that may help you:

Don't buy fresh vegetables simply because the price is low. It doesn't pay to buy more vegetables than you can use without waste. Most fresh vegetables can be stored for 2 to 5 days, except for root vegetables, which can be stored from one to several weeks.

It's "penny foolish" to buy fresh vegetables affected by decay. A few cents extra for vegetables in good condition is a good investment

Fresh vegetables are usually at their best quality and price at the peak of the season when they are in plentiful supply. USDA will notify consumers through newspapers and other media when vegetables are in abundant supply across the country.

Be careful to prevent injury to fresh vegetables when you are picking them out in the store. The consumer pays for carelessness in the long run.

USDA inspector examines scallions during harvesting by Navajo Indians in Arizona.

Be sure to check the label on canned, frozen, and dried vegetables. Besides describing contents of the package, the label may tell you the grade, variety, size, and maturity of the vegetables; seasonings; number of servings; cooking directions; and give recipes or serving ideas. Fair packaging and labeling regulations require that the label give the net contents in total ounces as well as in pounds and ounces if the package contains 1 pound or more, or less than 4 pounds. This should make it easier for you to compare prices.

Don't buy cans of vegetables that leak or bulge at either end. Bulging or swelling indicates spoilage. Dents in cans do not harm the contents unless they have actually pierced through the can or sprung the seam.

Packages of frozen vegetables should be firm. Because frozen vegetables should be used immediately after they have defrosted—to avoid loss of quality and possible contamination—do not buy packages that are limp, wet, or sweating. These are indications the vegetables have defrosted or are in the process of defrosting. Packages stained by the contents may have been defrosted and refrozen at some stage in the marketing process. The vegetables may not be contaminated, but refrozen vegetables will not taste as good as those that are freshly frozen.

Buy the quality and style of canned and frozen vegetables to fit the use you plan to make of the vegetable. Grade A or Fancy vegetables are the pick of the crop and may cost more than Grade B or C vegetables. They are good for a special luncheon or dinner. Grade B or Extra Standard vegetables may not look or taste quite as good as Grade A vegetables, but they are good served alone or in casseroles or gelatin salads. Grade C or Standard vegetables are just as nutritious as Grades A and B, but they don't look as attractive. They are more likely to be used in making soups or purees, and they also may be used in souffles.

Some vegetables, such as beets, are also sized when they are processed whole, so that you can buy processed whole beets of about the same size. This sizing also adds to the cost of the processed product, but whole vegetables of about the same size are very attractive as a hot vegetable or as a cold salad.

Fancy-cut vegetables, such as french-style green beans or julienne carrots (french-style and julienne are both sliced lengthwise) usually cost more than other cut styles and, because they are more attractive, are intended for use as hot vegetables or cold salads.

Short-cut green beans, diced carrots, and tomato pieces are examples of the least expensive styles of processed vegetables, and the styles that are best used for soups, souffles, or stews.

Whether you buy fresh or processed vegetables, knowing how many pounds or what package or can size to buy is sometimes a problem. The serving size commonly used for adults is ½ cup, and for young children, ¼ cup. But of course, how much you serve depends on your preference for the particular vegetable, whether or not you include the juice in the serving, and if you plan to allow for second helpings, especially for a company dinner.

To help you make a good buy, and use your purchase wisely, the qualities to look for in fresh vegetables and the styles of canned and frozen vegetables

Guide to Amounts of Vegetables to Buy to Serve Your Family

Vegetable and style	Approximate amount of cooked vegetable obtained from—				
	Frozen vegetables		Canned vegetables (drained)		1 lb. of fresh vegetable as purchased—
	Size of container (ounces)	Cooked, Cups	Size of container (ounces)	Heated, Cups	Cups
Asparagus, cut	10	1¼	14	1⅓	1¾
Beans, green or wax, cut	9	1⅔	15½	1¾	2¾
Beans, lima	10	1⅔	16	1¾	1⅛
Beets, sliced, diced or whole			16	1¾	1⅞
Broccoli, cut	10	1⅓			1½
Brussels sprouts	10	1½			2¼
Cabbage, shredded					2⅓
Carrots, diced, or sliced	10	1⅔	16	1¾	2⅛
Cauliflower	10	1½			1½
Corn, whole kernel	10	1½	[1] 16	1⅔	
Kale	10	1⅛	15	1⅓	2⅔
Okra	10	1¼	15½	1¾	2¼
Peas	10	1⅔	16	1¾	1
Potatoes	9	[2] 1⅔			[3] 1¾
Spinach	10	1¼	15	1⅓	2
Summer squash, sliced	10	1⅓			2
Tomatoes			[4] 16	1⅞	

[1] Whole kernels with liquid; a 12 oz. can of whole kernels, vacuum pack, provides 1¾ cups.
[2] French fries.
[3] Mashed.
[4] Undrained.

that are available are given in the list that follows. Grades of several of the more familiar canned and frozen vegetables are described so that you can determine differences in quality for yourself.

Most people tend to cook and serve vegetables plain, buttered at all times. Yet there are many delightful ways to prepare most vegetables. With each vegetable listing, ways are suggested to serve vegetables so that your family will really enjoy them.

Artichokes. This vegetable has a delicate, nutty flavor that makes it first choice among gourmets.

Artichoke hearts—the tender inner part of the vegetable—are available frozen and canned. Artichoke hearts are also packed in vinegar and sauces, to be used like pickles or as hors d'oeuvres. Canned whole artichokes may be used like fresh artichokes.

When you buy the fresh vegetable, look for plump, globe to cone-shaped artichokes that are heavy in relation to their size, and have thick, green, fresh-looking petals or leaves which tightly enfold the bud.

To clean fresh artichokes, hold them under running water or dip them in a pan of cold water. With a sharp knife, cut off about 1 inch from the top and trim off the thorny tip of each leaf with a pair of scissors. Cut off stem and pull off any loose leaves around the bottom. Artichokes discolor rapidly after they are cut. To keep them light before cooking, put them in a pan of water with vinegar or lemon juice added, about 3 tablespoons for each quart of water.

To cook whole artichokes, place them upright in a deep saucepan in about 3 inches of boiling, salted water. Cover pan and cook until tender, about 15 to 45 minutes depending on size and variety. They are tender when you can easily pierce the stalk or readily pull out a leaf. Drain upside down.

A popular sauce for hot artichokes is made by combining ⅓ cup melted butter or margarine, ½ teaspoon of salt, ¼ teaspoon pepper, 1 teaspoon sugar, ¼ cup lemon juice, and 2 tablespoons minced parsley. Heat a minute or two, until flavors blend. Dip the tender end of each leaf into the sauce before you eat it.

Cooked fresh or frozen artichokes and canned artichokes may also be served cold. French dressing, oil and lemon juice, or thinned mayonnaise are good dressings. Split fresh artichokes lengthwise and remove and discard the chokes before serving. Cold artichokes are especially good served with shrimp or crab meat salad, or with tomato wedges, olives, and dill pickle.

Asparagus. There are two types of asparagus—green and white. Green asparagus is sold fresh, frozen, and canned; white asparagus is mostly canned. Whole spears and tips (the most prized part of asparagus) are more expensive than cut styles of frozen or canned asparagus.

Fresh asparagus should have closed, compact tips and smooth, round, tender spears, with a rich green color covering most of the spear. Tips that are open or spread or spears that are angular or ridged are signs of aging.

Fresh asparagus should be washed thoroughly. Scrub the stalks gently with a vegetable brush and scrape off the scales if they are sandy. Break off the stalks as far down as they will snap easily. Usually the white portion is tough.

Asparagus may be left whole, cut into 1½-inch pieces, or sliced diagonally, making thin slanting slices about 1½ inches long. Cut several stalks at one time on a cutting board.

To cook whole asparagus, tie them in a bundle with a band of foil, and stand the stalks upright in about 1 inch of boiling salted water in a deep pan. If you cook asparagus laid flat in the pan, place them on a strip of foil so that they can be removed by lifting the ends of the foil strip. Cover and cook until stalks are just tender when pierced with a fork, about 10 to 20 minutes.

Oriental cooks cut asparagus into thin slanting slices and cook them until barely tender. Use ¼ cup water and 3 tablespoons of vegetable oil to cook about 3 cups of cut asparagus. Sprinkle with salt and pepper and monosodium glutamate and cook for 3 to 5 minutes.

Asparagus is good either hot or cold. Pour lemon-butter sauce or hollandaise sauce over hot asparagus; or add diced, hard-cooked eggs to a medium white sauce to serve over it. Or you can sprinkle crisp bacon bits or toasted blanched almonds over hot buttered asparagus. Some like italian dressing on asparagus.

For Chive Asparagus, slowly heat one 3-ounce package of chive cream cheese and stir until soft and creamy. Pour over hot asparagus.

For Marinated Asparagus, chill cooked whole asparagus. Top it with french dressing and snipped parsley.

For Asparagus with Croutons, dice bread in tiny squares and brown them in a little butter or margarine in a frying pan. Season with salt and pepper, garlic salt, curry powder, or any favorite herb. Sprinkle over hot buttered asparagus.

Beans, Green and Wax. Called string beans before the development of stringless varieties, or snap beans, pole beans, or bush beans when they are fresh, the canned and frozen products are usually known as green beans and wax beans. Wax beans are so called because of their waxy yellow color. There is little difference in nutritional value of the two types of beans, but green beans are more common.

Styles of both frozen and canned green and wax beans are whole, french (julienne or shoestring), and cut. Beans cut diagonally are called "kitchen cuts" or "home cuts."

Fresh snap beans should be crisp and firm but tender, with a bright green or yellow color. Thick, tough, fibrous pods are overmature.

Green and wax beans may be served in vegetable salads, either hot or chilled. Often they are marinated and served cold alone or with other salad vegetables. Snap beans also are a good ingredient of stews and soups. Cooked fresh or frozen beans and canned beans can be used interchangeably in most recipes.

Asparagus served with new potatoes and garnished with peas, celery, and white sauce.

There are many ways to prepare fresh green or wax beans. You can leave them whole, snap or cut across into 1-inch pieces, cut on the diagonal in thin pieces, or—slice them lengthwise with a sharp knife or put through a bean slicer. Wash and snip off the ends before you cut them.

To cook fresh snap beans in a small amount of water, add beans from 1 pound as purchased to ½ or 1 cup boiling water in a saucepan. If you wish, add ½ teaspoon salt. Cover pan. Cook the shortest time possible until just tender for the best flavored beans —12 to 16 minutes for 1-inch pieces, slightly less time for diagonal and lengthwise cut, and slightly more time for whole beans.

Flavor with salt, pepper, and butter or margarine, and serve hot. For a more sophisticated dish, beans may be served like asparagus with a hollandaise, cheese, or mushroom sauce. Some folks like to add bacon or salt pork before cooking to give a special flavor to beans.

A recipe from Greece called "Yahni" combines 1 pound green beans, a sliced onion, and 1½ cups canned tomatoes or 3 fresh tomatoes. Cook cut-up beans in a very small amount of water for 10 to 15 minutes, add the onion and tomatoes, and season with vegetable oil, salt, and pepper. Add a few pieces of cooked lamb or other meat, if desired, and cook slowly for ½ hour.

Other countries have modified this recipe by adding a minced garlic clove, chopped green pepper, diced celery, and chopped parsley. These ingredients may be cooked for a few minutes in butter or margarine before adding beans.

Beans, Lima. Practically all the lima bean crop is processed into canned or frozen products, but a small supply of local or "home-grown" fresh limas may be found in food stores in summer and fall.

Fresh lima bean pods should be well filled and have a bright appearance. Lima beans from pods that are dried, shriveled, or yellow are more like dried limas in flavor.

Several types of lima beans are canned and frozen. Fordhook variety, a name often shown on labels, has large, thick beans. Several varieties of limas have small, thin beans; these are usually called baby limas. Lima beans are white, yellow, or green, depending on their maturity when harvested. Each color has its own flavor. Green limas are usually the youngest beans.

Speckled butter beans are another variety of lima bean, found mostly in frozen form. They are larger than most other lima beans and have a different flavor.

U.S. Grades A and B lima beans are less starchy than Grade C, and baby limas are less starchy than the larger beans.

Cook fresh lima beans in a small amount of boiling salted water for 25 to 30 minutes, or until tender. Add seasonings and butter or margarine.

Fresh, frozen, or canned lima beans can be used in this recipe for Green Lima Bean Casserole.

GREEN LIMA BEAN CASSEROLE

6 servings, ⅔ cup each

½ cup milk
1 can (10½ ounces) condensed cheese soup
1 cup diced celery
¼ cup cut-up parsley
2 cups cooked green lima beans
½ cup canned french-fried onion rings

Blend milk with soup. Add celery, parsley, and lima beans. Place mixture in a baking dish. Top with onion rings. Bake at 350° F. for 45 minutes.

Beets. Beautiful, rich-red beets can liven up any meal. Young beets (small beets from 1½ to 2¼ inches in diameter) are usually sold with the tops still attached, and older beets (usually larger than 2¼ inches in diameter) with the tops removed. (See "*Greens, cooked,*" for discussion of beet tops.)

Canned beets are available whole, sliced, quartered, diced, and in strips. They may be served as a hot dish or used in cold salads. Beets prepared in a slightly thickened, sweet vinegar sauce are called Harvard beets.

Fresh beets should be firm and round, smooth over most of their surface, and have a rich, deep-red color. If they are bunched, you can judge their freshness fairly accurately by the condition of the tops. Decayed or badly wilted tops indicate lack of freshness, but the beets may be usable if they are firm. Avoid elongated beets with rough, scaly areas around the top surface—they may be tough, fibrous, and strong flavored.

The red color pigment in beets is extremely soluble in water, so it's best to cook fresh beets whole in their skins with a little of the beet tops and roots left on them. Use enough boiling salted water to almost cover the beets. The red pigment is more stable if a little vinegar or lemon juice is added to the water.

Depending on size, the cooking time for young beets varies from 30 to 45 minutes and for older beets from 45 to 90 minutes. When the beets are tender, remove them from the water, cool slightly, and slip off the skins, stems, and roots by rubbing with your fingers. Beets may then be served whole, sliced, diced, or cut into strips. Season to taste with salt and pepper or other spices, and add butter or margarine, lemon juice or vinegar as desired.

BEETS IN ORANGE SAUCE

6 servings, ½ cup each

¼ cup sugar
¾ teaspoon salt
2 tablespoons cornstarch
¾ cup orange juice
2 tablespoons lemon juice
1 tablespoon butter or margarine
3 cups drained sliced beets, canned or cooked

Mix sugar, salt, and cornstarch in a saucepan. Stir in the orange juice and cook until thickened, stirring constantly. Remove from heat and stir in lemon juice and fat. Pour sauce over beets and heat.

Broccoli. The tender young stalks and branches and their bud clusters (or heads) are the edible part of broccoli.

Fresh broccoli has firm, compact bud clusters that are dark green or sage green, sometimes with a pronounced purplish cast. None of the small flower buds should have opened enough to show the yellow color, and the stalks and branches should be firm and tender. Broccoli that is wilted or has spread bud clusters, enlarged or open buds, or a yellowish-green color is overmature or has been on display for too long.

The highest quality frozen broccoli, with its compact bud clusters, looks much like the fresh product. Second quality broccoli may have slightly spread bud clusters. Frozen broccoli is prepared as whole spears or stalks, short spears or florets (the head with a short portion of the stalk), broccoli cuts or pieces, and chopped broccoli.

The fleshy stalks of broccoli take longer to cook than the blossoms, so fresh broccoli may be cooked like asparagus, with the stalks standing in boiling salted water and the buds cooking in the steam. Or the broccoli may be cut in pieces and the stems cooked a short time before adding the buds. Large stalks may be sliced lengthwise and they will then cook as quickly as the florets. Short cooking and little water tend to preserve the nutrients and flavor.

Serve broccoli spears with a tart sauce made by mixing 2 tablespoons of lemon juice, 2 tablespoons melted butter or margarine, and 1½ teaspoons prepared horseradish with ½ teaspoon salt, 1½ teaspoons sugar, and ½ teaspoon paprika. Mix well and pour over hot broccoli.

Chopped broccoli is a flavorsome party food when it is used in a souffle and served with creamy mushroom sauce.

Brussels Sprouts. Fresh brussels sprouts should be firm, bright green, free from blemishes, and have tight-fitting outer leaves. Sprouts with yellow or yellowish-green leaves, or leaves which are loose, soft, or wilted, are not a good buy. Small holes in the leaves or ragged leaves may be signs of worm injury.

Frozen sprouts are trimmed and have the outer leaves removed, but otherwise closely resemble fresh sprouts.

When preparing fresh sprouts for cooking, remove any yellowed leaves and trim off a bit of the stems. Wash fresh sprouts thoroughly in cold water and soak in cold salt water for 30 minutes to an hour to remove insects if any are present.

Cook fresh sprouts in a small amount (not more than 1 cup to 1 pound of sprouts) of boiling salted water in a saucepan. Cover pan and cook for 15 to 20 minutes or until just tender. Overcooking may produce a strong flavor and discoloration and cause loss of vitamins. Drain, add butter or margarine, salt, and pepper, or any other seasonings you prefer.

Brussels sprouts are delicious served with either cheese sauce or hollandaise sauce. Sprinkle buttered breadcrumbs or chopped nuts over the top for that special company dinner.

Cabbage. Smooth-leaved green, crinkly-leaved green Savoy, and red cabbage are the three groups of cabbage. All three types are suitable for cooking or serving cold in salads, but the Savoy and red varieties are more in demand for slaws and salads. (See "*Greens, salad,*" for discussion of Chinese cabbage.)

Good heads of cabbage are firm or hard, heavy for their size, with crisp leaves. The outer leaves should be free from serious blemishes. These outer or "wrapper leaves" are usually discarded, but too many blemished leaves cause extra waste. Old cabbage (cabbage that has been stored) may lack green color, but is satisfactory if the leaves are not wilted or discolored. If the leaves have separated from the base of the head, the cabbage may be too old.

Sauerkraut is the only form of processed cabbage available in food stores. The shredded cabbage is fermented in a brine of its own juice and salt. Some is flavored with peppers, pimientos, tomatoes, or various spices. It is available canned and in refrigerated packages, and at times a semifresh product is sold from barrels or similar containers.

Cook fresh cabbage the shortest time possible and use very little water to save its high nutritive value. Never overcook cabbage because the flavor gets strong and it loses its crisp texture.

The cooking time in a saucepan is short—only 3 to 10 minutes—for shredded cabbage of different varieties. Finely shredded cabbage can also be cooked in a frying pan in a small amount of fat (1 tablespoon) and water (2 tablespoons), and ½ teaspoon salt for each quart of shredded cabbage. Cover pan to hold in steam. Cook over low heat until vegetable is tender in 6 to 8 minutes.

For a different flavor, cabbage can be cooked in milk. Add 1 quart shredded cabbage to 1½ cups milk, and simmer for 2 minutes. Mix 2 tablespoons each of flour and melted fat and add a little of the hot milk. Stir this mixture into the cabbage and cook for 3 to 4 minutes, or until thickened, stirring constantly. Season to taste with salt and pepper.

Cabbage slaw, hot or cold, is a favorite in many countries. The cabbage is chopped coarsely or shredded in thin strips, as preferred, and a favorite dressing and seasonings are added. A little vinegar, salt, sugar, and pepper is sufficient for some palates. Sweet or sour cream salad dressing or mayonnaise is preferred by others. To prepare hot slaw, make a hot salad dressing and stir in finely shredded cabbage. Cover and heat a few minutes before serving.

Red cabbage will retain its red color during cooking if vinegar or lemon juice is added to the water.

In Europe and the Near East, cabbage leaves also are used to wrap around meat rolls. Cook the cabbage leaves until wilted (about 5 minutes) in boiling water. Wrap around a meat filling and place in heavy frying pan. Add 2 cups tomato juice, cover, and cook 30 minutes.

Carrots. The carrot is a versatile vegetable and it is good when served alone or in combination with meats or other vegetables.

Fresh carrots should be reasonably well formed, smooth, firm, and have a good orange color. Watch out for excessively rough or cracked carrots, or carrots with large green areas at the top.

Canned and frozen carrots are available whole, quartered, diced, as strips, and round slices (cuts). Canned small baby carrots are especially flavorful.

Fresh carrots are easy to prepare. First wash them well and pare or scrape to remove the thin skin. A vegetable parer does the job quickly; or leave the skin on if you like. Leave whole, dice, or cut into round slices or lengthwise strips.

Cook young, whole carrots for 15 to 20 minutes and older ones 20 to 30 minutes. Sliced or diced carrots may be cooked in as little as 10 minutes. Use a small amount of water, only ½ to 1 cup for 6 servings of carrots; add ½ teaspoon salt and 1 teaspoon sugar to the water, if desired. Cover the pan so carrots will cook in the steam.

Carrots can also be baked, particularly when you are planning an oven meal. Cut the carrots in half and place them in a casserole with ¼ cup water, 2 or 3 tablespoons butter or margarine, and a sprinkle of salt and pepper. Cover the casserole and bake at 375° F. for 45 minutes, or until carrots are tender. Whole carrots also may be baked with roasted meats, adding them in the last 45 minutes before the meat is done.

Some good carrot combinations are:

- Carrot strips and whole green snap beans cooked with a little dill seed, sugar, and salt in the cooking water and served with italian dressing.
- Braised carrots and celery cooked in margarine and a little water.
- Carrots and onions, cut finely and cooked in bacon fat or margarine in a tightly covered frying pan.
- Carrots diced and creamed with peas and new potatoes.

Carrots are also good sliced raw as a crisp relish; shredded or sliced in salads, either alone or with other vegetables; glazed in honey or brown sugar; or combined with meats in the main dish. Carrots are often used to give color to soups.

For a very elegant carrot casserole, combine 3 cups of cooked, sliced carrots (fresh, frozen, or canned) with 1 can (10½-ounce) condensed celery soup, and 1 cup of shredded process cheese in a baking dish. Mix 1 tablespoon melted butter or margarine with ¼ cup of fine dry breadcrumbs and sprinkle on top of carrots. Bake at 350° F. for about 20 minutes to brown crumbs.

Cauliflower. Fresh cauliflower sold at retail is generally wrapped in clear plastic film with most of the green outer leaf covering (the jacket leaves) removed.

The white, edible portion of cauliflower (the curd) should be clean, compact, and white to creamy-white. A slightly "ricey" texture will not hurt the eating quality if the curd is compact. If the jacket leaves are attached, good green color is a sign of freshness.

Frozen cauliflower is separated into florets, ready to cook. Grade A frozen cauliflower looks almost like the fresh product. Grade B often looks slightly gray or brown but turns white when cooked.

To cook fresh cauliflower, cut away the tough outer leaves and part of the core. The head may be left whole or separated into florets. Whole cauliflower will cook in boiling water in 15 to 25 minutes; florets in 8 to 15 minutes.

Cauliflower will discolor if overcooked. Also, it can pick up an unattractive yellowish cast if cooked in a hard or alkaline water. Adding a teaspoon of lemon juice to the water will help to keep the cauliflower nice and white.

Because of its bland flavor, cooked cauliflower goes very well with many sauces—white, cheese, or mushroom, or the more highly flavored hollandaise or vinaigrette sauces. To add interest, sprinkle the cauliflower with fine breadcrumbs lightly browned in butter, and garnish with chopped fresh parsley.

Spices and herbs that go well with cauliflower are caraway seed, celery salt, dill, mace, and tarragon. Use them sparingly to enhance the natural flavor of the cauliflower. In India, cauliflower is cooked with ginger, cloves, cardamom seeds, and cinnamon sticks. In Spain, grated orange rind is sprinkled on top. Scandinavians prefer a dill sauce.

If you want to cook cauliflower like the Chinese do, slice each floret thinly. Place 1 quart florets in a heavy pan, sprinkle lightly with salt, and add ⅓ cup hot water. Cook covered about 5 minutes or until slightly crisp. Add 2 tablespoons each butter or margarine and heavy cream. Heat for 1 or 2 minutes longer and serve with cut-up chives or parsley sprinkled on the top.

Celery. Celery has many uses, both as a raw and cooked vegetable. Its crunchy goodness is important in salads, sandwich fillings, and as a relish or snack food. Raw celery stuffed with creamy cheese or other filling is an old standby.

Most celery found in retail stores is of the thick-branched green varieties (it's known as the "Pascal" type), although Golden-type blanched celery may occasionally be available. Celery hearts are the tender inner branches of the stalk.

Freshness and crispness are a must in celery. The stalk should have a solid, rigid feel. Outer branches should be light to medium green with a glossy surface. Small leaflets at the top of the stalk should be mostly green and not more than slightly wilted.

Celery is usually cut up for cooking in a small amount of salted water, using about ½ cup water, ½ teaspoon salt, and 1½ pounds celery for 6 servings, ½ cup each. Cook for about 15 minutes in a tightly covered pan. Season the drained celery with salt and butter, or add a white sauce. Season the sauce with curry, celery seed, dill seed, or freshly grated nutmeg.

To make Celery Au Gratin, put cooked celery in white sauce in a baking dish, cover the top with breadcrumbs, and dot with butter or sprinkle with grated cheese. Bake in a hot oven (400° F.) until it is lightly browned.

Creamed celery is also good combined with cooked green pepper strips, green beans, or green peas.

Corn. Sweet corn may have either white or yellow kernels, but yellow varieties make up most of the commercial production.

When you buy fresh sweet corn, look for ears that are well covered with bright, plump kernels and husks that are fresh and green.

Ears with small underdeveloped kernels are immature, and ears with very large, tough, deep-colored kernels are overmature. Avoid the ears with dented or shrunken kernels. Corn with husks that are yellow, wilted, or dried should be checked carefully for dented kernels.

Processed sweet corn is found in many forms, styles, and grades. Canned corn may be cream-style with the kernels cut into smaller pieces so as to have the consistency of a very thick cream; whole-grain style, with the kernels generally whole and packed in a relatively clear liquid; and vacuum-pack whole grain, with little or no free liquid. Most canned corn is prepared from yellow or orange varieties, but some white corn also is canned. "Shoe peg" corn, a whole-grain white corn, has small, narrow kernels with a distinctive flavor.

Most frozen corn is whole-grain yellow corn. A considerable amount is frozen on the cob.

Both canned and frozen corn may have peppers or pimientos or other foods added for flavor or appearance.

Much processed corn is packed according to U.S. grades, with the USDA grademark on the label:

U.S. Grade A is tender and succulent, free from defects, and has excellent flavor.

U.S. Grade B is slightly more mature and more chewy than grade A, reasonably free from defects, and has a good flavor.

U.S. Grade C is more mature and

starchier than grades A and B, but it is flavorful and nourishing.

Fresh sweet corn loses its good flavor quickly after it is picked because the sugar turns into starch as a result of enzymatic activity.

For best quality retention, do not remove husks from fresh corn until it is to be cooked. Remove silks with a stiff brush. Add a teaspoon of salt to a large pan half full of boiling water. Cook corn on the cob for 5 to 15 minutes, depending on its age and freshness. Serve the corn hot with plenty of butter or margarine, and pass the salt and pepper.

Corn in cream is a good way to use corn cut off the cob, either raw or cooked. Start with 3 cups of corn kernels for 6 servings. Cook the kernels for 8 to 10 minutes with 2 tablespoons of chopped onion in 3 tablespoons butter or margarine. Add 1 cup of sweet cream, 1 teaspoon sugar, and salt and pepper to taste. Heat and stir until hot.

If preferred, use sour cream instead of the sweet cream, or cream cheese softened with milk. Add a half teaspoon curry powder if you like.

Cucumbers. Cucumbers should be a good green color and firm over their entire length. They may also have some white or greenish-white color and still be top quality. They should be well shaped and well developed, but not too large in diameter. Ignore the many small lumps on their surfaces; this is typical of good cucumbers.

Overgrown cucumbers (those with large diameters) and cucumbers of a dull color, turning yellowish, are likely to have tough flesh and large hard seeds. Cucumbers with withered or shriveled ends may be somewhat bitter.

Food uses for fresh, raw cucumbers are numerous. They can be sliced or diced and added to tossed salads or fancy molded salads; cut lengthwise into sticks for the relish tray; sliced and served with vinegar or sour cream; or scooped out and filled with a favorite salad mixture.

Cucumbers are also delicious cooked, although this use is less common than others. Sliced cucumbers are cooked slightly and served with thin cream sauce or hot vinegar, sugar, and crisp bacon bits. They are also used to make baked stuffed cucumbers.

But of course the principal use for cucumbers is in pickling, either at home or commercially.

Eggplant. Fresh eggplant, one of the more delicate vegetables, is of good quality when it is firm, heavy, smooth, uniformly dark purple, and free from scars or cuts.

Poorly colored, soft, shriveled, or flabby eggplants are usually bitter or poor in flavor.

Frying is perhaps the most well-known way in the United States to prepare eggplant. The eggplant is cut into ½-inch strips, dipped in batter, and cooked in either deep or shallow hot fat until browned. The batter is made by mixing 1 cup flour with ½ teaspoon salt, 1 egg, 1 cup milk, and 1 tablespoon vegetable oil, and beating until smooth. Drain fried eggplant on paper towels and sprinkle with salt. Serve hot and pass the grated Parmesan cheese for those who like this flavor combination.

French-fried eggplant sticks are also available in frozen form.

Greens, Cooked. Many species of plants are grown for use as "greens." The better known kinds are spinach, kale, chard, collards, turnip, beet, mustard and broccoli leaves, dandelion, and sorrel. Many others, some of them wild, are also used as greens.

Good quality greens are fresh, young, tender, free from blemishes, and have a healthy green color. Beet tops and ruby chard have a reddish color.

Avoid leaves with coarse stems, yellowish color, or those that are soft, wilted, or dried. Look carefully for signs of insects, particularly aphids. They are sometimes hard to see, and even harder to wash away.

Various leafy greens are available in canned or frozen form. Among them are collards, kale, mustard, turnip greens (often with immature turnips), poke salad, endive, and swiss chard.

Spinach is processed in "whole leaf" and chopped styles, sometimes with various sauces and flavorings. The highest grade of these products is produced from young, tender plants.

Fresh greens can be delicious when properly prepared. Well-cooked greens have a bright color and sweet flavor and are almost crisp. When greens are overcooked, the green chlorophyll pigment turns to an olive brown color, the texture becomes soft and mushy, and the flavor is strong.

To prepare greens for cooking, discard any bruised, wilted, or yellowed outer leaves, and cut off tough or dried stem ends. Strip kale leaves off the woody midribs.

Wash thoroughly, using plenty of water for leafy greens.

Lift greens out of water and repeat washing until no grit settles to the bottom of the pan.

Spinach and other tender greens need only the water clinging to the leaves after washing to cook them in a tightly covered pan. Less tender greens need more water. Reduce heat after steam begins to escape, and cook slowly so that the water does not boil away. The secret to success in cooking greens is to cook until they are just tender and still slightly crisp. Cooking time varies from 3 minutes for tender spinach to 30 minutes for mustard and turnip greens. Kale and chard take 10 to 15 minutes.

Add 1 or 2 tablespoons butter, margarine, or meat drippings to greens before cooking, if desired. For variety, add bits of crumbled bacon, diced cooked ham, or chopped hard-cooked eggs to the cooked greens.

Serve greens with lemon juice or with light cream and horseradish. Other interesting ways to prepare greens are scalloped, molded, or creamed; in a fondue or a souffle; with cheese sauce or mushroom sauce; Dutch style with bacon, vinegar, and sugar; in soups, in omelets, or in salads. (See "*Greens, salad.*")

Wilted spinach, such as the old-fashioned wilted lettuce, adds color and zesty flavor to a meal.

WILTED SPINACH

6 servings, ⅔ cup each

3 slices bacon
2 tablespoons flour
1 tablespoon sugar
1 teaspoon salt
2 tablespoons bacon drippings
¾ cup water
¼ cup vinegar
1 quart coarsely chopped raw spinach

Cut bacon in ½-inch pieces and fry until crisp. Drain bacon and save the drippings. Blend flour, sugar, and salt with the bacon drippings. Stir in water and vinegar and cook until thickened, stirring constantly. Pour the hot vinegar dressing over spinach, add bacon, and toss to mix.

Greens, Salad. Lettuce is the most important salad plant grown in the Nation. Four types are generally sold: Iceberg, Butterhead, Romaine, and Leaf.

Iceberg lettuce is by far the major type. Heads are large, round, and solid, with outer leaves medium-green. Inner leaves are a lighter green.

Butterhead lettuce, including the Big Boston and Bibb varieties, has a smaller head than Iceberg. It is slightly flat on top and has soft, tender, pale inner leaves that are oily or buttery to the feel.

Romaine (or Cos) lettuce plants are tall and cylindrical with crisp, folded, dark-green leaves.

Leaf lettuce has broad, tender, succulent, fairly smooth leaves that vary in color depending on variety. Grown mainly in greenhouses or on truck farms for local sale, leaf lettuce is very delicate and usually not suitable for long distance shipping.

The leaves of Iceberg lettuce and Romaine should be crisp. Other types of lettuce have a softer texture, but the leaves should not be wilted. Look for good, bright color—the shade of green varies with variety.

Heads of Iceberg lettuce that are very hard and lack green color are overmature. They may have a less attractive flavor. Heads of irregular shape or with hard lumps on the top may have overgrown central stems, causing excessive waste and a slightly bitter flavor. Check the lettuce for tan or brown areas on the edge of the leaves. Slight discoloration of the outer or wrapper leaves usually will not hurt lettuce quality.

Chicory or endive has narrower, crinkly leaves with notched edges. Escarole leaves are much broader and less crinkly than those of chicory. Chicory plants often have "blanched" yellowish leaves in the central portion of the head. Witloof or Belgian endive is a compact, cigar-shaped plant which is creamy white from blanching.

Chinese cabbage is an elongated plant resembling celery. Some of the varieties develop a firm stalk, while others have an open, leafy form.

Watercress is a small, round-leaved plant that grows naturally (or may be cultivated) along the banks of fresh-water streams or ponds. Its spicy flavor makes it a favorite for use as a garnish or in mixed green salads.

All these salad greens should look fresh and crisp.

Different types of lettuce have distinctive roles to play in salad making. Iceberg lettuce is good served alone or in combination with other greens, vegetables, or fruits, as well as with meat, poultry, and fish salads. Boston or Butterhead lettuce is excellent in tossed green salads and as garnishes, but it is too soft to combine with fruits and vegetables. The small leaves of Bibb lettuce are a salad by themselves with a french or a russian dressing. Romaine lettuce retains its crispness in tossed salads and is famous for its use in Caesar Salad made with a special dressing and garlic-flavored croutons. Leaf lettuce is delightful in a spring salad bowl combined with other greens, carrot curls, and chopped green onions, and tossed with italian dressing.

The use of lettuce in sandwiches is almost universal. It is also popular prepared as "Wilted Lettuce," which is lettuce served with a hot bacon, vinegar, and sugar dressing.

When salad greens are brought into your kitchen, discard any bruised leaves. Wash the greens thoroughly, and dry them well before refrigerating.

To obtain whole leaves of Iceberg lettuce, cut or twist out the core and run water through it to loosen the leaves. Drain well on paper towels. For tossed salads, tear greens into bite-size pieces. For other uses, cut lettuce into wedges or shred it with a sharp knife.

Raw spinach is also used as a salad green.

The tossed green salad is by far the most popular salad. It is easy to make and a timesaver. Use one or two or more kinds of greens and tear into bite-size pieces to make about 2 quarts. In the salad bowl, finely chop 1 garlic clove, add salt and pepper, and a bit of dry mustard if you like; mash the seasonings together. Add 1 tablespoon vinegar or lemon juice and ¼ cup of salad oil. Add greens just before serving and toss to mix.

This basic salad can be varied by adding artichoke hearts, raw cauliflower, celery, chives, or green onions, cucumbers, raw mushrooms, radishes, tomatoes, or any cold, cooked vegetable. Fruits like apples, avocados, grapes, pineapple, or oranges also can be added to the tossed salad; or you can add cut-up cheese, hard-cooked eggs, cooked meats, or seafood.

Raw spinach salad is a refreshing taste sensation. Shred the spinach, add french or italian dressing, and garnish with grated hard-cooked eggs or sliced tomatoes.

Mushrooms. Cultivated in caves, cellars, or special houses, the mushroom is an edible fungus with a cap (the wide portion on top), gills (the many rows of paper-thin tissue underneath the cap), and a stem.

Young mushrooms of small to medium size with a white to creamy-white cap surface are the best quality. The caps should be clean and tightly closed around the stem. If the caps are partly open, the exposed gills should be no darker than light tan or pink.

Avoid mushrooms with pitted or

badly discolored caps, or those with wide open caps and dark, discolored gills.

Smaller mushrooms are canned in several styles: Whole (including the stems), as buttons (the top only), sliced, and stems and pieces. They are sometimes processed in butter and broiled before canning. Frozen mushrooms are available in most of the same styles.

Wash fresh mushrooms in cold water and then cut off the tips of the stems. It is not necessary to peel them. To prevent mushrooms from darkening during cooking, use lemon juice. Slice by cutting from the round side down through the stems, or remove the stems and use the caps, saving the stems for another use.

Lightly brown fresh mushrooms in butter or margarine before using them in combination with almost all foods.

When using canned mushrooms in place of fresh, the contents of three 4-ounce cans equals 1 pound fresh mushrooms cooked. Browning canned mushrooms in butter or margarine before you add them to other foods makes their flavor more distinctive. Drain the liquid from caps, slices, or pieces of canned mushrooms. Then lightly brown the mushrooms in a little butter or margarine the same as you would fresh mushrooms.

CHINESE-STYLE MUSHROOMS

6 servings, ⅓ cup each

1 pound fresh mushrooms
2 tablespoons vegetable oil
2 tablespoons soy sauce
2 tablespoons water
1 teaspoon sugar
1 tablespoon cornstarch

Wash mushrooms and cut vertically into thin slices. Cook mushrooms in hot oil in frying pan for 3 minutes, stirring as needed.

Combine other ingredients and stir into mushrooms. Cook for 2 minutes more until the juice is translucent.

Okra. Okra is a seed pod harvested in the immature stage well before the pods or seeds have begun to harden.

Small whole okra pods and pods cut into rings are available both canned and frozen. Canned fermented okra is partially fermented in a salt brine and has an acid, krautlike flavor. Usually firm, with a bright green color, canned fermented okra may be served as a vegetable, but is usually used in soups or other foods. Small okra pods, pickled at home or commercially, are a favorite in the South.

The pods of fresh okra should be tender, bright green, free from blemishes, and less than 4½ inches long. The tips should bend with slight pressure. Pods with a pale, faded color, a hard body, or tips that resist bending are tough and fibrous.

Scrub fresh okra pods well before cooking. Cut off stem end, leave small pods whole, and cut large pods in ½-inch slices. Add ½ cup salted water to 1¼ pounds okra for 6 servings, and cook until barely tender, 10 to 15 minutes. It may also be steamed until just tender. (When overcooked, okra may develop a gummy consistency.) Serve with melted butter or margarine or hollandaise sauce.

For french-fried okra, dip pods in beaten egg and fine bread crumbs, or in cornmeal, then fry in deep fat or shallow fat.

Chicken Gumbo is perhaps the most famous use for okra. To diced chicken meat and broth are added okra cut in ½-inch pieces, and tomatoes, celery, green pepper, onion, and parsley, all cut finely. Simmer until vegetables are tender. Season to taste with salt and pepper. Add cooked corn or cooked rice, if you wish. Proportions of ingredients and seasoning can be varied to suit the taste.

A favorite in the South is Creole Okra, made by combining cooked okra and a spicy creole sauce made with tomatoes, chopped onion, green pepper, and seasonings.

Onions, Mature. The many varieties of onions grown for fresh market fall into three general classes: Globe, Granex-Grano, and Spanish. All three classes may be yellow, white, red, or brown, but commercial production mainly consists of yellow-skinned varieties.

Globe onions are the most common class, and are considered primarily cooking onions. They are predominantly round to oval, rather strong flavored, and small to medium in size.

Granex-Grano are medium- to large-size onions. Mild in flavor, they are ideal for serving raw or cooked. Their shape tends to be top-shaped or flattened. Bermuda onions fall into this class.

Spanish onions resemble the globes in shape, but are generally much larger. Often called "sweet Spanish," they are mild flavored and ideal for salads or slicing.

Good-quality onions should be dry, hard or firm, and have small necks. They should be covered with a thin, papery outer skin and be reasonably free from such blemishes as green sunburn spots or sunken, leatherlike areas.

Avoid onions with a thick woody center in the neck or which have fresh sprouts.

Onions are also available frozen and canned whole and as french-fried onion rings. Canned whole onions are usually packed in a salt brine. Top-grade canned whole onions are fairly uniform in size and shape.

Onions can be baked, boiled, fried in butter or margarine, french-fried in rings, or made into delicious french onion soup.

For Baked Onions, cut peeled onions in half crosswise. Use 2 pounds of medium-size onions for 6 servings. Add just enough water to cover bottom of a baking pan. Sprinkle with salt and pepper and cover pan. Bake for 30 minutes. Top with 1 cup of buttered bread cubes and bake uncovered 15 to 20 minutes longer, or until cubes are brown and onions are tender.

Whole onions can be cooked in boiling salted water for 15 to 30 minutes, depending upon size. Add a medium white sauce to cooked onions to make creamed onions. Top with buttered bread crumbs and bake for 25 minutes for scalloped onions.

To make french-fried onions, peel Spanish, Bermuda, or mild white onions and cut into ¼-inch slices. Separate into rings, dip in evaporated milk or a mixture of 2 cups milk and 3 eggs, then into flour, coating each ring well. Fry in hot deep fat at 370° to 385° F. Drain on paper towels and sprinkle with salt.

Onions, Green; Shallots; and Leeks. Green onions, shallots, and leeks are sometimes called "scallions."

Green onions are ordinary onions harvested very young. They have very little or no bulb formation and their tops are tubular. Shallots are similar to green onions, but grow in clusters and have practically no swelling at the base. Leeks are larger than shallots, have slight bulb formation and broad, flat, dark-green tops.

These salad vegetables should have fresh, crisp, green tops and firm, well-blanched (white) portions extending 2 or 3 inches up from the root end.

Yellowing, wilted, discolored, or decayed tops indicate the bulb is flabby, tough, or fibrous. Bruised tops will not affect eating quality of the bulb.

Parsley. Parsley can be a valuable addition to your diet, used as a seasoning in many foods as well as a decorative garnish. Both curled-leaf and flat-leaf parsley are produced.

Look for fresh, crisp, bright-green leaves. Slightly wilted leaves can be freshened by trimming off the ends of the stems and placing them in cold water. Yellowed or badly wilted leaves are signs of aging.

Parsnips. Parsnips of good eating quality are small- to medium-size, well formed, smooth, firm, and free from serious blemishes.

Large coarse parsnips are apt to have a tough or woody center, and badly wilted and flabby parsnips are usually pithy or fibrous.

For cooking, leave parsnips whole or pare and cut into lengthwise strips, slices, or cubes. Allow 1½ pounds for six ½-cup servings. Scrub parsnips and cook whole in boiling salted water until tender. Plunge into cold water and slip off skins. Cook pieces in ½ cup boiling salted water for 8 to 15 minutes.

Canned peas and mushrooms in casserole topped with white sauce, bread cubes, and paprika.

Parsnips also are good baked in a covered casserole at 350° F. for 40 to 45 minutes. Serve with melted butter, margarine, or cream and seasonings to taste. Or mash the parsnips and serve with a little grated orange rind.

Glazed Parsnips are the choice for some menu combinations. Cut cooked parsnips into strips or large pieces and heat them in a sirup made by blending ¼ cup brown sugar, 2 tablespoons butter or margarine, and 1 tablespoon of water. Cook over low heat until sirup is very thick, and vegetables are well coated.

Peas, Green. Only a small part of the commercial production of green peas is shipped to fresh market. The bulk of the crop is canned or frozen.

Fresh pea pods should be bright green, slightly velvety to the touch, and well filled. Pods which are swollen, light in color, or flecked with gray may contain tough, poorly flavored peas. Pods containing very immature peas are usually flat, dark green in color, and may have a wilted appearance.

Peas, both canned and frozen, are among the most popular processed vegetables. Two types of peas are used for canning—the smooth-skinned early or early June type and the dimple-skinned or sweet type. Most peas for freezing are the sweet type, especially developed for deep-green color.

U.S. Grade A or Fancy canned peas are tender and flavorful, and their color is the typical soft pea-green. The juice is slightly green and waterlike. Off-color peas are rarely found in a can at this grade.

U.S. Grade B or Extra Standard canned peas may be slightly mealy, but have a very good flavor. Their color may be variable—and a few off-color peas or broken peas may be in a can. The liquid may be a slightly cloudy, light green.

U.S. Grade C or Standard canned peas tend to be slightly mealy, and do not taste as sweet as Grades A and B. They are a dull pea-green and some blond or cream-colored or broken peas may be in a can. The liquid may be very cloudy with a starchy flavor.

Like fresh corn, fresh peas should be used soon because they begin to lose tenderness and sweetness shortly after they are picked from the vine.

Cooked peas may be served with butter or margarine, in a cream sauce, in vegetable salads, in soups and stews, and in combination with many other foods. Several pleasing combinations follow:

- Creamed peas and new potatoes with chopped chives or chopped spring onions.
- Peas and crisp-cooked celery with chopped canned pimiento for a touch of color, sprinkled with salt, pepper, and savory seasoning.
- Peas and corn in light cream topped with lightly browned ham slivers.
- Curried peas and onions using fresh or frozen peas and small, white cooked onions.
- Buttered peas cooked with thinly sliced mushrooms and a thinly sliced onion.
- Old-fashioned peas and carrots, dressed up with chives and cream cheese thinned with milk to desired consistency.

For a fresh springtime flavor, add freshly chopped or dried mint, grated lemon peel, and butter or margarine to the cooked green peas. Marjoram and oregano are two other seasonings that lend unusual flavors to peas alone or paired with other vegetables.

Peppers. Most peppers you find in food stores are the sweet green type.

Peppers should be medium to dark green, relatively heavy for their size, and have a glossy sheen and crisp, firm walls or sides.

Peppers with very thin walls (indicated by light weight and flimsiness) and peppers that are wilted or flabby should be avoided, as well as those that are cut or punctured.

Frozen peppers are convenient to use for stuffing or as garnish. Both green and red peppers (fully matured green peppers) are frozen whole, with or without stems, as well as halved, sliced, and diced. Red and green peppers are occasionally available in cans, too.

Sweet peppers are good either raw or cooked. For some uses, as in antipasto, they need to be peeled. This is easy to do if the peppers are first roasted in a very hot oven (450° F.) for 3 to 4 minutes, or over a hot flame until the skin is blistered and dark. Cool the peppers in cold water and rub off the blackened skin.

Brief parboiling for about 5 minutes in boiling salted water is desirable if peppers are to be stuffed. First cut off the tops and remove the seeds and ribs. After heating, drain well and fill with some well-seasoned mixture of cooked meat and rice or mashed potatoes, rice and cheese, or even corned beef hash. Pour 1 cup water or tomato sauce around peppers. Bake at 375° F. for 30 minutes if stuffing is precooked, an hour if not.

Sweet peppers are delicious, too, cut in strips, cooked briefly in garlic-flavored vegetable oil, and seasoned to taste with salt and pepper.

To make a popular Italian Antipasto, cut peeled peppers into even strips and arrange them on a plate. Top each strip with 1 or 2 anchovy fillets, and sprinkle with pepper, olive oil, and capers.

Stuffed green peppers are delightful for salads. Try filling the crisp green peppers with a colorful mixture of lightly cooked and marinated vegetables—carrot cubes, snap beans, and cauliflower pieces. Any of your favorite salad mixtures is made more glamorous when it is served in a pepper shell.

Potatoes. In general, potatoes can be classed as long or round and white, red, or russet. It would also be desirable to classify potatoes for use, as boiling, baking, or frying. Unfortunately, this is not possible because of the wide range of growing and storage conditions as well as personal preferences.

New potatoes are freshly harvested and not fully mature. They often have skinned areas. Late crop potatoes are harvested at a more mature stage and put into storage for winter and spring shipment. They are generally considered more suitable for baking than new potatoes.

Look for reasonably smooth, well-shaped, firm potatoes that are free from blemishes. In new potatoes, some amount of skinned surface is normal, but large skinned and discolored areas are undesirable.

Avoid potatoes with gouges or bruises (they'll mean waste in peeling), those with a green color, or those that are sprouted or shriveled.

Processed white potatoes are available in many forms: Canned, small whole potatoes in salt brine; french-fried shoe strings vacuum-packed, and ready to eat; frozen french-fried in many sizes and shapes; frozen deep-fried small, whole potatoes; sliced or diced products; and patties or puffs made from mashed potatoes; and the frozen, unfried products—ready-to-cook patties, or whole, sliced, diced, or shredded potatoes.

Dehydrated potatoes are also available in many attractive forms. Among the most popular for home use are flakes or granules to make mashed potatoes.

The ways to prepare potatoes are endless. They may be used frequently in meals because of their bland flavor and of the variety of ways to serve them—roasted, baked, boiled, mashed, fried, creamed, browned, french-fried, hash browned, in salads, stews, and soups.

The baked potato is almost an institution in America and other countries as well. Potatoes can be baked either at 350° F. (along with other foods) for 1 hour 10 minutes or in a very hot oven (450° F.) for 40 minutes. When the potatoes feel soft and are easily pierced with a fork, they are done. Cut a cross into top of each potato and press the sides of the potato to open it and let the steam out.

Butter and dairy sour cream are well-liked accompaniments. Other interesting garnitures are chopped green onions and chives, minced parsley, caraway seeds, chopped dill, minced red peppers, sliced stuffed olives, toasted sesame seeds, or crumbled fried bacon or salt pork.

Potato salad, one more American favorite, can be varied in dozens of ways by adding ingredients such as diced cheese or diced ham or other cooked meat. In Finland, they add diced carrots, diced beets, and salted herring. In Sweden, additional ingredients may include chopped apple and diced cucumbers, with sliced egg for decoration.

Radishes. Good quality radishes are medium sized (¾ to 1 inch in diameter), with good red color, and they are plump, round, firm, and crisp.

Very large or spongy radishes are likely to have pithy centers. Dark, discolored spots may indicate decay or aging. Yellow or decayed tops of bunched radishes are signs of overage, but don't always mean the radishes are of poor quality.

Wash radishes well and cut them in attractive ways to use on the relish plate or to garnish salads.

Squash. The many varieties of squash can be divided into two general classes: Summer and winter.

Summer squash is harvested while still immature, at a stage when the entire squash is tender and edible. The yellow crookneck, the large yellow straightneck, the scalloped greenish-white or yellow patty pan, the slender green zucchini, and Italian marrow are all summer types.

Winter squash is marketed only when fully matured, when the rind has become hard and tough. Butternut, buttercup, banana, green and blue hubbard, the small corrugated acorn, and green and gold delicious are among the winter types.

Summer squash should be firm, well

formed, and have a glossy, fresh appearance. Summer squash with a dull appearance and a hard, tough rind is stale or overmature. Such squash will usually have enlarged seeds and dry, stringy flesh. Winter squash should be heavy for its size (this means it has a thick wall and more edible flesh) and have a hard rind. Slight variations in rind color will not affect flavor. Winter squash with a tender rind is immature and has poor eating quality.

Canned and frozen summer squash is made from small succulent squashes usually cut crossways. Several varieties are available, including the flavorful zucchini.

Canned and frozen winter squashes, very similar to pumpkin, are usually cooked and ready for use as a vegetable or in a pie filling.

Fresh summer squashes should be scrubbed clean, but do not need to be pared. They may be left whole or cut into slices or cubes. They are best cooked in a very small amount of water (about ¼ cup for 6 servings) in a covered saucepan for 8 to 15 minutes.

For flavoring, during cooking add finely chopped onion or chives, a tablespoon of butter or margarine, or a bouillon cube. A sprinkle of sugar gives summer squash a fresher taste. Cook over low heat until squash is tender, then uncover and boil rapidly for a few minutes to evaporate excess liquid. Be careful not to overcook. Summer squash will have better acceptance when it is slightly crisp and holds its shape.

For baking, whole, young zucchini squash are a good choice. When almost cooked, slit lengthwise and add strips of cheese. Bake until cheese is melted.

Small, hard-type squashes are often cut in half and baked, and served in the shell. Larger squashes are cut into individual servings. Seeds and stringy portions should be removed before cooking. Add butter or margarine, brown sugar, and salt and pepper, as desired, and bake it in a hot oven (400° F.) for 30 to 60 minutes, or until tender. Covering the squash with foil for the first half of the baking period allows it to steam and shortens the baking time. For unexpected interest, sprinkle a little cinnamon or nutmeg on squash before baking, or mix ¼ cup of orange juice frozen concentrate, ¼ cup honey, and 1 teaspoon salt; put some of the mixture in each squash cavity.

Sweetpotatoes. Two general types of sweetpotatoes are grown commercially.

One type, sometimes called "Yams" or "Porto Ricans," has a soft, moist texture when cooked and very sweet, orange to orange-red flesh. Depending on variety, the skin may be orange, pale rose, or copper-red.

The second type, when cooked, is firm, somewhat dry and mealy, and has pale orange to light yellow flesh. The skin is usually a light yellow to fawn colored. The popularity and production of this type has dwindled rapidly.

Processed sweetpotatoes come in diverse forms, from only partially cooked to almost ready to eat. Canned sweetpotatoes may be vacuum-packed, without any liquid, in a sirup, or solid pack (solid pack is tightly packed with little liquid). They are canned whole, mashed, or as pieces. Frozen sweetpotatoes are available whole or halved, peeled or unpeeled, baked, stuffed in a shell, sliced, french cut, diced, mashed, and sometimes formed into cakes.

Dehydrated sweetpotatoes need only hot water added to produce a mashed sweetpotato that can be served with butter or used in recipes calling for mashed sweetpotatoes.

Fresh sweetpotatoes should be well-shaped and firm, with smooth, bright, uniformly colored skins.

Sweetpotatoes can be boiled, baked, browned, fried, or candied, or used for making pies, custard, cookies, and cakes.

For best flavor and nutritive value, always cook sweetpotatoes whole in their jackets—it takes 35 to 55 minutes in boiling water and about 35 to 60 minutes in a hot oven (425° F.). The moist type cooks in less time than the mealy type.

Delicious Sweetpotato Puff can be prepared from either fresh, canned, or dehydrated sweetpotatoes.

SWEETPOTATO PUFF

6 servings, ⅔ cup each

2 cups mashed sweetpotatoes
¾ cup hot milk
3 tablespoons butter or margarine
¼ teaspoon salt
¼ teaspoon allspice
1 tablespoon grated orange rind
2 eggs

To the sweetpotatoes add the milk, fat, salt, allspice, and orange rind. Mix well. Separate eggs. Beat the egg yolks and add to sweetpotato mixture. Beat egg whites until stiff, and fold the potato mixture into the whites. Place in a baking dish and bake at 350° F. for 45 minutes.

Tomatoes. The tomato is a colorful and a nutritious asset to any meal, served in soups or salads, vegetable dishes, sauces, spicy relishes, and preserves for breakfast, lunch, or dinner.

Best flavor usually comes from "home-grown" tomatoes produced on nearby farms because these tomatoes are generally allowed to fully ripen on the vine. Many areas, however, now ship tomatoes which are picked after the color has begun to change from green to pink. These have flavor almost as satisfying as "home-grown" tomatoes.

Canned tomatoes are usually peeled and packed in their own juice but they may have some added tomato pulp or semisolid paste. The higher grades have a better color, usually more whole than broken pieces, and are free from peel, core, and other defects. U.S. Grade A Whole is a special grade, consisting principally of whole tomatoes.

Many canned tomato specialties, different from those you may usually buy, are becoming available. They include pear- or plum-shaped tomatoes, slices, dices, and other forms which are firm and have little juice. Many of these may be used in salads.

Fresh tomatoes should be well formed, smooth, plump, well ripened, and reasonably free from blemishes. For fully ripe fruit, look for an overall rich red color and a slight softness. Softness can be detected with gentle handling. For tomatoes less than fully ripe, look for firm texture and color ranging from pink to light red. Green tomatoes should be kept at room temperature away from direct sunlight to continue ripening.

Avoid overripe and bruised tomatoes (they are both soft and watery), tomatoes with distinctly yellow areas around the shoulder, those with deep growth cracks.

When fresh tomatoes are plentiful, serve them sliced, stuffed, in salads, or baked whole. Cut fresh tomatoes in half, and broil or bake them. To perk up the flavor, top with grated cheese or buttered crumbs, salt, and paprika. Fresh or canned tomatoes are fine in combination with almost any other vegetable.

Green tomatoes are used for frying, pickling, and combining with other foods.

Either green or ripe tomatoes cut in ½-inch slices can be fried in a small amount of hot fat. Dip the slices into flour, salt, and pepper or in fine, dry breadcrumbs before frying.

For a luncheon or dinner, Baked Stuffed Whole Tomatoes are a real treat. Stuff them with cheddar cheese, chips of crisp bacon, and some of the tomato pulp scooped from the center. Top with more bacon and cheese and pop into the broiler until browned slightly. Another popular stuffing for tomatoes, Savory Crumb Stuffing, is made from a quart of soft breadcrumbs, 1 teaspoon of poultry seasoning, and salt to taste. Cook 1 chopped onion and ¼ cup chopped celery in ¼ cup butter for about 5 minutes, and mix with breadcrumbs and tomato centers. Stuff tomatoes and bake at 375° F. for about 15 minutes.

Turnips, Rutabagas. The most popular variety of turnips has white flesh and a purplish tinting of the upper surface.

Rutabagas are distinctively yellow-fleshed, large-sized relatives of turnips. Rutabagas are usually coated with a thin layer of paraffin to prevent shriveling and loss of moisture. The paraffin is easily removed by peeling before cooking.

Good quality turnips are small or medium sized, smooth, fairly round, and firm. If sold in bunches, the tops should be fresh and green. Rutabagas should be heavy in relation to their size, smooth, round to moderately elongated, and firm. Both should have only a few leaf scars at the crown and very few fibrous roots at the base.

Avoid turnips or rutabagas that are soft or shriveled, cut or punctured. Those that are light in weight for their size are likely to be tough, woody, pithy, and strong flavored.

Rutabagas and turnips are cooked in the same way—peeled and cooked in large pieces if they are to be mashed, or cut into small cubes if they are to be buttered or creamed. Turnips may be cooked whole in 20 to 30 minutes; cut-up turnips take only half as long to cook.

Turnips and rutabagas are excellent additions to stews and soups, enhancing the flavor of the other ingredients, as well as their own.

A vegetable medley of cooked diced turnips, diced carrots, and green peas makes a pretty color and interesting flavor combination, seasoned with salt and pepper, and butter or margarine.

For a special occasion, creamed turnips can be topped with shredded cheddar cheese and baked in a moderate oven just long enough to melt the cheese. Cooked turnip sticks sprinkled with lemon juice, finely chopped onion, and parsley is another interesting way to vary this vegetable.

Raw turnips, with their nippy flavor, are good additions to the relish tray or the salad bowl.

For further reading:

U.S. Department of Agriculture, *Family Fare: Food Management and Recipes.* Home and Garden Bulletin 1, Washington, D.C. 20250, 1966.

——— *Home Canning of Fruits and Vegetables.* Home and Garden Bulletin 8, Washington, D.C. 20250, 1965.

——— *Home Care of Purchased Frozen Foods.* Home and Garden Bulletin 69, Washington, D.C. 20250, 1967.

——— *Home Freezing of Fruits and Vegetables.* Home and Garden Bulletin 10, Washington, D.C. 20250, 1967.

——— *How to Buy Fresh Vegetables.* Home and Garden Bulletin 143, Washington, D.C. 20250, 1967.

——— *Shopper's Guide for Canned Peas.* Program Aid 728, Washington, D.C. 20250, 1966.

——— *Storing Perishable Foods in the Home.* Home and Garden Bulletin 78, Washington, D.C. 20250, 1967.

——— *Storing Vegetables and Fruits in Basements, Cellars, Outbuildings, and Pits.* Home and Garden Bulletin 119, Washington, D.C. 20250, 1966.

——— *Vegetables in Family Meals.* Home and Garden Bulletin 105, Washington, D.C. 20250, 1968.

This vegetable platter combines carrots, beets, green snap beans, and swiss chard.

Bernice K. McGeary
Malcolm E. Smith

Nuts, a Shell Game That Pays Off in Good Eating

Nuts in a bowl are attractive and taste tempting any time of the year and are an American tradition during the Thanksgiving and Christmas holidays. There is a certain satisfaction in obeying that impulse to crack and eat some of them.

Nuts play an important role in our diet. They rank high for good eating and nutrition.

The many kinds of nuts, broadly speaking, are marketed in just a few forms: In the shell or as shelled kernels; and raw or roasted.

Mixed kinds, in demand both for appearance and variety of flavor, are perhaps the most popular in-shell nuts. They are usually made up of almonds, brazil nuts, filberts, pecans, and walnuts. But each kind of these in-shell nuts can also be found singly at many food markets in late fall and early winter. Other kinds of nuts commonly offered for sale in the shell are coconuts, peanuts, and pistachios, and sometimes pine nuts—the last three generally roasted.

In-shell peanuts are available to most consumers in the roasted form known as "ball-park peanuts." Actually, peanuts belong to the pea and bean family, but they are classified with nuts because they are similar in use and food value. A major difference is that around half of the peanuts produced go into peanut butter.

Raw nut meats most likely to be on the grocer's shelf are walnuts, pecans, almonds, and black walnuts. They are offered in a variety of packages, qualities, and sizes of pieces at a wide range of prices. Raw shelled peanuts, brazils, filberts, and cashews appear in relatively few stores to supply a limited demand.

A price comparison between in-shell and shelled nuts may be of interest to you as a buyer. For a method of approach, say that a pound of English walnuts in the shell costs 60 cents, and 1 pound contains approximately 7 ounces of kernels. This cost, compared with the retail price of 7 ounces of nutmeats, tells the story. One pound of other kinds of in-shell nuts will yield these approximate ounces of nutmeats: Almonds, 6½; brazils, 8; filberts, 7; pecans, 6¾; and black walnuts, 3½.

Roasted, mixed salted nuts usually include three or more kinds. Peanuts, cashews, brazils, almonds, and filberts are used most. Percentage of each in a mix varies widely among commercial packers, and is reflected in prices. Peanuts are often the least expensive nuts, and this creates an incentive to use more of them in the mix. In view of this fact, some packers label their packages either "with peanuts" or "without peanuts."

Some nuts on the market are dry roasted. The term "dry" simply means that no fat has been added. In addition, there are low-calorie peanuts which have had a high percentage of the fat removed. Since much of the flavor of nuts is in the fat, "defatted" ones are milder in peanut flavor.

Bernice K. McGeary is a Nutritionist with the Consumer Use of Foods Staff, Human Nutrition Research Division, Agricultural Research Service.

Malcolm E. Smith, now retired, was a Marketing Specialist, Fruit and Vegetable Division, Consumer and Marketing Service.

Volumewise, processed coconut is one of the most important nuts. It is marketed almost exclusively in sweetened, grated, or shredded forms. Its flavor and texture are similar to fresh coconut. Sometimes, more perishable coconut that is labelled "fresh" is sold in stores where it can be quickly moved for immediate use.

Grade standards have been established for a number of kinds of nuts by the Consumer and Marketing Service of the U.S. Department of Agriculture. Use of standards is not compulsory, nor are packers of nuts required to mark containers with grade designations. However, if a package of nuts is so marked, the packer is legally obligated to make the contents meet requirements of the grade specified. Hence, a grademark on a container is a reliable indicator of the quality. The upper grades provided in each of the existing standards are listed in a table below.

Inspection service is made available at cost to the nut packing industry by the Consumer and Marketing Service and cooperating State departments of agriculture. Government inspectors will, upon request, determine and certify the quality and grade of a specific lot of nuts.

Some packers of nuts have contracted with USDA's Inspection Service to have "continuous inspection" at their plants. Inspectors are present in such plants at all times. A packer agrees to place high-quality nuts in his packages in return for the privilege of printing the U.S. Department of Agriculture quality shield or the statement "USDA Inspected" on his containers. This shield indicates the best quality grade, and the "USDA Inspected" indicates a very good quality.

Selection of nuts deserves care. Like the cover of a book, the shell of a nut may be deceiving. Fully developed shells can contain defective or poorly developed kernels even though the shells may be bleached or dyed and waxed to improve their appearance.

Price alone is not a reliable basis for judging quality of either shelled, unshelled, or roasted nuts. Price tags may be governed by kind, size, form of nutmeats, a name, or other factors rather than the actual quantity and quality of the nut kernels.

The best aid to the shopper is a statement on the label which shows that the nuts are of a certain U.S. grade, or they have been subjected to USDA inspection, or both.

When nuts are ungraded or do not carry the inspection mark or USDA shield, you will especially need to look for other signs of quality. Sometimes experience will teach you that certain brand or packers' names are meaningful. There are more guides which are related to particular forms of nuts.

Most in-shell nuts are found in the colorfully printed "see-through" bags or "window" boxes. Although these

U.S. Grade Standards for Nuts

Kind of Nut	Grade	Description of quality
In-shell		
Almonds	U.S. No. 1	Best quality.
Brazils	"	" "
English walnuts	"	" "
Filberts	"	" "
Pecans	"	" "
Mixed nuts (almonds, brazils, filberts, pecans, and English walnuts).	U.S. Extra Fancy	Best quality and largest sizes. At least 10 percent but not over 40 percent of each kind in the mixture.
	U.S. Fancy	Same quality and mixture, but permits smaller sizes of some kinds.
Shelled, raw		
Almonds	U.S. Fancy	Best quality.
	U.S. Extra No. 1	Almost the best—permits a few doubles and broken.
	U.S. No. 1	Very good quality—permits more doubles and broken.
English walnuts	U.S. No. 1	Best quality.
Pecans	U.S. No. 1	" "
Peanut butter	U.S. Grade A	" "

containers allow somewhat limited observation of the contents, label information may be helpful to the consumer. Nuts which are available in bulk permit thorough, unobstructed examination of individual nuts for good or bad factors which determine the quality.

Nuts with clean, bright shells are likely to contain good kernels. Shells that are dull, dirty, or stained, and those that are cracked or broken are sometimes indicative of defective kernels inside. More important is weight of individual nuts in proportion to their size. The heavier the nut, the meatier the kernel.

Good coconuts are relatively easy to select. First, shake the coconut to determine that it has a large amount of liquid or "milk." This is the most important indication of freshness. Then examine the "eyes," those three small, circular, depressed areas near one end of the coconut. Eyes should be solid—not cracked or punctured. Finally, look over the entire shell to make sure it is not cracked.

Chestnuts can be deceiving in appearance, but there are a few criteria which may guide shoppers. Heavy weight is the best single indication of a sound, fresh kernel. Shells should be somewhat glossy and should be pliable under pressure from the fingers. They should also be free from mold.

Choosing shelled nuts may be a confusing matter to the consumer who is faced with a large assortment of small packages. The task can be made easier and more successful if a few general factors relating to quality are known.

In transparent containers, the contents can be seen, yet nutmeats are protected from oxidation and contamination. Vacuum-packed metal cans more completely protect the contents from effects of air, light, and contamination, but shoppers cannot inspect the nuts before buying.

As a rule, broken kernels or "pieces" are less expensive than whole kernels or "halves" of the same kind of nuts. The smaller pieces are just as well or better suited for a great many uses.

Exposed flesh of broken or chopped nutmeats should be light colored and look fresh, though color will vary somewhat with the kind of nut. Yellowish, oily appearance indicates aging with probable stale flavor or possible early stages of rancidity.

Color of the skin covering the nutmeat may also vary with the age and kind of nut. Although lighter color is generally considered preferable, this is largely a matter of appearance.

Large amounts of powdery material and "chaff" or "meal" in a package may be due to poor screening before packing. However, plastic bags sometimes create static electricity and attract particles which give an exaggerated impression of the amount of meal present.

Close examination of nutmeats in transparent containers will give assurance that they are apparently free from spoiled kernels and pieces of shell.

Roasted and salted nuts can be chosen by most of the same basic quality guides as for shelled, raw nuts. Sometimes the advice of a reputable merchant is helpful.

Keeping quality of nuts depends on the way you treat good ones. Under poor conditions, some kinds become inedible within a month. Ideally stored, these same kinds of nuts have retained top quality for 5 years.

Most nuts can soon lose flavor or develop off-flavor and darken, or they can mold if not protected from air, heat, light, and excessive moisture.

Rancidity is perhaps the worst enemy of kinds of nuts that are highest in fat. Generally speaking, nutmeats are 50 to 70 percent fat, except for coconuts that are 35 to 40 percent fat, and chestnuts with only a trace. The fat reacts with oxygen from the air to cause "oxidation" or development of rancid flavor and odor.

You can keep in-shell nuts that are highest in fat in a cool, dry basement throughout the winter. Shelled ones retain top quality in tightly closed containers in the refrigerator for 6 months or more, or in the freezer at 0° F. for 2 years. The high-fat nuts keep longer at low temperatures or unshelled and unroasted. Shelled nuts also keep longer if kernels are unbroken (less surface exposed to air), vacuum packed, or are processed with preservatives.

Peanut butter, consisting of roasted and ground peanuts, will deteriorate less rapidly after the container is opened if it is refrigerated.

Fresh coconuts and chestnuts are more perishable than other nuts. If refrigerated, coconuts will keep up to a month and chestnuts should keep several months. Chestnuts must be treated differently from other nuts. They are more like a starchy vegetable and need to be stored in loosely covered containers or ventilated plastic bags. This prevents accumulation of moisture on the nuts but keeps them from becoming dry and hard.

To freeze nutmeats, pack them in tightly closed containers or in plastic bags. Wrap chunks of fresh coconut tightly to expel the air from around them. Cover fresh, shredded coconut with liquid (milk) drained from the coconut. Blanch chestnut meats before freezing them; cook frozen ones without defrosting.

Nuts are versatile foods. They are shared with the monkeys at the zoo, and they go to the fanciest party. Nuts also "dress-up" any part of a meal—fruit cup or soup, main dish or stuffing, salad or salad dressing, vegetable or vegetable sauce, all types of breads, and a multitude of desserts.

Preparation of nuts may be complete if you buy them already shelled. They are available whole, cut, broken, or ground; and they are either raw or roasted in a number of ways. Some kinds are blanched. Processed coconut is grated or shredded in different ways and it comes in varying degrees of moistness. In-shell nuts, on the other hand, may require considerable time and attention before they are usable.

Shelling nuts is a slow, awkward process for some persons—fun only for snacking. Experience brings more speed and ease and less broken nutmeats. Hard shells may be easier to crack if nuts are first soaked in warm water several hours or overnight. Nutmeats will come out less broken too,

Coconut yule log—frosting with coconut over a jelly roll.

Above, three peanut flavored drinks and peanut butterscotch squares. In photo on opposite page, Roll It In Peanuts is the theme.

but will need to be dried before storing.

To prepare a fresh coconut, pierce the "eyes" and drain out the "milk." Place the coconut on a firm surface and strike it with a hammer in several places to crack the shell. Remove nutmeat from the shell. Separation is easier if the coconut is either baked at 325° F. for about 25 minutes or is frozen before cracking. Then use a vegetable parer to remove the brown skin from the coconut meat.

Removing thick skins from some nut meats gives them a more delicate flavor and better appearance.

"Blanching" is a common term for this process.

To loosen skins of raw almonds or peanuts, let them stand in boiling water for about 3 minutes or roast them. The skins should then slide off easily. Loosen the skins on filberts by baking them at 300° F. for 10 to 15 minutes. Let shelled chestnuts stand in boiling water for 2 minutes. Remove a few nuts at a time, cool slightly, and peel them. Reheat chestnuts that are difficult to peel.

Roasting nuts is an ancient custom. Flavor and color usually become richer and nuts are more crisp when roasted or toasted. There are a few nuts, peanuts being most common, which so often reach the consumer roasted that many people have never tasted raw ones. Freshly prepared nuts are always best. It is quick and easy to roast or toast them for snack treats or for use in recipes, but watch them carefully because nuts scorch easily!

To roast or toast nutmeats or processed coconut in the oven, spread in a shallow pan. For richer flavor and more even browning, mix a teaspoon of oil or melted fat with each cup of nuts. Bake at 350° F. for 5 to 12 minutes until lightly browned, stirring occasionally. Salt the hot nuts, if you desire. Add a little fat to help make the salt cling, if needed.

Nutmeats or processed coconut can also be toasted in a heavy pan on top of the range. Heat them slowly for 10 to 15 minutes until lightly browned, stirring frequently.

Roast in-shell peanuts in a shallow pan at 350° F., stirring occasionally, about 18 minutes or until skins slip off easily and kernels are a rich brown.

"Chestnuts roasted on an open fire" are an American legend. Along with extinction of the native chestnut went frequent appearance of this nut in the home. If you are tasting roasted chestnuts for the first time, you will be surprised to find that the nutmeats are sweet and have been softened by cooking. Their texture is somewhat like cooked potatoes; both are starchy foods. And if you're roasting chestnuts for the first time, you may be shocked and have an oven to clean, too, if you are unaware of another characteristic of these nuts. They will explode unless the shells are slit before heating to allow steam to escape. Of course, some say that one nut should be allowed to "pop" and thereby announce that all are roasted.

For roasting chestnuts, slash each nut through the shell on the flat side. Place them, cut sides up, on a baking sheet. Roast at 400° F. about 20 minutes until tender.

Using nuts as food was a custom of North American Indians. Colonists no doubt found their inheritance of nuts provided both subsistence and good eating. Nutmeats were added to stews or were ground into meals for breads or puddings. Some were even made into milklike beverages.

Old recipes using acorns as human food only make conversation today—the squirrels can have these nuts. On the other hand, imagine where we would stand without some of the kinds of nuts handed down to us—black walnuts, filberts (cultivated hazelnuts), and pecans.

When nuts are a part of foods, they contribute rich flavor, give contrast in texture, and make a pleasing garnish.

You can substitute any common nut, except chestnuts and coconut, for another kind in recipes. Each nut will, of course, add its own special flavor. Salted nuts should not replace unsalted ones unless salt can be reduced in the recipe. Any peanuts used should be roasted or toasted ones unless they will brown in preparation of the food. Do not use ground-up nuts or peanut butter for other forms of nuts.

The black walnut is the only common nut with such full flavor that it is almost never roasted. It is often the primary flavor of a food.

Nut brittle is especially good when made with most any kind of freshly roasted nuts, including mixed ones. You can even brown raw peanuts right in the candy as it cooks, if desired.

Soups have been one of the least likely places for nuts to appear. The author of the expression "soup to nuts" perhaps never thought of combining the two. Now they seem to be used this way to some extent around most of the world. You can use pecans to make Cream of Nut Soup into a Mardi Gras special or use cashews for a San Juan version. For a Ghana-like peanut soup, use peanut butter.

To keep nuts crisp in foods, add them just before serving or use them as a garnish. Dry or toast any limp nuts such as frozen, defrosted ones before using them.

To extend nut flavor in foods, use small pieces, roast or toast them, or use more highly flavored nuts. Flavor is enhanced when nuts are used with brown sugar instead of white or by adding a little maple or almond flavor to some foods.

Macadamias and pine nuts are not as widely known as nuts that are more available and perhaps lower in price. Either is a real treat.

Macadamias look much like hazelnuts, but are competitors of cashews for flavor. They are good raw, but only roasted ones may be available to you unless you live where they are grown, in Hawaii and California.

Pine nuts are a Biblical food. The many varieties of these pine seeds come under the broad name, "pignolias." Common ones in Europe and Brazil are longer than the popular, tiny "Indian" nuts of our Southwestern States. Some European varieties have a slight turpentine flavor unless the nuts are cooked. The "piñon" (Spanish for pine), which includes Indian nuts, is the most common kind. Confectioners like this nut for a dainty garnish.

Pine nuts are used in all kinds of foods and make gourmet mixed, salted nuts.

You can "experiment" with nuts. Special recipes are not always needed. It takes only a little imagination to make "company fare" of plain food. Many good old standbys are even better with nuts. Start in with these suggestions:

Add toasted nuts to creamed or saucy meat dishes or vegetables.

Serve sour cream with nuts on meat or baked potatoes.

For waffles, biscuits, or muffins, stir nuts into blended dry ingredients before adding liquid.

Mix crisp bits of bacon with peanut butter for a sandwich filling, or use peanut butter and cheese slices for a grilled sandwich filling.

Add nuts to meat, to poultry, or to seafood salads.

Try slivered or sliced nuts in tossed vegetable salads.

Make tiny cream cheese-nut balls to add to jellied salads.

Mix coconut with a food color for garnish.

Roll ice cream balls in tinted or toasted coconut or chopped nuts. Freeze balls separately until set.

Use toasted coconut or toasted, chopped nuts as a quick topping for cream pie or ice cream pie.

Sprinkle cupcakes with nuts before baking to eliminate icing them.

Here are some recipes:

SUGAR AND SPICE NUTS

About 3½ cups

1 tablespoon butter or margarine, melted
1 egg white, slightly beaten
1 cup sugar
½ teaspoon salt
1½ teaspoons cinnamon
¾ teaspoon nutmeg
¾ teaspoon allspice
2 cups mixed nuts (almonds, English walnuts, and pecans)

Stir cooled fat into egg whites. Add nuts.

Mix the sugar and spices. Spread about one-fourth of the mixture in a large, shallow baking pan.

Coat a few nuts at a time with the remaining sugar and arrange in pan. Sprinkle rest of sugar on nuts.

Bake at 300° F. about 18 minutes until lightly browned. Stir gently to separate and coat nuts. Cool and store in closed containers.

SOUTHERN NUT CHESS PIE

9-inch pie

1 cup brown sugar, packed
½ cup granulated sugar
1 tablespoon flour
2 eggs
¼ cup milk
½ cup butter or margarine, melted
1 teaspoon vanilla
¾ to 1 cup chopped pecans or roasted (unsalted) peanuts
9-inch unbaked pastry shell

Mix sugars and flour. Beat in eggs and milk. Stir in fat, vanilla, and nuts. Pour into pastry shell.

Bake pie at 375° F. for 40 minutes or until a knife inserted in the center comes out clean.

NUT CHESS TARTS

In place of pastry shell, separate the dough into 12 parts. Roll thinly and fit into 2½-inch muffin tins. Add filling. Baking time will be shorter than for the pie.

BLACK WALNUT BREAD USA

1 loaf

⅔ cup light brown sugar, packed
¼ cup shortening
2 eggs
2 cups unsifted flour
2 teaspoons baking powder
½ teaspoon baking soda
½ teaspoon salt
1 cup milk
1 cup chopped black walnuts

Beat the sugar, shortening, and eggs until creamy.

Mix dry ingredients thoroughly; stir alternately with the milk into the egg mixture. Mix nuts with the last portion of the flour before adding to the batter.

Pour into a greased 9- by 5- by 3-inch baking pan. Bake about 1 hour, or until a toothpick inserted in center comes out clean.

Cool 10 minutes before removing from pan.

PARTY NUT BREAD

Use ½ cup pecans, English walnuts, or brazils for the nuts. Add ¾ cup chopped, candied fruit and 1 teaspoon grated lemon rind with the nuts to the dry ingredients.

NUT BRITTLE

1½ pounds

2 cups sugar
½ cup light corn sirup
⅔ cup water
2 tablespoons butter or margarine
1 teaspoon vanilla
½ teaspoon baking soda
1½ cups roasted, salted nuts

Combine sugar, sirup, water, and fat in a large, heavy saucepan. Cook, stirring only until sugar dissolves. Then cook mixture to 300° F., or until a few drops form hard, brittle threads in cold water. Remove from heat.

Stir in remaining ingredients. Pour over a greased baking sheet. Pull thinner while cooling, if desired. Cool and break into pieces.

Note: To use raw peanuts, add them and ¼ teaspoon salt to the sirup at 238° F., or when a drop makes a soft ball in cold water. Continue to cook as above.

CREAM OF NUT SOUP

6 servings

1 tablespoon butter or margarine
2 tablespoons finely chopped celery
2 tablespoons finely chopped onion
2 tablespoons flour
1 cup milk
2 cups chicken broth or bouillon
¼ teaspoon hickory salt or Worcestershire sauce
1 cup salted pecans or cashews, finely chopped
Salt and pepper, as desired
Paprika or minced parsley, as desired

Melt fat in a large, heavy saucepan. Add celery and onion; cook, stirring frequently until tender.

Blend in flour. Gradually stir in liquids, hickory salt or Worcestershire sauce, salt and pepper, and nuts. Bring to a boil and cook 1 minute longer, stirring as needed.

Garnish with paprika or parsley.

CREAM OF PEANUT BUTTER SOUP

Reduce flour to 1 tablespoon in the above recipe. Blend in ¾ cup peanut butter before adding liquids. Omit other nuts.

SUNDAE NUT SIRUP

6 servings

½ cup pecans or English walnuts, chopped
2 tablespoons butter or margarine, melted
¼ cup brown sugar, packed
2 tablespoons water
2 tablespoons light corn sirup

Stir the nuts in the fat over low heat until lightly browned. Add the remaining ingredients. Simmer for 2 minutes.

Serve warm over ice cream.

An array of nuts—including Indian nuts (pine nuts or piñon), coconut, cashews, pistachios, pecans, mixed nuts, Macadamias, and peanuts.

Andrea C. Mackey

Cereals, the Staff of Life, Take on a New Importance in Today's World

Cereal grains are taking on new importance in the diets of today's people and those of the future.

All important civilizations were founded on the cultivation and use of one or another of the cereal grains. The early civilizations of Babylonia, Egypt, Greece, and Rome were based on the growing of wheat, barley, and the millets. The ancient cultures of India, China, and Japan were based on the rice crop. The Inca, Maya, and Aztec civilizations in the New World depended on their crops of corn.

Cultivation of the cereal grains began so long ago that their earliest history cannot be pinpointed exactly. However, we know they have been man's most important food plants since the dawn of history.

The cereal grains are the dried seeds of cultivated grasses which belong to the family Gramineae. They are rice, wheat, oats, barley, corn, rye, grain sorghum, and millet.

Cereals have stayed with us through the centuries for many reasons. One or more can be grown almost anywhere, thus making possible a food supply in nearly every corner of the world. They give high yields per acre in comparison with other food crops. They can be stored compactly for long periods and transported cheaply. They are palatable and nutritious.

All cereals consist of three parts: The bran, the germ, and the endosperm.

The whole grains are concentrated sources of needed nutrients, being especially valuable sources of starch, protein, the B vitamins, iron, and phosphorous. The protein of cereals is not complete. But the addition of other foods such as milk or meat supplements the cereal protein, thus enabling it to become a valuable nutrient to the body.

The cereal proteins are low in two essential amino acids, lysine and tryptophan. By "essential" we mean that these amino acids must be provided in the food that we eat for the protein needs of our bodies. We cannot manufacture them for ourselves from other things we eat.

Even now steps are being taken to improve the nutritive value of grain protein. Our agricultural geneticists have been developing strains of the cereal grains that will provide good sources of all the amino acids, including lysine and tryptophan. It looks as if, in the near future, the cereal grains produced by the everyday farmer will be nearly complete foods in that they will provide the bulk of nutrients needed by man for his daily food. He will still need to include sources of other nutrients such as vitamins A and C, which we now obtain from fruits and vegetables, and some minerals, such as calcium, which Americans usually get from milk.

In the United States, our dietary needs are met by including foods from four categories in our meals: The bread and cereal groups, meat group, milk group, and vegetable and fruit group.

The grains serve as food not only for man but for animals. Their unparalleled importance as food and feed, as well as their industrial use, imparts great economic value to the

Andrea C. Mackey is Professor of Foods and Nutrition at Oregon State University, Corvallis.

cereal grain crops. For example, corn yields starch which can in turn be converted to corn sirup. The germ of the corn grain is pressed to yield oil. Both the corn sirup and corn oil are common household materials used in food preparation.

Climate determines where each of the cereal grains can be grown.

Rice is the principal food of about half the world's people. About 95 percent of the world rice crop is produced and consumed in the southeastern part of Asia from India to Japan and the adjacent tropical and subtropical islands. The United States, however, is the biggest rice exporter in the world—although it has less than 1 percent of the world's rice acreage.

Corn is largely a New World crop, about half the world acreage being in the United States. In South America, the principal corn-growing countries are Argentina and Brazil.

Sorghum grain is fairly important throughout the world but particularly so for human food in India and Africa. Millets are used as food primarily in eastern and southern Asia, parts of Africa, and parts of the Soviet Union.

Wheat is the most widely cultivated of all cereal grains. It is grown in all countries lying in the temperate zones.

Rye can be grown in the colder climates. Winter rye, planted in the fall, can survive winter temperatures as low as 40° below zero. It is grown beyond the Arctic Circle in Finland and in Russia as far north as the border of Siberia.

More than 80 percent of the world acreage of oats lies in the moist, cool, temperate areas of North America, northern Europe, and Soviet Russia. In the United States, more than three-fourths of the crop is grown in the North Central States.

Barley is an important crop in many countries with a temperate climate. In the United States, the leading barley growing areas are in California, North Dakota, South Dakota, Minnesota, and Montana.

In early times, cereals were cooked by parching the whole grain. The grains were also ground between stones to form a coarse meal. This was made into heavy, unleavened flat bread or was boiled with water to make a porridge. Flat bread has been found along with parched or uncooked stores of wheat, barley, and millet in the ruins of the Swiss lake dwellers who lived six to seven thousand years ago. It has also been found in Egyptian tombs.

Today's consumers want convenience, high nutritive value, palatability, and attractive appearance in their foods. They get all this in cereals. Now the cereal grains come to the market in many different forms. Products made of corn, oats, rice, and wheat are most common. For convenience, we may think of cereals in two categories—those to be prepared by cooking and served hot, and those that are ready to eat as they come from the package.

The first ready-to-eat cereal was developed back in 1893. What an interesting new idea this was! And what merchandising problems must have arisen, for it was an entirely new type of product. It did not take long for the idea to catch on, however, and ready-to-eat cereal appeared on breakfast tables everywhere.

Next, in 1894, the first flaked cereal product was developed by Dr. John Harvey Kellogg.

Soon after, Charles W. Post produced a ground, ready-to-eat cereal. And in 1902, Alexander Anderson developed the first puffed cereal.

How are puffed grain products made? A manufacturer says that they really are shot from "guns." The "guns" are loaded with grain, and heat and pressure are built up. The pressure is suddenly released, and puffed kernels shower from the guns in a noisy explosion.

Today the homemaker can make her selection of ready-to-eat cereals from among 100 or more items, brands, and package sizes on the supermarket shelves.

Today's cereals not only have a

Noodles Romanoff with chops.

variety of taste appeal, but they also have added convenience. One of the chief appeals of the ready-to-eat cereals is their "no cooking" convenience. However, the traditional uncooked cereals now offer some of the same benefits. Some are "instant." Add hot water and they are ready to eat. Others take but 1 to 5 minutes of cooking time. Contrast this with the same kinds of cereals that 25 years ago took from 30 minutes to 3 hours to cook!

The quick cooking feature is achieved by cereal manufacturers in several ways. The grain may be precooked, then dried. A small amount of disodium phosphate may be added, or the cereal may be modified during manufacture with a small amount of enzyme preparation. All these processes make it possible for water to reenter the grain very rapidly, thus speeding up the cooking time.

The packaged cereal grains that are to be cooked should not be washed. To do so removes valuable nutrients, especially the B vitamins. Except for macaroni products, it is best to cook cereals and rice in just enough water so that the water will be completely absorbed. Pasta products (macaroni) are usually cooked in an excess of water. However, some recipes call for cooking them in meat broth in sufficient quantity so all of the liquid is absorbed.

The processing of cereals is a bigger enterprise in the United States than in any other country. They are manufactured here and exported throughout the world. The fabulous breakfast cereal industry originated in our country and has been propagated by our large cereal companies.

The story of grain as it moves from the farmer's field to the breakfast tables of the United States and many parts of the world is told by the Battle Creek Board of Education in a brochure,

Oatmeal bread.

"Inside Battle Creek." Farmers are the source of all grains, but grain directly from the field is not ready for processing. The farmers usually sell their grain to nearby elevators which clean and store the grain. They in turn sell the grain to elevators located near food processing centers, or directly to the food processors.

They may sell to brokers who act as intermediaries in supplying the needs of processors.

Following the purchasing of the grain, it is brought to the company's storage bins. It then enters the manufacturing chain which will result in the needed amount of the desired finished product. Marketing the finished cereals is regarded one of the many vital steps in routing the product to the customer.

To do a good job of marketing requires informing the public about the product, and creating and maintaining a demand for it. This is done by advertising. The cereals are shipped from the manufacturing plant to the retail stores, usually via food brokers or wholesalers, but sometimes directly to the warehouses of the large retail stores. When the packages arrive at the local market and are placed on the shelves, the homemaker should already be informed about them and she should be interested in trying them.

There are many uses for cereal grains.

Barley is sold as pearled barley which is popular for use in soups. It is the whole grain which has had the hulls and bran removed. Barley flour is used in baby foods and in breakfast cereals.

Corn is made into cornmeal or grits which must be cooked. Ready-to-eat corn flakes are made by blending grits with malt, sugar, and other ingredients, followed by cooking, rolling, and toasting.

Wheat and rye for human food are milled into flour. Rye flour is used for making bread. A high proportion of the wheat crop is milled into flour which in turn is used to create many kinds of baked goods, as crackers, bread, and cakes.

One variety of wheat (Durum) is made into macaroni type products. Wheat is also converted into breakfast cereals to be cooked and served hot, like farina, cream of wheat, and rolled wheat, and ready-to-eat kinds such as puffed, shredded, and flaked wheat.

Among the foods made from oats, rolled oats have been available for the longest time. In the ready-to-eat oats cereals, there are flaked, puffed, and shredded forms. Rolled oats, whether old fashioned, quick, or instant, are made from the whole grain, including the bran and germ.

Rice is boiled or steamed to prepare it for the table. It may be white polished rice, brown rice which retains part of the bran coat, or converted rice, which has been precooked and dried before polishing.

Consumer preference decides to a large extent which rice people buy. Brown rice has more nutrients (the B vitamins—thiamine, riboflavin, and niacin) but for many people doesn't have the sales appeal of polished white rice. Nor does brown rice cook up as fluffy and as quickly as some of the other rices. Converted rice or parboiled ranks next to brown rice in nutritive value. During the conversion process most of the vitamin B is forced into the interior of the grain and is not lost when the bran is discarded.

These differences are often adjusted with enrichment. Nowadays most of the breakfast cereals, whether ready to eat or to be cooked, are enriched by the addition of minerals and vitamins. Some are enriched with added protein.

Enrichment of grain foods with vitamins and minerals is of great importance to the nutritional well-being of many people. It is necessary that most of the calories consumed in the day's meals should carry with them a reasonable amount of nutrients, like the vitamins and minerals, to establish a balanced diet.

While whole grain cereals, containing as they do the bran and germ of the grain, have ample supplies of valuable vitamins and minerals, the bran coat tends to be somewhat firm and coarse even when cooked. Some people find whole grains harder to digest for this reason.

When processed into other forms attractive to a wide variety of personal tastes, the bran and germ are often removed, carrying with them much of the vitamin and mineral content. Enrichment returns these essential nutrients to the product, making the cereal equally or more nutritious than before processing.

To keep the flavor of cereals good from the time the package is opened until all the contents have been used, they should be stored in a dry, cool convenient place in the kitchen. By opening the cereal container carefully, it can be reclosed, thus helping to protect the food. It is also advisable to store cereals in a different place from soap or other products having strong odors.

Cereals should be kept in their original packages. The package label has important information. It identifies the product, tells how to cook it, and often gives a recipe which you may enjoy trying.

Cereals are inexpensive foods. It might be expected that those more sophisticated items like puffed or shredded enriched cereals would cost more than the grains from which they were developed. The cost of many ready-to-eat cereals having such special features as sugar coating and being crisply toasted is approximately four times as much as those that require cooking. When you remember you are buying food value—cereals are approximately 12 percent water while most other foods contain a much higher percentage of water—all cereals are among our least expensive foods. Each ounce of ready-to-eat or uncooked cereal has about 104 calories. One ounce is considered as an average serving.

Although spoken of as breakfast cereals, these foods readily perform special functions as ingredients in recipes intended for use at other meals. Their usefulness as ingredients is indicated by such recipes as the following:

"Date nut flake bread" in which whole wheat flakes, bran flakes, or corn flakes are used; "orange fluff pie" in which corn flakes are used to make the crust; or "easy-do tuna on buttery cereal crunch" in which creamed tuna is served over shredded wheat or bite-size cereals.

These recipes and a number of others were found in "Cereal Service Brochure," a publication of the Cereal Institute, Inc., 135 South LaSalle St., Chicago, Ill. 60603. This brochure will be sent to you without charge if you write for it.

CURRIED CHICKEN DELUXE

8 servings

Curried chicken:
1 cup chopped onions
½ cup chopped green pepper
¼ cup butter or margarine
¾ cup flour
5 cups chicken broth
or
3 cans chicken broth (12½ ounces each)
Salt to taste
2 tablespoons curry powder
4 cups chicken, cooked and diced

Saute onions and green pepper in the fat in a frying pan until tender.

Stir in flour.

Gradually blend in chicken broth. Add salt and curry powder.

Cook until thickened, stirring as needed.

Add chicken and heat thoroughly.

Serve over deluxe rice.

DELUXE RICE

½ cup slivered, blanched almonds
2 tablespoons butter or margarine
2⅔ cups water (or amount specified on package)
⅓ cup dried currants
1 teaspoon salt
2⅔ cups packaged precooked rice

Saute almonds in the fat in a frying pan until golden brown.

Add water, currants, and salt. Bring to a boil. Stir in rice. Then cover, remove from heat, and let it stand for 5 minutes.

Fluff with fork before serving.

PEANUT BUTTER CEREAL SQUARES

4 dozen pieces

5 cups toasted oat cereal rings
1 cup sugar-coated corn puffs
1½ cups sugar
1½ cups corn sirup, light
6-ounce package butterscotch bits
6-ounce package chocolate bits
¼ cup butter or margarine
3 tablespoons milk
½ teaspoon salt
2 cups peanut butter
2 teaspoons vanilla

Grease a 9″ x 13″ x 2″ baking pan.

Combine cereals; set aside.

Combine sugar, sirup, butterscotch and chocolate bits, fat, milk, and salt in large saucepan.

Heat, stirring until sugar melts.

Cook until mixture comes to a full boil. Then cook it 1 minute, stirring constantly.

Remove from heat.

Add peanut butter, vanilla, and cereals; mix well, and pour at once into baking pan.

Cool; cut into squares.

LASAGNA

4 large servings

4 ounces lasagna noodles
2 tablespoons butter or margarine
½ cup finely chopped onion
1 finely chopped garlic clove
½ pound ground beef
1 can (6 ounces) tomato paste
1 can (20 ounces) tomatoes
1 teaspoon salt
⅛ teaspoon pepper
¼ teaspoon basil
¼ teaspoon oregano
½ pound ricotta or cottage cheese
½ pound natural or process Swiss cheese slices
¼ cup parmesan cheese, grated

Cook lasagna noodles until tender, using package directions. Drain.

Separate lasagna and hang over

edge of colander or pan to allow for easy handling later.

While lasagna is cooking, melt fat in large frying pan.

Add onion and garlic and cook over moderate heat until tender. Add ground beef, and cook slowly, stirring frequently until red color disappears from meat.

Stir in tomato paste, tomatoes, salt, pepper, basil, and oregano.

Simmer 30 minutes, stirring occasionally.

In an 8-inch square baking dish, make three layers of meat sauce, lasagna, and ricotta, Swiss, and parmesan cheeses. Use about ⅓ of each for each layer, topping with parmesan cheese.

Bake at 350° F. until mixture is bubbly and cheese is lightly browned, about 35 to 40 minutes.

MACARONI, EGG, AND BEAN SALAD

6 servings

2 cups cooked and cooled elbow macaroni
½ cup mayonnaise
¼ cup french dressing
⅛ teaspoon hot pepper sauce
⅓ cup sweet pickles, diced
2 tablespoons vinegar
6 hard-cooked, cubed eggs
1 can (8 ounces) kidney beans, drained
Salt and pepper to taste

Mix all ingredients.

Chill and serve on lettuce or other salad greens. Garnish with watercress if desired.

STEAMED BROWN BREAD

2 loaves

1 cup rye flour
1 cup cornmeal
1 cup whole-wheat flour
2 teaspoons baking soda
1 teaspoon salt
¾ cup molasses
2 cups sour milk or buttermilk
1 cup seedless raisins

Mix dry ingredients.

Stir in molasses, milk, and raisins. Beat well.

Pour into two greased 1-pound coffee cans.

Cover cans with wax paper. Set on rack in deep pan over hot water. Cover pan tightly.

Steam for 3 hours.

Serve with butter or margarine.

PUMPERNICKEL

2 loaves

1½ cups warm water, 110°–115° F.
3 packages active, dry yeast
4 teaspoons salt
2 teaspoons caraway seeds
2 tablespoons shortening
½ cup molasses
2¾ cups sifted rye flour
3½ cups sifted flour

Measure water into mixing bowl and add yeast, stirring to dissolve. Stir in salt and caraway seeds. Mix in shortening, molasses, and rye flour until smooth. Mix in flour until dough can be handled.

Turn onto a lightly floured board; knead. Cover with a damp cloth. Let rise in warm place (about 85° F.) until double in volume. This will take about 1½ hours.

Punch down and let dough rise again until almost double.

Shape into two round, slightly flattened loaves.

Place on opposite corners of a greased baking sheet which has been lightly sprinkled with cornmeal.

Cover with damp cloth, and let rise until double in volume, about 1 hour.

Bake at 375° F. until brown, 30 to 35 minutes.

Brush loaves with fat after removing from oven. Cool on rack.

FRIED CORNMEAL MUSH

4 servings

Pour 2 cups cooked cornmeal mush into a loaf pan. Mush must be thick to mold.

Cover to prevent crust from forming. Chill thoroughly.

Cut in ¼-inch slices and fry in bacon drippings or other fat until crisp and nicely browned on both sides.

Serve hot with butter or margarine and with sirup or jelly and bacon or sausages if desired. (For a crisper crust, dip slices in cornmeal, then fry.)

WHOLE WHEAT PANCAKES

12 pancakes

1½ cups whole wheat flour
1 tablespoon baking powder
¾ teaspoon salt
3 tablespoons brown sugar
1 beaten egg
1¼ cups milk
3 tablespoons melted shortening

Thoroughly mix dry ingredients.

Combine the egg, milk, and shortening. Add to the dry ingredients and mix until smooth.

Drop the mixture from a spoon onto a hot, lightly greased griddle.

Cook until bubbles form on the top.

Turn and brown the other side.

VIRGINIA SPOON BREAD

6 servings

1 cup cornmeal
1½ teaspoons salt
2 cups scalded milk
2½ teaspoons baking powder
2 eggs, separated

Mix cornmeal and salt, stir into hot milk.

Cook over hot water until thick and smooth, stirring occasionally; cool slightly.

Stir in the baking powder and well-beaten egg yolks.

Fold in stiffly beaten egg whites.

Turn into greased casserole or 9-inch square pan.

Bake at 375° F. about 35 minutes, or until firm and crust is brown.

Serve from baking dish.

OATMEAL COOKIES

5 dozen cookies

¾ cup shortening
1 cup packed brown sugar
½ cup granulated sugar
1 egg
¼ cup water
1 teaspoon vanilla
1 cup sifted flour
1 teaspoon salt
½ teaspoon baking soda
1 cup raisins
3 cups rolled oats, uncooked

Place shortening, sugars, egg, water, and the vanilla in mixing bowl; beat thoroughly.

Sift together flour, salt, and soda; add to shortening mixture, mix well.

Blend in oats and raisins.

Drop by teaspoonfuls onto greased cookie sheets.

Bake at 350° F. for 12 to 15 minutes or until lightly browned.

Theresa A. Demus

Baking Treats Ad Infinitum: Breads and Tasty Pastry

Bread is one of man's oldest foods. It is referred to in the Old Testament as leavened and unleavened loaves and cakes. Over the world, bread is known by many names and is made from many grains—wheat, corn, rye, rice, oats, barley, buckwheat.

Bread continues to be an important part of our diet because the grains from which cereal foods are made are grown almost all over the world. These grains are readily available, produce high yields, and have low production cost. They also have excellent "keeping" qualities. Breads and the related cereal foods constitute the largest single item in the average diet. They are the greatest source of carbohydrates, furnishing many necessary calories. Enrichment and fortification of flour has greatly improved diets in which bread is the chief item.

When many of us think of breads, cakes, donuts, cookies, or pastries, we remember the irresistible aroma that drew us to the kitchen to swipe Mom's cookies.

Today, however, our markets provide bakery items ad infinitum. There are the ready-to-serve products, the partially-baked products, the ready-to-serve frozen products, the prepared frozen products, the canned prepared products, and the prepared mixes. These items are widely available, and there is considerable variety to suit individual needs and wants.

Ready-to-serve products have been baked and are ready for the table. Breads, sweet rolls, donuts, pastries, and cookies are among the numerous items of ready-to-serve products.

Partially-baked products are "half baked." Baking must be completed at home before serving. Available forms are loaves of bread, rolls, and buns.

Ready-to-serve frozen products are fully prepared products ready to serve after thawing. If desired, these products can be heated before serving. Cakes, pastries, some pies, rolls, and buns are sold in this manner.

Prepared frozen products have not been baked before freezing. They require baking before serving. Breads, pies, rolls, and hors d'oeuvres are available in today's market. These products must be kept frozen until used.

Canned prepared products must be completely baked before serving. Cookies, biscuits, and rolls are among the variety of products that can be purchased. Canned prepared products need to be refrigerated until used.

Prepared mixes are convenience preparations containing basic ingredients like flour, shortening, sugar, leavening. The consumer must add such ingredients as water or milk and/or eggs. Pie crusts, cakes, and roll mixes are available in this form. No refrigeration is needed for these mixes. They can be stored on the kitchen shelf.

Flours are made by grinding cereal grains to powders of varying fineness. A meal is coarsely ground flour.

Wheat is the preferred grain for flour. Present in wheat flour are the proteins—gliadin and glutenin. Gliadin is of a sticky nature which imparts adhesiveness to the gluten, while glutenin imparts tenacity and strength.

Theresa A. Demus is Director of the Consumer Services Staff, Office of the Assistant Commissioner for Education and Information, Food and Drug Administration.

Peach Paradise, above, and sourdough breads, below. To make Peach Paradise, start with large chiffon or angel food cake. Slice it into two layers and spread each layer with whipped cream. Freestone peach slices go between layers and are arranged on top. Combine layers and spread sides with whipped cream and toasted coconut.

The combination of these two very different proteins with water is known as gluten. Gluten is the elastic part of dough which allows the batter or dough to expand as gas is released from the leavening agent. When heated, it coagulates and forms the structure, imparting form and lightness to the product.

There are several types of wheat—durum wheats, hard wheats, and soft wheats. These wheats vary in the amount of protein they contain. Special blending of the wheat flours makes the flours more adaptable for special uses, for example:

- Pasta flours are milled from durum wheat which is high in protein, and their best use is to make noodles, macaroni, and spaghetti.
- Bread flours are milled primarily for the baker. They are a blend of hard spring and hard winter wheats. They may be bleached or unbleached. These flours are somewhat granular to the touch.
- Cake flours are bleached flours milled from soft wheats, and are the most finely ground of all the flours. Protein content of these flours is low.
- Pastry flours are generally milled from soft wheat; however, they can be made from either hard or soft wheat. These flours are used largely by bakers, and are unbleached.
- All-purpose flours can be blends of hard wheats or soft wheats or both, depending on what area of the country the wheat comes from. These flours are blended to obtain satisfactory results for general family cooking. Protein content is sufficient to make good yeast breads as well as quick breads.
- Self-rising flour is an intimate mixture of flour, sodium bicarbonate (baking soda), and one or more of the acid-reacting substances—monocalcium phosphate, sodium acid pyrophosphate, and sodium aluminum phosphate (baking powder).

Rye is second to wheat as a bread-making grain. This grain is used extensively with wheat in breads.

Rye flour is always darker than wheat flour. Bleaching has little effect on the color, but improves the baking properties. Rye gluten contains the same protein as wheat gluten, but in different proportions. Its proteins are very different in character and lack stability. Therefore, it is difficult to make a loaf of considerable volume.

Rye bread has a close texture and is difficult to bake. Pumpernickel is an example of an all-rye flour bread. Many varieties of bread are available currently with a rye and wheat grain combination.

Oats are rich in protein and are very nourishing although they are not suitable for breadmaking because they contain no gluten-forming protein.

Oats and oatmeal are important breakfast foods. They are also used with other flours to make tasty cookies.

Corn contains the protein gliadin but does not contain glutenin. This means that cornmeal cannot form gluten and must be used with a wheat flour for making breads. Cornmeal is used very extensively in the United States, particularly in the South, for making cornbread, spoonbread, muffins, and mush.

Barley is not normally used for breadmaking purposes. It is low in protein and fat. It is known for its high mineral content. This food is seldom used in our country except in soups.

Rice may be purchased as white (polished) or brown (unpolished) in varieties grouped as long grain, medium, or short grain.

Rice flour is milled from white rice. It is particularly useful in diets for persons who have allergies to other cereal grains. Rice flour can be used as a thickening agent or as flour in certain baked products such as cookies and pancakes.

Buckwheat is used only as pancake flour. It is not a true grain, but is used as a cereal.

In the refining, compounding, or processing of some foods, there is an unavoidable loss of vitamins and minerals. Enrichment is to replace or to restore the food by adding pure vitamins and minerals to the natural level of the original product.

Milling of low extraction fine white flour, cornmeal, and polished white rice results in unavoidable losses of some nutrients. The Food and Nutrition Board of the National Research Council, recognizing the deficiency of these products in vitamins and iron, recommended that all white flours be enriched. In the last several decades, the addition of thiamine, riboflavin, niacin, and of iron to wheat flour, macaroni and noodle products, farina, rice, cornmeal, and corn grits has been gradually introduced as a legally required procedure in a large number of States. Besides these four required enrichment ingredients, enriched flour and bread may contain two optional ingredients, calcium and vitamin D.

A food may be considered fortified when one or more ingredients have been added to provide certain nutrients that may or may not be present naturally in foods. For example, since milk in its natural state does not contain vitamin D, addition of the vitamin makes milk a fortified food. Today, both enrichment and fortification have become accepted routine steps in the manufacture of certain staple foods, and they contribute considerably to the nutritional welfare of our population.

What may start as mere enrichment may become modified to a combination of enrichment and fortification. Flour is a good example where enrichment was not limited to restoring previous natural values.

In setting legal requirements for enrichment of bread, human needs and the general dietary situation with respect to the nutrients involved were taken into consideration.

The Food and Drug Administration, an agency within the Department of Health, Education, and Welfare, is responsible for administering the Food, Drug, and Cosmetic Act, which also provides for the issuance of standards for food products, including bread. Enrichment of white bread began on a voluntary basis in 1941 and was made mandatory for all bakery white breads and rolls from 1943 to 1946. When this war measure was rescinded in October of 1946, more than half the States continued to require enrichment, and some processors and bakers continued to enrich their products on a voluntary basis.

Standards for bread and flour shipped in interstate commerce and labeled as enriched became effective August 13, 1952. Bread or flour identified as enriched must contain amounts of the four required enrichment ingredients (thiamine, riboflavin, niacin, and iron) in each pound of bread or flour as are written in the FDA regulations. Calcium and vitamin D are optional enrichment ingredients that may also be added to bread or to flour.

Food and drug inspectors maintain surveillance over the storage and transportation of grain in interstate commerce as well as in the flour mill to assure that adequate sanitation practices—and other safeguards—are followed. Flour labeled as "enriched" must contain the specified amounts of vitamins and minerals. FDA checks both by inspection and analysis to see that adequate amounts are present.

At the bakery, the FDA inspector checks the plant's storage areas, production line, equipment and facilities, and sanitation practices for evidence of conditions that may result in contamination. Besides visual examination, he takes samples of materials, ingredients, and in-line finished products to be analyzed. In the laboratory, the samples are checked for filth or contamination.

Most flours and bakeries come under the jurisdiction of State and local authorities. But the Federal Food, Drug, and Cosmetic Act of 1938 provided that foods shipped across State lines must be free from filth and must not be prepared or held under unsanitary conditions that cause them to become contaminated. Products in violation of this law should be reported to the nearest FDA office or, if produced in a local bakery, to the local health department.

In general, manufacturers are not required to state the ingredients on the label for standardized foods, except that the presence of any artificial flavoring, artificial coloring, or chemical preservative must be declared. The common or usual name on the bread or flour is in effect a statement by the manufacturer that the composition of his product will be what the consumer expects. It is therefore not ordinarily necessary for the label to state all the ingredients. When optional ingredients, such as bleaching agents, are used in flour, the label must state the word "bleached."

Label information must be conspicuously displayed and easy to understand. The label must contain the name and address of the manufacturer or distributor and an accurate statement of the amount of food in the package. The enrichment statement must also be included.

A nonstandardized bread product must list ingredients in order of predominance by weight to avoid consumer deception. All other information required for the standardized product is required for the nonstandardized food.

On the label of a loaf of bread you have probably seen the words "calcium and sodium propionate added to retard spoilage." The propionates have the ability of keeping bread from becoming moldy in the store or in your breadbox at home.

Sodium diacetate and lactic acid are also used in bread as mold or rope inhibitors. Rope is a bacterial infection that sometimes occurs in breads in hot and humid weather. It is identified by a strange odor resembling overripe pineapple or strawberries, by discolored crumb, and by a sticky and gummy consistency of the interior of the loaf. The rope bacteria is in the soil and in dust and can readily be transmitted to the dough. It is easy to understand why equipment must be scrupulously clean and a rope inhibitor must be used. The FDA has the responsibility of approving food additives as safe before they can be used in a food.

One should not buy cereal grain products by the size of package because this can be misleading. These products should be bought by weight. The cost may be determined by figuring the cost per ounce and the number of servings per package. Total cost of the contents of the package divided by the weight in ounces will give the cost per ounce.

Baked foods prepared at home are usually less expensive than those purchased ready to eat. Keep in mind that in the price of prepared products, you are paying for each step that is completed for you. However, when time is a precious element, sometimes it is more economical to buy prepared products rather than have to do the work at home.

Day-old bread is less expensive and just as nourishing as fresh bread, so take advantage of the day-old sales. Many consumers who have freezers may want to buy in quantity and freeze the products. This can mean a saving. Many times prepared products are on sale. If you have storage space in your refrigerator, these also are good buys.

Flours and meals are attractive to insect pests. This contamination can sometimes result from unsatisfactory storage conditions. To sidestep this problem, flour and meal should be stored in tightly covered containers in a cool, dry area. Flour held at high temperatures may become unusable. The flour container should always be cleaned thoroughly before a new supply is added.

Whole wheat products become rancid more quickly and are more difficult to store. Frozen baked products should be kept in the freezer at 0° F. or lower. Ready baked products can be frozen at the same temperature if wrapped and sealed properly.

Ready baked products also can be kept in the refrigerator if wrapped well. Refrigeration retards mold. Bread will become a little firmer in texture but its food value does not change. Breads that have been in the refrigerator can be freshened up by wrapping in aluminum foil and placing in a moderate oven for 10 to 12 minutes. Serve quickly.

Ready baked products can be kept in a breadbox, but keep in mind that bread picks up odors and it molds quickly, particularly in hot weather. The breadbox should be kept clean and dry.

Mixes can be stored on the kitchen shelf—but not in extremely warm temperatures. Ingredients in mixes deteriorate with storage. Depending on the ingredients, shelf life may be as long as a year.

Breads that have not been eaten when fresh need not be thrown away. They can be put to many uses. Biscuits, yeast rolls, bread, and muffins may be dried and ground to make dressings or meat fillings, for breading or topping in meats, poultry, fish, or vegetable dishes. In a container with a tight-fitting lid, the ground bread can be stored in the refrigerator for later use. Breads that contain fruit, nuts, or sugar can be used to great advantage in bread puddings.

Freezing is an excellent way of keeping foods. It retains freshness of the product. But don't expect anything better than what you have put in. Freezing will not enhance the flavor or texture. Freeze baked products the day they are baked.

It is important in freezing to have vapor- and moisture-proof, odorless, and tasteless materials in which to wrap the products. These materials should be durable but easy to handle. Plastic bags, heavy-duty aluminum foil, or wax- or plastic-coated paper are some of the popular materials which are used in freezing. Bread products should be thoroughly cooled before freezing.

Storage of bread should not exceed 3 months. Thaw breads at room temperature in the freezer container. It may take 1 to 3 hours. Rolls or muffins can be thawed at room temperature or placed unwrapped on a baking sheet and heated in the oven at 350° F. for 15 to 30 minutes.

Cakes with 7-minute frosting or boiled frosting should not be frozen. They tend to break down and become sticky. Unfrosted cakes stored more than 1 to 2 months are liable to lose some quality. Fruitcakes keep well for at least 1 year in a freezer.

Cakes should also be thoroughly cooled before freezing. Layer cakes may be stacked if a sheet of wax paper or its equivalent is placed between them before wrapping. I find that by taking one layer from the stack and cutting it in half and frosting it I have one half of a two-layer cake.

Frosted cakes should be frozen without being wrapped until frosting is frozen. Placing these cakes in a cardboard box is almost a must. This keeps the frosting from chipping or being smashed.

Thaw unfrosted cakes in freezer wrapping. Frosted cakes should be thawed without wrapping to prevent stickiness.

Cookies will keep about 6 months, baked or unbaked. Thoroughly cool baked cookies before freezing them. They can be stored in plastic bags or in sheet wrapping. Cookies thaw very quickly.

Most kinds of pies can be frozen, with the exception of custard. Cream pies can be frozen, but if your success isn't any better than mine, I would not recommend it.

Pie crust may be frozen in bulk, rolled in circles, or fitted and fluted in a pie pan. Circles should be stacked with two pieces of wax paper between layers so one may be removed without thawing the whole batch. The stack should be placed on a piece of cardboard, wrapped, sealed, and dated. Neither baked nor unbaked pie shells need thawing. Place pie crust in oven and bake as recipe directs. The top of double crust unbaked pie should not be cut before freezing.

When the term bread is used, it generally refers to quick breads or to yeast-leavened bread unless otherwise stated.

Orange crumble pumpkin pie.

Quick breads are what the name implies. They are relatively easy to make as well as being quick. Examples of quick breads are muffins, biscuits, waffles, pancakes, and coffeecakes. They are leavened with baking powder, soda, eggs, and steam.

There are three types of quick bread mixtures:

- Drop batter, such as is in a drop biscuit or muffins.
- Pour batter, as a pancake or waffle batter.
- Dough, such as rolled biscuits or dumplings.

Quick breads should not be overmixed. Overmixing develops gluten and causes tunnels and coarseness in the finished product. A good recipe will give the proper method for mixing. Quick breads always contain flour, liquid, fat, and leavening. They may also contain sugar, eggs, and flavoring. All-purpose (or family flour) is normally used for best results. If self-rising flour is used, read and follow directions on the package.

The difference between quick breads and yeast breads is the leavening agent. Quick breads are normally served hot, while yeast breads may be served hot or cold. Coffeecake and donuts are leavened breads but contain more sugar and fat and are considered good breakfast breads.

Each ingredient is an essential part of the finished product.

Flour is very basic in breadmaking

because it provides the gluten necessary in many baked products. Both hard and soft wheat flours make good yeast bread if used properly. The flour that's most used in breadmaking by the homemaker is all purpose.

Liquids are important to bind and mix the ingredients together. Water and milk are used in breadmaking. When water is used, the flavor of the wheat predominates. Italian and French breads and hard rolls are made with water.

Steam—In all batters and doughs, a certain amount of liquid is released to help leaven the mixture. In products where steam is the only form of leavening, the oven temperature must be hot to raise the temperature of the product to the boiling point quickly. Popovers and cream puffs are examples. Characteristic of these products are large central cavities.

Baking soda, baking powder, and yeast are used to produce carbon dioxide in breadmaking.

Pancakes, a pour batter product, make delicious and quick breakfast food.

Milk enhances the food value of the bread. Liquid or powdered skim milk can be used successfully in breadmaking. One-third cup of the skim milk powder to a pound of flour is a good proportion. Diluted evaporated milk is suitable and does not need to be boiled. If fluid milk is used, it should be boiled first. Condensed milk is sometimes an ingredient for making sweet breads.

A leavening agent is a substance used in flour mixtures which makes the cooked product porous or light. There are three leavening agents: Air, steam, and carbon dioxide.

Air can be incorporated into a product several ways: (a) By using beaten egg whites, (b) by creaming fat and sugar, and (c) by repeated sifting of the flour or by beating the mixture.

Baking soda used with an acid is simple and can be controlled easily. It does not develop flavor in the mixture as fermentation methods do. Baking soda, like baking powder, can leave a residue and in some cases may be undesirable. Sour milk and buttermilk are the acid-containing liquids used in this method. When fruit juice is an ingredient of a batter or dough, soda may be used to produce carbon dioxide. Soda and acid of fruit cut into cakes and cookies will combine to produce carbon dioxide.

All baking powders are combinations of an acid powder and baking soda in such proportion to form a salt. There are three kinds of baking powders: (1) Tartrate, (2) phosphate powders, and (3) sodium aluminum sulphate, often abbreviated as S.A.S.

The tartrate and the phosphate are single acting powders. The powders begin action as soon as the powder is mixed with the liquid. S.A.S. is a double acting powder; some action is begun when mixed with liquid and some takes place at oven temperature. Baking powder should be kept in tightly closed containers.

Yeast also produces carbon dioxide gas which aerates the dough and the final product and aids in its maturing or conditioning. It is available in moist or compressed yeast and as dry yeast. Dry yeast comes in foil packages and needs no refrigeration. Compressed yeast should always be stored in a cool place, preferably in a cool room or in the refrigerator at 42° F. If the temperature is lower, the yeast will keep for a longer period. If the yeast is frozen it will keep up to 3 months, after which there is a falling off in gas-producing power. Once yeast has been taken from the freezer and allowed to come up to a higher temperature, it should not be refrozen.

The primary function of salt in bread is to give flavor. Salt gives stability to the gluten to enable it to stretch without breaking as the gas expands. Salt prevents yeast from working too fast. For this reason some homemakers like to use more salt in the summer since the heat tends to speed up fermentation.

Sugar is not necessary in breadmaking from the standpoint of fermentation. But sugar does add flavor, improve texture, and increase browning potential. Sugar is a quick food for yeast, and occasionally it is added in amounts just to start yeast activity.

Fat and oil in bread improve flavor, add richness, and make it tender. They also help to keep bread moist.

Eggs provide a more delicate texture to breads as well as adding flavor. However, they are not essential in breadmaking.

Fancy breads may contain nuts, fruits, spices, and other flavorings.

One of the most *vital* steps in baking is measuring. Measuring is important in achieving a standard product each time it is made. After you select a recipe, do not alter the ingredients unless you know what the results will be, and you desire them.

Measuring equipment is inexpensive. Here is the basic equipment you should have: (1) A nest of measuring cups including ¼ cup, ⅓ cup, ½ cup, and 1 cup measure. Also available is a 1-cup and 2-cup graduated measuring cup with its capacity measure at the rim. (2) A set of measuring spoons including a ¼ teaspoon, ½ teaspoon, 1 teaspoon, and a tablespoon measure. (3) A measuring cup with the 1-cup line below the rim of the cup is good for measuring liquid ingredients. (4) A flour sifter. (5) A spatula to level off dry ingredients. A spatula looks like a knife but is straight on both sides and does not have a point. (6) A rubber scraper, which has many functions. It can be used to retrieve all the fat left in a measuring cup or to scrape batter from a bowl in mixing and when putting into a pan.

Recipes may call for sifted or unsifted flour. Sifted flour will be lighter in weight per cup, and substitution of sifted for unsifted flour is not advisable. Flour should be spooned lightly into a measuring cup and then leveled off with a spatula. Never shake the cup to level off the flour.

Brown sugar should be packed firmly in the cup. It should hold its shape when removed from the cup.

Sometimes brown sugar becomes lumpy. Sifting in a somewhat coarse sieve will help remove lumps.

Other sugars can be spooned into a cup, heaping slightly, and leveled off with a spatula. Should there be lumps, sift before measuring.

When measuring soda, baking powder, salt, and spices, the measuring spoon may be dipped into the container of the product and leveled off with a spatula. Some containers have paper covers that can be cut and used to level off the product.

Liquids should be measured in a liquid type measuring cup with the rim above the cup marker. This gives the opportunity to get the exact measure without spilling.

Above, apple crown pound cake. Right, the basic measuring equipment for baking: Liquid measuring cup, sifter, nest of measuring cups, measuring spoons, spatula, and rubber scraper.

In measuring a spoonful of liquid like vanilla or other flavoring, measure over an empty dish and not over other ingredients.

Butter, margarine, and shortening can be spooned from the container and packed firmly into a graduated or nest cup, leveling off with the rim.

The recipe you have selected will, as a general rule, give the size pan to use. Pans should be prepared before the mixture is begun. Should you use an oven glass pan instead of another type, lower your oven temperature 25° F. since the product may brown too quickly at the higher temperature.

Pans used for sponge or foam type cakes should not be greased or treated. However, jelly and cake roll cakepans are the exceptions and they should be lined with greased paper.

Pans used in shortening-type cakes should be greased and floured or lined with wax paper. To flour a greased pan, put approximately a spoonful of flour in pan and shake until pan is covered. Tap gently to remove excess.

The oven should always be preheated. Racks should be level and spaced well. In placing pans in the oven, keep in mind that the heat is the most even in the middle of the oven.

The two methods of combining ingredients in yeast breads are: The straight dough and the sponge methods.

In the straight dough method, the procedure should be (a) combining and mixing the ingredients; (b) kneading the dough—the dough should be kneaded until it is satiny (but batter doughs do not need this step. This dough is soft enough to form gluten by beating with spoon or mixer.); (c) allowing the dough to rise until dough has doubled in bulk; (d) shaping the loaves or rolls; (e) allowing them to rise again; and (f) baking at specified temperature and time.

In the sponge method of combining ingredients, there are two mixings. The liquid and yeast are combined, and just enough flour is added to make a thick batter. This mixture must be put in a warm place to rise. It will become light or bubbly. The rest of the flour, sugar, fat, and salt are added to the batter to make a dough that can be kneaded. The remainder of the procedure is like the straight dough method. In this method, less yeast is needed because of the length of time it has to grow. Also, flavor of bread made through this method is different but some prefer it.

The three general methods for combining ingredients for cakebaking are the muffin method, conventional method, and new speed method.

- Muffin Method—This is the method generally used in making muffins and is perhaps the simplest method. The three main steps are: (1) Sift dry ingredients together—flour, leavening, sugar, and salt (omit leavening and salt if self-rising flour is used). (2) Combine all the liquid ingredients—milk, beaten eggs, melted fat, and flavoring. (3) Add liquid to dry ingredients. Stir until mixed well.
- Conventional Method—This is considered the old-fashioned method of cake mixing. The procedures are: (1) Cream fat until light and fluffy. (2) Add sugar gradually and continue creaming until the two are blended well. (3) Add egg or egg yolks and beat until they are blended well with fat and sugar. (4) Sift dry ingredients together. (5) Add the flour mixture alternately with milk and flavoring, beginning and ending with the flour. (6) Fold the stiffly beaten whites into the well-mixed batter.
- New Speed Method—This method is known by several names, including baker's modified method or the one-bowl method. The steps in this method are: (1) Sift the dry ingredients together in bowl. (2) Add the fat, milk, and flavoring. (3) Beat vigorously for 2 minutes by hand (150 strokes per minute) or 2 minutes in the electric mixer. (4) Add the unbeaten eggs and beat for another 2 minutes. This method is extremely easy to use with an electric mixer. Texture of the cakes made by the speed method is very fine. The grain is finer and it may be described as "velvety" in contrast to

the feathery texture which is the aim of the conventional method.

To test cake for doneness, touch the top of the cake in the center lightly. If the indentation springs back, the cake is done; if the impression remains, the cake is not done. Another test is to insert a toothpick in the center of the cake. If the toothpick comes out clean, the cake is done. After baking, the cake should be removed from the oven to prevent dryness.

Icing helps to keep the cake moist as well as increasing attractiveness and palatability.

Plain pastry is made from flour, shortening, salt, and liquid. The fat is cut into the ingredients in pieces, or cut and rubbed in until mixture looks like fine breadcrumbs. Then the liquid is blended gradually either into all the mixture with a minimum of mixing, or into a part of the mixture. This mixture is blended in turn with the remaining fat and flour. If a liquid fat is used, it is added to the ingredients with the other liquid. Soft flours such as pastry and cake flours give a more delicate pastry than stronger all-purpose flour.

After the dough is mixed, it is rolled with a rolling pin with gentle pressure, lifting it with fingers only slightly, and then placed in position in pie tin with care to avoid stretching. Pastry which is to be baked as a single shell can be put on outside of the piepan and pricked with a fork before baking so steam can escape.

Plain and short-crust pastries can be modified by the addition of egg yolk, sugar, and other ingredients—such as nuts or dried fruit.

YEAST ROLLS

18 to 24 rolls

¾ cup hot milk
¼ cup shortening or oil
¼ cup sugar
1¼ teaspoons salt
1 egg
¼ cup water
1 package active dry yeast
About 4 cups flour

Mix milk, fat, sugar, and salt in a large mixing bowl. Cool to lukewarm.

Stir in egg, water, and yeast until yeast dissolves. Add 2 cups flour and beat until smooth. Gradually stir in more flour until dough leaves sides of the bowl.

Turn dough onto lightly floured surface and knead until smooth and elastic.

Place in a lightly greased bowl and turn over once to grease upper side of dough. Cover and let rise in a warm place (80° to 85° F.) until almost double in bulk, for 1 to 1¼ hours. Dough should rise until a light touch leaves a slight depression. Press the dough down into the bowl in order to remove air bubbles.

To make plain rolls, divide dough into small pieces and roll into balls about 1½ inches in diameter. Place in a shallow greased pan with the sides touching—or 1 inch apart if you prefer crusty sides.

Cover loosely and let rise in a warm place until double in bulk, 45 minutes to 1 hour.

Bake at 400° F., 15 to 20 minutes until browned.

Brush rolls with melted butter or margarine after removing them from the oven, if desired.

BISCUITS

12 biscuits

2 cups unsifted flour
1 tablespoon baking powder
1 teaspoon salt
⅓ cup shortening
About ¾ cup milk

Mix dry ingredients thoroughly. Mix in fat only until the mixture is crumbly.

Add most of the milk and stir to mix. Add more milk as needed to make a dough that is soft but not too sticky to knead. Knead dough gently on a lightly floured surface 10 to 12 times. Form into a ball.

Pat or roll dough to ½- to ¾-inch thickness. Cut with a floured biscuit cutter or cut into squares with a knife. Place on an ungreased baking sheet—

an inch apart for crusty biscuits; together for softer biscuits.

Bake at 450° F., 12 to 15 minutes, or until golden brown.

For cheese biscuits, combine ¾ cup shredded sharp or extra sharp cheese with the dry ingredients before adding fat.

MUFFINS

12 muffins

1 egg
1 cup milk
⅓ cup oil or melted shortening
2 cups unsifted flour
1 tablespoon baking powder
1 teaspoon salt
⅓ cup sugar

Beat egg until yolk and white are well blended. Blend in milk and fat.

Mix the dry ingredients thoroughly. Add liquid and stir until dry ingredients are barely moistened. Do not overmix. Batter should be lumpy.

Fill greased muffin tins half full of batter. Bake at 400° F., 20 to 25 minutes until browned.

For blueberry muffins increase sugar to ½ cup. Lightly blend in ¾ cup fresh or drained canned blueberries when combining liquid and dry ingredients. Do not crush berries.

PASTRY

8- or 9-inch pastry shell

1 cup unsifted flour
½ teaspoon salt
⅓ cup shortening
About 2 tablespoons cold water

Mix flour and salt thoroughly. Mix in fat only until mixture is crumbly.

Add a little water at a time, blending lightly. Dough should be just moist enough to cling together when pressed.

Shape dough into a ball. Roll out on a lightly floured surface or between two sheets of waxed paper. Fit carefully into the piepan. Lift edges and smooth out air bubbles. For baked pastry shell, trim pastry, leaving about an inch around the edge. Fold edge under and shape into an upright rim.

Prick bottom and sides well with a fork. Bake at 450° F. (very hot oven), for 12 to 15 minutes or until the pastry shell is golden brown.

Variation

Two-crust pie—Double the recipe. Form the dough into two balls, one slightly larger than the other. Roll out the larger ball of dough and fit into piepan. Roll out remaining dough for top crust; make several slits in crust to let steam escape during baking. Put filling into pastry-lined pan. Top with second crust. Fold edges of crusts under and press together to seal. Bake as directed in pie recipe.

CHOCOLATE CAKE

Two 8-inch layers

1¾ cups unsifted cake flour
1⅓ cups sugar
1 teaspoon salt
1 teaspoon baking soda
½ cup softened butter or margarine
1 cup buttermilk or sour milk
1 teaspoon vanilla
2 eggs
2 ounces (2 squares) unsweetened chocolate, melted, cooled

Mix dry ingredients well. Add fat and half of the milk; beat until creamy. Mix in remaining milk, vanilla, and eggs. Add chocolate; then beat until creamy.

Pour into two 8-inch greased and floured layer cakepans. Bake at 350° F., 30 to 35 minutes or until the cake's surface springs back when touched lightly. Cool cake for a few minutes before removing from the pans. When cool, frost as desired.

Note: For a loaf cake, use a greased and floured 9- by 12-inch cakepan. Bake about 40 minutes.

Lois T. Kilgore

How to Avoid Confusion in Fats and Oils Buying or Use

The housewife is often confused by the many edible fats on market shelves today. If you purchase and prepare foods, you're faced with deciding which of these many fats to buy. You must keep in mind the many uses of fats and make your selection according to your needs and food budget. You probably need a fat for shortening baked products and this may also be the same fat you use for frying. If you become familiar with the wide array of fats and their characteristics by reading the labels, choosing the fat that meets your needs will be easier.

Shortenings are edible fats used to shorten baked goods. A baked mixture of flour and water would be tough without the addition of proper amounts of fat or oil. Fats produce tenderness by surrounding particles of starch and strands of gluten. In this way the strands of gluten are kept short; hence, the name "shortening."

Although oils, butter, margarine, and lard may all be used as shortening agents, the products that have come to be known as shortenings are the vegetable fats or animal and vegetable mixtures that are plastic.

This means they are soft and creamy and may be easily molded or shaped.

Shortening as a food product is an American invention, growing out of the cotton-raising industry. The first shortenings, prepared by a blending of hard fats (edible tallows) and soft fats (cottonseed oil), were called compounds and were frankly conceived and marketed as substitutes for lard. In the beginning, the American meatpackers literally controlled the shortening industry, for they controlled the supply of hard animal fat which was an essential ingredient.

Solid fats are usually of animal origin and are composed of considerable amounts of saturated fatty acids which contain as many hydrogen atoms as the carbon chain can hold. Fats of vegetable origin are usually liquid oils and the unsaturated fatty acids are predominant. These may be monounsaturated with one reactive unsaturated linkage (double bond) which has two hydrogens missing; or polyunsaturated with two or more reactive unsaturated linkages (double bonds) with four, six, eight, or more hydrogens missing. (*Food, The 1959 Yearbook of Agriculture*, pp. 76–77, contains an excellent discussion on structure.)

Introduction of the hydrogenation process in about 1910 made the manufacturer of vegetable shortening independent. The hydrogenation process adds hydrogen to the unsaturated fatty acids, reducing their degree of unsaturation and transforming them to the corresponding saturated fatty acids. This changes the liquid oil to a plastic fat, and makes any blending with an animal fat unnecessary.

Since about 1933, further changes in the method of manufacturing hydrogenated shortenings have involved the addition of mono- and di-glycerides. The superior emulsifying properties of fats so treated cause a fine dispersion of the fat in the dough or cake and allow a higher ratio of sugar to flour.

Lois T. Kilgore is Professor of Home Economics, College of Agriculture, Mississippi State University. She is in charge of the Foods and Nutrition Laboratory at the Mississippi Agricultural Experiment Station.

These shortenings are described as "high ratio" or emulsified. They have become popular for use in cakes, sweet yeast doughs, and similar products. The shortenings have a lowered smoke point and are less desirable for frying.

For a long period of time there was an approximate parity in price between compound shortening and lard, but high production and undesirable qualities in lard caused a decrease in its price. Until recently, the lack of uniformity of lard and some of its properties such as odor, flavor, grainy texture, low smoke point, and susceptibility to rancidity have resulted in a greatly reduced usage of lard. Many years of research by government and industrial laboratories have improved the quality, uniformity, and functional properties of lard.

Shortenings of the all-vegetable-oil variety have always commanded a price above the compound shortenings. Retail prices of vegetable oils are even higher than hydrogenated shortenings.

In recent years shortening products containing lard or lard and beef fat blends have been refined, stiffened by hydrogenation, fortified with an antioxidant, deodorized, and in some cases superglycerinated to make them comparable to all-vegetable hydrogenated shortenings. From 1940 to 1963 the amount of lard used in shortenings increased 35-fold.

Commonly used food fats are complicated mixtures which do not have a sharp melting point but solidify over a wide temperature range. This fact is demonstrated when oils cloud on refrigeration. Many vegetable oils are "winterized" to prevent this, particularly salad oils. The process of winterizing an oil consists of chilling it to a temperature of 40° to 45° F. and removing the precipitated solid crystals by filtration. The resulting oil remains clear at ordinary refrigerator temperatures.

The first recognizable deterioration in fats, such as lard, oils, and shortening, is the development of rancidity. This is an oxidative change which in vegetable oils is inhibited by naturally occurring antioxidants. Since animal fats do not contain natural antioxidants to protect them, it is necessary to add chemical agents to delay the onset of rancidity. The U.S. Department of Agriculture has approved and specified the amount permitted for about a dozen antioxidants that may be used in animal fats.

Shortenings, whether of vegetable origin or mixtures, keep well at room temperature. But if a shortening is kept over a long period, it might be well to store it in the refrigerator. Allowing it to return to room temperature before use results in easier measuring and blending and also in a better pastry.

Only shortenings containing animal fats are inspected by USDA. A system of continuous inspection has been developed with the Federal inspectors placed in each plant to supervise the handling at every step. Inspection is concerned with facilities, equipment, sanitation, source and quality of raw materials, acceptable manufacturing practices, laboratory testing, and labeling. Only edible fats from U.S. inspected and passed carcasses may be used in animal fat shortenings.

When you see the familiar round stamp "U.S. Inspected and Passed," you know that the label is truthful and the product is wholesome and suitable for human consumption.

Standards of identity define what a food must contain to be called by a particular name. Congress has established a standard of identity for butter. The Food and Drug Administration has adopted standards of identity for margarine (oleomargarine), mayonnaise, french dressing, and salad dressing.

Butter must contain at least 80 percent milk fat, and nothing may be added except salt and coloring. USDA has set up standards for grading butter based on flavor, texture, color, and salt content. The Federal grading of butter is not compulsory, but the U.S. grade label on the outside carries the assurance that the butter has been tested by a Government grader.

Margarine or oleomargarine is a product made to resemble butter in which one or more optional fat ingredients are used along with or in place of the butterfat. Margarine was first made in France in 1870 when Napoleon III offered a prize for a butter substitute. Margarine, like butter, is a water-in-oil emulsion and must contain 80 percent fat. In making margarine, the melted fat is agitated with skim milk that has been pasteurized and which may have been cultured with a bacterial starter.

The flavor of margarine at one time depended to a large extent upon the treatment of the milk. Today, flavor is obtained principally by adding flavoring substances permitted under Federal standards of identity. Salt, preservatives, emulsifiers, vitamins A and D may be used as additives. The addition of 15,000 units of vitamin A per pound (which is the average amount found in butter), although not mandatory, is almost universal. However, the only way to be sure of the content of margarine is to read the label, since Federal regulations require full ingredient disclosure.

Suppose someone in your family is on a diet and has been cautioned to eat more polyunsaturated fat and less saturated fat. What does the manufacturer's label tell you?

The manufacturer must list the predominant ingredient first. For example, if the ingredients are listed as "liquid corn oil, partially-hydrogenated soybean oil, water, salt, etc.," this means the buyer may expect that there is more of polyunsaturated corn oil than of partially-saturated soybean oil in that margarine.

Now on the market are margarines significantly reduced in calories. These are currently very plainly marked as imitation margarine, and they only contain about half the amount of fat that real margarine must contain. Consequently the calories present in imitation margarine are about half of the amount found in margarine. Because of aeration, whipped margarine contains only about two-thirds of the calories in an equal volume of plain margarine.

Within the past 10 years, there has been a continuing increase in the use of margarine. This is probably owing to the fact that margarine has been substantially improved as a bread spread and that the retail price of butter in 1968 was about three times the price of margarine.

Deterioration of lards, shortenings, and salad oils (all of these contain no water) is almost wholly the result of oxidation caused by the combination with oxygen from the air. Butter and margarine contain water, and rancidity may be due to enzyme action or to micro-organisms that break down the fat and water into glycerol and fatty acid. If short-chain fatty acids are present, this breakdown will result in a rancid odor that can be detected at room temperature.

Fats from soybeans in shortening and margarine are also susceptible to reversion. This is a change in edible fats characterized by the development of an objectionable flavor. This objectionable flavor is quite often "fishy" or "painty." The high percentage of polyunsaturated fatty acids such as linolenic acid in soybean oil would make margarine produced with soybean oil very susceptible to reversion.

Since butter and margarine absorb odors so noticeably, they should be stored in covered containers in the refrigerator. If they are to be kept for a long period of time, they should be frozen.

It is well known that the shortening power of fats and oils varies with differences in temperature (particularly as this affects plasticity of fat), fat/flour ratio, and mixing techniques. However, several studies of tenderness in pastry have indicated that lard makes a more tender pastry than hydrogenated vegetable oil, whereas butter or margarine will produce the least tender pastry.

Further studies have shown that when increasing amounts of fats are added to pastry, optimum tenderness is achieved at lower levels with corn, cottonseed, or soybean oil than with any of the solid fats. Good quality pastries can be made with oils, lard, or hydrogenated shortening when the proper amount of fat and proper mixing techniques are used.

In this country, few desserts are as popular as pie. The success of a pie depends partly upon the quality of the crust. You, as the cook, have a number of decisions to make. You must choose the ingredients, amounts, methods of mixing, and temperature of cooking.

In a pastry made with hydrogenated fat, approximately ⅓ cup of fat per cup of flour is used. But with lard or oil, ¼ cup of fat per cup of flour is adequate. Lard and hydrogenated shortenings are cut into the flour with a pastry blender or two knives. Oil is stirred into flour with a fork either as water-oil mixture or just before adding water. Hot water may be added to a plastic shortening and stirred into the flour in the same fashion. Crusts made with oil or by using hot water are often more mealy than flaky. Pastry made with lard or hydrogenated shortenings are usually flaky as well as tender.

If you are not satisfied with your pastry, try different fats or oils using recommended recipes. Commercial companies spend a great deal of money on research to develop better recipes for their products, so their recipes are usually dependable.

Maybe your favorite dessert is cake. Fat in cake batter not only serves to make the crumb tender, but it entraps air during the creaming process and thus contributes to the leavening and increases the volume of the cake. Too little fat results in a dry cake that is not "velvety" and tender. Too much fat makes a crumbly, heavy cake which may fall in the center.

Plastic fat is melted when used in the muffin method of cake mixing. Oil may be used in a modification of this method, in which egg whites beaten with or without part of the sugar are added after combining the other ingredients. This cake is often called chiffon cake. Because of the difference in mixing and the higher ratio of sugar, do not try to substitute oil for solid fats in other cake recipes.

However, plastic fat in the conventional method of cake mixing does not need to be melted because it is creamed until it is light and fluffy. Flavoring is added while the fat is being creamed, for fat carries flavors far better than other ingredients do. Eggs serve as an emulsifying agent—to promote dispersion of fat.

The "quick mix" or "one bowl" method of mixing cakes was developed for the shortenings containing emulsifiers and makes especially good cakes with recipes that use a higher ratio of sugar to flour and other ingredients.

As previously stated, shortenings with emulsifiers have a low smoke point. When fats or oils are heated to a high temperature, decomposition occurs, and finally a point is reached at which visible fumes are given off. This is the smoke point. The fumes have an unpleasant odor and are irritating to the nose and eyes.

Food fried in smoking fats is likely to have an unpleasant flavor, and the fat will become rancid faster than fat which has not been heated to smoke temperatures.

An ideal fat for frying food is one that has a fairly high smoke point. Most cooking oils and all hydrogenated shortenings (without emulsifiers) have high smoke points. Smoke points vary for lards. Butter, margarine, and shortenings with emulsifiers have low smoke points and do not make good frying fats. Repeated use of a fat lowers the smoke point. Foods absorb more fat, which is undesirable, when they are cooked in a fat with a low smoke point.

A frying utensil that is relatively small in diameter is better for frying than a large one because the smoke point is lowered if a large surface of fat is exposed. Smoke point is also lowered by crumbs, bits of food, and flour. To remove such particles, fat is filtered through cheesecloth. Used fat should be stored in the refrigerator inasmuch as it is more susceptible to rancidity than unused fat.

Deep-fat frying is more of an art than a science, and experience is the best teacher. Are your french-fried potatoes soggy and greasy? Maybe your frying fat is not hot enough. The temperature of the fat should be 370° to 385° F. At this temperature a 1-inch bread cube will brown in 20 to 45 seconds. The potatoes should be cooked in small batches so temperature of the fat will not be lowered drastically. If you have time and want to make a real treat for the family, try this two-step method:

Pare the potatoes; cut lengthwise in ⅜-inch to ½-inch strips. Rinse strips quickly in cold water to remove surface starch, then dry them well. Heat deep fat (5 inches) in a 7-inch to 9-inch saucepan to 370° to 385° F. Place a layer of potatoes in a frying basket; lower basket gently into fat. Cook about 6 minutes (potatoes should be tender but not brown). Drain on absorbent paper. Repeat with another layer. When all potatoes have been cooked, reheat fat. Return two layers of potatoes at a time to basket and brown the potatoes in the hot fat. Drain, sprinkle with salt, and serve.

A delicious food that utilizes pan-frying is fried rice. A recipe tells how to prepare this Chinese food.

FRIED RICE

6 servings

1 teaspoon salt
1 tablespoon butter or margarine
1¾ cups water
1 cup rice, uncooked
or
3 cups cold cooked rice

Cooking Oil

½ pound fresh lean pork
or
1 cup cooked pork strips
4 scallions, medium size, cut up
1 pepper, chopped
3 tablespoons soy sauce

Add salt and fat to water and bring to rolling boil; stir in uncooked rice. Cover tightly and cook over low heat until tender, 20 to 30 minutes.

Uncover the pot for the last 5 minutes of cooking and fluff rice with a fork. To avoid spattering, dry rice in warm oven or use day-old rice.

Cut fresh pork into strips. Lightly cover the bottom of heavy frying pan with cooking oil. Brown pork strips quickly; cover to finish cooking. Remove pork to bowl.

Put scallions and pepper in frying pan; cover and cook until tender. Remove to bowl containing pork.

Add more oil to frying pan and fry rice until browned, stirring constantly.

Add pork, vegetables, and soy sauce. Toss lightly and serve.

Another important way that fats are used is in oil-in-water emulsions. Such food emulsions occur naturally as in milk or prepared as in mayonnaise and salad dressings. Actually, certain baked products like cakes and cream puffs are also emulsions. Mayonnaise is a stable emulsion of oil droplets in water. The emulsion is considered permanent because it is stabilized with egg yolk. The ingredients of mayonnaise are almost always vegetable oil, vinegar or lemon juice, eggs or yolks, and selected spices.

Salad dressing is a product which resembles mayonnaise. It contains essentially the same constituents except a cooked starch paste is substituted for part of the egg, and the amount of oil is thus reduced. Homemade french dressing is usually a temporary emulsion containing the same ingredients as mayonnaise without egg. Finely ground spices like paprika act here as emulsifying agents but are not sufficiently good emulsifiers to keep the oil and water phases from separating after a few minutes. Commercial french dressings usually contain small amounts of stabilizing ingredients such as vegetable gums or pectins and tomato paste or puree.

According to the U.S. Food and Drug Administration, mayonnaise must contain at least 65 percent oil, but commercially the oil levels run around

75 percent. Commercial french dressings must contain not less than 35 percent vegetable oil, and salad dressings must contain 30 percent oil as a minimum but often are found as high as 45 percent. Because of the cost difference in ingredients, mayonnaise is usually more expensive than salad dressings.

Salad dressings and french dressings contain about 50 to 60 calories per tablespoon, while mayonnaise contains around 100 calories per tablespoon. Imitation mayonnaises (reduced in oil content) are on the market, and these contain approximately 20 calories per tablespoon.

Variations can be made by adding chopped foods to mayonnaise, french dressing, or salad dressing. Some of the ingredients commonly added are green pepper, olives, pimiento, pickle, hard-cooked egg, celery, parsley, onion, horseradish, chili sauce, cream, raisins, cherries, nuts, pineapple, and Roquefort or cream cheese. Special low-calorie dressings which often contain less than 10 calories per tablespoon are made with very little oil, a fruit or vegetable base, and artificial sweeteners.

Mayonnaise is easy to make but certain precautions that may not be included in your recipe are: Too shallow a bowl will result in spreading the egg yolk into a thin film so that little or no mixing takes place at the beginning when thorough mixing is crucial. The oil, at room temperature, should be added in very small quantities at first and then more rapidly. If mayonnaise curdles during mixing or separates after it is made, you may start mixing again with an egg yolk or a tablespoon of water or vinegar. The curdled or separated mayonnaise must be added to the egg yolk or liquid. There is no value in adding the egg or liquid to the mixture.

This chapter would not be complete without mentioning peanut butter. This is the only nut butter produced commercially to any extent in this country. Peanut butter, which contains about 50 percent fat, is frequently

Peanuts.

used as a substitute for other fats in cakes, cookies, and candy. It is valued as a very nutritive spread because of its high fat, protein, mineral, and B-vitamin content.

If you are an adult and have held peanut butter in disdain since your childhood, try some. It has been improved with emulsifiers and stabilizers. Delicious canapes and sandwiches can be made by using peanut butter with additions of jellies, raisins, bananas, minced bacon, or pickle relish.

Verna A. Mikesh
Leona S. Nelson

Sugar, Sweets Play Roles in Food Texture and Flavoring

On each day, people everywhere say, "Please pass the sugar." Whether it's to sweeten the morning cereal or the midnight snack, sugar or a sweet in some form is a daily necessity.

Nutritionally, sugars, maple sirup, molasses, table sirup, jams and jellies, honey, and other sweets provide the body with the fuel to release energy. Artificial sweeteners provide sweetness—but no nutritional value. No one sugar or sweet is "more healthful" than another. The small amounts of minerals and vitamins in the unrefined forms are of little consequence in supplying an adequate diet.

Table sugar is one of our cheapest sources of food energy. The familiar white crystals are sucrose extracted and refined from sugar beets or sugarcane. Chemically, cane and beet sugars are the same. In cooking and preserving, they act the same.

Sugar performs many functions in cooking besides adding sweetness and enhancing flavors. It contributes to the lightness, color, and fine grain of baked products. Sugar softens the gluten strands of the flour, enabling them to expand with the action of leavening to give a light product. It furnishes quickly available food for yeast in bread doughs. Carbon dioxide thrown off by yeast growth expands the dough. Oven heat caramelizes the sugar giving the flavorful, crisp, brown crust we enjoy on baked products.

Sugar tenderizes egg protein. With sugar in a mixture, more air can be beaten into egg whites, and the foam will be more stable. This raises the temperature at which egg proteins coagulate. In an angel food cake, for example, the tiny air cells can expand before being set by oven heat. A smooth custard results from the slow coagulation of egg protein.

This recipe illustrates how sugar is used with beaten egg whites to make a delicious dessert.

MERINGUE TORTE

8 servings

3 egg whites
½ teaspoon baking powder
1 cup sugar
10 square (2-inch) soda crackers rolled fine (⅓ cup crumbs)
½ cup chopped nutmeats
1 quart of strawberries or raspberries, washed and trimmed
½ cup whipping cream
1 to 2 tablespoons sugar, as desired

Beat egg whites and baking powder until frothy. Beat sugar in gradually until the egg whites are stiff. Fold in crumbs and nutmeats. Spread on a greased 9-inch piepan. Bake in a slow oven (300° F.) for 30 minutes. Cool. Fill with the berries. Whip cream, sweeten with sugar, and spread over berries. Chill several hours.

Puddings, pie fillings, and dessert sauces owe their body and smoothness to sugar. To prevent lumping, mix the sugar and starch together before combining with the liquid. Improve the smoothness of hot cocoa by blending the dry cocoa with sugar before combining with the liquid.

Verna A. Mikesh is Extension Nutritionist and Leona S. Nelson is an Assistant Extension Information Specialist, with the Agricultural Extension Service, University of Minnesota, St. Paul.

Frozen desserts are smooth because sugar lowers the freezing point of the mixture to be frozen. This factor, plus stirring, makes tiny ice crystals in the food. The result is a smooth and a creamy product.

Candies and frostings further demonstrate the many physical and chemical characteristics of sugar. Vary the sugar concentration, temperature, agitation, and other ingredients to make a myriad of sweets.

The ability of sugar to change to invert sugar makes creamy fudge and fondant because invert sugar induces a very fine crystal structure.

Moisture, heat, and acid bring about this chemical change. Acid ingredients such as cream of tartar or chocolate accelerate it. The addition of corn sirup also aids in controlling the crystal size.

Candies such as butterscotch don't have any crystals due to the combination of invert sugar, high temperature, and corn sirup. They harden before they crystallize.

As the concentration of sugar in a sirup increases, the boiling temperature

Creamy pecan fudge.

Temperature and Tests for Sugar Cookery

Thread Test

Product	Temperature (°F.)	
Sirup	230–234	Sirup spins a 2-inch thread.

Cold Water Test

Drop sirup into very cold water.

Product	Temperature (°F.)	
Fondant Fudge, Penocha (Penoche)	234–240	Sirup forms a soft ball that flattens when removed from water.
Caramels	244–248	Sirup forms a firm ball that doesn't flatten when removed from water.
Divinity	250–266	Sirup forms a hard ball that holds its shape yet remains plastic.
Butterscotch Taffy	270–290	Sirup separates into threads that are hard but not brittle (soft crack).
Brittle	300–310	Sirup separates into threads that are hard and brittle (hard crack).

rises. A candy thermometer aids in making candy and frosting. The cold water test is less reliable, but many people use it.

Sugar preserves the color and flavor of fruit in the form of jams and jellies. The acid and pectin in the fruit, plus sugar, makes a gel. The cooked products keep without further processing because sugar minimizes the growth of micro-organisms.

Store white granulated sugar covered and in a dry place.

Other sugars (brown), molasses, honey, and sirup have many of the qualities of white granulated sugar because they are similar physically and chemically. They add interest to food with their distinctive flavors and special properties.

Brown sugar is brown and soft because some of the original sugar sirup remains around the crystals. The color varies from very light to the more robust-flavored dark brown.

Store brown sugar in an airtight container to keep it from drying out. Adding half of an apple in the container provides moisture, but check it occasionally for mold. Soften hardened brown sugar by heating it in a slow oven. It becomes harder than ever after cooling, so handle it while it is still warm.

Measure brown sugar by packing it into the measuring utensil. The sugar should retain its shape when the utensil is lifted off. Your grocer may also have the granulated form of brown sugar. Measure granulated brown sugar as you would white sugar. Follow package directions for substituting it in your recipes.

Powdered or confectioners sugar is very finely ground granulated sugar. A small percent of cornstarch may be added to prevent caking. Powdered sugar may need sifting to insure a smooth frosting and accurate measurement. You may like the new granulated form that measures easily and blends smoothly. It is more expensive but it's convenient.

Molasses that is a byproduct of sugar manufacture contains sulphur dioxide. Some manufacturers make an "unsulphured" molasses by concentrating the juice of sugarcane without the intention of making sugar.

High-grade mild molasses is used in table sirups. The darker kinds lend color and flavor to many cooked foods. In addition to sugar, molasses contains some calcium and iron.

There is little nutritional advantage in using crude blackstrap molasses, a byproduct of sugar manufacture.

Sugar-rich sorghum cane yields sorghum sirup. Those who enjoy its distinctive flavor use it as they would molasses and sirup. The market forms may contain invert sugar to prevent crystallization.

The American Indian discovered that the concentrated sap of the maple tree makes a delicious sweet. Maple sirup and maple sugar are expensive but highly prized for their flavor.

Not only is this prized flavor imitated, but often maple sugar and sirup are blended with less expensive sweets to pour over the pancakes of the budget-conscious consumer.

Making maple sirup requires time, labor, and skill. It takes about 40 gallons of sap boiled down to make 1 gallon of sirup or 8 pounds of sugar.

Color is the principal factor in grading maple sirup which meets all the other requirements for density, flavor, and clearness.

USDA grades for maple sirup are:

Light amber—U.S. grade AA; medium amber—U.S. grade A; dark amber—U.S. grade B; unclassified.

You can buy maple sirup in any quantity ranging from a gallon to less than a pint. Sirup in sealed containers keeps well at room temperature. Refrigerate open containers to prevent mold formation. Rebottle the sirup bought in large lots by heating it to 180° F. and sealing in sterilized jars.

Store maple creme in the refrigerator or freezer; store maple sugar at room temperature in a dry place.

Enjoy maple flavor with this dessert.

MAPLE-BAKED APPLES

Use 1 cup maple sirup and 1 teaspoon grated lemon rind for six apples. Choose tart baking apples. Pare about one-third of the way down and core. Place in a baking dish. Pour sirup and lemon rind over them. Bake 1 hour at 375° F. Baste occasionally with sirup. Serve warm with sirup and cream.

MAPLE SUNDAE

Warm maple sirup slightly. Pour over ice cream, and sprinkle with chopped nuts for a delicious sundae.

Corn supplies another sweet in the form of corn sirup. These sirups, white and dark, are made by subjecting corn starch to the action of acid or enzymes. Though less expensive than other sirups, they aren't as sweet and are used in candymaking, infant formulas, the manufacture of table sirups, and in other products requiring sweetening.

The grocer's shelf holds a large variety of the blended table sirups for pancakes and waffles. They include sugar, corn, and maple sirups in varying proportions as stated on the label. Other ingredients such as butter, salt, honey, sorghum, imitation flavoring, coloring, stabilizers, and preservatives are also included and listed.

Since maple sirup is the most expensive, and corn sirup the least, cost will vary with the amounts of each that are used.

Honey, the sweetest tasting of all sweets, contains some fructose, which is one-fifth sweeter than granulated sugar.

Color and flavor of honey are determined by the flowers from which the bees collect the nectar. Light-colored, mild kinds come from clovers. One of the darkest and most strongly flavored is from buckwheat. Citrus blossom, tupelo, sage, and basswood are well-liked, distinctive honey flavors.

Most of the honey on the market is extracted honey, that is, honey separated from the comb. Extracted honey in a crystallized form is called honey creme or honey spread. Comb honey is usually more expensive because it is difficult and costly to produce.

U.S. Grade A or U.S. Fancy indicates top grade honey. Next is U.S. Grade B. Flavor is a most important factor in honey grading, plus clarity and absence of defects. Color isn't a factor in U.S. grades.

Liquid honey can be bought in quantities ranging from a large tin pail to a small plastic squeeze bottle. Creme honey comes in plastic or paper-type tubs. One and one-third cups of honey weigh 1 pound.

Store honey tightly covered to retain its flavor and aroma. Keep it at room temperature to retard granulation. If it granulates, put the container in a bowl of warm water to melt the crystals. Honey stored over a long time may darken somewhat, but it will still be usable.

Cooked foods made with honey are slightly sweeter, have more color, and a different texture from those made with sugar. Baked goods remain soft as honey absorbs moisture from the air. Candies and meringues made with honey may absorb excess moisture, making them soft and sticky. Freezing intensifies the honey flavor in baked products.

For best results when using honey in cooking and baking, follow recipes especially designed for honey.

Try these foods for honey flavor enjoyment.

HONEY BRUNCH COCOA

5 servings

1 quart milk
2 sticks cinnamon
¼ cup cocoa
⅛ teaspoon salt
3 tablespoons honey

Scald milk with cinnamon sticks. Mix cocoa and salt; blend in ¼ cup hot milk until smooth. Add to scalded milk and stir in honey. Remove the cinnamon sticks. Mix with a rotary beater.

HONEY CORN MUFFINS

8 muffins

¾ cup sifted flour
1¼ teaspoon baking powder
½ teaspoon salt
⅓ cup cornmeal
1 egg, well beaten
⅓ cup milk
¼ cup honey
3 tablespoons shortening, melted
¼ cup pared diced apple

Mix the flour, baking powder, and salt. Stir in cornmeal. Combine egg, milk, honey, and shortening. Add all at once to cornmeal mixture; add apple; stir only enough to dampen flour. Spoon into 8 well-greased, 2-inch muffin pans. Bake at 400° F. for 15 to 20 minutes.

The array of jellies, jams, preserves, and marmalades on the grocer's shelf indicates that these are important food specialties. Calorie counters and special dieters can purchase varieties made with artificial sweeteners.

The Food and Drug Administration has established standards of identity for jams, jellies, and preserves. Among other things they must be made with no less than 45 parts of fruit to 55 parts of sweeteners by weight. If the product doesn't meet the composition requirement, then it must be labeled "Imitation."

In addition, the U.S. Department of Agriculture has developed grade standards in cooperation with the preserving industry. You may find a continuous inspection shield on the label or lid, but more often, it will be the red, white, and blue U.S. Grade A or Fancy designation. This means the product was packed under the Department's continuous inspection. This doesn't imply that products without the inspection or grademark are inferior.

Jelly adds a jewel-like sparkle to these cookies:

SCANDINAVIAN THUMBPRINT COOKIES

2 dozen cookies

½ cup butter or margarine
¼ cup brown sugar, packed
1 egg, separated
½ teaspoon vanilla
1 cup sifted flour
¼ teaspoon salt
¾ cup finely chopped nuts
Tart red jelly, as needed

Blend fat, sugar, egg yolk, and vanilla. Stir in flour and salt. Beat egg white slightly. Roll dough into 1-inch balls. Dip in slightly beaten egg white. Roll into finely chopped nuts. Place 1 inch apart on an ungreased cookie sheet. Bake 5 minutes at 375° F. Remove from oven; quickly press thumb gently into the top of each cookie. Return to oven and bake 8 minutes longer or until lightly browned. Cool.

Place a dab of red jelly in each depression.

There is a vast increase in the use of artificial sweeteners. Originally they were intended primarily for diabetics. But a weight-conscious society has adopted them as an aid to weight control. In this respect their effectiveness depends on the caloric regulation of other foods in the diet.

Artificial sweeteners may be saccharin, cyclamate, or a combination of the two. Any products which are artificially sweetened must show the ingredient that's used, along with the amount, on the label. These sweeteners are used in soft drinks, desserts, and other products being promoted as low-calorie foods. They may be bought for use as table sweetening or cooking, in tablet, liquid, or granular form.

Sweetening equivalents as stated on the container differ among these products. For cooking and baking, use recipes especially designed for their use. Remember that they don't have the preservative qualities of sugar. Jams and jellies made with artificial sweetener must be refrigerated after opening. Baked products may mold in a short time.

The Food and Drug Administration constantly checks artificial sweeteners for significant adverse effects at normal use levels. Manufactured products that contain sweeteners which are not designated on the label misbrand the product. This is why the Food and Drug Administration rules that the label must state these are non-nutritive artificial sweeteners recommended only for persons who must restrict their use of ordinary sweets.

A stop at the candy counter in almost any establishment points out the size of the American sweet tooth.

The choices range from a penny licorice whip to an elaborate box of fancy hand-dipped chocolates. Candies are part of our holiday fun: Fillers for Halloween trick or treat bags, Christmas hard mix, Valentine hearts, and multicolored jelly eggs at Easter. They have great social significance, as bribes or peace offerings, or expressions of love and joy.

"Please help yourself and pass the candy."

Walter R. Moses
Margaret F. Tennant

Beverages: Milk, Coffee, Tea, Juices, Chocolate

Without beverages our meals would be less nutritious and our working hours and social gatherings less enjoyable. Their use is wide, their types varied, and their history long.

Coffee drinking became a popular pastime in the coffeehouses of London in the middle 17th century where literary, scientific, religious, and political matters were discussed over cups of the steaming brew.

Tea has been used as a beverage since ancient days. In many countries the preparation and serving of tea is considered an art—Japanese women of good family sometimes receive up to 3 years' instruction in the ceremony.

During the conquest of Mexico in 1519 Hernando Cortez found the Aztec emperor Montezuma drinking "chocolatl" from great golden bowls and carried the idea back to Spain. The Spanish added cane sugar to the drink and served it hot.

Today in the United States consumption of these and other beverages is on the rise, except for milk which has served man as a food for thousands of years.

A recent nationwide survey by U.S. Department of Agriculture food economists indicates that more youths in the population, more snacking by people in general, and more money in the household budget resulted in a 15 percent increase in the amount of the beverages consumed at home during the 10 years from 1955 to 1965. Ten cents of the 1965 household food dollar was used for beverages other than milk, while approximately 8 cents was spent for the various types of fresh fluid and processed milk.

The trend has been away from milk as a beverage and toward more coffee, soft drinks, fruit ades, and punches. An average of 39 cups of milk (buttermilk, skim milk, chocolate milk, baby and diet formula) were consumed per household per week in 1965 compared to 46 cups in 1955. On the other hand, the number of cups of coffee increased from 38 to 48, soft drinks increased from 5 to 9 cups, while fruit ades and punches consumed rose from 1 to 13 cups a week. Tea and juices remained about the same with an increase of 1 cup for each. Away-from-home purchases added to these totals.

The United States not only produces a plentiful supply of milk, but also an abundant supply of fruit. Juices in many pleasing flavors and colors are used as appetizers with meals, as pickups between meals, as ingredients for the party punchbowl, and in other beverages. Raw materials for coffee, tea, cocoa, and chocolate must be imported.

Beverages and beverage materials are marketed in many forms. Milk, for example, may be packaged as whole fresh milk in bottles or cartons, often homogenized, nearly always pasteurized. It may be sold in the fluid form as skimmed milk; low-fat milk, with or without added nonfat solids; or as buttermilk—all of which require refrigeration. Sterilized milk, evaporated

Walter R. Moses is Chief, Food Case Branch, Bureau of Regulatory Compliance, Food and Drug Administration.

Margaret F. Tennant is a Public Information Officer in the Information Division, Agricultural Research Service.

Maryland student participates in taste test of grape juice. Before canned juice from grapes grown in different parts of the country was added to national school lunch menu for first time, USDA wanted to find out which of two types the children preferred.

milk, and sweetened condensed milk are marketed in cans. Nonfat dry milk is sold in bags, cartons, or packets, does not need refrigeration, and under proper storage conditions keeps for months.

Fruit juices are marketed as fluids in glass or cans; single strength or concentrated; pasteurized and refrigerated; or sealed in containers and heat-processed to prevent spoilage. Juices are also sold frozen, either single strength or concentrated.

Of the various juices, orange juice is marketed in the most diverse forms. Under the Federal Food, Drug, and Cosmetic Act, the Food and Drug Administration (FDA) has established standards of identity for the following forms: orange juice, frozen orange juice, pasteurized orange juice, canned orange juice, orange juice from concentrate, frozen concentrated orange juice, and also canned concentrated orange juice. To any of these, sugar or certain other specified sweeteners may be added with appropriate label declaration.

Each form of juice has its advantages and disadvantages. Most people prefer the flavor of fresh fruit juice. Such juice, however, contains enzymes and micro-organisms which quickly cause spoilage or lower the quality, even when the juice is kept chilled. Quality can be maintained by freezing, but the frozen single-strength juice is expensive to store and ship. It is inconvenient to handle, and few firms stock it.

Spoilage may be delayed by pasteurizing the juice. This process inactivates the enzymes and reduces the number of spoilage organisms but, unfortunately, it also changes the flavor. Pasteurized juice must be refrigerated. Most of the orange juice sold by grocery stores or distributed by dairies in glass or cartons has been pasteurized.

Canned juice is sealed into containers and processed by heat to kill the spoilage organisms so it will keep without refrigeration as long as the container remains sealed. The flavor of canned fruit juice is usually considered less desirable than that of other forms.

The juice prepared from frozen concentrated orange juice is commonly rated next to fresh juice in flavor and other desirable characteristics. The frozen concentrate retains its quality indefinitely when stored at the proper temperature. It is cheaper to ship and less bulky to store than the single strength juice, yet keeps some of the taste of the single strength juice mixed into the concentrate before it is frozen.

FDA has established standards for canned pineapple juice, tomato juice, and prune juice. However, no standards have been set for other popular juices such as apple, grape, or grapefruit. These nonstandardized juices are sometimes preserved with chemicals like sodium benzoate or sorbic acid. When used, such preservatives must be declared on the label.

There are on the market many beverages and beverage bases made in part from fruit juices. Some contain significant quantities of fruit juice or pulp. Those labeled as "juice-drinks" sometimes contain 30 percent or more juice. Nectars contain an even higher percentage of juice and pulp. Other beverages of this type contain little fruit or juice and derive most of their flavor from added acids, natural or synthetic flavoring materials, and other additives. Still others, including some dried or frozen concentrates, contain no fruit ingredients, being made entirely from synthetic colors, flavors, and other nonfruit ingredients.

Standards of identity for frozen concentrates for lemonade, colored lemonade, and artificially sweetened lemonade have been established by FDA. In May 1968 the agency published an order intended to do the same thing for certain nectars, ades, juice-drinks, cranberry juice cocktail, and other diluted fruit drinks. This order, which prescribed the minimum percentage of juice or pulp for each and required that the percentage be listed on the label, had to be stayed pending a requested public hearing.

The nutrient value of carbonated beverages is mainly in sugar and calories. Artificially sweetened carbonated drinks and drink bases are popular with persons on low calorie or sugar restricted diets. They provide few nutrients and are valuable only as thirst quenchers. These drinks come in bottles (returnable or nonreturnable) and in metal cans. Carbonated beverages, other than those that are artificially sweetened, must comply with FDA standards. Action on proposed standards for artificially sweetened soda water was postponed pending public hearings upon FDA's special dietary food regulations.

Because of the rapid rise in use of artificial sweeteners there has been concern about their safety. In 1955 and again in 1965, the Food Protection Committee of the National Academy of Sciences—National Research Council (NAS/NRC) evaluated all available scientific evidence on the safety of the artificial sweeteners and published reports which gave no basis for restricting special dietary use of the sweeteners.

In 1968, at the request of FDA, NAS/NRC reviewed recent research reports, and concluded that "totally unrestricted use of the cyclamates is not warranted at this time." In the Federal Register of April 5, 1969, FDA published a proposal to require labeling of foods containing cyclamates which would make it practical for consumers to limit their intake of cyclamates to recommended levels. The recommended maximum daily intake for adults is 3,500 milligrams—for children, 1,200 milligrams.

It is estimated that close to a third of the world's population uses coffee in greater amounts than any other

USDA coffee tester at work. He helps assure better quality coffee for schools, institutions, the military, and State and Federal agencies that use the testing service.

beverage, with coffee drinkers in the United States consuming around 50 percent of the supply.

Coffee is imported as green beans which must be blended, roasted, and are usually ground before they reach the consumer. "Coffee testers" who spend many years in developing their senses of taste and smell (the only way coffee can be appraised) use actual cup tests rather than physical characteristics of the coffee bean as a basis for combining different varieties. They try to balance costs with acceptable quality, and many blends are available at different prices. The only way to find the "right" one is to try different brands.

The flavor depends also upon the degree of roasting which brings out the "coffee taste" and the aroma not apparent in the coffee bean. People have different preferences depending upon region and national origin. A dark roast is generally preferred in the South, a light roast along the Pacific coast, and medium roast elsewhere in the United States. Some people may even prefer the almost black roast common in Italy, Turkey, and the surrounding areas.

Blends of coffee with chicory are popular in Louisiana and may be purchased elsewhere.

The device used for brewing coffee governs the choice of grind to a large extent, but it should be remembered that a finer grind permits quicker extraction with less loss of desirable flavor and aroma.

Instant coffees, first used by the U.S. armed forces in the field, now account for more than a fourth of the coffee prepared at home. They are available in a number of blends. Some are freeze-dried while others are prepared by various extraction, evaporation, and drying processes.

For those who do not like the stimulating effect of caffein, green coffee is sometimes steamed and soaked using a chlorinated organic solvent. Consumer preference for the "decaffeinated" coffee is for the instant or soluble type of product.

About half the people of the world drink hot or cold tea. Consumption in the United States is said to average about three-fourths of a pound per year compared to 10 pounds for Great Britain and for Ireland, perhaps the world's greatest tea-drinking countries. Instant tea and tea bags are contributing to the growing popularity of this beverage in the United States.

Teas may be selected from three classes: Green (from leaves that have been withered, rolled, and fired immediately); black (leaves have been fermented or oxidized before firing); and oolong (from partially oxidized or fermented leaves). They are usually imported, blended, and packed for sale to consumers. Americans have preferred black, whole leaf teas, particularly those labeled "pekoe" or "orange pekoe." These names designate the small first and second leaves next to the end of the tea shoots. Broken and cut leaves are utilized in tea bags.

Instant teas are made principally from the black teas and are available as either "pure" instant teas or with malto-dextrin as a carrier. Consumers are sometimes confused because a teaspoonful of the light, fluffy, pure form of instant tea contains the same amount of extracted tea solids as the heavier mixture.

Like coffee and tea, chocolate beverages are made from imported raw materials—in this case dried cacao beans. The manufacturer cleans, blends, roasts, and removes the shells, leaving the meat or "nibs." These are crushed in a process which generates enough frictional heat to liquefy the cocoa butter (the nibs average 54 percent cocoa butter content) and form what is known by the industry as "chocolate liquor."

That portion of the liquor used for cocoa is pumped into hydraulic presses to remove the desired amount of cocoa butter. This leaves a pressed cake that can be cooled, pulverized, and sifted into powder.

Breakfast or high-fat cocoa contains at least 22 percent fat, medium-fat cocoa (sometimes labeled simply as "cocoa") contains 10 to 22 percent, while low-fat cocoa contains less than 10 percent.

Chocolate may be treated with alkali to prepare "Dutched" or Dutch-process cocoa. This makes a darker beverage which looks stronger but actually has a milder flavor.

Chocolate and cocoa are often used to flavor milk or skimmed milk. When milk is made with chocolate, it may be labeled "chocolate milk." Milk or other dairy drinks made with cocoa should be labeled "chocolate flavored."

Cocoa, because of its popular flavor, is often used in food items intended for special diets. Some of these items are used "as is" while others are in dry form to be added to milk or skim milk.

Careful reading of labels is essential if you are to choose wisely from the big supply of beverages and beverage materials. The Federal Food, Drug, and Cosmetic Act (FD&C Act) and the more recent Fair Packaging and Labeling Act require accurate and informative labeling to help prospective buyers compare and make wise choices.

The principal display panel or panels must bear a prominent declaration of the identity of the beverage. If the beverage is standardized, the name is the one prescribed by the standard such as "orange juice from concentrate" or "club soda." In the absence of a standard, the designation must be the common or usual name, modified when necessary to indicate the form of the beverage as, for example, "coffee—drip grind." Also, an accurate declaration of the contents in terms of weight, volume, or count must appear on the principal display panel, usually in the lower 30 percent of the panel, printed in letters of prescribed height, and separated by specified distances from other printed information. Solids are normally declared by weight, liquids by volume. Some are declared by count and the volume or weight such as "100 tea bags—8 ounces."

Name and address of the manufacturer, packer, or the shipper must appear prominently, modified, when necessary, by some statement such as "distributed by." Ingredients must be declared in descending order of predominance unless the beverage is one where they are specified by a standard of identity. Standards prescribe which optional ingredients must be declared, if used. Always the label must state the presence of any artificial coloring, artificial flavoring, or a chemical preservative.

If intended for special dietary use, the beverage must be labeled with information about its vitamin and mineral content; percentages of fat, protein, and carbohydrates; the calories it will provide; or other information needed to guide the user. Names and percentages of artificial sweeteners must be stated.

Additives are sometimes listed by long, formidable, technical names. Consumers may rest assured that the beverages containing these are safe. Since its passage in 1938, the FD&C Act has prohibited adding any substance which would make the beverages injurious to health. The act was later amended to provide more positive protection by requiring pretesting of food additives and color additives in order to demonstrate that the proposed uses are safe.

Other helpful information is sometimes found on labels. They may bear directions for preparing, recipes, or information about the number and size of servings. Most milk and other dairy drinks are labeled "Grade A" to show that they have been produced under sanitary conditions and from raw materials which meet standards recommended by the U.S. Public Health Service and adopted by most States.

U.S. "Grade A" or U.S. "Fancy" markings on other beverages or beverage bases indicate that these meet the quality standards established by USDA.

Factors considered in grading include those affecting appearance, like depth and brightness of color, absence of flecks and excess sediment; and those affecting taste, like sweetness, acidity, the Brix/acid ratio (which measures the balance between sweetness and tartness), the amount of peel oil, and other characteristics. If a beverage has been packed under the voluntary inspection service provided by USDA, the label may bear the inspection shield showing that it was "Packed Under Continuous Inspection" and the grade may also be shown in the USDA shield.

Value comparisons are hard to make, not only because there are many beverages in different forms but also because individual taste preferences or dietary needs may outweigh price considerations. A coffee or tea that makes a distasteful brew is no bargain at any price. For dietary reasons some may choose skim milk or low-fat cocoa, while others need the nutrients in whole milk or chocolate. Prices of diluted juice drinks usually vary according to their juice content. Nutritive values do not necessarily vary proportionately.

The large "economy" size may cost less per pint, but offers no advantage if much of the product deteriorates before it can be used.

Available storage facilities may dictate the form or the amount of a beverage to be purchased. Frozen products must be stored in the freezer compartment, which should be maintained at between 0° (or below) and 5° F. Milk, orange juice (other than canned or frozen), and opened containers of other beverages should be kept in the refrigerator, preferably at a temperature no higher than 40° F.

Chocolate should be kept cool to prevent melting and should not be subjected to wide swings of temperature. Tea may be stored in any cool, dry place.

Coffee is more difficult to keep. The oils and other constituents that provide its flavor and fragrance are easily dissipated or, if exposed to air, are quickly oxidized to substances yielding disagreeable odors and tastes. In contrast, coffee is a rare treat when made from freshly roasted and ground beans in an atmosphere where the air is still full of the rich aroma released by roasting, grinding, and brewing.

By the time most roasted and ground coffee reaches the consumer, even when protected in vacuum-packed containers, much of its aroma and flavor have been lost. Once the container is opened, the loss speeds up. It can be retarded but not stopped by keeping the coffee container tightly closed and stored in a cool place. Coffee should be purchased in amounts small enough to be quickly used.

We drink tea and coffee partly because of the stimulating effect of the caffein they contain (cocoa or chocolate is mildly stimulating). If we want only this effect, it matters little how we prepare them. We might even enjoy the dark and bitter brew prepared by that champion tea-drinker, the Australian sheepman, by long boiling of the leaves in his blackened "billy-can" celebrated in the song "Waltzing Matilda." Most of us prefer to just sing about "Matilda" while drinking tea or coffee brewed in ways that do not drive off the constituents that provide pleasant aroma and taste.

Much of the tea and coffee served in the United States could be improved if the water used were of better quality. Usually we take whatever comes from the tap. Vendors of spring water no longer wander the

Shopping cart with cans of apple juice packed under continuous inspection by USDA, shown in Yakima, Wash. Note shields on cans.

streets shouting "Tea water! Come and get your tea water!" as they did in pre-Revolutionary New York.

Coffee is brewed in pots, percolators, dripolators, or any of several vacuum-type devices. Scientific research undertaken by the Coffee Brewing Institute since its formation in 1951 has shown that to make good coffee you should:

Start with utensils that have been thoroughly cleaned.

Use freshly drawn water.

Use the finest grind suited to your coffeemaking device.

Use plenty of coffee; the standard proportion of 2 level tablespoons per cup may be increased, if so desired. More coffee with less brewing time usually gives better flavor.

When you use a percolator, keep the heat adjusted to barely percolate. Percolate no longer than 5 to 10 minutes.

Keep coffee hot over low heat to avoid boiling and loss of flavor.

After the Mardi Gras balls in New Orleans, it is traditional for participants to go to the Old French Market to enjoy "cafe-au-lait," made by mixing equal portions of hot milk and strong coffee.

During the gay days of the Old Empire, the Viennese invented ways to serve whipped cream with coffee. Coffee with whipped cream is still called "Vienna coffee."

To make good tea:

- Add water to the tea as soon as it comes to a bubbling boil; do not let water boil since this drives out dissolved air which helps give tea its "bite."
- Prewarm the pot, which preferably should be of ceramic material.
- If using tea leaves, weigh out about one-third ounce per pint or measure 1 rounded teaspoon per cup. Use tea bags according to directions.
- Allow the tea to "draw" for 3 to 4 minutes unless milk or cream is to be added, in which case it may draw for 4, 5, or even 6 minutes.
- Separate the brew from the leaves, and keep it hot until served.

Sugar, lemon, cream, or milk may be added. Cream or milk mellows the taste, and casein in the milk causes the tannin which is in the tea to become insoluble.

For iced tea, brew 5 to 6 minutes and add extra tea (4 tablespoons tea to 3 cups boiling water).

Hot chocolate or cocoa can be made from these recipes:

HOT CHOCOLATE

6 servings

2 squares unsweetened chocolate
1 cup hot water
¼ cup sugar
Dash of salt
3 cups milk

Melt the chocolate in water in top of double boiler directly over low heat. Add sugar and salt; simmer 4 minutes with constant stirring. Place over hot water. Stir in milk. Heat to serving temperature and beat with rotary beater.

BREAKFAST COCOA

6 servings

⅓ cup cocoa
4 to 6 tablespoons sugar
⅛ teaspoon salt
½ cup water
3½ cups milk

Mix cocoa, sugar and salt, pour in water, and cook 3 minutes. Stir in milk and heat to boiling, but do not boil. Beat with rotary beater to prevent scum formation.

Juices usually require no preparation other than chilling. If ice is added, do not overdilute. Since sugar is hard to dissolve in cold liquids, sugar sirup is preferable if juices are to be sweetened. Sirup drained from canned fruits may be used for this purpose. This saves money and may add flavor.

Cookbooks contain pages of recipes for punches, varying from a simple mixture of 2 pints ginger ale and 1 pint of grapejuice, to some involving many ingredients and complex mixing instructions. Punchmaking offers ample room for study and imaginative experimentation.

Edward R. Thompson

The Pedigreed Pickle Is Here: New Quality in Old Favorites

Pickles, relishes, olives, and kraut are good by themselves, but more importantly they make other foods taste better. They can add sparkle and zest to a sandwich, a salad, a banquet, a beverage. They can provide a change in the texture and flavor of many foods.

America has always had a fondness for pickles and relishes. "On a hot day, in Virginia," wrote Thomas Jefferson, "I know of nothing more comforting than a fine spiced pickle, brought up trout-like from the sparkling depths of that aromatic jar below stairs in Aunt Sally's cellar."

Pickling—to keep food longer—is of ancient lineage, along with sun-drying, salting, and smoking. Pickling is still with us in many improved forms to provide a lengthy list of delicacies.

Perhaps it all started centuries ago when a naturally bitter olive fell into a briny lagoon and was found to be edible, tasty, and nourishing. Be that as it may, the art of pickling can be traced through thousands of years of recorded history.

Famous people of all eras have expressed a fondness for pickles. Cleopatra, we are told, found them a royal treat for flavor and zest; and believed they contributed to health and beauty. Pliny's writings mention spiced and preserved cucumbers. Napoleon esteemed pickles as a health-giving food.

Queen Elizabeth I was among the multitude of pickle fanciers. The list continues on to include George Washington, John Adams, and Dolley Madison.

In America, the pickle patch was an important adjunct to good living on colonial plantations. And pickles were highly regarded by all the pioneering generations because, under frontier conditions, pickles were the only zestful, juicy, green, succulent food available for many months of the year. In colonial days, and much later on the farm and in the villages, homemakers expected to "put down" some pickles in stone crocks—and to "put up" pickles and pickle relishes in glass jars. It remained for the commercial pickle packers, however, to utilize the discoveries of scientific research in developing the most perfect pickles ever produced.

Pickles are a product of natural fermentation—either of the vegetable or food ingredients or of the liquid surrounding them. This fermentation process, carefully controlled by the amount of salt used, the temperature, herbs, spices, and other factors, develops the flavor, color, aroma, and texture desired for the particular kind of pickles.

Manufacture of pickles has moved with modern science from the small plant where mistakes were often made, quality was uncertain, and losses heavy; to the larger, well-equipped, sanitary food plants where all the processes are controlled and a myriad of pickles, relishes, and similar products are prepared and attractively packaged for your use.

A modern pickle packer uses varieties of cucumbers far superior to those used previously for pickling, yet

Edward R. Thompson is Assistant Head, Standardization Section, Processed Products Standardization and Inspection Branch, Fruit and Vegetable Division, Consumer and Marketing Service.

manufacturers strive constantly to improve the strains. Soil, rainfall, and location all have a decisive effect on development of just the right kind of tender, flavorful cucumber for pickling. Agriculturalists and scientists have supplied growers with improved varieties and advised farmers as to the best methods of planting and cultivating in order to produce firmer, meatier cucumbers.

Cucumbers are picked at a time when most of them are of the sizes particularly wanted by the packer. The bulk of this work has been done by hand. In the larger "pickle patches" of today, a strong trend is toward mechanically harvesting the cucumbers very quickly and at the peak of their quality.

Since most pickles are cucumber pickles or contain cucumber pickles in a mixture, let's talk mostly about them. Because of the way they are made they are called either "cured pickles" or "fresh pack pickles." Each has its own characteristics of flavor and texture.

- Cured pickles have been slightly fermented in a salt brine for several months. They are then de-salted and washed. The pickling process is completed in a vinegar solution, also a fermentation product, and seasoned to give the flavor characteristics desired. The curing process imparts subtle flavor changes and produces edible acids in the pickles themselves. They are usually crisp, dark green, and somewhat translucent.
- Fresh-pack pickles are relatively new in the market. In this process the cucumbers are packed directly into the containers, and covered with a pickling solution containing vinegars, other acids, flavorings, and other suitable ingredients to give the desired characteristics to the pickles. The containers are then sealed and pasteurized with heat to preserve them. Fresh-pack pickles have not been fermented and retain something of the flavor of fresh cucumbers. They are usually a light yellow-green color and are not usually as salty or as acid as the cured type. "Fresh-pack" is often shown on the label.

In modern day pickling, cucumbers to be cured are hauled to salting stations close to the growing regions. The newly harvested cucumbers go there for a thorough cleansing and careful sorting for defects and sizes. Speed is essential while the cucumbers are at their peak of perfection, and it is provided by very efficient, modern machinery.

For cured pickles, the selected cucumbers are put in a salt water bath in vats, where controlled fermentation takes place. The salt is added gradually, according to an exact formula, and it penetrates the pickles slowly, evenly, and thoroughly.

After weeks and even months of such curing, the cucumbers are called "brine stock." The brine stock may then be removed from the salting station to the finishing plant, according to the plant's schedule. Cucumbers for fresh pack are hauled directly to the packing plant since they must be processed within a few hours.

The kinds of pickles you can buy are almost as infinite as the kinds of cooking that exist. You may sometimes be confused by the number of different styles, colors, and shapes that fill the shelves. However, all cucumber pickles are related to one or another of an easily-remembered handful of basic kinds. Here are some typical variations. If you keep these in mind, you can easily find your way around the pickle department of your favorite food store and get just the kind you want.

Dill Pickles. Dill pickles are flavored primarily with dill, an aromatic herb, which may be supplemented by various mixed spices. They come in three variations. Genuine dill pickles are prepared entirely by a lengthy process of natural fermentation with the various herbs. Processed dill pickles are started as regular brine stock, and finished later in a dill solution; they possess somewhat better keeping qualities than the genuine dill pickles. Between these sometimes you may find an "overnight dill" pickle. This is a quickly fermented variation of the genuine dill pickles produced by stopping the fermentation after only a day or two through placing the pickles in cold storage. These pickles retain some of the flavor of the fresh cucumber, along with the dill flavor. Like the genuine dills, they are commonly sold in bulk.

The label may indicate that many of these dills are "kosher" or "kosher-style" pickles. The term "kosher" has religious significance in accord with Hebrew law. However, in the United States it also has come to mean that these pickles are more highly spiced, including onion and garlic flavors. Most dill pickles are large or medium in size. They may have been cut into strips, slices, cubes, or in any manner.

Sour Pickles are brine stock pickles which have been finished in vinegar with spices. While normally packed whole, they may be cut in strips, slices, or in any manner. There are a number of different styles such as sour mixed pickles—produced by combining sour cucumber pickles with the other sour pickled vegetables such as cauliflower, onions, peppers, all cut into small convenient pieces. Sour relish or piccalilli includes finely chopped sour pickles, sometimes packed alone and sometimes with other finely chopped sour cured vegetables. Chow chow is similar to sour mixed pickles except for the addition of a mustard sauce flavored with spices such as yellow and brown mustard seed, turmeric, garlic, cinnamon, cloves, ginger, nutmeg, cayenne and black and white pepper.

Sweet Pickles start as sour pickles from which the vinegar has been drained. They are finished in sweet, spicy liquors which are added from time to time until the desired degree of sweetness is attained. A lengthy aging process follows. Sweet pickles are available in many variations such as the following: sliced sweet pickles, chips or wafers—plain sweet pickles cut crosswise into discs; candied chips—extra sweet, sliced sweet pickles; sweet dill pickles—made from genuine or

Picnic bean dishes: Dill pickles help season the cold salad of green beans, while sweet pickle relish spices the made-in-minutes baked beans.

processed dill pickles instead of sour pickles and frequently cut lengthwise as well as crosswise; mixed sweet pickles—sweet pickles combined with other sweet pickled vegetables, such as cauliflower, onions, sweet pepper, and green tomatoes; sweet relish or piccalilli—finely chopped sweet pickles sometimes combined with other finely chopped sweet pickled vegetables.

Some of the pickles that are classified as cured type are also available in the fresh type pack.

Among them are fresh-packed dill pickles, fresh-packed sweet pickles and mild sweet pickles, fresh-packed sweet relish and mild sweet relish, fresh-packed sweetened dill pickles, and fresh-packed sweetened dill relish.

Pickles belong to a larger family of foods with many of the same characteristics and which add interest and zest to your meals. Many other fruits and vegetables are pickled commercially or by homemakers. Some you may find on the store shelf are: peach, pear, crabapple, watermelon rind, beet, onion, okra, peppers, tomatoes—ripe or green, and green beans.

You may also find a variety of relishes you might remember from childhood—or perhaps never have heard of, such as: pepper-onion, tomato apple-chutney, tomato-pear chutney, horseradish, and corn relish.

Sauerkraut belongs in this large family of foods, too. Good sauerkraut—brined, fermented cabbage—has a pleasant, characteristic, tart, and tangy flavor. It is crisp and firm in texture, creamy white in color, and free from specks and core material. It is used hot in many ways, for instance as a main dish with meat, or in most of the ways pickles are used—cold as a side dish, in sandwiches, on a salad plate, or in a mixed pickle and relish platter.

Cured olives also belong in this family since they are used in much the same manner. Serve them the way you would cucumber pickles—whole or chopped, sliced or stuffed.

As with many of the other foods you buy, pickles and relishes are packed quite often according to U.S. grades. These grades with their definitions of styles, forms, and kinds help manufacturers to properly make and accurately label the products they offer for sale. U.S. grades also help the store buyers to buy what they know you want. Some of these foods have on their labels an indication of their grade—such as U.S. Grade A or U.S. Grade B. These marks show that the food has been packed according to the official U.S. standards and meets requirements of the grade. If the label shows by an official USDA mark that the product has been packed under the continuous inspection of the U.S. Department of Agriculture, you will know it was packed in a good commerical plant, in a sanitary manner.

When you make your selection in the store:

- First look at the whole pickle display including the product as seen through the glass container. You can usually tell whether the cucumbers are whole, sliced crosswise, sliced lengthwise, unevenly cut, or finely cut as in a relish. You can also choose the size you want. Cucumber pickles come in seven regular sizes from the midget to the extra large. You can often examine the jars of mixed pickles and relishes to see what ingredients are used and in what proportions.
- Read the labels; they give much useful information. For one thing, labels may suggest kinds and styles you have never heard of. Information on the label that can help in your selection includes: the kind of pickles—sweet, sour, or dill, the size or number in the container, whether they are the cured or fresh type, and the amount of product in the container.
- Note the prices asked; they vary considerably from item to item and brand to brand. This is often because some types are much more costly to make. Small whole cucumbers, long processes, and more costly spices and other ingredients are reasons for higher priced items. They may well be worth the higher price for some purposes. Small whole cucumber pickles would

not be a good buy, however, if you intend to slice them into a salad or a sandwich.

• Buy different kinds to add variety to your meals and to learn what your family really likes.

Most everyone knows what pickles and relishes can add to our meals—from sandwich to meat loaf to holiday dinner. Perhaps we don't know everything they can do. Here are some ways you can use pickles and relishes:

In the lunchbox alone or in the sandwich mix.

A sprinkle of chopped pickle or relish in almost any soup.

Diced in stuffings, meat loaves or meat dishes, fish, salads, creamed or buttered vegetables.

Diced pickles, olives, or relishes in scrambled eggs.

Pickles or their liquids in sauces for meats, fish, fowl, egg dishes.

The liquid from pickles in almost any dressing or to baste the meat.

Wherever a bit of spice or herb flavor is needed.

You can keep pickles and relishes unopened for several months. After opening, store them in the refrigerator. Natural acids in the food and the surrounding liquor tend to inhibit the growth of molds and bacteria.

Pickles and relishes will not keep for an indefinite period, however. Discard any open jar if the product is very discolored, if it has an offensive odor, if gas bubbles appear, or if the product displays any unusual softness, mushiness, or slipperiness.

Here are a few pickle recipes.

DILLY FRANKS

8 servings

¼ cup butter or margarine
8 frankfurters
1½ cups catsup
½ cup water
2 teaspoons (or to taste) chili powder
⅔ cup chopped dill pickles
2 medium-size onions, chopped
8 frankfurter rolls

Melt fat. Add frankfurters; cook over medium heat until browned on all sides. Combine catsup, water, chili powder, pickles, and onions; mix well. Add to frankfurters. Cook over low heat, stirring occasionally, 10 minutes. Serve frankfurters on rolls.

PICKLESICLES

These are simply the largest dill pickles you can find, with ice cream sticks inserted for easy handling and eating. Serve them nestled in a big bucket of ice. Just for fun you can paint the sticks with ordinary vegetable coloring. Instead of ice cream sticks, you can use plastic picnic butter spreaders as handles. Children love picklesicles!

SALAMI PICKLEWICHES

Cut large dill pickles in half lengthwise. Cut two pieces salami and one piece process Swiss cheese to size of pickle. Place slice of cheese between slices of salami and insert in pickles, sandwich fashion. Chill.

CALORIE COUNTERS' STUFFED CELERY

6 servings

¼ teaspoon Worcestershire sauce
½ cup cottage cheese
⅓ cup (about 2 each, 2 by ⅝ inches) chopped sweet gherkins
¼ teaspoon salt
1 tablespoon chopped celery leaves
6 celery stalks, cut in 8-inch pieces

Combine Worcestershire sauce, cottage cheese, gherkins, salt, and celery leaves; mix well. Spread cheese mixture on celery stalks. Calories per serving: about 29.

WEIGHT WATCHERS' STUFFED MUSHROOMS

Mix together ½ cup chopped sweet mixed pickles and ½ cup chopped apple. Stuff 8 large mushroom caps with mixture. Calories per serving: about 23.

For further reading:

Pickle Packers International, Inc., 108½ East Main Street, St. Charles, Ill. 60174. Various consumer and recipe bulletins.

Helen Carlisle
Richard L. Hall

Be an Artful Seasoner With Spices and Herbs

Spices and herbs have added flavoring to food since the dawn of civilization. They are a part of our history—Marco Polo and Columbus sought them. They are a part of our literature—Chaucer, Shakespeare, and Lewis Carroll mentioned them. And, of course, they are an important part of our food. Spices give their distinctive character to spaghetti and chili, to goulash and pumpkin pie, and to a variety of other everyday and exotic dishes.

We often use the word "spice" in a very broad sense. We speak of the "spice shelf," or of "spice cookery." Here we mean any aromatic fresh or dried plant material added to food primarily for its flavor. But when we speak of "spices and herbs," we use the term in a much more limited sense.

Strictly speaking, spices are aromatic natural products which are the dried seeds, buds, fruit, flower parts, bark or roots of plants, usually of a tropical origin.

Examples include pepper (dried berry); cloves (dried, unopened flower buds); cinnamon (bark); and ginger (a rhizome or rootlike stem).

Herbs are the aromatic leaves and sometimes the flowers of plants, usually of temperate zone origin. Examples include "parsley, sage, rosemary, and thyme," to quote from a quite recent popular song.

A seed is the aromatic, dried, small, whole fruits or seeds of plants, usually of temperate origin. Examples are anise, caraway, and sesame.

Most of these products are available in whole and ground forms in cans and bottles. Or you can have the fun and benefit of growing many of the temperate zone herbs and seeds in your own garden, although their flavor quality may be unpredictable.

Spices, herbs, and seeds owe their flavor to two classes of substances found in them.

One class contains certain aromatic substances, called "essential oils," which are responsible for the aroma and much of the flavor. Because these oils evaporate readily, they are quickly lost from ground spice unless the spice is kept cool and in a tightly closed container. The whole spice contains these oils still trapped in undamaged cells, and it retains its flavor much longer.

A number of spices, including black pepper, red pepper, and ginger, contain the other class of substances which cause pungency or "bite," bitterness, astringency, and other flavor sensations. While most of these latter components are not lost with age, the evaporation of the essential oils—due to age or to poor storage conditions—changes the flavor and robs the spice of much of its original value.

At times spices may become infested by so-called "stored grain" insects such as the insects that attack flour and cornmeal. Members of the red pepper family and some of the dehydrated vegetables are particularly prone to infestation.

The consumer who is interested in maintaining maximum quality on her

Helen Carlisle is Home Economics Director and Richard L. Hall is Vice President-Research and Development with McCormick & Company, Inc., Baltimore, Md.

Fancy Tea Bread, above, is spiced with cardamom, crushed saffron, and mace, and the bread is glazed and sprinkled with decors. Chicken Breast Gourmet, below, is spiced with poultry seasoning and other seasoning, crushed coriander seed, black pepper, whole cloves, and whole allspice.

spice shelf should observe the following points:

- The container—A tightly closed, screw-cap glass jar is best. Cans and cartons are inexpensive and convenient but cannot be sealed or resealed. Apothecary jars will keep the romance but not the flavor.
- The location—A cool, dry location away from bright light or sunlight is best. Enemies of flavor quality are heat, moisture, air, and light, in that order. You need not refrigerate spices, but the spot often picked for convenience—over the range—is the worst.

Under average conditions, one should expect to be able to keep whole spices for several years—almost indefinitely. Whole leaf herbs are somewhat less durable, and will lose their freshness in a year or two; color often fades sooner. Ground spices are seldom at their best after a year. Members of the red pepper family, red and chili pepper, paprika, and bell pepper flakes lose quality in 6 months. In warm, moist climates, as in the Gulf States, deterioration is much more rapid. Tightly closed containers in humid climates are always a great help.

Good seasoning is an art, but easy and fun to learn. The best flavor is one so smooth and well blended that individual flavor notes are hard to pick out or define. We have all heard some appreciative guest say, "My, this is good. What is in it?" We can be certain that if the flavor were so strong or simple that he could tell what was in it, he would not have liked it as well.

There are no hard-and-fast rules for the use of spices. Two general hints:

- Experiment; be adventurous.
- Underseason, rather than overseason.

Beyond this, it is possible to list certain general groups of spices which possess flavors that lend themselves especially well to certain foods. Such a list suggests some likely uses, but every spice can be used much more broadly. Desirability of each use is a matter of personal preference.

"Sweet" spices include allspice, cardamom, cinnamon, cloves, coriander, ginger, nutmeg, and mace. Poppy and sesame seeds are in this group. Sweet spices go very well with pastries, fruit dishes, nuts, and ham. Of course, they can be used with good effect with many other foods besides these.

Another group might be called "protein spices," since they are often used with meat, fowl, fish, egg, and bean dishes. This group includes red pepper, celery, chili powder, curry powder, marjoram, monosodium glutamate or MSG (which is not really a spice but a flavor enhancer), sage, mustard, poultry seasoning, thyme, and rosemary.

"Salad herbs" go especially well in salads and vegetable dishes. Basil, caraway, celery, parsley, and tarragon are in this group.

A number of seeds are frequently used in baking breads and crackers. Caraway, poppy, and sesame seeds are the most popular.

Finally, several spices, herbs, and seeds are useful in so many ways that they belong to several groups. Among them are dehydrated onion and garlic, oregano, mace, marjoram, paprika, and, of course, black pepper.

The recipes which follow illustrate how spices may be used to lend variety to food that would be rather commonplace without them.

EXOTIC FRUIT MEDLEY

4 servings

Sauce:
½ cup packed brown sugar
1 tablespoon arrowroot or cornstarch
1 teaspoon lemon bits
¼ teaspoon allspice
¼ teaspoon mace
¼ teaspoon fennel seed, crushed
1 tablespoon lemon juice
½ cup water

Fruit:
2 bananas, cut in 2-inch pieces
2 peach halves
2 pear halves
2 slices pineapple, cut in halves
8 orange sections
12 Bing cherries

Combine ingredients for sauce.

Cook, stirring constantly, 2 minutes or until thickened.

Arrange fruits in a shallow pan.

Spread a part of the sauce over the fruits.

Broil around 5 minutes; turn fruit and spread with remaining sauce. Broil 5 minutes.

Serve it with ham, turkey, chicken, or pork.

SAVORY MUSTARD SAUCE

About 1½ cups

1 cup packed brown sugar
¼ cup dry mustard
1 tablespoon arrowroot or cornstarch
¼ teaspoon salt
1 teaspoon beef flavor base
½ cup hot water
2 tablespoons lemon juice
2 eggs, beaten

Combine sugar, mustard, arrowroot, and salt.

Dissolve beef flavor base in hot water. Add to sugar mixture along with lemon juice. Mix well.

Stir in beaten eggs and cook over low heat or in double boiler, stirring, 10 minutes or until sauce thickens.

Serve it with ham, fried shrimp, or roast beef.

ORIENTAL RICE

6 servings

3 tablespoons butter or margarine
Dash cloves
¼ teaspoon cinnamon
¼ teaspoon cardamom
⅛ teaspoon allspice
⅛ teaspoon saffron
⅛ teaspoon black pepper
2 teaspoons garlic salt
2 tablespoons instant minced onion
1 cup long-grain rice
3 cups boiling water
½ cup raisins
½ cup toasted, slivered almonds

Melt butter or margarine in large saucepan. Add cloves, cinnamon, cardamom, allspice, saffron, pepper, garlic salt, onion, and rice; mix well.

Stir in boiling water; cover and simmer 25 minutes.

Add raisins and let stand, covered, 5 minutes.

Sprinkle the almonds over the top before serving.

BOHEMIAN GOULASH

6 servings

2 pounds round steak, cut in ½- by ½- by 2-inch strips
2 tablespoons butter or margarine
¾ teaspoon salt
1 tablespoon instant minced garlic
2 tablespoons instant minced onion
1½ teaspoons caraway seed
2 teaspoons dill seed
1½ cups water
Cooked noodles or rice, as desired
1 cup dairy sour cream

Brown the steak strips in butter or margarine.

Add salt, garlic, onion, caraway seed, dill seed, and water.

Simmer for 1 hour or until meat is tender, stirring occasionally.

Serve over noodles or rice and top with sour cream.

For further reading:

AMERICAN SPICE TRADE ASSOCIATION, *The Magic of Spices*. American Spice Trade Association, New York, 1964.

CLAIBORNE, CRAIG, *The New York Times Menu Cook Book*. Harper & Row, Publishers, Inc., New York, 1966.

COLLINS, MARY, *The McCormick Spices of the World Cookbook*. McGraw-Hill Book Co., New York, 1964.

MACMILLAN, H. F., *Tropical Planting and Gardening*. MacMillan & Co., Ltd., London, 1952.

MUENSCHER AND RICE, *Garden Spices and Wild Potherbs*. Comstock Publishing Co., Ithaca, N.Y., 1955.

OCHSE, J. J., AND OTHERS, *Tropical and Subtropical Agriculture*. The MacMillan Co., New York, 1961.

PARRY, JOHN W., *The Story of Spices*. Chemical Publishing Co., Inc., New York, 1953.

Food and Your Life

Thelma J. McMillan

Your Basic Food Needs: Nutrients for Life, Growth

Think for a moment of the microscopic speck of substance you were the day you started life as a single cell. What you are today reflects many things—how sound were your inherited instructions on how to build and operate a human body, what has been your life program of rest and exercise, how good have been your medical care and community and personal sanitation practices, and what emotional and intellectual stimulation the environment has provided. But these influences alone could not have changed you from that single cell.

Continually through the years the inherited instructions present in that first cell have been followed to rearrange food substance into the living tissue which is you. The process never stops, even if you are no longer increasing in size. Such an intricate system is possible only by constant exchange of substance composing the cells. In this exchange, there is always some leakage, with destruction and loss from the body and necessary replacement from food. Bone, fat, muscle, organs, blood—all participate in this constant change of material. You may be an exact duplicate of what you were a year ago, but you are to a very large extent of new substance.

The tools to carry through the body reactions have come from food. Some, such as the vitamins, come directly; but others, such as the hormones, must be made in the tissues from food substance.

Fuel to drive the reactions comes from food. A person is aware of the energy it takes to climb stairs, and he may recognize that energy is always being used by the heart and the diaphragm muscles. In addition to such muscular activity requiring energy, a myriad of invisible chores must be done—moving substances through cell membranes, joining molecules to form tissues, collecting waste material to be excreted—to mention only a few.

We are, in a very real sense, what we eat. The common stuff of life in the cells of animals and plants are the nutrients. Group names for the nutrients are carbohydrates (starches and sugars), proteins (amino acids), fats, vitamins, minerals, and water. All but the last two exist because the plant has formed them from carbon dioxide of the air, salts of nitrogen and minerals from the soil, and water, with the use of the energy of sunlight. Animals live on the plants, either first or second hand. The job of a person's digestive system is to break up plant and animal material into the common nutrients. This includes splitting big carbohydrate molecules to simple sugars and splitting big protein molecules to their constituent amino acids. The body absorbs these common substances and uses them to form and operate its own structure.

No one food gives us the nutrients in the amounts we need. It is true that the amino acid assortment in beefsteak matches that in your muscle, but what about the mineral for your bones? The animal bone lies on the dinner plate. The minerals it contains will have to be supplied to your system

Thelma J. McMillan is Professor of Food and Nutrition, College of Home Economics, at Iowa State University, Ames.

by other foods, primarily milk. Neither meat nor milk do much to satisfy your needs for vitamin C—fruits and vegetables do. Many other examples can be given. Ultimately, we find a mixture of plant and animal products proves most successful and pleasant in providing enough of each of the nutrients for our tissues.

The living system is an outstanding example of cooperation and interdependence. Each nutrient may have its special part to play, but it has no independence. A change at any point in the total integrated system can bring change and adjustment throughout the system. No sharp dividing line exists between structure and function of the body, nor even body substance and the fuel supply. Perhaps no accomplishment of the body illustrates as well the multiple and interdependent action as does the resistance to infection, in which many nutrients are involved in different ways. This unity and interdependence should be borne in mind as we consider the contribution of various nutrients.

A man who weighs around 160 pounds may be made up of about 100 pounds of water, 29 pounds of protein, 25 pounds of fat, 5 pounds of minerals, one pound of carbohydrate, and one-quarter ounce of vitamins.

Only the vitamins, in their minute amounts, seem to play no part as structural components of the body. Most of the mineral material is calcium and phosphorus, found deposited in the protein framework of bone and tooth cells to create a hard tissue able to bear weight and pressure. Carbohydrate is a component of nerve fibers.

Fat has been identified as a structural component of every cell wall and every membrane within a cell. Perhaps the most startling observation is that about half the dry weight of the brain is fat. In other parts of the body, certain cells are adapted to hold large amounts of fat, and the fatty tissue which they form helps to round the contours of the body, to cushion and support body organs, and to insulate the body.

Although we cannot look upon the carbohydrate and fat as sources of fuel only, most of the body content of each is present for that purpose.

The main structural units of the body are the many different protein molecules that the body makes from the amino acids it has obtained from the proteins of food. There are 20 amino acids, and a specific protein will contain most or all of these 20 in certain proportions and arranged in a certain sequence. We can learn to choose our food so that enough of each amino acid is readily available, but we have to depend on our heredity to know how to arrange them properly into the proteins characteristic of the different tissues of the body.

Vitamins and most of the minerals find their use as tools for carrying through the body's reactions. Usually, the vitamin will be combined in the cell with a specific protein to form an enzyme. The enzyme has the shape and chemical properties to bring about changes in various nutrients and body products. For instance, in the daily activities of the cell, amino acids must be joined to form proteins, proteins must be joined to form cell structures, food fat must be modified to one's own tissue fat, energy of the food must be made available. The body has a tremendous number of enzymes to use for all these specific reactions just by changing the proteins combined with the various vitamins. Minerals also play a part in some of these enzyme systems.

In a few cases, vitamins and minerals are parts of some highly specialized substances other than enzymes. Examples include: Vitamin A is part of pigments in the eye which are used in vision; iron is part of the hemoglobin molecule that carries oxygen to the cells; and iodine is a part of the hormone thyroxine.

The only fuels our systems can use are carbohydrates, fats, and proteins. If you made a bonfire of dry food, you could see part of the energy released as light and feel part of it as heat. When the carbohydrates, fats, and

Meeting basic food needs is a pleasant adventure with a variety of good foods.

proteins are oxidized in our bodies, energy contained in their molecules is caught up in the formation of other molecules, ones which will be involved in muscle contraction, for instance. Eventually, much of the energy of the food does escape as heat, something we are aware of when we exercise heavily. Carbohydrates and proteins each provide us with 4 calories per gram of the nutrient in the food, and fats provide 9 calories per gram. (Both the gram and the calorie are units of measure. The gram is a weight unit equal to one twenty-eighth of an ounce; the calorie is a unit of measure of energy.)

A mixture of these three fuels is used throughout the day by body cells. We are choosing to eat in such a way in the United States that about 10 to 12 percent of the fuel is supplied by protein, about 44 percent by fat, and about 46 percent by carbohydrate. This means that if a man is spending 2,500 calories per day, he must take in about 480 grams, or a bit over a pound, of fuel. This is not the weight of food which would contain the nutrients; it is the weight of the dry nutrients alone. So man cannot look forward to condensing his fuel supply for the day into a handful of easily swallowed capsules.

Water occupies a unique position in the health of the body. It is a solvent for most molecules and permits them to interact more readily. In addition, water makes possible the movement of materials into the body, out to all of the cells, and then away to eventual elimination.

Water takes priority over all other nutrients in our need for an uninterrupted supply. The amount in the body tissues can easily fluctuate a pint or two, which means that the weight will fluctuate a pound or two as a result. Heavy loss of water, as on a hot day or in a steam bath, demands prompt replacement if danger is to be avoided. Only in certain illnesses, such as those of the heart or kidney, does the amount of water which is held increase markedly. These conditions must have a physician's attention to the disease rather than the person's manipulation of his water intake.

Both the food supply and the body regulatory processes affect the quantity of a nutrient which is present in the tissues. Compare protein and fat, for instance.

Severe limitation on protein supply can reduce the body content and stunt growth. However, generous protein will not provide short parents with tall sons for the basketball team nor the office worker with the bulging biceps of a weight-lifter. Severe limitation on fuel supply leads to wasting of body tissues and starvation. On the other hand, when the intake of fuel consistently exceeds the expenditure, no apparent limit exists on how plump a person may become. Another contrast can be drawn between vitamins A and C. Beyond certain limits of intake of vitamin C, the body content does not increase, while generous intakes of vitamin A will lead to continued increase in the amount in the liver, even to the point of harm.

That amount of a nutrient which accumulates in the body as a nonfunctioning surplus is referred to as "stored." Fat, carbohydrate, minerals, and vitamins A, D, E, and K are nutrients which can be stored. Protein and the water-soluble vitamins—including thiamine, niacin, and riboflavin—cannot be stored.

As more of a nutrient is eaten, more of it is absorbed from the digestive tract into the body. When the nutrient cannot be stored, the excess of the absorbed material is excreted, principally in the urine. In the case of the energy-yielding nutrients, protein is not stored and carbohydrate is stored in only limited amounts. None of the fuel supply, however, is wasted. Both protein and carbohydrate can be converted to fat in the body and may be stored in the fat depots.

The concept of storage can be misunderstood and unwarranted assumptions made. There is never a daily turnover or loss of all of a nutrient from the body cells. If any nutrient is eliminated from the diet, the amount in the body does not immediately drop to zero. Instead, there is a long period of slow depletion, in which the body makes what adjustments it can to the stress of lack of supply. Damage slowly becomes severe enough to be recognizable. The supplies of those nutrients which can be stored will protect the body for much longer periods than will the available amounts of nonstored nutrients. The ability to have reserves of nutrients is no guarantee that any are present. As with your financial reserve in the bank, a period of deposition or storing up must precede any withdrawal.

In everyday practice of good nutrition, the aim is to operate the body close to the top concentrations of protein and water-soluble vitamins, and to provide for reasonable storage of fat, minerals, and fat-soluble vitamins. Our present year-round good food supplies make this possible. Reserve supplies in the body are called upon when the intake is interrupted, as in illness; when the demand is especially great, as in the periods of very rapid growth of the child, pregnancy, or sustained activity; and when loss is especially heavy, as in the drain on iron stores caused by blood loss, or other losses during illness.

The ability to build up stores of certain nutrients is a mixed blessing. With continued storage of excess fuel intake, the result can be obesity and its complications. This is the only case where the unwanted excess has come from foods.

Medical reports have been made of people who became ill from excessive intakes of vitamin A and vitamin D over a period of time. The toxic quantities always came from excessive use of concentrated medicinal sources of the vitamins. Not enough occurs naturally in foods to be toxic. In fact, vitamin D is the one vitamin which does not even occur in our foods in particularly useful amounts, and its addition to milk has been an excellent health measure for the country. Unfortunately, vitamin D has been added to a wide variety of foods on the market. It is hoped that in the future the addition of vitamin D can be limited to milk, including fresh, canned, and dried milk. The amount of the vitamin D formed in the skin upon exposure to sunlight is never a part of the problem of excess.

The individual minerals vary markedly in the amount of each that is present in the body, the conditions of storage, and the possibility of harm from excess. It is the trace minerals that are sometimes involved in problems of excess. The source of the excess is not the food per se, but some contamination which has occurred. We have learned we must protect our food supplies against contamination with copper and zinc resulting from incorrect use of containers. The Food and Drug Administration has found a number of occasions when it was necessary to identify and stop the flow of certain minerals into the food supply.

Regulated addition of iron to refined grain products, iodine to table salt, and fluorine to drinking water are necessary parts of our supplies of these nutrients, but it is a mistake to assume that just any amount of any mineral is beneficial. Mineral compounds should never be handled casually; a child can be fatally poisoned by swallowing a handful of iron pills.

Let us consider the possibilities for a person to select a food intake that will not provide enough of one or more nutrients. For fuel and water we have the sense of hunger and the sense of thirst to help to guide us. For some nutrients, our need is so small in comparison to the amounts in any selection of food we might make that we always have been successful in meeting our needs. Examples of such nutrients are the vitamins biotin, pantothenic acid, and vitamin E, as well as such minerals as copper and zinc. Some nutrients have been problems in the history of man. Certain of the diseases known through the centuries have been found to result from marked deficiencies of one or more nutrients.

Following is a list of the historic names of these deficiency diseases and of the nutrient which is involved:

Scurvy—vitamin C; simple goiter—iodine; beriberi—thiamine; pellagra—niacin; and rickets—vitamin D and calcium.

We have inherited no name for vitamin A deficiency but use two terms for the eye symptoms involved, night blindness and xerophthalmia. In recent years the term kwashiorkor has come to be accepted for severe calorie-protein malnutrition, typically in the very young.

The historic deficiency diseases are all too common in some areas of the world today. In the United States, classic cases are so rare that teaching hospitals are very grateful to have an occasional one for young physicians to observe. This is not to say that we have yet reached the goal that each person receives the benefit of a fully adequate diet.

Effects of different levels of intake of nutrients upon people have been studied carefully. Definite benefits to health result from increases in the nutrient intake beyond the disease-prevention level. The exact point at which any further increase will bring no possible benefit is difficult to establish firmly. For these reasons, recommendations for nutrient intake made by nutritionists include what is called a safety factor, an amount of the nutrient beyond that having demonstrable effect. This is to provide the margin of security and certainty that most of us like to have in everything that we do, whether it be in highway driving, family financial planning, or swimming. Too large or too small margins of safety can be self-defeating, wasting resources in one fashion or another. The establishment of dietary goals does require carefully weighed judgments.

The leadership task of setting recommendations in the United States is entrusted to the Food and Nutrition Board of the National Research Council, which periodically reviews the research information and publishes a table of Recommended Daily Dietary Allowances for the nutrients. The greater the difference is between the recommended allowances and the intake of a population group or an individual, the greater the need for a change in habits of food intake.

Many people in the United States eat food which meets the nutrient recommendations; some do not. It is easy to evaluate your food intake and determine the group to which you belong. The recommended amounts of the nutrients have been translated into amounts of common types of foods by the U.S. Department of Agriculture in its Daily Food Guide. Compare what you are eating with this guide. The results will let you know whether you are permitting yourself the security of a generous nutrient intake.

Evaluation of the food intake alone cannot be used to provide reliable information on the existence, cause, or treatment of any signs of ill health. Such information comes from an evaluation of the person, the intricate self that is the net result of the interaction of nutrient supply, heredity, and environmental influences.

In succeeding chapters of this book you will find information on what nutrients more often are in a short supply in the food eaten by families in this country, what may be done to influence food habits so that the nutrient intake will be adequate, and a very practical guide to selection of an adequate diet for yourself and your family.

For further reading:

U.S. Department of Agriculture, *Food for Fitness: A Daily Food Guide.* Leaflet 424, Washington, D.C. 20250, 1964.

LEVERTON, RUTH M., *Food Becomes You.* Iowa State University Press, Ames, Iowa, 1965.

MICKELSEN, OLAF, *Nutrition Science and You.* Scholastic Book Service, New York, 1964.

Mary M. Hill

Creating Good Food Habits—Start Young, Never Quit

Food habits begin to form almost as soon as a child is born. They result from repeated experience with food and are modified, rather easily in the early years, as experience changes.

The first modification is in spacing meals to eliminate nighttime feedings. Later, a variety of foods are added to the baby's diet.

Food habits the child forms while very young and the modifications he makes as he grows and develops are good food habits when they meet his current individual needs for nutrients and for food energy. The child's needs change while he grows and matures, and so his food practices need to be adapted as these changes occur.

The greater the variety of foods which children know and enjoy, the easier it is to make these adaptations as they are needed.

There are several conditions in life that influence the assortment of foods a person will eat. One is the socioeconomic level into which a child is born. The foods a mother gives her baby must be selected from the variety of foods available to her economically. The young child of the poor family gains experience primarily with low-cost foods. These may or may not be good choices. The fact remains that the variety of foods that this child learns to eat and to enjoy is limited by cost.

The young child of a wealthy family will probably have experience with a greatly different variety of foods. Again, these may or may not be good choices. The variety of foods this child learns to eat and enjoy is not limited by cost but undoubtedly is limited by one or more of the other conditions of life that influence choices.

The ethnic background of the family influences the variety of foods and the methods of food preparation that the young child experiences. If the family came fairly recently from a rice-eating country, rice will probably be one of the first foods the young child will learn to eat.

Religion may also influence the variety of foods that a child experiences. Some groups forgo certain foods at all times and some abstain from the use of particular foods at specified times. The foods that will be given to a young child in one of these families will naturally be in line with dictates of the family's religion.

The most direct influence, however, is the parents themselves—their food preferences, attitudes toward food, and their information about the nutritive value of foods.

It is extremely difficult for a mother not to communicate in some way her dislike for a food she is feeding her child because she believes "it is good for him." Often the child resists this particular food even when the mother consciously tries to mask her own lack of preference.

It is difficult to interest a small child in a food which one family member refuses even to taste. How often that Johnnie will not eat a particular food because his father complains every time the food is served!

Sometimes the experiences parents

Mary M. Hill is a Nutritionist, Consumer and Food Economics Research Division, Agricultural Research Service.

have had cause them to severely limit the variety of foods they make available to their children. For example, on visiting a school where an informal breakfast survey was in progress some years ago, we found the school nurse concerned about one child's breakfast records. The little girl reported she had cream of wheat, brewer's yeast, bonemeal, and rose hip powder for her breakfast every morning. Investigation revealed that her parents had been interned in a concentration camp during World War II. Upon liberation, they were taken to England for treatment of the severe dietary deficiencies they had suffered. The therapeutic diet included brewer's yeast, bonemeal, and rose hip powder. These parents wanted to be sure their child would never suffer as they had. This, of course, is an extreme instance, but many parents today limit the variety of foods because of their beliefs about health and the wholesomeness of food.

We have named several conditions that tend to limit the variety of foods our children learn to eat and enjoy. There are other conditions that tend to extend the variety of foods that children will eat.

Fortunately, children do not spend all their formative years in the confines of their homes under the influence only of the immediate family. Most children, at an early age, have experience with other children. How many times have you heard a child say to his mother, "I want some of what Janie has." Often this is an opportunity to help a child learn to enjoy some fruit or vegetable that has been previously rejected.

As the child grows older, he has experience with other adults whom he comes to regard highly. His first teacher often becomes important to him. If the teacher has a wholesome attitude toward food and sets a good example, she helps to extend the variety of food that the child will accept and enjoy.

Drastic changes in the food supply also may extend variety. For example, during the food rationing of World War II, families were forced to use or to increase the use of foods that had not been on their usual shopping list. After the rationing was over some people, particularly children and young folks, had discovered foods such as a variety of fish that they could eat with enjoyment.

Children who participate in the National School Lunch program often learn to know and enjoy foods not usually available to them in the home. Repeated experiences with desirable food practices tend to help the child develop good eating habits.

Family mobility tends to acquaint children with a wider variety of foods. Fortunately, families usually stay in one place long enough for the family members to acquire a taste for some of the new foods.

If an individual's food choices, day after day, fail to meet his needs for energy and nutrients, his food habits are poor and over time will cause health problems.

The U.S. food supply has such variety and abundance that food combinations which will lead to an adequate diet are innumerable.

Acceptance of a wide variety of foods increases the likelihood and ease of achieving an adequate diet, but is no assurance that such a diet will result. Some information about combining of foods is necessary.

Nutritionists have translated recommendations of the Food and Nutrition Board, National Research Council-National Academy of Sciences, into servings of food and compiled them into reliable, easy-to-follow food guides. One such guide, "Food for Fitness—A Daily Food Guide," is available from the Office of Information, U.S. Department of Agriculture, Washington, D.C. 20250.

This guide divides food into four broad groups, allowing a great deal of choice within each group. If the specified number of servings from each food group are eaten, a good nutritional foundation will be assured. Extra servings of these and other foods to round out meals and to meet individual needs for food energy are desirable.

It is much easier to develop and maintain good food habits in young children than it is to correct any poor habits as children grow older. Considering the way most people in the United States live and work today, this requires the concerted cooperative efforts of all those who deal with children at meal or snack time. Here are some pointers:

• At home. Parents profoundly influence the attitudes and habits of their children. Children develop preferences for particular foods from the assortment of food served them. Likes or dislikes are developed upon the basis of flavor, consistency, texture, and the like.

All food rejected may not be disliked. Children may refuse to taste foods they see other family members avoid or those that for some reason are unappealing to them. When the latter occurs, it is wise to wait until another day and matter-of-factly offer the food again.

During the preschool or prenursery school years, parents are solely responsible for providing the nutritional guidance which results in desirable eating habits—setting a good example and providing a good variety of foods. By this means, parents convey to their young children that all food is good and should at least be tasted. A wholesome attitude toward food and a willingness to accept new foods or different methods of preparation is the first big step in developing and maintaining desirable eating habits. We eat food because it tastes good! The fact it is good for us is a bonus rather than an acceptable reason—to young children—for eating it.

After they enter school, children continue to need an example set for them at home, especially at breakfast time. One way to provide such an example is for both parents to allow enough time every morning to eat an adequate breakfast themselves.

Parents influence schoolchildren as well as preschool tots. Parents who are permissive so long as suitable choices are made often find it easier to guide their children when selections need modification. Boys and girls will often add the milk or fruit needed to round out the meal if they can have the "poor boy" or "hero" sandwich they want.

Learning to eat a variety of foods will proceed faster if parents will serve at home the important foods studied in school or that are included in the school lunch. Parents can also help their children to establish good food habits by encouraging them to participate in the school lunch even though the children may not yet have learned to enjoy some of the foods served.

In recent years, mothers working, consolidation of schools, and other changes in family and community life cause millions of children to eat some of their meals away from home and often without any supervision. Responsibility for the food habits of these children becomes a shared one.

• In nursery school. Although parents do and should have responsibility for the nutritional health of their children, the nursery school can support the home by serving for meals and snacks a variety of foods which contribute very substantially toward meeting the child's daily needs for nutrients and food energy. Children respond better to food if the surroundings are pleasant and the adult is understanding but firm about it being time to eat together.

Further, the child should have an opportunity to participate in activities that will help him extend the variety of foods he will eat. Tasting parties and games at snack time that motivate the child to taste unfamiliar or previously rejected foods are very good activities for this purpose.

The greatest contributions the nursery school can make to achievement of good eating habits are (1) providing well-chosen foods that look good and taste good to the children and (2) a continuing wholesome attitude toward all food on the part of adults who work with the children.

• In the school classroom. The classroom teacher has many opportunities to reinforce good teaching begun in the home by including at all grade levels well-chosen experiences with food in the classroom. Accurate nutrition information suitable to the age and maturity of the children can also be presented in such subject matter areas as health, science, social studies, and language arts.

In the primary grades, it is important that children learn that all food is good. Up to this time, the child has had the opportunity to learn to eat the foods included in the family food pattern. Now he can increase the variety of foods he knows by becoming familiar with those included in the food patterns of his classmates and the children he learns about.

The teacher takes the place of the mother during the school day. Her enthusiasm for all foods influences the children to taste unfamiliar ones.

If the child has a good example to follow both at home and at school, he will probably enjoy learning to identify the various foods he eats and to investigate and compare the flavors, textures, and consistencies. It is not expected that he learn to enjoy all foods equally well but it is important that he be willing to taste all foods offered to him. If either teacher or parents display a poor attitude toward foods, confusion often results and the youngster may limit the variety of foods he will eat.

In grades four through six, children are learning how to find answers to many questions. These children need the opportunity to decide for themselves that food really does make a difference in how one looks and feels and how well children grow. In these grades, nutrition guidance often becomes a part of science teaching, and plant growing or animal projects become a means of learning that the kind and amount of food eaten are important to health.

Children of this age often resist getting up in the morning and tend to dawdle while preparing for the day. Thus this group, especially the older ones, often alter earlier good habits by skimping or skipping breakfast. Food habit surveys of schoolchildren reveal that this poor practice tends to persist on through the school career.

Simple breakfasts that children can safely and easily prepare for themselves are good projects at this grade level. These need not always be the usual combinations we associate with breakfast but may be planned around some leftover food basic to family cultural patterns. This is an excellent opportunity to teach children what to put with the preferred food to make a good breakfast of it.

For example, in a neighborhood where many Spanish-American families use beans and rice almost as regularly as other families use bread, children could be encouraged to add tomato juice or some other source of vitamin C and a glass of milk to their usual breakfast of beans and rice.

It is also necessary for pupils to learn that an adequate diet can be made up of many different food combinations. While children are studying other countries in their social studies classes, it is natural that they should include something about the eating patterns of the people.

Teachers who have taught units of this kind report that children enjoy them and seem to learn readily to understand children of other nations and cultures.

Secondary school students are ready to review in an organized fashion the facts they have learned about food in the elementary school. They can then apply those facts as they gain an understanding of the processes involved in utilizing food to meet body needs. Both boys and girls need to develop this understanding in addition to some facility in making wise choices for themselves.

Desirable attitudes and habits developed in the elementary school years will benefit the boys and girls during adolescence and later as adults. Understanding what happens to food after it is eaten, and ability to select meals which are good nutritionally and a pleasure to eat will encourage students to continue to make good selections for themselves and for any children they may have in the future.

• In school feeding programs. Schools that participate in the federally sponsored school feeding programs have an important resource within the school for providing nutrition guidance to boys and girls. We know it is important for boys and girls to acquire nutrition information, but we learned long ago that being told what to eat to insure good nutritional health does not necessarily result in better food habits among children or adults whose food practices need improvement.

Boys and girls need to have repeated experience with desirable food practices over an extended period if good habit formation is to result. The school lunch and breakfast programs can provide children this day-by-day experience throughout the school career by serving nutritionally sound meals that children will eat.

In any group feeding operation, whether it is a family group of three or four persons or a school population of 300 or 400, it will not be possible to completely please everyone at every meal. No one enjoys all foods equally, but everyone can learn at least to taste all the foods served and possibly acquire a taste for some previously avoided.

School feeding programs continually provide opportunities for boys and girls to eat a good lunch daily—in some schools, breakfast also is served—and at the same time to increase the variety of food they can eat with pleasure. The wholesome attitude of parents and teachers toward all food and the pleasant atmosphere created by a friendly school feeding staff influences students to take advantage of the opportunities to learn to eat well by eating the good meals available every day.

This learning is most likely to take place when meals are planned with a realistic understanding of the children and the communities being served. Meal patterns prescribed by the U.S. Department of Agriculture assure well-balanced meals but are flexible, and preferred foods may be included.

New foods or those most generally avoided are often served as part of a lunch featuring hamburgers, spaghetti, or some other food of high appeal. Thus, the principles of habit formation and learning are applied along with principles of good nutrition.

School feeding programs are most successful when parents, teachers, and administrators understand the objectives and problems involved and cooperate by giving their support.

• Snacks at home and away from home. In recent years there has been less emphasis upon the advisability of limiting food intake to three meals daily. One or two additional small meals or snacks have become a part of our culture. Nutritionally, this is satisfactory so long as the total daily intake of food meets the individual's need for nutrients and does not exceed his need for calories.

Unfortunately, the choices often made at snacktime are relatively concentrated sources of calories but do not contribute much to nutrient needs of the individual.

One way to improve this situation is to make wholesome snacks available to all family members at times and places where snacks are eaten. The family's larder should include good snack choices such as cheese, peanut butter, fruits, raw vegetables, fruit or vegetable juices, and milk.

Gathering places for teenagers and snack bars for office or other workers should be encouraged to at least have

A good lunch served in pleasant surroundings.

fruit and milk vending machines as well as candy and soda pop vending machines.

Food habits are closely associated with the individual's sense of security, and any modification, particularly as he grows older, will require strong motivation.

Modifications in food habits need to be made to adjust to the decreased need for calories as people grow older. The number of overweight people one sees is testimony that they have failed to make the adjustment. For the most part this must be credited to lack of motivation rather than lack of information. How to motivate people to make these adjustments is still an area that needs further study.

Some people are meeting their need for calories—are not overweight—but are eating a combination of foods that do not supply recommended amounts of all nutrients. It is difficult for such individuals to see a need for change inasmuch as they maintain a desirable weight and thus do not associate any symptoms of poor health they may have with eating habits. Cause and effect are not easily demonstrated.

Much needs to be learned about how to help people make modifications when they are needed. We do know, however, that those who have a good attitude toward all food, a spirit of adventure that prompts them to taste new foods or to try new methods of food preparation, can adjust more easily to modifications in diet whether for health reasons or as a result of limited availability of foods familiar to them.

Faith Clark

A Scorecard on How We Americans Are Eating

The average American diet, as measured by the food available for consumption, is varied and sufficient to feed our population well.

Amounts of food estimated to have been used per person per day in spring 1965, the date of our latest household food consumption survey, were 10½ ounces of meat, poultry, and fish (or enough for about two servings a day); about one egg; nearly 2½ cups of milk or its equivalent in milk products; close to 4 ounces of potatoes and sweetpotatoes; and a little over a pound of vegetables and fruit, including juices.

Also, about 3½ slices of bread and 2¼ ounces of other bakery products; around 3 ounces of flour and other cereal products; 2½ ounces of sugar and other sweets; nearly 2 ounces of fats, oils, and salad dressings; plus beverages, nuts, mixtures, and condiments. Some of these are wasted, of course, but, even at that, the amounts would appear to be generous.

All this provides plenty of calories, protein, minerals, and vitamins to meet the goals set by nutrition specialists. This does not mean, however, that everyone in the Nation is well fed.

There is great variation in the amounts of foods used by individuals within each household and by different groups of households. One of the principal factors affecting the kinds and amounts of foods that people eat is their purchasing power—roughly equated with income. But the other important factors are the habits and preferences that influence choice—a complex set of conditions that result from people's education, sociological backgrounds, and situations.

Comparisons of present-day food consumption are available with earlier years and with other countries. A few facts help to place our present-day pattern in perspective before we go on to answer the question "How Well Are Americans Eating?"

One of the most notable changes in our food consumption in recent years has been the increase in use of meat. Meat is one of our most preferred foods. When there is more money to spend, some of it is likely to be spent for meat, poultry, or fish. In our statistics we frequently group these main dish items together.

In the last two decades production of meat and poultry on a per capita basis has increased substantially. We have also had an increase in real incomes in the United States. As a result, families at all incomes have shared in the increased consumption. By spring 1965, urban families in the lowest third of the income distribution were consuming more meat, poultry, and fish than families in the highest third did in spring 1942. And wartime rationing of meat was not in effect at that time in 1942.

Milk and milk products have not risen much in consumption as have meat, poultry, and fish. In fact, there was a decrease in the amounts used by the families at all three income levels between 1955 (when a survey was made) and 1965.

Consumption of grain products has

Faith Clark is Director, Consumer and Food Economics Research Division, Agricultural Research Service. She has taken part in five nationwide food consumption surveys.

decreased slightly at all income levels. Potatoes also have declined, but the use of more processed potatoes in recent years has helped stem the drop in consumption. There have been slight downward shifts in use of other vegetables and fruits since the end of World War II. Increases in consumption of processed products have not made up for the decreases in use of fresh products.

Higher income families consume more of meat, poultry, and fish, milk and milk products, and fruits and vegetables than do the lower income families. Grain products are used in larger amounts by low income families. There is relatively little difference in the use of potatoes. These are broad generalizations, however. There are many exceptions of individual foods within these major groupings.

U.S. food supplies are abundant and generous in animal products compared with those of many countries. The latest World Food Survey made by the United Nations Food and Agriculture Organization shows that amounts of animal protein ranged from 8 grams per person per day in the Far East and 14 grams in the Near East to 62 grams in Oceania and 66 grams in North America.

But even in this affluent country, not all share in our abundance. From a nutritional standpoint, many make poor choices although they could well afford to make selections that would be rated nutritionally good.

In our recent nationwide survey we found that about half of the U.S. households had food supplies that we described as good, that is, they met the Recommended Dietary Allowances (RDA's) of the Food and Nutrition Board for seven nutrients. About a fifth had food supplies that we called poor—because they furnished less than two-thirds of the RDA's in one or more of these seven nutrients. The remainder were fair—somewhere in between good and poor.

Note that we are not saying that the fifth with poor diets were hungry or malnourished. Poor diets in the long term are, usually, conducive to poor nutrition, but the occurrence of poor diets is not synonymous with hunger or malnutrition. There is no way to relate the findings from our food consumption studies directly to malnutrition and the health of the American people. It was not designed for that purpose. Physical examinations and biochemical tests would have been needed.

So far, we have been citing statistics based on household food supplies. In measuring such supplies we have not been able to allow for waste nor have we allowed for differences in the consumption of food and in the needs of household members.

At the time of the survey of household food usage in a week, we also obtained information on food intake of members of the families during the 24 hours preceding the time the interviewers called at their home. This information has been tabulated and provides, for the first time, a national profile of the foods eaten by men, women, and children of different ages.

With some 15,000 in the survey, representing almost 200 million of us living in housekeeping households, it is not easy, however, to reduce the statistics to neat pictures of a typical breakfast, lunch, and dinner. For one thing, people eat much more frequently than three times a day. In 1965 we found that 16 percent of the men 20 to 34 years of age had something to eat or drink six or more times a day. The proportion decreased with age—13 percent for men 35 to 64 and 5 percent for men 65 years and older. The percentages were only slightly smaller for women.

Describing a representative or average breakfast, noon, or evening meal is almost impossible. The best we can do is to add together foods that are either used interchangeably in meals or have like nutritive value.

Some of the chief factors that affect the kinds and amounts of food individuals eat are their sex, age, size, and activity; their incomes and ability to buy; their food choices and habits,

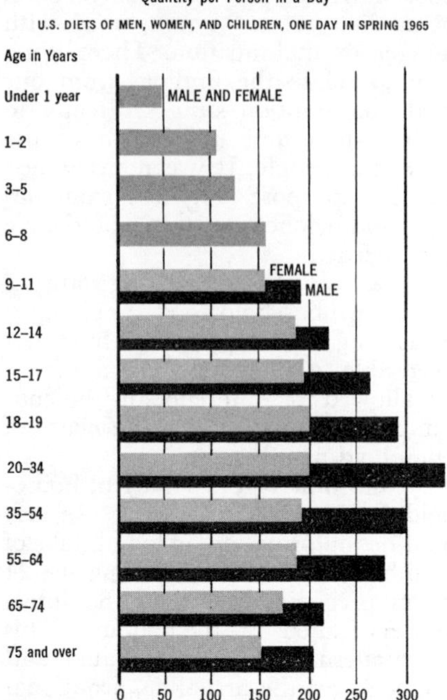

which are in turn affected by ethnic background; and many other conditions affecting family and childhood patterns of living.

Always important, as we have already emphasized, is the availability of foods in markets or from the home farm or garden.

Our nationwide survey of the food intake of individuals in 1965 showed that men and boys eat larger quantities of most types of foods than women and girls of the same age. This is especially true for bread, other baked goods and cereals; meat, poultry, and fish; fats and oils; and sugars and sweets. For vegetables and fruits, there is less difference.

Average amounts of all foods used by men and women 20 to 34 years of age are shown in the table on p. 272.

For most foods, consumption peaks for males in their late teens and early adulthood. For example, the average amount of meat, poultry, and fish eaten by men 20 to 34 years is considerably higher than amounts eaten by either younger or older males. The peak years for grain products are a little earlier—between 15 and 20 years of age. For beverages other than milk and fruit juices, the years between 20 and 55 are the highest. For milk and milk products, the largest use after infancy is by boys between 9 and 20. After 20 years, consumption drops off sharply.

For females there tends to be less difference between age groups in amounts of food eaten than for males. For example, the average amounts of meat, poultry, and fish eaten by girls and women between the age of 12 and 74 differ relatively little. The peak years for grain products are 12 to 14. From age 15 years and on, consumption drops slightly. Beverages other than milk and juices, though generally used in smaller amounts by females than males, show much the same consumption pattern by age for the two sexes. Use of milk and milk products by girls

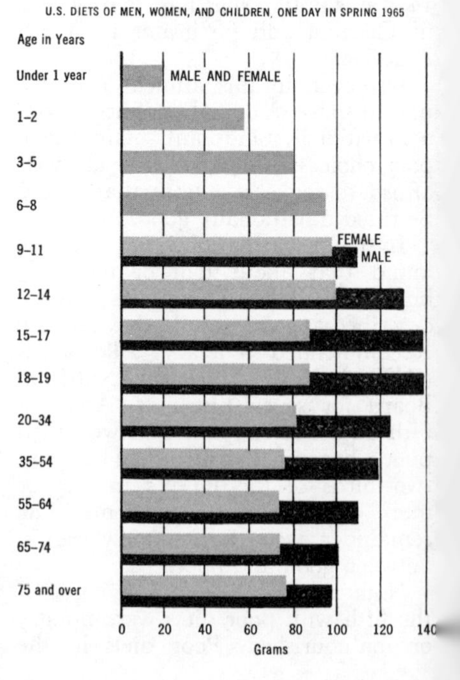

and women declines consistently beyond the 9 to 11 age group. The low point is reached at the 35 to 54 year age group, with a slight upturn after 55.

Vegetables and fruits are used in quite similar amounts by adults of different age groups. There is less regularity to patterns of use, partly because it is more difficult to summarize types and amounts used.

In judging how well people eat in our research studies, we take into account the Recommended Dietary Allowances for each of 22 different sex and age groups. These are the same guides for good nutrition established by the Food and Nutrition Board of the National Academy of Sciences—National Research Council which we use in judging the nutritional quality of household diets.

When the total amounts of each nutrient in the average diets of these 22 groups—as revealed by the 1965 survey—were compared with the Recommended Dietary Allowances, the results showed that:

VEGETABLES AND FRUITS

Quantity per Person in a Day

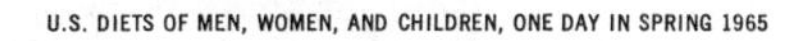

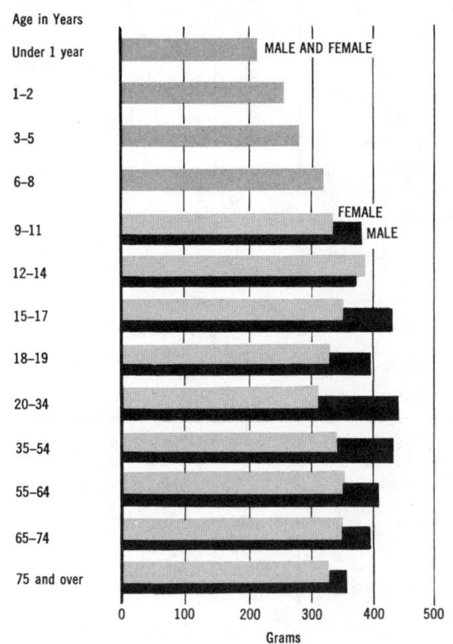

MILK AND MILK PRODUCTS (CALCIUM EQUIVALENT)

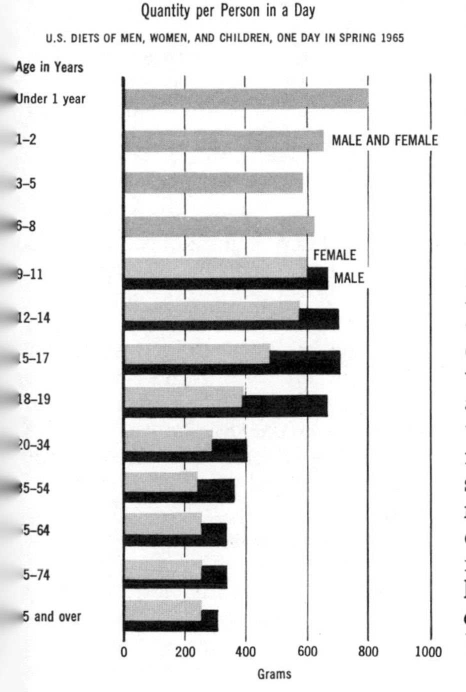

Average diets for most sex-age groups approached or were above the Recommended Dietary Allowances for calories and five of the seven nutrients we studied: protein, vitamin A value, thiamine, riboflavin, and ascorbic acid.

Calcium and iron furnished by the day's food, however, were more than 30 percent below recommended allowances for several groups, especially of girls and women. The iron in diets of infants and children under 3 years was 50 percent below recommended amounts. However, the Food and Nutrition Board does not expect the recommended allowances for iron for some age groups to be met by ordinary food products. The Board does expect ordinary diets to provide at least 6 milligrams per 1,000 calories. That level was not reached in the diets of children 1 through 8 years and of boys and girls 9 through 19 years.

In general we found that the diets of

NUTRIENT INTAKE BELOW RECOMMENDED ALLOWANCE

Average Intake of Group Below Recommended Dietary Allowance, NAS–NCR, 1968

U.S. DIETS OF MEN, WOMEN, AND CHILDREN, ONE DAY IN SPRING 1965

Sex-Age Group	Protein	Calcium	Iron	Vitamin A value	Thiamine	Riboflavin	Ascorbic acid
MALE AND FEMALE:							
Under 1 year			••••				
1– 2 years			••••				
3– 5 years			••				
6– 8 years							
MALE:							
9–11 years		•					
12–14 years		••	•••		•		
15–17 years		•	•				
18–19 years							
20–34 years							
35–54 years		•					
55–64 years		••					
65–74 years		••					
75 years and over		•••		•		••	•
FEMALE:							
9–11 years		•••	••••		•		
12–14 years		•••	••••	•	•		
15–17 years		••••	••••		••		
18–19 years		•••	••••	•	•		
20–34 years		•••	••••		•	•	
35–54 years		••••	••••		•	••	
55–64 years		••••			•	•	
65–74 years		••••	•	•	••	••	
75 years and over		••••	•	••	••	•••	

BELOW BY:	
1–10%	•
11–20%	••
21–29%	•••
30% OR MORE	••••

males met the recommended allowances for more nutrients than the diets of females. Except for iron, the average diets of children under 9 years were above recommendations. The diets of several age groups of girls and women were below recommended amounts of several nutrients—vitamin A, thiamine, and riboflavin in addition to calcium and iron. Older men (over 75 years) had diets low in calcium, vitamin A, riboflavin, and ascorbic acid.

With averages below the recommended allowances for some sex-age groups, it is safe to conclude that some persons within those groups had diets in need of improvement. Where averages fell to more than 30 percent below recommendations, as in calcium and iron for some sex-age groups, the proportions of persons with diets in need of improving were almost surely high.

The proportion of calories derived from fat ranged from an average of 39 percent for infants to 45 percent for men 20 to 64 years of age. The Food and Nutrition Board does not include an allowance for fat in the Recommended Dietary Allowances—nor a recommendation on the percentage of calories that should come from fat. Percentages as high as 40 percent, however, are considered too high by some authorities.

Income and the quality of diet are closely related. This relationship is easier to describe for household diets than for the diets of men, women, and children of different ages separately. In the 1965 household study, we found that of the families with incomes under $3,000, about a third had what we called poor diets. Of the families with incomes of $10,000 or more, about a tenth had poor diets. Thus income was definitely related to the quality of the diet.

Yet even at the highest income level, a sizable proportion of families had poor diets. Food habits, not the ability to purchase, were the dominant cause of poor diets for this group. Some families at almost all income levels

DIETS AT 3 LEVELS OF QUALITY, BY INCOME, 1965

U.S. households, one week in Spring

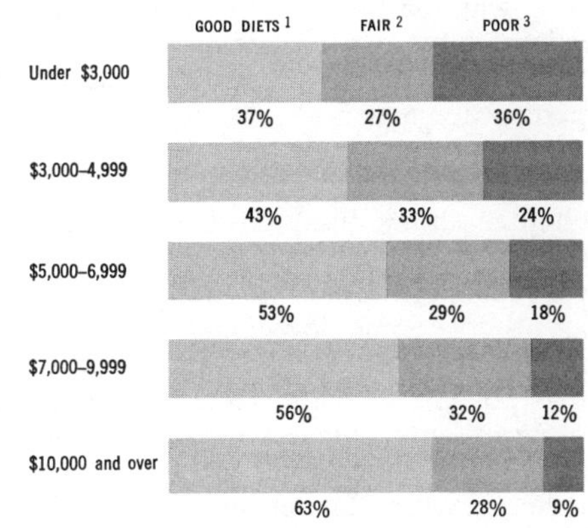

[1] Met recommended dietary allowances (1963) for 7 nutrients.
[2] Met at least ⅔ RDA for 7 nutrients but less than RDA for 1 to 7.
[3] Met less than ⅔ RDA for 1 to 7 nutrients; is not synonymous with serious hunger and malnutrition.

either do not know which foods to select in order to make up a good diet or they do not have any desire to choose these foods.

There is relatively little difference in the nutritive quality of the diets of families in different regions of the United States. A slightly higher proportion of families had poor diets in the South and North Central region than in the Northeast and the West, according to the 1965 survey.

Differences in regional food patterns are smaller than formerly. Improvements in processing, transportation, and storage have made it possible to have consumption of the same foods throughout the Nation. Seasonal fluctuations are also less pronounced than years ago.

There are still some very important differences, however, between the way people eat in the South and the rest of the United States. In the 1965 survey, households were classified into the four broad Census regions: Northeast, North Central, South, and West. Households in the South had the lowest average consumption of milk and milk products. They also used the least bread but the most flour, sugar, fat, and eggs—indicating more home baking than in the other regions.

Families in the South used about the same amount of meat, poultry, and fish as in the other three regions, but their choices within this group were different. Southern families used a larger share of the total as pork, poultry, and fish. But they used a smaller share as beef and lunch meat than the other regions.

Rural-urban differences are also much less pronounced. Farm families now produce on their own places about a third of their food. Only 10 years ago, the proportion was about 40 percent. And of course many years ago, the proportion was still higher.

The greatest difference between farm and urban food consumption is still in flour and cereals. In 1965 farm households used more than twice as much of these foods as urban families. Their use of more fats and sugars is partly related to their use of larger quantities of flour and cereals. Farm families use smaller amounts than city families of purchased bread and other bakery products, soups and other type purchased mixes, and all the types of beverages—soft drinks, coffee, ades and punches, and alcoholic beverages.

Ten years ago farm families used almost a fifth more milk per person than urban families. Because of the decline in use of home-produced milk, their consumption is now almost the same.

Another difference between rural and urban families is the extent to which they eat some of their meals away from home. Although a larger proportion of rural families is now buying food—either meals or between-meal food and drink—for consumption away from home than 10 years ago, the proportion is much less than that of urban families.

In a week in the spring of 1965, some 62 percent of the farm families spent money for either meals or snacks for eating away from home, with an average expenditure of $6.16 a week for those families making any such expenditure. Of the urban families in the survey, 72 percent spent money for food away from home during a week with an average expenditure of $9.42 a family. Interestingly enough, almost the same proportion of the total expenditure was for between-meal food and drink for the two population groups—25 percent for farm families and 22 percent for urban.

The information presented in this chapter shows that, on the average, diets in the United States are good, but that some groups are not doing as well as others. Some low-income families need help in extending their purchasing power—through food assistance programs and education programs that help them make better use of existing incomes. Many higher income families also need guidance in meeting their nutritional needs from the great abundance of foods available.

The age groups which need special emphasis are teenage girls and women and older men.

They need assistance in selecting foods which will provide increased amounts of calcium, iron, and several vitamins.

Foods needed are those stressed in the USDA's Daily Food Guide—milk and milk products; meat, poultry, and fish, eggs, dry beans, peas, and nuts; enriched and whole grain bread and cereal products; and vegetables and fruits, especially those rich in vitamin A and ascorbic acid.

Most age groups need guidance in selecting foods that are not overly rich so that the proportion of calories derived from fat in the diet is kept to a moderate level—at least below 40 percent of the total calories.

Average Amounts of Food Eaten in One Day by Men and Women 20 to 34 Years of Age
Spring 1965

Food (as served)	Unit	Men	Women
Milk and milk products:			
Milk, milk drinks	cups	1¼	¾
Cream, ice cream	cups	¼	¼
Cheese	ounces	⅓	⅓
Eggs	each	1	½
Meat, poultry, fish:			
Beef	ounces	4	2¼
Pork	ounces	3½	2
Other meat	ounces	¼	¼
Poultry	ounces	1¼	¾
Fish, shellfish	ounces	½	¼
Mixtures	ounces	2¾	1¾
Legumes, nuts:			
Legumes, mixtures	tablespoons	2	1¼
Nuts, nut butter	tablespoons	½	¼
Grain products:			
Bread, rolls, biscuits	slices	5¼	3
Other baked goods	ounces	2¾	1¾
Cereals, pastes	ounces	1½	1¼
Mixtures	ounces	1½	1½
Tomatoes, citrus fruits:			
Tomatoes	cups	¼	¼
Citrus fruit	cups	¼	¼
Dark green and deep yellow vegetables	tablespoons	1¼	1¼
Potatoes	cups	½	¼
Other vegetables and fruit:			
Other vegetables	cups	½	½
Other fruit	cups	½	¼
Sugars, sweets:			
Sugar	teaspoons	4¼	3¼
Sirup, honey, molasses	teaspoons	1	½
Jelly, jam, gelatin desserts	teaspoons	2¾	2¼
Candy	ounces	¼	¼
Fats, oils:			
Table fats	tablespoons	1¼	¾
Other fats, oils	tablespoons	1¾	¾
Beverages other than milk, juices, and alcoholic drinks:			
Tea	6-ounce cups	¾	¾
Coffee	6-ounce cups	2¼	2¼
Soft drinks	12-ounce bottle	½	½

Audrey C. Burkart

Smarten Up and Snack Right! Here's How to Do It

Each year we Americans pop into our mouths the equivalent of $2 billion worth of potato chips, pretzels, nuts, corn chips, puffed snacks, crackers, spreads, and other snacks.

The 1965 *Household Food Consumption Survey* conducted by the U.S. Department of Agriculture showed that we ate 83 percent more potato chips than in 1955. That means our potato chip consumption increased nearly five times the percentage increase in our population (17 percent). Other snack foods that showed an increase were carbonated and noncarbonated soft drinks, along with punches, crackers, donuts, and candy.

The National Soft Drink Association reports that in 1966 the average American drank almost 18 gallons of drinks such as cola, root beer, fruit-flavored beverages, etc. In 1960, 20 million cases of dietetic soft drinks were produced. By 1966 the number spiraled to more than 400 million cases, and who can guess what the future will bring?

It has been predicted that we will have more leisure time in the future and if this becomes a reality, the importance and popularity of snack foods will probably increase, too. Of course, if we are not relaxing we are usually in a hurry trying to keep appointments and get things done. Here again snacks and snack type eating have come in handy.

The point is that snacks have become part of our food pattern. Snacks are associated with happiness, fun, good times, socializing, and enjoyment. They can also be associated with unwanted and unnecessary calories, spoiled appetites, and "binge" eating in response to frustration and insecurity.

Let's think about the foods you ate yesterday. How many foods were part of a regular meal? For example, the sweet roll or peanut butter cracker sandwich you had during the coffee break at the office or at home after everyone had left for the day. The soft drink you had at 3 p.m. with just one cookie. Remember last night as you were watching TV? What was on the table next to you? Maybe potato chips or pretzels. And when you went shopping, didn't you buy a candy bar to munch as you drove home to prepare the family's dinner? Last but not least, on what have you always prided yourself when you were entertaining guests? Could it be tuna-stuffed puffed pastries?

To say all snacks are "bad" would be like saying there is only one way to cook potatoes. The contributions that snacks can make to the daily food pattern in energy, protein, vitamins and minerals can only be judged after one learns how they are being used and what kinds of foods are being discussed. For example, is the beverage a substitute for a more nutritious one like milk, or is the food part of an already good meal pattern like an ice cream dessert at 8 p.m. while watching TV? A snack can include anything from a pizza "with everything" to potato chips, or from a thick milkshake to a cup of bouillon.

Audrey C. Burkart is an Assistant Specialist in Foods and Nutrition, New Jersey Cooperative Extension Service, College of Agriculture and Environmental Science, Rutgers University—The State University of New Jersey, New Brunswick.

Let's find out the role snacks can play in the lives of many Americans.

What about the higher calorie snack foods like donuts, pastries, candies, and soft drinks? Are they forbidden? No, just as long as (1) they do not replace those foods that are needed by the body such as meat, milk, fruit, vegetables, and enriched bread and (2) the added calories do not contribute to a weight control problem.

The preschool child is growing, but not as fast as he did during his first year of life. Because of this, he may show a decreased interest in eating, much to his parents' dismay. But he is still growing, and he is taking an interest in things going on around him. He is an imitator. During this period of life, he will be introduced to the family's meal pattern, which will probably become his own. So it is very important he starts on the "right foot," and that means the snacks he eats as well. Whether or not he is given a mid-morning and a mid-afternoon snack should be determined by his growth needs and his appetite at mealtimes, not just to develop the habit of eating between meals or as a "reward" for being a "good" boy.

If snacks are served, they should be small in size so his appetite will not be dulled for the next meal. Perhaps your child eats better if he is given a little at a time. Then the snack may include foods not eaten at mealtime, such as his breakfast orange juice, a great source of vitamin C, or milk, so good in calcium and protein. Keeping his lunch or dinner dessert until mid-morning and evening respectively can solve many problems, too.

If your preschooler is a good eater at mealtime, any snack should still be counted as a part of his overall meal pattern.

The preschool child usually enjoys raw fruits and vegetables like a wedge of pared apple, a cube of cantaloup (another good source of vitamin C), or a carrot stick (a tasty way to enjoy some vitamin A). Oatmeal cookies with raisins are tasty and a good source of iron, too. All these foods can help the child develop his chewing ability, and supply some necessary roughage besides helping to fulfill his need for energy, vitamins, and minerals.

Overly sweet cakes, cookies, and candy should be avoided since they tend to dull the appetite and promote development of a "sweet tooth." Many authorities agree that the road to overweight begins here, so this is another good reason to make sure the snacks given are not above and beyond the child's energy needs and that they be considered part of his overall meal pattern.

A child attending nursery school is in a whole new world. To begin with, his mother is no longer present to tell him what to do, breakfast is at an earlier hour, and he now has the companionship of others while playing and eating.

The mid-morning snack for the nursery school child is important to prevent fatigue. It provides needed energy and may help prevent lunchtime problems when the child is overtired. Since there may be a long timespan between lunch and dinner at home, a mid-afternoon snack might be in order.

The kinds of foods enjoyed by children of this age include vitamin C-rich fruits such as orange sections, cantaloup, or citrus juices including orange or blended orange and grapefruit juices. Pared and unpared apples and dried fruits are other taste treats.

Raw vegetables like carrot sticks, celery curls, turnip slices, and green pepper sticks (another good source of vitamins A and C) are also very well received. Graham crackers, toast sticks made with enriched bread, and plain or hard whole wheat crackers are favorites, too.

There are times when the mother of a nursery school child may complain that her child picks at his dinner after school. It may be he is overly tired, or should not have a mid-afternoon snack. The nursery school teacher and the parents should always be in touch so this kind of problem does not become a hardship for the child.

Milk and oatmeal cookies make a nutritious afternoon snack for an elementary school child.

The world of many elementary schoolchildren includes that wondrous thing called an allowance. And after all, what could be greater fun than buying something with your very own money? Unfortunately, when it comes to food, this is frequently of the "junk" variety. Help your child select foods that contribute more than just calories. A piece of fruit or a container of milk or ice cream might be good.

If your child does not buy his own snacks, you can be sure he will come home hungry after school. Here, as with the younger child, the size of the snack should not be so large that it dulls the appetite for dinner. If you have a child this age, why not try one of the following energy-, protein-, vitamin-, and mineral-packed afternoon snacks: peanut butter with crackers, half of a cheese sandwich, a cold leg of cooked chicken, a small glass of milk with a cookie, fresh fruit, or raw vegetables? The energy-packed dried fruits such as apricots, an excellent source of vitamin A, or prunes and raisins, both good sources of iron, are ideal foods to satisfy the "sweet tooth." To some children on a cold winter's day, a cup of hot soup hits the spot and tides them over until dinner. In short, make your children's snacks work for them.

To the teenager, food in general and snacks in particular are a way of life! The proverbial "hollow leg" seems to apply to many since this is a period of rapid growth. Yet many teenagers are reported as falling short of the mark where nutrition is concerned.

The teen years are a time of striving for independence, concern for physical appearance, and desire to conform to the peer group. All these characteristics are reflected in food patterns.

Studies have shown that teenagers tend to skip meals (and not always just breakfasts, either) and to consume many snacks. Some studies indicate girls tend to snack more than boys, although other studies show no such relationship. A 1966 study of 122 teenagers showed that boys and girls had different snack preferences. The boys tended to enjoy in this order of popularity the following foods for snacks: (1) cereals and breads, (2) pie, cake, pastry, and cookies, (3) soft drinks, (4) milk, (5) fruit, (6) eggs, meat, and cheese, (7) ice cream, (8) candy, (9) potato chips, and (10) vegetables.

In contrast, the girls enjoyed in order of preference: (1) pie, cake, pastry, and cookies, (2) candy, (3) fruit, (4) cereals and breads, (5) ice cream, (6) soft drinks, (7) milk, (8) eggs, meat, and cheese, (9) potato chips, and (10) vegetables. It was also noted that the types of snack foods selected had little or no relation to amount of body fat in either the girls or the boys.

Other studies have shown that girls tended to snack more frequently than boys. Girls were figure conscious. Unfortunately, to achieve their goal of a slender figure they frequently selected foods that contained little more than calories. They also showed a tendency to skip meals. Since girls are faced with a greater possibility than their mothers of having a child early in life, it is imperative that they *now* learn to eat those foods that can help prepare them for the future.

Snacking—a teenager's delight.

Since meal skipping and high-calorie snacks have been found popular with the teenagers, why not "jump on the bandwagon" by helping them to enjoy more nutritious snacks. How? By having the refrigerator stocked with the right "makings." For example, three snack favorites include pizza, hotdogs, and hamburgers. All three are sources of protein, vitamins, and minerals. So why not have some salad fixings like carrots, celery, and green peppers in addition to citrus fruit "conspicuously available" next to the meats. If you the homemaker, sometimes called the "gatekeeper" of the food, have these foods available and do a little prompting, not preaching, they will be used. Teenagers want to be healthy and attractive, and getting the point across that the right snacks can help them attain their goal can be very effective.

The same approach can be used where beverages are concerned. Cola beverages need not be outlawed, but you can spark an interest in serving something different by putting a blender into operation to make some luscious and cooling milkshakes, either plain or with fruit. Ice cream specials are usually well rated by teenagers. Would you be surprised to learn that both boys and girls pride themselves on being good hosts and hostesses to their friends? They do!

Does your teenager enjoy cooking outdoors? Fine. Here is another opportunity to help him learn to take care of himself and become a good host. Let him try serving kabobs to his friends. Made with a less expensive cut of beef, cubed, and skewered along with green pepper and tomatoes, they are sure to please. On this one skewer you will find energy, protein, and vitamins A and C. Just what a teenager needs! If hamburger is the choice, stimulate interest in serving a colorful salad alongside, like a tossed green salad or cole slaw. A sparkling fruit punch which bubbles with the addition of ginger ale, and served from a pitcher, can be a taste treat. Cold milk, either whole or skimmed (both good sources of calcium), is enjoyed by most teenagers, so always have it available.

For a smaller snack, grilled cheese sandwiches or chili buns are fun to make and eat. Cheese snacks are a good choice for the nonmilk drinker.

A snack breakfast could very well solve the problem of your morning sleepyhead. Have a meat or cheese sandwich ready or else pack him an extra sandwich to take on the schoolbus. The traditional breakfast orange juice can be obtained just as well from a whole orange that is packed with the sandwich.

To be sure, most teenagers can eat a big snack an hour before mealtime and then sit down to a full dinner. This is fine if his body needs it, and if he is active enough to use the calories. Today, however, many busy teenagers are not physically active, and these are the ones who have an overweight problem. To help them over this hump, have some of the lower calorie snack foods available, like fresh fruit, gelatin desserts, and puddings made with skimmed milk. For those who should gain weight, the thick milkshake, pie alamode, and nuts are the thing.

Would it be a shock if I told you that adults are not perfect in their eating habits either? The morning coffee break is a case in point. Frequently this consists of a cup of coffee with or without sugar and milk, and possibly a sweet bun. For many, this is more than just a mid-morning break. It is breakfast and a poor one at that.

Calories are high, but little else often is contributed in the way of protein, vitamins, and minerals. How much better it would be if the cafeterias and mobile coffee carts were stocked, in addition to coffee, with oranges, orange and tomato juice, milk, individually wrapped cheese wedges (another way to get calcium), portion-packaged enriched ready-to-eat cereals, and cottage cheese with fruit. Having something different to stimulate interest in more nutritious snacks can help adults, too.

Homemakers are busy people, and many do not take time to sit down to eat. Snacks such as cookies and other munchables can become a mainstay during the day. All too frequently you watch, much to your horror, the bathroom scales soar to new heights. If you don't sit down for a complete breakfast or lunch, use the "missed" foods for your snacks. In the long run you may be "eating" fewer calories and if the foods are carefully selected, you will be fulfilling your food needs.

Snacking rates very high with many senior citizens primarily because snacks are convenient and frequently associated with a social occasion, like having visitors. A survey made in one Iowa county revealed that those over 75 years of age snacked less than those in their early 60's. The foods most frequently listed were cookies or breads. Coffee, tea, and Postum were also listed, while milk was more popular with people living in cities than in rural areas.

A survey made in Rochester, N.Y., of a selected group of beneficiaries of old-age survivors and disability insurance revealed that, based upon nutrient relationships, milk and the other dairy products and fruits were very

Snacks can be a nutritional asset or liability.

All set for a dip-in.

popular between-meal foods. Overweight, denture, and digestive problems are frequently found in the older age group. In many cases, the appetite and the interest in food is irregular.

Depending on the physical condition of the individuals, the following kinds of snack foods can help fulfill their nutritional needs: cooked and canned fruit, fruit juices, calcium and protein foods like eggnogs, custards, and puddings.

Open-faced sandwiches using cooked ground beef, tender cooked chicken slices, or other favorite and available meat "fillings" can be a fun way of getting some protein.

To the person watching his weight, every calorie must count. Frequent snacking of high calorie foods or larger servings of a reduced calorie food such as candies and cookies made with sugar substitutes or dry roasted nuts, may help you defeat your own purpose. This means you should take advantage of the many lower calorie, appetizing foods that make excellent festive snacks. Many of your friends will be happy to know that while you are watching your party calories you are helping them do the same. Here are a few party snack ideas. Check your favorite cookbook for recipes.

Fruit and vegetable ideas for drinking, nibbling, and dipping: Cranberry-pineapple cocktail; orange-grapefruit juice with mint sprig; vegetable juice "on the rocks"; hot tomato-bouillon in mugs; fruit kabobs made of pineapple wedges, banana slices, cherries—for a dip, try a french dressing; garnish tray including—radish roses, carrot curls, marinated cauliflower, stuffed cucumber, stuffed mushroom, and stuffed celery; for dippers try—carrot sticks, cauliflower florets, turnip sticks, strawberries, cooked shrimp.

Meat, fish, and egg ideas: Miniature meat balls on toothpicks; meat slice cornucopias around cheese sticks; ham roll-ups with cottage cheese spiced with onion soup mix as a filling; cooked shrimp and olives on toothpick; deviled eggs; open-faced sandwiches using rye or wheat wafers and topped with thin slices of meat—garnish, with pimiento, green pepper, or parsley.

Milk and cheese ideas: Cheese tray including cheddar cubes, Edam, Swiss; cheese ball; yogurt dip excellent for such fruit dippers as strawberries, melon slices, etc.; milk coolers.

Throughout this article, three points have been repeatedly emphasized in the snack suggestions given: (1) snacks should be selected to supply the body with vitamins, minerals, and possibly protein, in addition to energy, (2) all snacks must be considered as a part of the total day's food intake if they are to be to your advantage without contributing to such health problems as being overweight, and (3) snacks should not interfere with the appetite for the next meal.

Helen Denning Ullrich

Food Planning for Families at 3 Different Cost Levels

You can feed your family nutritionally adequate meals at widely different costs. If you want to prepare a basic mixture of soy and wheat flour, dry milk powder, vegetable oil, and some purified vitamins and minerals, you can feed your family for only a few cents a day. Most American families, however, take pride in choosing among the wide variety of foods found in our grocery stores.

In March of 1969 it was estimated that a family of four with two school-age children could be adequately fed for one week on a $28.80 low-cost food plan, a $36.90 moderate-cost food plan, and a $45.10 liberal plan. Your own grocery bills may be larger than these costs. The figures quoted include only food eaten at home or carried in lunches from the home food supply.

You should have a plan in mind when food shopping. Careful planning will bring more satisfaction and variety from the food you choose. By planning meals, you can ensure that they include foods from the four basic food groups. This may not mean deciding on the precise menu for Wednesday's or Friday's dinner, but merely making a general plan for the week. The other members of the family may also enjoy planning some of the meals. The kinds and amounts of food that you buy will depend on how often you shop and how much refrigerator, freezer, and general storage space you have.

A family food plan should include certain basic foods to provide for quick meals, emergencies, and unexpected company. These staples and supplies will vary according to available storage space and family food preferences.

Good shopping habits save time and money, and reduce impulse buying. Make a list of needed items, allowing for adjustments and for substitutions. Check the newspaper ads and take advantage of specials. Some stores advertise specials good for part of the week; others feature discount prices. Some offer quality, service, convenience, and stamps. Compare prices. Know what you are paying for.

Consider the family eating patterns when you buy food. Packed lunches, or irregular meal hours, or frequent snacks require special planning. When meal patterns vary from the normal three a day, it takes special care to ensure that foods from the daily food guide are included. Such foods as crackers, potato chips, pastries, soft drinks, and punches can add considerably to your food budget while contributing little besides calories to the nutritive value of the diet.

The cost of food does not reflect its nutritive value. Hamburger and high-priced steak have about the same food value. Each family has to decide how much it wishes to budget for food. A budget close to the USDA low-cost plan does not allow for many frills. It requires skill in buying, storing, and preserving food to insure that the family is nutritionally well fed.

Most partially prepared foods cost more than foods that require all the preparation at home, and fewer of them are included in low-cost food

Helen Denning Ullrich is Associate Specialist in the Department of Nutritional Sciences, University of California, Berkeley. She is also project director and editor of the Journal of Nutrition Education.

budgets. When the homemaker is busy outside the home, however, she may find the time saved by partially prepared foods worth the extra money.

Setting a price limit for the dinner main dish is helpful—for example, $1 for a family of four with a low-cost budget, or $1.50 to $2 on a more liberal budget. The vegetables (other than potatoes) and desserts, respectively, might cost not over 25 to 30 cents for the low-cost budget. Check your food plan and decide your own price limits. Fluctuation in such items can unbalance a tight budget.

The average family will spend about half its food budget for milk, meat, and eggs, about a fifth on fruits and vegetables, and the rest for all other food purchases. On a low-cost budget, more is usually expended for cereal, milk products, and eggs, and less for meat. Each family will spend differently for food, depending on its needs, and the homemaker's time, equipment, skills, and energy. In some families, several members may share the meal planning, marketing, cooking, and serving. This also influences the food budget.

A listing of needed items, a week's menu, and newspaper ads are useful in planning a shopping list. At grocery store, adjust plans to take advantage of specials.

In planning meals for the family, choose foods from each of the four basic food groups—meat, milk, fruit-vegetable, and bread-cereal—according to the family needs. Costs vary widely for foods within each group.

Meat, fish, poultry, eggs, dried beans, and nuts are important protein foods. Most families spend more than a third of each food dollar for foods in this group. The lean meat of steak, roast, stew, and ground meat has the same nutritive value. Because the amount of bone, gristle, and fat varies in the different cuts of meat, the price per serving must be figured for the edible portion in a pound of meat. The following is a general guide to the number of 3-ounce servings of cooked lean meat per pound: Much bone or gristle—1 or 2 servings; medium amount of bone—2 or 3 servings; little or no bone—3 or 4.

Poultry contributes the same high-quality protein, minerals, and vitamins to the diet as does meat. To compare costs of whole, cut-up, and selected parts of poultry, divide the price per pound by the percentage of edible meat. Whole and cut-up birds contain 51 percent edible meat; legs and thighs, 53 percent; breast, 63 percent; wings, 50 percent; and backs, 42 percent. If whole chickens sell for 39 cents per pound, the cost per pound of meat is 78 cents.

Like meat, fish is a good source of protein. Costs of fish vary widely. The popular shellfish are the most expensive; canned tuna is often the least expensive. Nutritive value is about the same in most kinds of fish.

Nuts are also an excellent source of protein. Peanuts and peanut butter are the only items in this group that are in the low-cost range. Unshelled nuts cost less than shelled and processed nuts. Some types, like walnuts, pecans, and almonds, are used in prepared foods to give texture and flavor.

Two eggs will provide about the protein equivalent to a serving of meat. They are also an excellent source of iron. Grade, size, and color of eggs do not affect the food value, but do influence the price. Choose the grade and size to fit your needs and budget. In March 1969 pricing, two grade A large eggs were about two-thirds the cost of 4 ounces of regular ground beef.

Dried beans, peas, and lentils, as another good source of protein, may often be served in combination with some animal protein for the main dish. These foods are inexpensive, but they do take a long time to cook. Canned cooked beans are timesavers and also a good buy.

Milk and the other dairy products supply most of the calcium in the American diet in addition to their protein content. Cost of milk varies, depending on whether it is obtained from a grocery store, a special milk depot, or by home delivery. Half gallons and gallons generally cost less than quarts.

Nonfat dry milk is the least expensive form and is low in calorie content. Evaporated milk, which is also more economical than fresh whole milk, has about the same number of calories when diluted. Many families save considerably by using some nonfat dry milk in combination with fluid whole milk; while others use the reconstituted type almost entirely. When the dry milk and water are mixed well in advance and the milk is allowed to chill in the refrigerator, it is very satisfactory. If you use nonfat milk which is not enriched with vitamin A, you should include additional amounts of dark-green and deep-yellow vegetables in the diet to replace the vitamin A which is removed from the whole milk with the fat.

Compare prices carefully on cheeses. Bulk cheese is usually the best buy, but not always. If your family uses any sizable quantities, a large brick of process cheese may well be the most economical.

Imitation dairy products are often available at a lower price than the natural product. But when comparing prices, be sure that products are also comparable in nutritive value.

The vegetable-fruit group can reflect great cost differences depending upon the season of the year, or the abundance and popularity of the food, and whether it is fresh, canned, frozen, dehydrated, or specially prepared.

Fruits and vegetables rich in vitamins A and C should be included on every shopping list whether for a low, moderate, or a liberal budget. They offer more food value for your money.

Four servings of vegetables and fruits should be eaten every day. You should serve foods rich in vitamin C daily, and those high in vitamin A at least every other day. Choose from potatoes and other fruits and vegetables to complete the four servings.

Canned and frozen fruits and vegetables are about equal to fresh in food value. Some fruits and vegetables are available fresh almost the year round, and the price varies only slightly. Others have a peak season when the supply is greatest and the price usually lowest. Compare prices of fresh, frozen, and canned products when deciding on the best buy. Because there is waste in fresh fruits and vegetables, figure the price per serving when you compare prices.

In addition to many choices of fruit juices, today's market offers products made to taste like fruit juices. If you are buying a beverage as a source of vitamin C, be sure it contains enough to provide the family needs. Compare costs on the reconstituted volume. Cost of the substitute juice may be the same as or slightly less than that of the natural juice. Then consider the other nutrients contained in the natural juice, and compare the flavor, convenience, and enjoyment of the product when you make your decision.

Potatoes provide calories and some of the nutrients in your meals inexpensively. A low-cost budget will include more potatoes than will the moderate or liberal budgets. Dehydrated and frozen potatoes, both very convenient products, have been used increasingly in the past few years. Still, the very popular instant mashed potatoes and frozen french-fried potatoes are not yet as inexpensive as the medium-sized nonbaking potato.

Plan four servings daily of whole grain, enriched, or restored breads and cereals. Foods in this group include bread, cooked and ready-to-eat cereal, crackers, flour, cornmeal, grits, spaghetti, noodles, rice, macaroni, and baked goods such as muffins, biscuits, cakes, and cookies. If any of these products are not whole grain, enriched, or restored, they do not count as servings from this food group.

A low-cost food plan will include more foods from the bread-cereal group than will a more moderate or liberal plan. Enriched cornmeal and wheat flour are probably the most economical choices in this food group. Many people find they can cut their budget by making their own biscuits, cornbread, and yeast bread. When the family is large, savings are considerable. Enriched and entire whole-wheat breads usually cost about the same per pound. The specialty types of breads, rolls, and prebaked, refrigerated, and frozen goods are frequently not enriched and cost more.

Breakfast cereals which require cooking are a good buy in nutrition and are usually less expensive than ready-to-eat cereals. Since almost all breakfast cereals are enriched, fortified, or whole grain, they contain B vitamins and iron.

Ready-to-eat cereals come flaked, shredded, granulated, puffed, sweetened, and toasted. Through the development of freeze-drying it is now possible to combine many different kinds of fruit with cereals. Family preference plays a big part in choosing cereals. The influence of advertising, prize in the box, and the value of the boxtop affect the children's choice.

First, read the label to see if the cereal is enriched. Then check the weight and price and cost per serving as box sizes can be misleading. The range of monthly costs for different types of cereal for a family of five, serving 1 ounce per person every day, is as follows: Cereal to be cooked—$2.20 to $4.61; ready-to-eat—$4.02 to $7.52; sugared—$5.36 to $7.71; individual packages—$8.18 to $9.49.

Cereals promoted as extra high in certain nutrients often are higher priced. Some of the sweetened cereals are not enriched with added nutrients.

The macaroni family, which includes spaghetti, egg noodles, vermicelli, and pastina, as well as macaroni, is available in an amazing array of lengths, shapes, and sizes. Most but not all of these products are enriched. Read the label. Macaroni combines well with small amounts of meat, fish, poultry, cheese, and eggs to make nutritious, low-cost main dishes. When frills are added, like sour cream, mushrooms, pimiento, and special cheeses, they become moderate- to liberal-cost dishes.

While nonenriched, white milled rice may cost less than precooked or converted rice, it is much lower in food value and therefore may not be a bargain.

With the present interest in the unsaturated fats, many new fat and oil products with wide price ranges have appeared on the market. Margarines requiring no refrigeration are the least costly. Often the store's own brand is the lowest price in this group. Next come the softer refrigerated margarines and then the whipped types. Butter is usually higher priced than margarine.

Vegetable oils also have a rather wide price range. Olive oil is the highest in price; next are the single vegetable oils, like safflower and corn; and lowest in price are the products called vegetable or salad oil, which may be a mixture of many different vegetable oils.

When foods are in limited supply, as at the beginning or end of the season, the price is usually higher. This is also true if the supply is limited as a result of crop failure, or if fewer animals are being raised.

Foods in low or limited demand are usually high in price—for example, artichokes, avocados, and papayas. Foods grown only in certain localities are sometimes higher. Dates grown in the desert areas of California and cranberries grown in the bogs of New England and Wisconsin, however, are enough in popular demand to result in a moderate price.

Choose package size that best suits family needs. Read labels for information on nutritive value, weight, and price. Compare prices per serving.

Popular interest in such foods as duckling and guinea hens is limited. Those foods are used only for special occasions even on a liberal-cost budget.

Food in the large-size container is generally less costly per pound than in the small size. If the large size fits the family needs and storage space, it can save a nice amount in the family food budget. A large size may be too much, however, for a small family.

Most of the fresh foods in the market today are of good quality. Fancy or prime quality food is the most expensive. Poor quality fresh fruits and vegetables can be a poor buy because blemished, bruised portions must be discarded. The nutritive value may also have diminished. Nutritive value of the different grades of meat, fish, and poultry does not change, but the lower grades may require more preparation. Use the lower grade canned fruits and vegetables when they are going to be cut up or cooked in casseroles or mixtures and the like.

Specialty items like packaged beef stroganoff, frozen shrimp cocktail, cheesecake mixes, and canned pickled artichokes are convenient but usually more expensive than when prepared at home. Popular foods such as frozen orange juice concentrate, canned concentrated soups, the powdered coffees, canned spaghetti, and yellow and devil's-food cake mixes are usually less expensive than the similar fresh or home-prepared foods.

Advances in food processing provide new convenience foods on the grocer's shelves almost daily. As the demand for these foods builds up, cost of production can be lowered. The concentrated, frozen, and canned fruit and vegetables may be less expensive because there is less waste and weight to transport and handle than with the fresh product. Removing water and discarding inedible portions of the food reduces the bulk weight, and the perishability. The resulting efficiency is reflected in reduced costs.

Highly perishable convenience foods like the ready-to-eat baked products can cost up to twice as much as the home-prepared products. Expensive packaging, frequent replacement, and a rather large variety add to marketing costs. Consider other factors in addition to price when trying to decide whether a convenience food is a good choice. Preparation time and effort can be a major item. For example, frozen beef stew needs only to be heated. Preparation time for the same stew made from scratch, in the home, would be about 40 minutes plus about 2 hours of cooking time. If a money value is put on the preparation time at home, the frozen stew would be cheaper. The necessary defrosting and cooking time for frozen food may not be a timesaver when a meal is to be served in a hurry. It may be faster to broil hamburgers, warm a can of peas, and prepare instant mashed potatoes than to heat up a frozen dinner.

In some cases the quality of the home-prepared product may be considered better. For example, it may contain larger quantities of the high-priced items like meat. The quality differences may or may not be important to the individual.

Most of the convenience foods now list the number and the size of servings on the package. Use this information to compare prices between the fresh, partly prepared, or entirely prepared product which may be fresh, dried, canned, or frozen. Often a new convenience food is placed in the grocery store at a promotion or introductory price, which can be a sizable saving.

You can prepare your own convenience foods. Make your own basic dough, pie crust, and cookie mix. Prepare extra quantities of a recipe and freeze part of it. A large cut of meat can be cut into steaks, roast, and stew meat—each section frozen for future needs. Canning and freezing foods when they are in plentiful supply means part of the preparation is already done. It can be a big saving to your food budget, if you have the needed time.

Nutritive value of the menus is about the same. It is typical that the liberal budget food pattern is also a higher calorie pattern. The calorie needs can be adjusted, however, by making the size of the serving either larger or smaller. (See menus, p. 285.)

The same food is often suggested on different menus but in a different form. Garnishes like pickles, olives, and potato chips add only cost and calories and little nutritive value. The low-calorie soft drinks contribute only to the cost. When frozen concentrate lemonade (1 quart) is 16 cents, a 6-ounce serving is 3 cents, compared with 5 to 10 cents for most soft drinks. The low-cost menu was planned to include more vitamin A-rich vegetables to replace vitamin A lacking in unenriched dry nonfat milk.

Cost of protein-rich foods varies from the relatively inexpensive peanut butter to moderate-priced bologna and expensive sliced, boiled ham. Many families use bologna because they feel it is a low-cost meat.

Meat combined with spaghetti paste

A Day's Menu at Different Costs

	Low	Moderate	Liberal
BREAKFAST			
	Orange juice (canned)	Orange juice (frozen)	Sliced oranges
	Oatmeal with reconstituted nonfat milk	Wheat flakes with whole milk	Sugarfrosted rice cereal with fruit and half-and-half
	Enriched white toast	Whole wheat toast	Sweet rolls
	Margarine	Margarine	
	Jelly	Jelly	
	Reconstituted nonfat milk for children	Whole milk for children	Whole milk for children
	Instant coffee	Coffee	Coffee
LUNCH			
	Cream of tomato soup (made with dry nonfat milk)	Dehydrated onion soup	Frozen tomato bisque
	Peanut butter and raisin sandwich (enriched bread)	Bologna sandwich (enriched bread)	Boiled ham on dark rye bread
	Celery and carrot sticks	Head lettuce salad, thousand island dressing	Deviled egg, pickles, olives, potato chips
	Reconstituted nonfat milk for children	Whole milk	Whole milk for children
	Instant coffee		Coffee
SNACK			
	Lemonade	Cider	Low-calorie soft drink
	Oatmeal cookies	Brownies	Assorted butter cookies
DINNER			
	Spaghetti with meat sauce	Beef stew with potatoes, carrots, onions	Standing rib roast
	Winter squash	Tomato and lettuce salad with mayonnaise	Baked potato
			Zucchini, onion, and cheese casserole
			Romaine salad with blue cheese dressing
	Biscuits		
	Margarine		
	Bread pudding	Custard	Toffee ice cream
	Reconstituted nonfat milk for children	Whole milk for children	Whole milk for children
	Instant coffee	Coffee	Coffee

contains less protein than stew and roast beef, but the protein in biscuits and bread pudding will make up the difference.

Deciding what foods to buy for the family depends upon many factors: family likes and dislikes; size of family and ages of family members; number of meals eaten at home; the kinds of meals—normal three meals a day versus irregular meal times, frequent snacks; the amount of money available for food; time available for shopping and for preparing food; skill in planning, preparing, and in serving food; storage and cooking facilities; and who does most of the planning, purchasing, and cooking.

Careful planning will result in good meals and a satisfied family. No two families will come out with the same answer.

Ellen H. Semrow

Money Stretching Ideas for Making Your Food Dollar Go F-u-r-t-h-e-r

A food dollar is precious. It purchases food to satisfy hunger. It brings familiar foods to the table where all can share in the warm, happy feeling that comes from enjoying food together. Used wisely, your food dollar can do all this and more. It can, with planning, provide foods to help each family member, young and old, become the energetic and healthy individual that he wants to be.

The person purchasing and serving food should know the value of every dollar. Although a certain amount of food money is placed in the pocketbook each week, some of it goes for away-from-home meals. And it may be called on to cover emergencies—a doctor or car repair bill; the purchase of new shoes. In that event, how to make the most of what is left calls for pennypinching with know-how.

To have food in the refrigerator, in the cupboard, or on the pantry shelf and cash on hand means future meals. Planning can do much to bring about this security.

Each family's plan is theirs alone. It changes as the family grows in number and in years. It changes with the season, with prices for food.

To have cash on hand, you may purchase food by the meal or by the day. Or you may purchase only the foods needed as you can afford them and round out the commodities you receive. Also, you may be forced to shop often because you share a kitchen or because the equipment and storage space do not fit your needs.

Payday is shopping day for many. A family may spend a certain amount, trying to purchase food to last out the week. Because of tradition, another family may purchase expensive regional or imported items, adding other foods as dollars allow.

Families far from shopping centers must have food supplies to last more than 2 weeks. Each trip costs money.

Others can afford to pursue and purchase quantities of bargain-priced foods for future use. And those with gardens have a supply of fresh, canned, or frozen foods.

Working homemakers purchase more convenience foods than stay-at-homes do. Often it is the children who shop, cook, and serve meals when mothers cannot be at home. For such families, teamwork in planning and doing is a necessity.

To use food money well, first consider the food needs of every family member. Then weigh these against the dollars you have to spend. Get the most for the least by:

- Picking from the plentiful foods in planning meals and snacks.
- Shopping from a prepared list.
- Spending the food money in stores stocking a wide variety of good foods, where the average price means lower grocery and meat bills for you week in and week out.

One homemaker may plan weekly menus as she studies food advertisements. Another is so skilled she can see in her mind's eye each of the meals she will prepare for the family and guests,

Ellen H. Semrow is Director, Consumer Service Department, of the American Institute of Baking, Chicago, Ill.

making use of best buys. Both will have other choices in mind should they be disappointed in the "special offers" or discover that the supermarket is sold out of what they wanted. Both types of homemakers plan and use shopping lists as guides. Experience has taught them that this is a good way to save energy and money.

How to Make a Shopping List:

Jot down the needed items as food supplies run low.

Inventory the refrigerator, freezer, and shelves. First, plan uses for your leftovers.

List the same kinds of foods and supplies together.

Watch food advertisements. Foods in plentiful supply are at the peak of their quality and are reasonably priced.

"Specials" may be closeouts, to be sold before the new crop or pack arrives at the store.

Shop newspaper pages, compare all prices, the ones in small print as well as big offerings.

Those caught in the low-income squeeze who cannot afford newspapers, and those who cannot read even the free advertisements, can by working together with others plan purchases and shopping trips. Sharing talents, experiences, and expenses is one way to obtain more for less. Community helpers may advise on the good buys, show how to use new foods, organize shopping trips. They may make transportation available at cost.

Place perishable and frozen foods last on your list. Purchase them just before "checking out."

Be sure your shopping list contains the foods needed for each person, on each day.

Do servings from the meat group total at least two? Include dry beans or peas, eggs, and cheese with meat.

See that four or more servings of enriched or whole-grain breads and cereals are included.

Servings of fruits and vegetables should add up to four. Include deep-green and yellow vegetables and vitamin C-rich fruits or juices.

Plan for three to four cups of milk a day for children; two cups for adults. Include milk used in cooking. Cheese counts here.

Total the food costs, omitting cleaning and household supplies. If cuts are needed, start in trimming and substituting.

Money-Saving Suggestions:

Rethink meat. It takes about a third of the food allowance. Plan entrees around less-tender cuts. Pick those with the most meat to eat for money spent. If pig ears, snouts, and tails are used often, be sure to include additional red meat. Lunch meats are

Cost per Serving of Commonly Used Fresh Pork Variety Meats*

Retail cut	Servings per pound	Price per pound in pennies											
		19	21	24	29	31	34	37	39	41	44	47	49
		Cost per serving											
Pork—fresh:													
Chitterlings, Pig ears, Pork snouts, Hog fries	3	6+	7	8	9+	10+	11+	12+	13	13+	14+	15+	16+
Hog maws, Pork liver	2	9+	10+	12	14+	15+	17+	18+	19+	20+	22	23+	24+
Neck bones, Pork tails	1	19	21	24	29	31	34	37	39	41	44	47	49

*Information developed from personal interviews with packers, retailers, and public aid workers in the Chicago area, 1968.

costly. Plan more large roasts and use some of the meat for sandwiches. Pass up chicken parts; cut up a whole bird. Use fish if the price pinch is less.

Bulk cheese costs less per pound than sliced or grated cheese.

Run in favorite recipes with stretchpower; extend the meat or fish with bread, rice, noodles, and pasta—spaghetti, macaroni, etc.

Plan uses for dry beans and peas.

Buy cereals that require cooking instead of ready-to-serve ones.

Use vegetable shortening, margarine, and butter to thriftiest advantage.

Scan luxury snacks such as potato chips, popped corn, corn puffs. Of this group, pretzels cost less per ounce. Private label brands and larger packages normally cost less per ounce for like quality.

Soft drinks cost less per ounce in returnable bottles than in disposable cans or bottles. Save on larger-sized bottles and lesser-known brands.

Skip costly low-calorie, instant or convenience meal items. Example: Buttered toast spread with preserves is cheaper than fruit-filled popups.

Choose from abundant and low-cost vegetables and fruit rather than from unusual or imported varieties. Buy the least expensive forms, whether fresh, frozen, or canned. Example: Root vegetables such as sweetpotatoes or white potatoes, turnips, carrots, and beets might take the place of Puerto Rican plantains, yautias, and yucas.

Select lower grades wherever you can without losing appetite appeal and usefulness. An example: Grade B eggs can be used for baking and for some egg dishes.

The locally grown beans, dried or canned, are cheaper than imported beans.

Select juices and drinks for vitamin C value. Rule out fruit-flavored choices supplying only sugar.

Bread cubes and noodles give stretchpower to this Rosy Beef Romanoff.

Substitute dried or evaporated milk for part of the fresh milk.

If you have made every possible saving and still find yourself spending more than you should, replan the menus. Begin by cutting quantities of meat, poultry, and fish; vegetables and fruits less rich in vitamins A and C. Add more bread, cereals, potatoes, and dry beans and peas. Keep quantities of milk and cheese, green and yellow vegetables, tomatoes, and citrus fruits and juices the same.

With menus planned and shopping list ready, two more decisions need to be made—where to shop and how.

Prices vary with store policy and location, even within the city. For savings, patronize a cash-and-carry store. Which one? Ask yourself these questions:

Does the store stock a wide variety of food? Is there a consumer adviser to help you? Does it offer value, quality, and freshness at lowest prices? Are the surroundings neat and clean?

Are the fresh meat and produce counters filled with quality items, trimmed to reduce waste, and reasonably priced? Can you examine bagged produce? Is the added cost of feature games, stamps, check cashing services, and perhaps hot coffee, in addition to ample parking space, worth it to you?

Shopping special offers means going from store to store. Consider transportation, time, and energy. Such a trip may offset savings. You may fare better with one-store shopping where pricing policy and services suit your needs. Recheck prices often. Compare items with those advertised by competitors to be sure that you get your dollar's worth.

Careful buyers can save even in times of a price pinch. Staples offer biggest savings: enriched flour, rice, and bread; margarine; sugar; and the simple convenience foods like some biscuit and cake mixes. Canned chicken soup and instant coffee are usually good buys. Plan your available kitchen time so you can save by cooking from scratch.

Pointers for Pricers:

Know the grades for food quality developed by the U.S. Department of Agriculture.

Read labels and inspection stamps.

Compare sale prices with the stock prices. Spotlighted product displays may suggest a bargain. Check the shelves. The featured price may be the usual price. Look for a competing product of the same size and quality. You may save here.

Think about quality in terms of use. Why use fresh tomatoes when canned ones will do?

Compare costs of various forms of food—fresh, instant, dried, frozen, or canned; enriched or unenriched. Buy the type which suits needs and food likes. Example: Frozen spinach, free from waste, may cost less per serving than fresh. Enriched bread costs no more than the unenriched kind.

The seasonal food prices should be noted. Keep track of the trends. Buy when prices are down. Substitute when prices are up.

Take advantage of private label items when the quality and price are right.

Think of cost per serving or portion rather than price per pound, especially when it comes to meat. Cuts high in bone and fat cost more per person than cuts with little waste. Example: Spareribs versus rolled pork loin.

Buy all cereal foods by the cost per ounce or pound.

Buy foods that store well and in largest sized packages which can be used in a reasonable length of time and not hog shelf, freezer, or refrigerator space.

Judge values in fresh fruits and vegetables. Make your own selection, handpick whenever you can. Use thought and care in handling perishables. Adding to spoilage adds to costs.

Do not buy merely because the price is low. Buy to suit your needs.

Consider produce in season and grown nearby.

Look for signs of decay, bruises, or blemishes. Choose only sound items.

Select fruits such as apples, peaches,

and melons for use, and thus reduce waste. Example: Why hand a huge apple to a small girl who can eat only a small apple?

Small produce may be sold by measure. Check containers for loose pack; for fancy items on top, culls on the bottom.

Develop the habit of doing mental arithmetic while you shop. For easy division, round out servings or ounces and prices and get approximate costs.

Always shop from a list. Try to shop alone, when the store is not crowded. Impulse buying is less when one is not under pressure from prodding shopping carts and clamors for goodies. If children are along, they should be present at the checkout counter to learn firsthand that food costs money.

If the man of the house does the shopping, then he should be in on preparation of the list. Children old enough to take part should be included.

Be the consumer's best friend when you shop. Treat all merchandise you handle as if you were paying for it. Place unwanted goods back where they belong. Handle shopping carts with care. Any loss or damage to merchandise or property increases supermarket costs, costs for which the consumer always pays.

Select packaged foods carefully. The packaging may be worth more than the contents. Examples: Individually wrapped or trayed cookies in special boxes, heat-and-eat dinners, imported foods like crackers and oatmeal in tins.

Be sure all canned and packaged items are in good condition. Check milk cartons for dripping. Inspect butter cartons with care. Get what you pay for. Look at egg cartons for wet or dry egg solids. Open lid carefully. Don't buy if any eggs are cracked. Close properly.

Check processing dates on all packages carrying them. Buy those with the most recent datemark.

Watch the scale. It should carry an inspection stamp showing it has been checked for accuracy. Be sure it registers zero before item is weighed. Have weight checked on bagged produce.

Watch the checker as your bill is rung up on the cash register. Follow each entry to be certain you are charged only for actual purchases and that prices are right. Ask for a "recount" if you feel an error has been made.

With experience in planning and shopping you will learn that price alone does not always mean a best buy. You will know how to pick foods for their real value.

Prompt and proper storage of food in the home saves food value, flavor, texture, and appearance. Spoilage and waste can undo savings.

Foods that do not require refrigeration at all, or none until the package or can has been opened, keep best when tightly sealed and stored in a dry, cool spot away from light and heat. In hot, damp climates, some foods must be placed in covered containers for protection. Keep only short supplies of these. Make certain that containers and shelves are clean.

Refrigerator temperature should be 35° F. to 45° F. To store, always cover or wrap foods to prevent moisture loss. Use most perishable items first. Leftovers won't be skipped if kept at front of shelves.

Freezer temperatures should be zero or lower. The food taken from the freezer can be only as good as that which you put in, provided that it was wrapped properly and was not stored overlong. Freeze foods which mean real savings. All packages should be labeled with date, kind, and amount of food. Freeze only 2 pounds for each cubic foot of space every 6 hours. If you have a large freezer, jot down items and dates as you store. Scratch each package off the list upon removal, the oldest first.

If meat is boned out, wrap and freeze the bones. When enough are on hand, make soup.

If there is a special on ground beef in large packages, divide into portions before wrapping and freezing; some for meat sauce for spaghetti, some shaped into individual patties.

Ham trimmings can stand short-time freezing. Use with greens.

When ground beef has to show up on the family menu every other day, try Beef Balls Potpourri for variety. Ingredients include stuffing, a tomato sauce, thin slices of peeled cucumber, strips of green pepper, and onion rings.

When you have to create meals from but few ingredients, using them more than once a day, sameness shows up fast. Ban monotony and waste through pennywise preparation. Discover new ways with foods. You can learn how to make even third-time-around food far tastier by attending demonstrations or classes or by using tested recipes.

• Peanut butter sandwich fillings can be different. Add applesauce, chili sauce, or orange juice and grated rind to it; enough to make it spreadable. Scones, hushpuppies, brownies, and fruit salad dressing can be made with peanut butter.
• Flick bread slices in and out of an egg-milk mixture, coat slices with cornmeal or breadcrumbs, pan fry for new flavor and texture.
• Cut biscuit dough and bread into different shapes. Serve with new spreads. Cube or crumb bread trimmings.
• Fry rice Chinese style and serve it under a blanket of hot, thick tomato sauce garnished with bits of fried ham or sausage and shredded Cheddar cheese. Or, layer hot rice, chopped ham, sour cream and shredded Cheddar cheese in a baking dish, finishing off with cheese; bake in a hot oven for 10 minutes.

Do not repeat flavors or colors on a menu—apple salad and apple pie, red beets and red cabbage.

Too many strong aromas at any one meal, such as garlic, onion, and cabbage, can ruin appetites.

Recipes are needed when you are learning to use strange foods. Introduce new dishes with this plan: Offer them at dinner, serving small portions along with familiar foods. Children tend to accept a new food if parents show they like it.

Food wastage is less with the tested recipes. Preparation is easier, dishes are tastier, failures are fewer when measuring spoons and cups are used. Always measure dry ingredients with dry cups and spoons. Pots and pans of the right size are important, too. If you lack equipment, it helps to think about how to do it with what you have on hand.

Clock your time and ability to cook and serve meals. Remember that a few well-chosen foods, all on the table at the right time, make a more satisfactory meal than many carelessly prepared dishes straggling along.

Homemakers with little kitchen time, who cannot afford heat-and-eat foods, can divide some favorite recipes into steps. Decide what can be prepared on the night before and safely refrigerated, then what must be done at mealtime in a few minutes. Such recipes, when planned into menus, give these bonuses: Savings in time and money, balanced meals, happier people at the table.

Quick-cooking foods are best started after all who will eat are at home. Overcooking and extra-long holding of foods rob the eating quality. If foods must be served at different times, prepare those which can be held over or reheated.

Check foods as they cook to avoid scorching, especially those cooking in little water.

Use a sharp knife for carving meat. Remember: Attractively sliced meat, when arranged on a platter or placed on a plate, looks elegant.

All foods should be picture pretty, alone or together. Their colors, shapes, sizes, and textures should flatter each other.

Foods have right serving temperatures. Ice cream at zero is too cold. Refrigerate it a short time, letting the flavor bloom before serving. Mashed potatoes are delicious when hot, sad when cold. Bananas taste best at room temperature.

Breads and rolls are good at either room temperature or oven-warm.

Use these facts: Tart foods sharpen appetites; sweets dull them. Crunchy or crisp foods add texture contrast: hard rolls with the soups and stews, crisp toast with creamed dishes.

Show off foods to advantage. The right tablecloth, place mats, dishes, glassware, and flowers can light up a meal. Wrongly used, they turn off appetites—orange juice in purple glasses, for instance. If you can have but one set of dishes, stick to a plain design and light colors. Pick clear glassware. With these, and color in tablecloths and the decorations, you can avoid problems.

Ways to encourage good eating include a change of pace in meal service. Surprise the family with an occasional indoor or outdoor picnic. Use fanfare upon special days. Rather than rush through a meal to see a TV show, make it a tray supper.

Each person is an individual. Appetites vary with age and how one feels at the moment. Keep servings small. Let each ask for more as long as he eats what is on the plate.

Snacking dulls the appetite, wrecks food budgets. Eating a week's supply of apples in 1 day not only spoils the desire for other food, it discourages the cook. Check food binges. Snacks should be part of the food plan.

You have three assets in leftovers—savings in time since they are already cooked, an extra stretch for the food budget, and variety.

The trick to using leftovers is to change their appearance and step up the flavor as much as possible. One-dish meals and scalloped dishes (various cooked foods heated in sauce) make a changeover easier. You can extend the meats and vegetables with dumplings and biscuits; with rice, macaroni, noodles, and bread cubes. You can top off such entrees with french-fried onion rings, Chinese noodles, or seasoned croutons. Eye appeal doubles when colorful ingredients like chopped tomato, pimiento, green onions, chives, or green pepper are added to toppings.

Omelets and french toast are more tasty with bits of leftovers. A small amount of cooked vegetables can stand an hour or two in french dressing for added flavor. Strips of leftover meats and cheeses make salads hearty.

Second-time-around fruits—cooked, canned, or fresh—can be added to cottage cheese. You can replan these into desserts along with other fruits. They, like vegetables, can be added to flavored gelatins, chilled in molds, and turned out on lettuce or shredded cabbage.

Encourage the eating of salads and soups by adding seasoned, toasted bread cubes before serving. Cubes also can become puddings, fruit desserts, or stuffings. Crumbs can be used to coat foods for frying. Doughnuts can be split, spread with marmalade, and broiled for a moment. Renew cakes and cookies by serving them with fruit sauces and ice cream.

When it comes to getting the most out of food money, one thing more is necessary. It is the enthusiastic and thrifty-minded homemaker who prepares food with imagination and joy and serves it with pride. She creates the atmosphere for enjoying food. To her, as it should be to every one of us, food is precious.

How To Use Table:

Assume chuck roast (bone-in), lamb shoulder roast, and Boston butt (bone-in) are all 59 cents per pound. Which is the more economical choice? Just match the price per pound with the meat cut you are comparing. Reading the table under the 59 cents per pound column shows chuck roast at 30 cents per serving, lamb shoulder roast at 24 cents per serving, and the bone-in Boston butt at 20 cents per serving. Servings are from 2½ to 3½ ounces of cooked lean meat.

(Marketing Information for Consumers, Cooperative Extension Service, Ohio State University, Columbus.)

Cost per Serving of Red Meat and Poultry

Retail cut	Servings per pound	Price per pound											
		29	39	49	59	69	79	89	99	109	119	129	139
		Cost per serving											
BEEF:													
Sirloin Steak	2½	12	16	20	24	28	32	36	40	44	48	52	56
Porterhouse, T-bone, Rib Steak	2	15	20	25	30	35	40	45	50	55	60	65	70
Round Steak	3½	8	11	14	17	20	23	25	28	31	34	37	40
Chuck Roast, bone-in	2	15	20	25	30	35	40	45	50	55	60	65	70
Rib Roast—boneless	2½	12	16	20	24	28	32	36	40	44	48	52	56
Rib Roast—bone-in	2	15	20	25	30	35	40	45	50	55	60	65	70
Rump, Sirloin Roast	3	10	13	16	20	23	26	30	33	36	40	43	46
Ground Beef	4	7	10	12	15	17	20	22	25	27	30	32	35
Short Ribs	2	15	20	25	30	35	40	45	50	55	60	65	70
Heart, Liver, Kidney	5	6	8	10	12	14	16	18	20	22	24	26	28
Frankfurters	4	7	10	12	15	17	20	22	25	27	30	32	35
Stew Meat, boneless	5	6	8	10	12	14	16	18	20	22	24	26	28
LAMB:													
Loin, Rib, Shoulder Chops	3	10	13	16	20	23	26	30	33	36	40	43	46
Breast, Shank	2	15	20	25	30	35	40	45	50	55	60	65	70
Shoulder Roast	2½	12	16	20	24	28	32	36	40	44	48	52	56
Leg of Lamb	3	10	13	16	20	23	26	30	33	36	40	43	46
PORK—FRESH:													
Center Cut or Rib Chops	4	7	10	12	15	17	20	22	25	27	30	32	35
Loin or Rib Roast	2½	12	16	20	24	28	32	36	40	44	48	52	56
Boston butt—bone-in	3	10	13	16	20	23	26	30	33	36	40	43	46
Blade Steak	3	10	13	16	20	23	26	30	33	36	40	43	46
Spare Ribs	1⅓	22	29	37	44	52	59	67	74	82	89	97	104
PORK—CURED:													
Picnic—bone-in	2	15	20	25	30	35	40	45	50	55	60	65	70
Ham—fully cooked:													
bone-in	3½	8	11	14	17	20	23	25	28	31	34	37	40
boneless and canned	5	6	8	10	12	14	16	18	20	22	24	26	28
shankless	4¼	7	9	12	14	16	19	21	23	26	28	30	33
center slice	5	6	8	10	12	14	16	18	20	22	24	26	28
POULTRY:													
Broiler, ready-to-cook	1⅓	22	29	37	44	52	59	67	74	82	89	97	104
legs, thighs	3	10	13	16	20	23	26	30	33	36	40	43	46
breasts	4	7	10	12	15	17	20	22	25	27	30	32	35
Turkey, ready-to-cook:													
under 12 lbs	1	29	39	49	59	69	79	89	99	109	119	129	139
12 lbs. and over	1⅓	22	29	37	44	52	59	67	74	82	89	97	104

Harvye Lewis

A Food Guide for the Ages, From Baby to Gramps

Each of us has an individual need for food, yet we usually like to eat with others. Socializing with food is one of the more pleasant aspects of our way of life. We like to share meals with friends and family. In contrast to the hospital tray, these meals may be adapted to personal requirements by changing the size of servings and making a few substitutions.

Differences in activities, body size, and stages of growth are the main reasons for individual food needs. The quantity of food for a person is usually measured in terms of energy or calories. Building materials are proteins and minerals, especially calcium, phosphorus, magnesium, and iron. Reactions are continuously going on in the body to use our food for energy or for tissue building. Vitamins are necessary for these reactions.

Energy needs increase with body size and activity. The minimum energy need for maintaining muscle tone and functioning of internal organs is called basal metabolism, and this amounts to approximately 1,700 calories in a young man and to 1,400 in a young woman. Because of their smaller size, children require fewer calories than adults even though their energy expenditure is higher per unit of body weight. Activity may cause variations in energy need amounting to several thousand calories per day. Persons in the same profession may have avocations that run the gamut from watching television to playing tennis. Man's use of gasoline and electricity to perform work formerly accomplished by muscles is causing Americans to get fat.

Research on nutritional needs has been going on since before the turn of the century, and there is a scientific background for planning meals. Since the early 1940's the Food and Nutrition Board of the National Research Council has reviewed the available information at five-year intervals and brought out the publication *Recommended Dietary Allowances*. The amounts of nutrients recommended are the requirements plus a safety factor in most cases. These allowances were the basis of *A Daily Food Guide*, prepared by the U.S. Department of Agriculture. Included in the guide are four food groups: Milk, meat, vegetable-fruit, and bread-cereal. By using the suggested amounts of foods from the four groups, you can plan adequate diets without much knowledge of nutrition. Knowing something about the reasons for individual needs and the contributions of various foods makes the job easier and the reasons for planning more compelling.

Formation of tissue in the child, pregnant woman, or convalescent requires only a small quantity of food beyond that needed to supply energy. The main difference for them is in the proportion of various nutrients. The nursing mother also has a special need for the building nutrients, as the baby is growing rapidly in the first year. Protein is the class of organic compounds present in the largest amount in the animal body, and it is synthesized from amino acids, which are supplied by dietary proteins from plant

Dr. Harvye Lewis is Professor of Food and Nutrition at the School of Home Economics, Louisiana State University, Baton Rouge.

and animal sources. The other building materials are inorganic elements, those present in bone being needed in the largest amounts.

Baby and Mother. Beginning with conception, food needs for the baby and mother are inseparable. Sometimes a young or adolescent mother is still completing the laying down of her own body tissues. Pregnancy is a physiological stress for the healthy, well nourished woman, and an even greater hazard for the older woman whose body stores have been depleted by numerous pregnancies. The outcome of pregnancy is often a healthy baby, regardless of the lack of attention paid to the mother's diet, yet considerable evidence indicates there are benefits from an adequate diet during this time. The mother's health may be undermined by depletion of her body stores.

During pregnancy, there are hormone changes, increased fluid retention, increased basal metabolism, increased absorption of certain nutrients, and changes in the digestive system. Because of these changes, one should not assume that the needs during a pregnancy are a sum of the requirements for the nonpregnant woman plus those of the developing fetus, yet it appears reasonable to expect the mother to need more of some nutrients. The *Recommended Dietary Allowances* in the 1968 revision lists the amounts of calories and nutrients above those for the nonpregnant young woman.

The recommended allowance of an additional 200 calories during the latter half of pregnancy is an approximation and is not right for all women. Whether the woman was underweight or overweight at the start of pregnancy, her height and activities all affect her energy need. The increase in basal metabolism may be offset by the decrease in activities during the last months. Weight gain should be regular throughout a pregnancy and should total 22 to 26 pounds for most women.

The National Research Council recommends that the consumption of protein, calcium, phosphorus, and folic acid be increased significantly during pregnancy. Vitamin D, which is not included in the normal allowances of adults, is added because of its relation to mineral absorption and utilization. The additional protein amounts to 10 grams per day, which may be furnished by adding 1½ cups of milk. The milk also takes care of the recommended additional 0.4 gram calcium and contributes other nutrients.

Iron needs for women are being studied at present, as there is evidence that many females have borderline or poor reserves. The iron needs of the developing fetus may cause iron deficiency anemia during or following pregnancy. On the other side of the picture, there is a saving of body iron by cessation of menstruation and increased absorption of dietary iron.

The present recommendation for all women during the childbearing period is 18 milligrams per day. For most women this should be sufficient during pregnancy. In order to provide 18 milligrams of iron, it is necessary to include meat, generous amounts of the green vegetables, and enriched or whole-grain cereals. Liver is the most potent food source of iron and supplies other nutrients as well. A diet which includes two servings of meat, poultry, or fish, one egg, two green vegetables, two other vegetables, four slices of bread, one cup of breakfast cereal, and one or more fruits will supply enough iron without running up the calories. To this should be added 3 cups of milk and other foods to take care of the energy need.

Generous use of green vegetables to supply iron will more than supply the additional amounts of vitamins A, C, and folic acid recommended for the pregnant woman. If the extra calories are furnished by enriched cereals, milk, and vegetables, the increased allowances for the B complex for the pregnant woman are readily met. Vitamin D is supplied by fortified milk plus small amounts of margarine and a few other foods.

The main difference between the pregnant woman's diet and that of her husband is more milk and stress on iron-rich foods. He may have no objection to eating the same foods, making some adjustment for his own calorie needs. The increased amounts of nutrients recommended for the pregnant woman may be furnished by the diet without vitamin or mineral supplements.

Despite improvements in infant formulae, breast feeding is still strongly recommended. One explanation of the reason infants thrive better on human milk is that it promotes the growth of favorable intestinal bacteria which stop the growth of less desirable ones. Some pediatricians advocate breast feeding as a foolproof method rather than because of superior nutritional qualities. Another favorable aspect is the close mother-child relationship.

For many mothers the need for more food during nursing may be achieved by relaxing the restrictions normally necessary for weight control. Approximately 1,000 calories beyond the usual diet before pregnancy is needed for an average milk yield. At this time a mother's energy needs for activities will probably be higher as she takes on the responsibilities of a baby and resumes her household chores.

The main increases in the nutrient allowances during nursing are the addition of 20 grams of protein and 3,000 International Units of vitamin A. Minerals and other vitamins are the same or slightly higher than the amounts recommended during pregnancy. Folic acid and vitamin B_{12} allowances are lower than during a pregnancy. One pint of milk and one egg added to the diet which was adequate before pregnancy will furnish all the protein and almost half of the additional vitamin A. Using milk as the source of the extra protein contributes to the mother's fluid need during nursing. Continued emphasis on the green vegetables, recommended during pregnancy, will supply the rest of the vitamin A, iron, and other minerals and vitamins.

The newborn baby needs higher levels of all nutrients in relation to size as compared with all other ages. He needs these materials for rapid growth and because of a higher metabolic rate. The premature or low-birth-weight infant may have insufficient body stores of some nutrients, along with decreased ability to absorb fat and fat-soluble vitamins; thus feeding problems are compounded. Babies will vary in energy requirements because of differences in size and in activities. A baby that cries a lot may double his energy need. In relation to body weight, the infant's needs for both energy and protein decrease rapidly during the first year.

Successful use of cow's milk in feeding infants involves meeting nutritional requirements of the child, avoiding digestive difficulties, and preventing infection. Cleanliness in handling all the equipment and heat treatment of the milk will lower the chances of infection. Pasteurization and sterilization of the milk also cause the formation of small curds, which are more digestible.

Cow's milk is richer in protein, comparable in fat, and lower in sugar than human milk. Except for vitamins C, D, and niacin, it contains more vitamins and minerals. Babies may tolerate milk from the carton; however, it is usually modified. Whole milk is diluted with water to lower protein and minerals, and sugar is added to bring the calorie level back to that of human milk. Evaporated milk has largely replaced fresh milk in infant feeding. A common modification is 3 ounces evaporated milk, 7 ounces water, and ½ ounce cane sugar.

As the sterilization process destroys ascorbic acid (vitamin C) in milk, the artificially fed infant should be given a supplement of 35 milligrams daily beginning during the first few weeks. Infantile scurvy is the only classic deficiency disease which has not been virtually wiped out in the United States. If vitamin D has not been added to the milk during processing, the baby should be given 400 International Units per day.

Full-term infants with nonanemic mothers have reserves of iron which

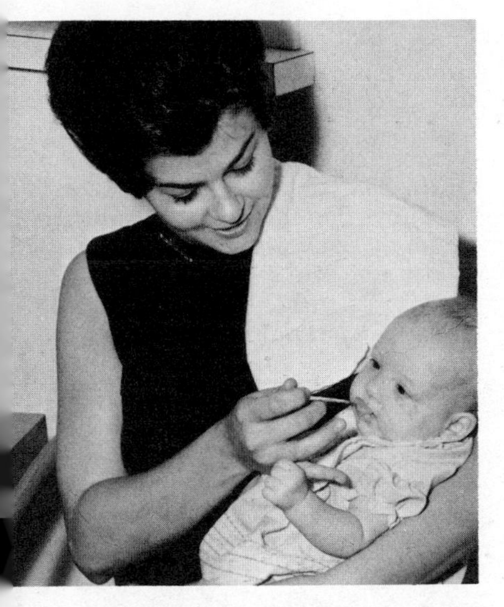

Foods supplying iron are usually first given to infants at two or three months of age.

should last about 6 months. During the first 2 or 3 months, a food high in iron is gradually introduced. Then more solid foods are added, and by the time that he is 6 months old the baby should be eating cooked cereals, strained fruits, strained vegetables, egg yolk, and homogenized meat. These foods may be cooked along with those prepared for the family, and then strained; or they may be purchased in small containers ready for use.

A baby gains in weight and length according to his own pattern, and failure to make a steady gain indicates something is wrong. As the child grows older, the calories and nutrients needed in relation to size decrease. Toward the end of the first year, although the age may not be the same for all, as growth slows down so does the baby's enthusiasm for food. Weight gain during the second year amounts to about a third that of the first year, and is slower between ages 2 and 6 years than at any time until after puberty is reached.

The Growing Child. Now that the baby can chew, it is no longer necessary to spoon strained or mashed vegetables into the little mouth. His hands are useful in putting many things in his mouth, including some food. As the child gives up baby foods and experiments with the new textures and flavors of the family meals, he may reject many items. This show of independence, together with a smaller appetite, may lead to pleading, bribing, scolding, and threatening by the parents. Meals become a battle, and it isn't always the larger person who wins. The child may capitalize on being the center of attention and not eat anything. This frightens the mother, and she may cater to his wishes, thus starting the pattern of strong likes and dislikes which may complicate his life for years to come.

When a child refuses to eat, food should be offered without comments about the desirability of eating. After a reasonable length of time—no longer than 20 minutes—the plate is removed, and nothing is offered or allowed until the next meal. Even a strong-willed child will capitulate by the third day.

Because of the small appetite characteristic of a young child, the quality of the diet becomes even more important; a small amount of food must now supply the materials for tissue building. He can't afford to fill his small capacity with foods that supply only energy, as soft drinks and candy, etc. Avoiding such fillers is a challenge to the mother, since there are temptations at the grocery store, drug store, grandmother's or the neighbors', and the ice cream truck that invades the neighborhood.

Amounts of nutrients needed by a preschool child are similar to those for a baby, although slightly higher.

With increasing size, the child requires more food; yet in relation to body size, there is a continued decrease in food needs except during the adolescent growth spurt. A list of foods which almost meet the recommended allowances for the various nutrients for a preschool child follows. Additional food to raise the calorie value should take care of the remainder of the nutrients, except for vitamin D.

Vitamin D milk is the only food source of this vitamin, and the usual fortification is 400 International Units per quart. If the child drinks only 1 pint of milk, it may be necessary to supply 200 International Units of vitamin D by a concentrated source. Preparations of vitamins should be used with care, for there are dangers in consuming too much of the fat-soluble ones: A, D, E, and K.

Learning to eat new or different foods is part of the preschool program.

Diet for a preschool child should include: 1 pint of vitamin D milk; 2 ounces of lean meat, fish, or poultry; ½ cup orange juice or some source of vitamin C; 1 egg; 2 slices enriched bread or other cereal; ½ cup cooked yellow or green leafy vegetable.

Amounts of food listed will not furnish enough daily food for a child, but there are numerous possibilities for supplements. The servings may be larger while other fruits, vegetables, butter or margarine, cereals, and simple desserts are suitable. Glasses that fit their small hands and items that are easily transported from dish to mouth encourage young children to consume what is put before them. Even though learning to handle the spoons, forks, glasses, liquids, crackers, etc., may involve many spills and crumbs, children enjoy company at meals. Sometimes the little ones seem to enjoy the meals in the nursery school more than those at home.

The rest of the diet should not be "empty calories." Sweets, especially sticky candies, promote the growth of micro-organisms which cause dental cavities. In preparation for the coming years when weight control is necessary, the child needs to learn to eat vegetables and fruits. The large amount of water in these foods causes them to have lower calorie values than meat, desserts, and bread.

Preadolescents. In preadolescence, a child needs larger amounts of the same kinds of food that the younger child eats. Going to school makes it necessary for him to have a routine schedule for meals. The preschool child who is not hungry when he wakes up may play for a while before breakfast. This behavior pattern doesn't fit in with carpools, buses, and the school bell. A child who comes to school without breakfast is at a big disadvantage in making the most of his intellectual powers. Although the candy and soft drinks available in some schools can allay the child's hunger, they may cause him to have very little appetite at lunchtime.

It is not imperative that a child consume the traditional bacon, eggs, and toast breakfast. Any food which may be prepared quickly and consumed easily is suitable. Many persons enjoy a glass of fruit juice first. If this isn't well accepted, the child may consume a source of vitamin C later in the day. Fats and proteins are digested more slowly than carbohydrates, thus delaying the empty feeling that soon follows a high carbohydrate meal. Eggs are economical and easily prepared sources of protein and iron; however, they are not irreplaceable in the child's diet.

Fruit juice, milk, and ready-to-eat cereal make a breakfast for the elementary school child that is quickly prepared and easily consumed.

The elementary school child may consume 1 cup (½ pint) of milk three times a day. As his appetite dictates, the amounts of meat, bread, fruit, and vegetables are increased. During these formative years the youngster should be encouraged to eat many different foods. Along with promoting good health, the School Lunch Program has contributed to teaching children good eating habits. Regulations under the National School Lunch Act of 1946 specify that the Type A lunch contain, as a minimum, 1 cup of whole milk, 2 ounces of protein-rich food, three-fourths cup of two or more vegetables or fruits or both, one slice of whole-grain or enriched bread or its equivalent, and 2 teaspoons of butter or of fortified margarine.

Adolescents. Adolescence is a period of rapid growth and of maturation, which may occur between the ages 10 and 20 years. On the average, girls reach this stage of development about 2 years earlier than boys. There is evidence that good nutrition, which promotes growth throughout childhood, is related to maturing early. At the same time that the adolescent has accelerated nutritional needs, there are many psychological and social pressures. At this age any deviation from the average in state of development may be upsetting. The tallest member of the seventh grade class, usually a girl, is as self conscious as the smallest boy.

During the growth spurt the formation of muscles, of bone, and blood requires ample supplies of the building materials: protein, calcium, and iron. A slight rise in basal metabolism and the constant activities of adolescents are also responsible for greater food consumption than in earlier and later periods of life. Most teenagers are forever hungry, and mothers are hard pressed to keep enough food on hand. This is an opportune time to introduce new foods and to overcome some of the

Maryland elementary students with their school lunch. USDA administers the National School Lunch Program, which helps teach children good eating habits.

dislikes the child developed when his appetite was more finicky. Along with the opportunity for improving food habits, however, is the possibility of developing worse ones.

Following the pattern suggested for younger children, the adolescent boy might eat: 4 cups of milk; 6 ounces of meat; ½ to 1 cup of orange juice; 4 slices of bread; ½ cup of a green or yellow vegetable; enriched cereals and bread; fruits and vegetables.

The foods listed in amounts will take care of the boy's need for protein, minerals, and vitamins, provided a green leafy vegetable or several less potent sources of iron are eaten. The adolescent girl may drink only 3 cups of milk, but her need for iron is even more critical after she begins menstruating. Meat, fish, poultry, enriched bread and cereals, green leafy vegetables, dried fruits, and egg yolk are the main sources of iron. Ice cream, peanut butter, hamburgers, cookies, and other popular foods may complete the rest of the diet. There is no advantage in consuming more than a quart of milk daily. Moreover, the girl who is restricting her calorie intake should leave off the extra serving rather than the foods supplying the building nutrients.

Many adults look back on adolescence with less than fond memories because physical and emotional problems, some related to nutrition, are common at this time. Overweight, undernutrition, anemia, and acne stand out among the physical defects which may bring on psychological problems. As if being different from his peers is not serious enough, the overweight child has the prospect of becoming an overweight adult, a situation affecting health as well as looks. Whether being overweight is caused by too much food or too little activity, the solution is a change in one or both to achieve energy balance.

The overweight adolescent needs the same kinds of food as the underweight or normal weight person, except in smaller amounts. Size and number of servings of even the meats, breads, vegetables, and milk have to be controlled. Rich desserts and many of the usual snack foods may be replaced with fresh fruits, tomatoes, carrot strips, celery, and the like. Instead of a "crash diet" to take off pounds immediately, the goal is developing eating habits which one can live with indefinitely. But even these habits require downward revision with time.

Underweight adolescents may or may not be satisfied with their state. Girls often desire to look like fashion models whereas boys would like to be athletic in appearance at least. Infections are more frequent among underweight persons. Anemia may occur in both sexes at this age, although the monthly blood loss places the girl in the more dangerous position. Meats, eggs, enriched breads, the green vegetables, and other sources of iron are dietary insurance against nutritional anemia, which is often responsible for a poor appetite and lack of weight gain. Acne is a condition which is related to hormone changes—rather than diet, and adolescents should not be promised that a good diet will clear up their skin problems.

As these boys and girls acquire more independence and eat away from the home, their diets have less supervision. Snacking between meals is a way of life at this age. Unfortunately, however, the snack foods are often those high in fat and sugar, furnishing only energy. Even the beanpole adolescent may develop habits which make weight control difficult in later years.

Adults. During the later teens and early twenties, growth ends and maturity is reached, thus reducing the need for the building materials. Basal metabolism is gradually declining, and usually physical activities slow down. As a person advances in his profession, his life normally becomes more sedentary. The homemaker becomes more skilled with practice, and laborsaving appliances may reduce her energy need even further. As was true for the growing child, each adult has an individual requirement for nutrients and calories related to age, size, sex, activity, and state of health. Slight excesses of nutrients are not considered harmful; however, the calorie intake must be adjusted to avoid becoming overweight.

Compared with a growing person, an adult has a lower need for protein and calcium—so milk consumption may be reduced to 2 cups a day. Men usually consume adequate amounts of iron without making an effort; while women must be sure to consume rich sources of iron until after menopause. A dietary source of vitamin D is not considered necessary for adults, except for pregnant and nursing women. The amount consumed by drinking milk with vitamin D added is considered safe. The recommended allowances of vitamins A and C are about the same as for the younger person, but these are easily furnished by a serving of green or yellow vegetable and a serving of citrus fruit or tomatoes. Along with the lower energy need there is a lowering of the recommendations for the B vitamins.

The main nutritional problem of many adults is weight control. Generally, a person should maintain his normal weight at age 25 for the rest of his life. As one adds years there is a need to subtract calories. At the same time protein, minerals, and vitamins are still very necessary. Foods high in fat—pastries, rich cakes, salad dressings, gravies, and nuts—supply small amounts of nutrients in proportion to their energy values. Frying adds fat to the food no matter how well it is drained on absorbent paper. Sugar, candies, sirups, jellies, soft drinks, and the alcoholic beverages are also sources of "empty calories." An adult has some choice as to which foods to leave out. Certain foods—meats, milk, fruits, vegetables, and cereals or bread—are needed for nutrients and calorie value. Crash diets for weight reduction are dangerous and often fail to accomplish the desired results.

Oldsters. Aging is continuous from conception on, and it is as hard to specify which birthday makes one

A meal like this supplies nutrients and calorie value needed by adults.

aged as to predict the exact year that puberty occurs. Calendar and physiological age are not the same. We have all known folks active in their eighties and others who became feeble much earlier. During aging there are losses in cell mass and perhaps impairment of the remaining cells so that organ systems function less efficiently. This may be observed in changes in the eyes, ears, digestive system, and kidney. The oldster also has the accumulated insults from accidents, infection, and environmental factors, including food. Nutrients supplied to the cells throughout the years affect the aging process and resistance to disease.

One change that definitely accompanies the aging process is a decreased energy need. Basal metabolism and, usually, activities are slowing down. On the average, men and women in the 55- to 75-year span need 300 to 400 calories less per day than they did during the 35- to 55-year period. The amounts of the B-complex vitamins are proportionately lowered too. There is no evidence that cellular changes affect the need for nutrients; so the recommendations for protein, calcium, vitamins A, C, and E are the same as for the younger adult. After menopause a woman's iron need is no higher than a man's.

Although the healthy person needs no special dietary alterations in old age except for fewer calories, a number of ailments do affect the kind and amount of food needed. Many older people need to do more than control weight; they actually need to reduce. Lack of teeth or poorly fitting dentures affect the kinds of acceptable food. Surveys have shown that oldsters often substitute bread for meat and vegetables, probably because of the ease in chewing as well as the expense. The blender is useful in making steak acceptable to a person without teeth.

Digestive difficulties and constipation are common and may cause the elderly person to reject some foods. For chronic conditions, many oldsters require special diets which become their way of life. Perhaps research will eventually find ways of controlling these diseases as with many others. Even now some deteriorative changes may be alleviated by good nutrition earlier in life.

With our great array of food, adequate diets for all of us at any age are possible without great effort. A person's individual needs may be furnished in various ways. Foods which supply energy, protein, minerals, and vitamins are available in the grocery store, the school, restaurant, and elsewhere.

Nutritious food tastes good. A daily pattern to provide the nutrients should be as habitual as dressing, brushing teeth, and other routine activities. The specific items are dictated by the resources and time available. Meals served at home may be purchased almost ready to serve or they may represent hours of loving preparation. Vitamin pills and other dietary supplements are usually unnecessary. Promotion of good health by eating the right foods is easy and pleasant.

Marjorie B. Washbon
Gail G. Harrison

Overweight, and What It Takes to Stay Trim

How to lose weight, preferably without effort, receives constant attention in the press and conversation. Not all of this information is wrong; but much is a mixture of fact, half-truths, and pure imagination. How can you know what to believe, especially when the information is often presented as a "new, scientific discovery"? After all, science has progressed to voyages around the moon. Yet easy ways to lose weight are still elusive. Unravelling the mysteries of the human body is proving more difficult than conquering outer space.

An easy way to lose weight is not yet in sight nor is it realistic to expect one. There has been, however, gradual accumulation of knowledge from continual experimentation, some of which has been treated in popular writings. The purpose of this chapter is to present an overview of what we know and don't know about the causes and correction of obesity.

There are sound health reasons for a concern about weight reduction although, admittedly, much of the current interest is motivated by desire for a fashionable figure. Most people know that overweight is considered a health hazard, particularly in relation to diseases of the heart and circulatory system. Most life insurance companies charge higher rates to the grossly overweight just as they do for other high risk categories—such as smokers and the accident-prone.

The connection between extreme overweight and several diseases is well documented. It is also known that the greater the degree of obesity, the greater the risk. But it is not clear just how much excess weight—or excess fat—constitutes a danger. Neither are we sure whether the primary health risk is overweight or overfatness.

Most of us agree there is little to say in favor of overweight and most of us, too, are acquainted with some of the more basic facts about weight reduction. The implications of these facts are less well understood.

Just about everyone knows, for example, that you accumulate extra fat by taking in more food than you can use up in energy output. And, conversely, that you lose body fat when you eat less food than you require for your energy expenditure. Most people know, also, that the term used to measure energy is calories. Possibly no word in the English language is more maligned. We count calories; we regret them; we blame them.

But scientifically speaking, calories are simply units to measure energy, just as inches or miles are units to measure distance.

We need food energy. Without it, the body could not function. But keeping it functioning at a constant weight requires a balance between intake and outgo. Many factors affect both sides of this energy equation.

We all use energy in two distinct ways: (1) to maintain those basic processes necessary to life, including growth and (2) to accomplish physical

Marjorie B. Washbon is Professor of Human Nutrition & Food, N.Y. State College of Human Ecology, Cornell University, Ithaca, N.Y.

Gail G. Harrison is Extension Associate, Department of Human Nutrition & Food, N.Y. State College of Human Ecology, Cornell University.

activity. The precise amount needed in each category varies greatly from one person to another.

By far the greatest proportion of our calorie need is accounted for by the basic, on-going processes of life—the work needed to keep the heart beating, the lungs breathing, the kidneys eliminating waste products, the cells of the body repairing themselves, new tissues being built during growth, and production of heat to keep body temperature normal. All of these processes require energy. The energy needed to maintain them is called the basal metabolic rate, or the BMR.

Many conditions affect the BMR, and thus the total caloric needs of a given individual. Among these are size, the body composition, age, and hormonal factors. The larger person, with a greater amount of muscle and bone, requires more energy for basic metabolic demands than the smaller person. Age is another influencing factor. Basal metabolic rate increases during periods of growth and decreases gradually throughout adult life.

About the only controllable factor affecting basal metabolic rate is the rare situation of hormonal imbalance. Occasionally the occurrence of thyroid insufficiency will slow BMR down. In these relatively rare and easily detected cases, therapy with thyroid hormone alleviates the condition. More often the imbalance in the energy equation must be attacked from the standpoint of food intake, exercise, or both.

Besides the BMR, the other major factor affecting energy needs is exercise. And this you can control. An important reason for the increased incidence of overweight today is the limited physical activity that everyday living demands of most of us. A conscious effort to increase our physical activity deserves more attention than it has had in the past. Even a few years ago, it was common to teach that exercise was of little or no value in weight control. Unfortunately, the erroneous ideas on which this teaching was based still persist.

One such fallacy is the notion that exercise automatically increases appetite and thus any beneficial effects are canceled out. This doesn't have to be true, especially with moderate activity. Actually, more data are available to support the opposite situation. That is, reducing activity to a low level may not be accompanied by less eating.

A second misconception is the belief that it takes a lot of exercise—more than most people will do—to use significant amounts of energy.

This is true enough if you are talking about the short term of a few weeks. But, over a period of months or years, even small increases in exercise can make a difference in how much you weigh, providing the activity becomes a daily habit.

Some increase in exercise is especially significant for many older folks and others whose caloric needs are low, when keeping extra weight off may seem almost an impossible problem. If such persons are to maintain their weight, the choice may rest between making the effort to get some regular exercise—or continually being a little hungry.

For the person who has always been overweight, exercise may be an even more complicated problem. The overweight teenager, for instance, may not be proficient in sports and feel self-conscious, and so he may habitually underparticipate. Thus, lack of exercise is not only contributing to his obesity; it is also a result of his obesity. A vicious circle develops that is difficult to break. Studies have also shown that the obese individual often gets less physical exercise than the person of normal weight even when engaged for the same length of time in the same sport. This is simply because he moves less.

The other side of the energy equation—the energy taken in as calories from food—is equally important. The amount of food we eat is not regulated solely by our need for calories. Would that it were! We humans are social beings, and often we eat to please our hostess, to share in the sociability, to relieve frustration, boredom, or loneliness, or just because the food is there—even if we are not particularly hungry!

We also adjust our food intake according to the expectations of society—and those expectations aren't always clear-cut and simple. Definitions of what's-good-to-do may contradict one another, creating a vague feeling of guilt. For instance, the ideal of the Clean Plate Club is still with us. The Puritan ethic of "waste not, want not" is part of our culture. Coupled with an abundance of food available, this conflicts with the ideal of a slim figure.

Because more than physical need is involved in controlling the amount we eat, many of us fail to adequately adjust our intake to our caloric need.

Much remains to be learned before all the pieces are in place in the complicated puzzle of our energy balance. Emotional, genetic, and metabolic factors may be important influences. Many of these are at present only notions in the minds of researchers—as yet a long way from being of practical value to the person who wants to lose some weight.

Most people realize there is some connection between heredity and body weight. You may have observed that overweight tends to run in families, but again the issue is not simple.

We know definitely that the body build—the general size and shape of the body, including bony structure and musculature as well as the fat distribution—is inherited. Bony structure cannot be changed, and muscle development can be changed only within rather narrow limits. It is a fact that some of us are tall, large-boned, and heavy. Others are long and lean. Still others are short, round, and stocky. Normal variations in body build are the subject of a whole science, called somatotyping. There are three basic somatotypes or extremes of body build: ectomorphy, mesomorphy, and endomorphy.

The ectomorphic individual has a long, lean body build. The skeletal structure is light and muscle development is usually small. Ectomorphs are seldom overweight, but may have the opposite problem of being too thin. They often seem to be able to eat relatively large amounts of food without gaining weight.

The mesomorphic person has a large, heavy frame and heavy muscle development. The "ideal" football player type of a person with broad shoulders and lots of muscle could be classified as mesomorphic. The scales may read high for the mesomorph because of heavy bone and muscle structure, even if he is not too fat.

The endomorphic person typically has soft, round body contours and is well covered with body fat. Endomorphs often have trouble maintaining reasonable weight.

Most of us are a combination of two of these types. An extreme ectomorph, endomorph, or mesomorph is really quite rare. But most people do exhibit one of these particular body builds predominantly.

What does all of this mean for the person who wants to lose weight? It means that overweight and overfatness may not be the same thing. A person with a large bony frame and heavy musculature is not as fat as a person of the same height and weight who has a small skeleton and less muscle development.

Understanding the difference between overweight and overfatness is

THREE EXTREMES OF BODY BUILD

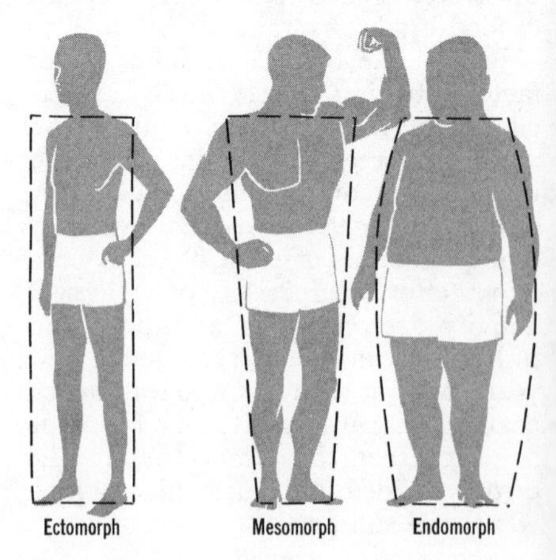

important because it is the basis for setting realistic goals for weight reduction. The amount of fat on the body can be changed, but the basic body build cannot. Nor can you expect to eliminate localized fat deposits, such as heavy thighs on an otherwise nonobese person. Fat distribution of this type cannot be selectively controlled by diet or exercise.

Less well established is whether heredity affects total fatness as well as bone, muscle structure, and fat distribution. Research relating the number and size of fat cells in the body to obesity may some day help clarify the mystery of heredity and obesity. But what we do know about heredity and body build is sufficient to help us realize that what is a realistic goal for one person may not be realistic for the next. And as knowledge about the relation of heredity to body fatness increases, it may be more and more possible to identify those individuals who are predisposed to easy weight gain and to help them prevent obesity in the first place, rather than limiting our attacks on the problem to helping the person who is already too fat.

It is easy to see that some people will, because of their basic body build, have more trouble maintaining reasonable weight than others. Obesity is a physical problem, and it may be a psychological one as well; but it should not be made a moral issue. It is highly unfair to classify every individual who has a weight problem as a weak-willed glutton, as our society too often does.

Since people differ so much in their inherited body builds, how can you know what is the best weight for you? The most widely used standards are height-weight tables. While these have some valid uses, an honest look in a full-length mirror will probably be as reliable an indicator as any chart in telling you whether or not you are too fat.

The limitations of some of the charts may be clearer if we discuss the origins of a few in current use and the differences among them. There are two types of charts in general use today: those which report the average weights of a large number of people, and those which recommend desirable weights.

In 1959, average weights of a large, insured adult population were published by the Society of Actuaries. These tables of average weights have been widely used since. Their reliability is limited because only insured individuals were considered and because measuring techniques were not standardized. But these tables do show that both men and women tend, on the average, to gain some weight as they get older.

Back in 1960, the Metropolitan Life Insurance Company published the widely-used "Tables of Desirable Weight," based upon data from the Society of Actuaries. These desirable weights were substantially lower than the previously published "average" weights. They were designed to be applied to adults 25 years of age and older. The desirable weights were based on the fact that, in the insured population, the person who maintained what he weighed at age 25 had the lowest mortality risk. No change, therefore, was made for age, but weight ranges were given and allowance was made for small, medium, and large body frames. While this was a step in the right direction, no indication was given as to how one might decide what type of body frame he had.

Another table of desirable weights in current use is based upon data on heights and weights of individuals 20 to 30 years old, as obtained by the U.S. Department of Agriculture. The USDA table assumes that the weight that is desirable in your mid-twenties is the best weight for later years, too.

To use the table, first find in the left-hand column your height, without shoes. If you have a small frame, your weight should probably be no lower than the weight in the "low" column and no higher than the weight given in the "average" column. If you have a large frame, use the "average" and "high" columns to determine your desirable weight range. If your frame is about average, your weight should probably be somewhere close to the average for your height.

There are a number of other tables in use besides those mentioned. All have the disadvantage that they only consider weight. They say nothing about fatness, which may be more the point in question.

Techniques and standards for judging fatness are needed, but as yet no such standards are in general use. Several methods are being tested in research situations, however. One of the most promising is the skinfold measurement, or "scientific pinch" as it is sometimes called. Special calipers are used to measure the fat pad just under the skin at certain specified points on the body. Researchers have been able to correlate these measurements with total body fatness. Someday we may see the skinfold calipers routinely used in the physician's office along with the scale, but at present their use is limited largely to research situations.

There is no doubt, then, that height and weight alone are not the only factors to consider in deciding whether a person is too fat. Also involved are appearance, general health, and some indication of relative fatness. Many experts would rather define desirable weight as the weight at which you feel your best and look your best, rather than by any chart or table.

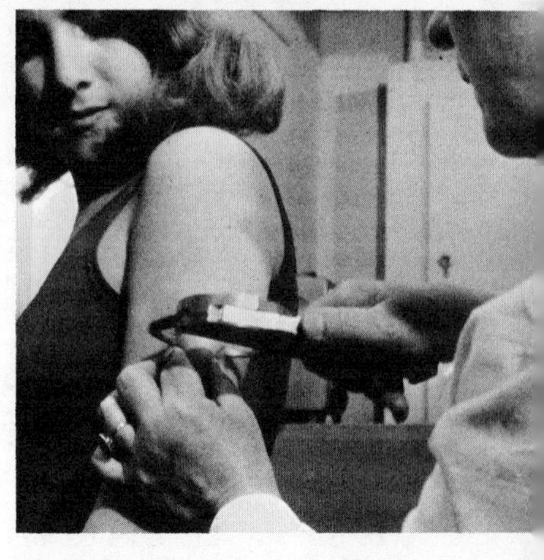

Using skinfold calipers to measure fat pad on upper arm, at Cornell University's Graduate School of Nutrition.

Weights of Persons 20 to 30 Years Old

Height (without shoes)	Weight (without clothing)		
	Low (pounds)	Average (pounds)	High (pounds)
Men			
5 feet 3 inches.....	118	129	141
5 feet 4 inches.....	122	133	145
5 feet 5 inches.....	126	137	149
5 feet 6 inches.....	130	142	155
5 feet 7 inches.....	134	147	161
5 feet 8 inches.....	139	151	166
5 feet 9 inches.....	143	155	170
5 feet 10 inches....	147	159	174
5 feet 11 inches....	150	163	178
6 feet............	154	167	183
6 feet 1 inch........	158	171	188
6 feet 2 inches.....	162	175	192
6 feet 3 inches.....	165	178	195
Women			
5 feet............	100	109	118
5 feet 1 inch.......	104	112	121
5 feet 2 inches.....	107	115	125
5 feet 3 inches.....	110	118	128
5 feet 4 inches.....	113	122	132
5 feet 5 inches.....	116	125	135
5 feet 6 inches.....	120	129	139
5 feet 7 inches.....	123	132	142
5 feet 8 inches.....	126	136	146
5 feet 9 inches.....	130	140	151
5 feet 10 inches....	133	144	156
5 feet 11 inches....	137	148	161
6 feet............	141	152	166

Evaluating the weight status of children is even more complicated. Every child has his own individual pattern of growth; some children experience the adolescent growth spurt, for instance, several years earlier than do others. And during puberty, perfectly normal changes in fatness occur due to sexual maturation. It would be unreasonable to apply the same standard for desirable weight to all youngsters of the same age or of the same height even if we could allow for the differences in body build.

Some tools have been developed which are useful in evaluating children's weight status. One such tool is the Meredith growth chart, widely used by pediatricians and in schools. This type of chart shows growth progress in both height and weight, allowing for a wide range of normal variation at every age.

Anyone who has tried to lose weight

is acquainted with another aspect of weight reduction. Weight loss is difficult to achieve and to maintain for many people. The low rate of success, measured by continued maintenance of weight loss, is disheartening to the reducer and to the clinicians who work with the problem. There is some comfort in realizing that the picture is probably brighter than published figures show. Many who achieve success may do so upon their own without ever seeking help and thus are never counted in the statistics.

Nevertheless, there is no question that losing weight and keeping it off is an obstinate problem for many, many people. Understanding some of the reasons won't in itself correct the problem, but it may help the would-be reducer to know the challenges that he is up against.

One reason for a poor success in weight reduction programs is incomplete knowledge of the relevant facts. Let's consider a few illustrations.

Many people fail to realize that obesity has multiple causes. Take, for example, the common experience of weight gain during the first year of marriage. But what caused the excess of food? A rewardingly appreciative husband, perhaps. Should the new wife be helped to realize that she cherishes her husband more effectively by not tempting him to overeat? When obesity is long-standing, the causative factors are much more complex. Treatment requires insight beyond "eat less, exercise more."

In addition, there is a great deal of popular ignorance about the caloric value of food, despite all that has been written about it. Most people have a general idea which foods are high in calories, defined as furnishing many calories in a small amount. But there are many misconceptions.

Bread, for example, has a high calorie image. To many people, this means white bread; but whole wheat, rye, or diet bread are often thought of as substantially lower in calories. Instead, they are roughly equivalent.

Meat enjoys a low-calorie image. Meat is not low calorie in the amounts usually eaten. Calorie values in tables are usually given in 2- or 3-ounce servings. This means one small hamburger, one frankfurter, or one small pork chop. Servings are commonly twice this size. Further, many meats contain a good deal of fat which cannot be trimmed off.

One general rule about caloric content of foods may prove useful. Fat contains, weight for weight, over twice as many calories as carbohydrate or protein. Cutting down on the amount of fat in the diet (substituting

These boys are both 16, but obviously at different stages of maturity. Each is of normal weight, but the two cannot be judged by the same standard.

skim milk for whole milk, for instance) may be the most efficient way to trim calorie intake.

Few people realize, too, that the overweight person doesn't always eat more than his slender peer. Many studies support this in the adolescent; some show it for the adult. If a person is already eating very little, further restriction may seem unrewarding unless the individual is either prepared for very slow progress or learns to adjust his activity pattern upward.

Finally, there is the human desire for overnight results which has some basis in ignorance. Even when food intake is highly restricted, weight loss is bound to be slow. At the rate of a 1,000 calorie deficit a day—which is fairly severe—the mathematical prediction is for a weight loss of about 2 pounds of fatty tissue a week, though the scales may register differently because of the individual variations in retention and loss of water.

The deep-rooted character of food habits is also responsible in part for failure of weight reduction programs. Each of us has an individual set of food habits which began forming with the first food we swallowed. By the time we are adults, these food consumption patterns have become as much a part of us as the way we walk, the way we speak, the way we think. Anyone who has tried to learn a different language as an adult knows how difficult it is. Changing food habits can be just as difficult.

People do learn new languages—and can learn to change food habits, too. But in either case, it takes strong motivation and a great deal of practice. The habit of eating less has a chance to persist only when the effort has been made for a long enough time to provide adequate practice. This means a program sensible enough to permit staying with it, and accompanied by a deep enough motivation to make the effort worthwhile.

These characteristics are lacking in many weight reduction programs, which is one reason many people have learned from experience to expect failure. And indeed, one of the most unlikely candidates for success is the person who has tried to maintain a weight loss and failed.

Further, attitudes toward life often influence attitudes toward food. The person who is more concerned about today than some indefinite tomorrow may prefer to take his chances with overweight rather than to forgo the certain pleasures of eating. This may be especially true at middle age or older when the social pressures for a slim figure have lessened.

Sometimes these personal attitudes are part of a cultural pattern which does not put a high premium upon slenderness. Some studies, for example, suggest that the higher your socioeconomic status, the lower the prevalence of obesity. Perhaps slimness is not equally important at all social levels.

Another reason for lack of success is failure to recognize that restricting food intake creates a stress with which the reducer must be able to cope. Whether we realize it or not, food fulfills many needs other than absolute hunger. Foods we learned to like as children mean the security of home and family; food or beverage often becomes synonomous with sociability; food may be a comfort in loneliness or in grief.

These are only a few such associations—and their relative importance varies with the individual. It is important to remember that these uses of food are perfectly valid and should never be discredited. Restricting food, without an adequate substitute, may create more problems than it corrects.

Because food supplies psychological as well as physical needs, there may be times in your life when you should not try to reduce—if you are under severe stress, for example. Or if you are in the process of altering another habit pattern, such as smoking. One stress at a time is enough.

This recitation of the barriers to achieving and maintaining weight loss may have left you with a feeling of futility. This is, of course, not our purpose. It has been our aim instead to give you a sound basis for appraising what you read and hear about weight reduction.

For instance, we hope this review has helped you see a major fallacy in the oddball diets so often promoted in popular writings. Such diets may be effective in dropping the first several pounds. But they do little to prepare you to continue the battle after the first skirmish is won. The only true test of success is in not regaining.

Our review would be incomplete without a few words about the parts of the enigma which are as yet unanswered. We have chosen to present these in a question and answer format, pointing out how far present knowledge goes and what still remains to be learned.

• What controls appetite? Appetite controlling mechanisms have been clearly identified and located in the brains of animals. When the area which controls satiety is destroyed, the animal eats voraciously and so becomes obese. It is reasonable to assume that a similar physiological mechanism operates in humans. But we are not yet sure how the mechanism works—what tells it to decide "I've had enough" or "I'm hungry." And in humans the study of any physiological control is complicated by the psychological factors. The possibility of enough knowledge to attack the problem of obesity from this angle is not yet in sight.

• Are some people really more efficient in their utilization of food than others? Certainly this seems to be true to many overweight people, but there is little research evidence to support it. There are some recent indications that an obese animal, when reduced, uses food more efficiently than before. Whether or not this applies to man is not clear. Someday we may be able to say that the obese person metabolizes food in a different way than his slender friend, but that day is not yet at hand.

• Does frequency of eating affect the conversion of food to fat? Experimental work in animals provides evidence that frequent small meals, or nibbling, produces more body protein and less body fat than eating the same number of calories in a single meal. These results have been demonstrated in rats but have not been shown consistently in other species. Studies in humans have been negative, too. So far, therefore, spaced feeding is just a matter of an individual choice—assuming, of course, that extra feedings do not mean extra calories.

• Does the proportion of protein, fat, and carbohydrate in the diet make a difference in how fast you lose weight? Diet plans appear periodically which promise spectacular results by drastically altering the amount of protein, fat, or carbohydrate in the diet. A prominent one has been the high fat-low carbohydrate regime in various versions. When investigated under controlled conditions, none of these have produced any more weight loss over a period of time than would be expected from the caloric deficit that they provide.

Such drastic diet alterations, including total fast or starvation diets, have occasional use in clinical situations. But they can be highly dangerous for the self-treated individual and obviously are not a sensible basis for long-term regulation.

We have been talking so far of what we know about weight reduction and what remains to be learned. How can you put these facts to work?

A standard plan for everyone is neither sound nor sensible. We are all different. We gained weight for different reasons; we want to lose weight for different reasons; we differ in age, health, and general life circumstances. The first step for anyone who is serious about losing weight should be working out a personal plan with his physician. The time will be well spent.

There are certain circumstances which call for special approaches to weight control. It is outside the scope of this chapter to deal with all the possible problems, but we will mention a few of the important factors in dealing with specific overweight problems.

The overweight child, for instance, needs special consideration. We have already pointed out that the fat child, especially if his genetic inheritance predisposes to easy weight gain, very often carries his physical and psychological burden for a lifetime. Developing eating and exercise habits which will prevent accumulation of excess fat must begin early in life if he is to avoid all the frustration of being an overweight individual in a slender society. If the chubby toddler or school-age child is to achieve more reasonable proportions, he requires understanding and knowledgeable help from his parents and physician.

Often the most realistic approach is to forgo absolute weight loss in favor of holding the weight relatively constant while height catches up.

Prospects for the child born with a predisposition to obesity will decidedly improve if and when parents abandon the old notion that a fat child is a healthy child. This isn't to say that every child should be a string bean. Most children go through stages of relative chubbiness prior to growth spurts in height; and like the adults, children are blessed with individual and different body builds. But it is quite unfair to a child to encourage his chubbiness as a baby and toddler and then to suddenly condemn it as he approaches adolescence.

The adolescent is perhaps more conscious of his appearance than is any other person. Many teenagers worry about their weight when there is no basis for real concern. One study of teenage girls showed that although only about 15 percent of the girls studied could be classified as obese, almost two-thirds had dieted to lose weight, and 37 percent were on diets on the day of the interview!

These results may reflect in part the fact that dieting was "the thing to do." But many of the girls probably felt they were too heavy even though their weight was mainly due to heavy bone and muscle structures. Many teenagers need to be helped to set realistic goals for their body weight in order to avoid fruitless and sometimes dangerous fad dieting.

But what of the adolescent who *is* too fat? Many are. Here again it is important to distinguish between longstanding, persistent obesity and the more common transient period of chubbiness which often precedes the adolescent growth spurt. Rapid growth in height will usually remedy the latter situation in a few months' time. But the adolescent growth spurt will not streamline the youngster who has been fat since childhood.

During adolescence, when awareness of the opposite sex and of one's own body is at a high point, obesity is especially difficult to cope with. Achieving emotional independence—which is none too easy for any teenager—is particularly difficult for the obese youth. The overweight adolescent needs help not only in controlling his weight, but in accepting himself as a person. Sympathetic, unchastising support from parents, teachers, physician, and peers is of paramount importance.

Because the adolescent is in a phase of rapid growth and development, nutritional needs are high even for the obese. It is extremely important that nutrient intake be adequate even when calories are restricted.

Often the most successful approach to weight reduction for the obese teenager is moderate caloric restriction coupled with a program of increased physical activity. Such a program has psychological as well as physical value, since increased participation in activity may help break a habit of withdrawal from social situations. And certainly an approach which does not restrict caloric intake too severely is to be preferred at a time of life when so many other stresses are present.

Adults. Let's turn now to the problems of weight control in adulthood. We have pointed out that the obese child all too often remains obese throughout his life. But many obese adults were not fat as children. Why do these extra pounds accumulate? The easy answer is too much food. This is true as far as it goes. But what special conditions of adulthood particularly predispose toward an excess weight gain?

One common concern for women is extra weight gain during pregnancy. Pregnancy poses special problems because two conflicting sets of circumstances are operating. On the one hand the mother realizes it is important to get the right kind and amount of food. At the same time she also knows that excess weight gain increases the risk of complications during pregnancy. Added to these conflicts may be the vague confidence that the extra weight will disappear after the baby is born. As many women can attest, it often doesn't.

The paradox is further compounded by the belief that calorie needs increase during pregnancy. This is true in part. Extra calories are needed during the last part of pregnancy for the growth of the fetus and increased metabolic rate. But this added requirement may be more than offset by the reduced activity as moving becomes less and less comfortable. Many women, therefore, may have no net increase in calorie needs.

Another peak period of weight gain for women may occur during menopause. This may have a physiological basis, but probably psychological and activity factors are involved as well.

The slow, steady weight gain which is common after 35, but sometimes starts even earlier, is another example of adult obesity and is as common among men as it is among women. It is particularly hard to cope with because the pounds arrive almost unnoticed. By the time 10 or 20 pounds of excess have accumulated, the pattern of living which produced them is well established. The soundest advice is prevention before the scales begin to creep up.

Energy needs are bound to decrease in adulthood unless you make a conscious effort to increase them. Part of the decrease is the slow but consistent reduction in the basal metabolic rate. Part is likely due to a decrease in physical activity as you acquire more laborsaving possessions and less active leisure interests.

Women at least have a potential brake on adding weight because of their motivation for slimness. Most men are less concerned with their figures and may be motivated only when enough weight has accumulated to become a health concern.

It may be of interest to know, too, that you get fatter as you get older even if your weight stays the same. To say this another way, active tissue is gradually replaced with fat, starting in early adulthood. So some of that "spare tire," less-than-lean feeling is inevitable as middle age progresses.

Possibly you are one of the lucky ones whose appetite control mechanisms automatically balance energy intake with needs. But many people are not that fortunate and have to make a conscious effort to achieve this balance.

As part of a program of prevention, it just makes good sense to keep reasonable track of your weight. Even a small change in your pattern can add or subtract several pounds in a few months. One slice of toast for breakfast instead of two, for example, decreases your intake 60 to 100 calories or more, depending on how much butter and jam you like on your toast. Couple this with a half-hour brisk walk and you have a calorie deficit of well over 100 calories a day. This may mean only a pound or so a month—but it also means 10 to 12 pounds in a year!

The same principle applies if you are already the owner of extra pounds. The difference is only one of degree. That is, losing weight requires a more substantial change in food intake and exercise than the goal of avoiding weight gain.

There is no one best diet plan for

reducing. Choosing the best one in a given circumstance is a very individual matter. Everybody can lose weight assuming a sufficient and continued change in the energy equation, but the same way will simply not work for everyone.

Some people need the support of others, perhaps a group of fellow reducers. Some will do the best by themselves.

Some find it easier to eat five or six times a day. Others say that frequent eating means to them only more frequent temptation.

Some do best on a slow and steady routine, perhaps a pound a week or even less. Others need the encouragement of more rapid weight loss.

Some people want a flexible plan. Others need the crutch of definite rules—often the more rigid the regulations, the better. Probably the most common example is counting calories. Another is the formula diet. Sometimes the rules dictate eating specific foods at certain times, or eating foods in specific combinations. There is nothing inherently wrong in these approaches, as long as the plan is nutritionally adequate. Just remember that they function as a prop for those who wish one. But there is nothing magic about them.

No matter how you choose to lose weight, remember there are some basic ideas you should begin with:

Talk with your physician first. There may be good reasons why you shouldn't try to lose weight; or there may be medical reasons for special considerations in your choice of a plan of action. Your doctor is the one to decide.

Set a realistic goal for weight reduction, based upon your doctor's evaluation and taking your basic body build into account.

Don't fall prey to the claims of miracle aids to weight loss. There is no easy way to lose weight. The only way to make it easier is to really *want* to lose weight—more than you want to eat!

Choose a diet you can live with. All food has caloric value. You'll want to avoid some high-calorie foods, but it's not wise to cut out your favorite foods altogether. And remember that alcohol is not without calories. One double martini is at least the caloric equivalent of a piece of pie.

Remember that exercise does use up calories. And especially with moderate exercise, increased appetite isn't a necessary result. Try to build some exercise into your everyday habits.

Plan your exercise pattern as carefully as you do your diet. For many people, learning to get more physical exercise is harder than learning to eat less food.

Don't be discouraged by day-to-day fluctuations in weight. The clothes that you're wearing and the time of day make a difference in your weight, as do variations in fluid retention which are common during weight loss. It makes more sense to weigh yourself once a week than every day.

Try to "diet quiet." The person on a diet can make a conversation pretty dull. And he can make life uncomfortable for others by making them feel guilty about the food that they're eating.

Be prepared for "help" from others. Family and friends may worry about you, especially after you've lost a few pounds. They will undoubtedly feel sorry for you if they realize that you're going without food you want. Steel yourself against their remarks and keep your determination up!

Keep in mind that the ultimate measure of success in weight reduction is not getting the pounds off, but keeping them off. All your efforts to lose weight should continue, not for a week or a month, but for the rest of your life.

For further reading:

U.S. Department of Agriculture, *Food and Your Weight.* Home and Garden Bulletin 74, Washington, D.C. 20250,

Public Health Service, *Obesity and Health.* Publication No. 1485, U.S. Government Printing Office, Washington, D.C. 20402.

Bernice K. Watt

Nutritive Values of Foods, and Use of Tables Listing Them

Like the millions upon millions of snowflakes, no two alike but in some aspects similar to others, so our foods are unique in their individual makeup yet each has some of the characteristics of others. No matter how we regard food, simply as a necessity of life or as something which we also enjoy, to our bodies it is the nutrients in the foods that count. All of the 50 or more nutrients now known to be needed for good health are abundantly available from food.

Our fund of knowledge continues to increase about our needs for nutrients, their occurrence in foods, and the effects on nutrients of processing and preparing the products that we eat. As this knowledge increases, tables of food values for research workers and others with specialized problems become longer and more complicated. Fortunately, for selecting foods and planning or evaluating our everyday diets, information about those nutrients which are best known is usually adequate.

The nutrients that are best known include protein; fat; carbohydrate; calcium; iron; vitamin A value; three of the B-vitamins, thiamine, riboflavin, and niacin; and ascorbic acid, also called vitamin C. Of these, protein, fat, and carbohydrate are energy-yielding nutrients. Energy is measured in units called calories. Food energy is, of course, a dietary essential and it too needs to be included in tables of food values. Often, however, in the emphasis put on counting calories, other essentials are ignored.

In several special situations, like the manned space flights, water content of the diet becomes important and so water is assessed along with other nutrients in the foods for astronauts. Although we do not need to consider the water content of foods for our usual diets, this information is useful for identifying the particular form of some items and often for making comparisons between foods.

Tables of food values are useful sources for reference to these data. Tables cannot provide information for all the foods we may want to eat, however, and at times it may not be convenient or practical to consult a reference table. It is well, therefore, to have in mind as part of our general knowledge, some information about the nutritive values of our basic foods.

One way to acquire a background on the nutritive value of foods is to study them in groups by type of origin, since each of the natural groupings makes a highly significant contribution of several dietary essentials and smaller or negligible contributions of the others. Besides this, it may be helpful to consider together two or more groups with such similar properties that they are often used interchangeably in meal planning.

As a practical basis in considering foods as sources of nutrients, we may group them as follows: Milk and the other dairy products; eggs; meat, poultry, and fish; dry beans and peas and nuts; vegetables and fruits; grain products; fats; and sugars. Similarities and differences in the major

Bernice K. Watt is a Nutrition Analyst, Consumer and Food Economics Research Division, Agricultural Research Service.

nutrients provided by these groups and by some foods within the groups are noted in the paragraphs below. A few of the lesser known nutrients are mentioned as they also are important and it is well to remember that nature has provided them for us.

Whole milk, outstanding for its calcium, is a good source of vitamin A, riboflavin, vitamin B_{12}, and of good quality protein. It provides important amounts of many other nutrients, too, but has only a negligible amount of iron and cannot be depended on for ascorbic acid.

Dairy products that retain milk fat carry the vitamin A value; skim milk retains the other nutrients important in whole milk but provides only a little more than half the number of calories. One factor in the differences in nutritive value of the different types of cheese is that some cheeses are made from whole milk while others are made from skim or part skim milk.

Eggs are an excellent source of protein of high quality and are one of the few foods in which nature provides vitamin D. The yolk has vitamin A and vitamin D, iron, calcium, and most of the B-vitamins including vitamins B_6 and B_{12} as well as fat and protein. The white of the egg has riboflavin and protein but only small amounts of most other nutrients. Ascorbic acid is not needed by the developing chick, and eggs do not contain this vitamin.

Meat, poultry, and fish, like most other foods of animal origin, are good sources of high-quality protein. They are good sources, too, of most of the B-vitamins including vitamin B_6 and vitamin B_{12}. Pork in particular is an especially good source of thiamine. All the red muscle meats are notable for their content of iron. Except for liver, the items in this group have only small amounts of ascorbic acid or vitamin A. Likewise, they have little calcium unless some of the bone is used, as it often is in canned salmon, sardines, some other fish, and pickled products.

Dry beans and peas and nuts are used sometimes as main dishes. All are concentrated sources of food energy, with their high content of protein in addition to considerable carbohydrates or fats or both. They are good sources for a number of minerals including magnesium. For generations, soybeans have been the main source of calcium in the diets of many oriental peoples. Foods in this group are also good sources of a number of the B-vitamins.

Peanuts and their products are outstanding for their content of niacin. The content of fat in nuts is high, except in chestnuts. For many kinds of nuts, fat makes up half or more of the weight.

Vegetables and fruits can be considered as one big group. These foods are a major source of most vitamins and minerals. Ascorbic acid occurs abundantly in the citrus fruits, strawberries, cantaloups, vegetables of the cabbage family, and in numerous other fruits and vegetables.

The succulent vegetables and most fruits have a high content of water and only small amounts of the energy-yielding nutrients. A firm head of lettuce, for example, may be 95 percent water. Even so, it has appreciable amounts of minerals and vitamins, more in the darker green leaves than in the bleached inner parts. Potatoes, sweetpotatoes, bananas, and some winter squashes have less water, from only about 70 to 85 percent, but more carbohydrate than lettuce and other leafy or tender vegetables.

Except for avocados, fruits and vegetables have only small amounts of fat. The orange-colored and dark green products like carrots, broccoli, spinach, turnip greens, and some varieties of sweetpotatoes, have particularly high vitamin A values.

Cereal grains and the products made from them are predominantly carbohydrate in their composition but also contain appreciable amounts of many other nutrients. Cereals have some protein. Because of the large quantities used, cereals contribute considerable protein to our diets.

All of the whole grain or near whole grain forms of cereals we use as food—whole cornmeal, oatmeal, brown rice, whole wheat flour or cereal, dark buckwheat and rye flours—have important amounts of thiamine, vitamin B_6, vitamin E, iron, and many other nutrients including a number of trace elements recently found essential. The minerals and vitamins are concentrated in the outer portions of the grains, and if these outer layers are removed in milling and processing, much of their original vitamin and mineral content is reduced. However, many of our cereal products have had nutrients added to them.

Fats are important in our diets and occur in many foods—milk, meat, nuts, dry legumes, cereal grains, and other seeds—from which they are separated and made into products convenient for our use. Butter oil, rendered fat from animal tissues, and refined oil from plant sources are our most concentrated sources of energy value. They have more than twice the calories of either protein or carbohydrate, the other energy-yielding nutrients present in foods.

Fats are sometimes classified as saturated or unsaturated. A chemist describes a fat as unsaturated if its fatty acids can combine with hydrogen and as saturated if they already are combined with all the hydrogen they can hold. Polyunsaturated is used to describe those fatty acids that can take up hydrogen at more than one place in their structure.

The fats in foods of plant origin usually have a higher content of the polyunsaturated fats, including the essential fatty acid, linoleic acid, than is present in the fats of animal origin. Two important exceptions are coconut oil and olive oil. These have less polyunsaturated fat than other commonly used fats of a plant origin. Cholesterol is another constituent of fat. It is present only in foods of animal origin. Egg yolk, liver, brains, kidney, and shellfish are all among the more concentrated sources for cholesterol.

The two commonly used table fats, butter and margarine, are well-known sources for vitamin A. Other fat-soluble vitamins may be present in the fats and oils prepared from plant sources. Salad dressings are often included with the fats because some form of separated fat is a major ingredient for most of them.

Sugars of the various kinds, sirups, candies, honey, molasses, jellies, and jams are all concentrated sources of carbohydrate. Small amounts of other nutrients are present in some of the less refined products. Molasses has more mineral matter than brown or unrefined sugars, corn or other sirups.

A question about values published in tables of food composition which is raised over and over is, why do values for foods shown in one table differ from the figures in another table? There are many reasons. The quantities of a particular food for which calories and nutrients are shown are not always the same in the various tables. Apparent discrepancies in nutritive values for an item are often resolved when the weights of food for which these values are reported are taken into consideration. Unfortunately, weights are not always stated and thus the measures are often only approximations.

Many of the packaged or processed items we buy have had nutrients added in their manufacture. For some products there are limitations upon the kinds and amounts of nutrients that may be added. For example, Federal enrichment laws state the minimum and maximum levels for iron, thiamine, riboflavin, and niacin which must be observed in certain cereal products if they are labeled as "enriched." Margarine in this country customarily has vitamin A added, nonfat dry milk may have vitamins A and D added, each according to specified Federal regulations.

A great many other products have one or more nutrients added in their manufacture, and for most, there are no Federal regulations that govern selection of the nutrients or of the amounts that may be added. For these foods, the kind and extent of fortification may be changed at any time at the manufacturer's discretion. The label must state, however, what is added. General figures published in the tables cannot keep pace with the changes that this kind of fortification can introduce.

Values shown in tables for foods prepared from recipes should be considered solely as estimates. For prepared products such as these, the calorie and nutrient content will vary considerably depending upon the recipe used, and the recipe is the prerogative of the cook.

As an example, lemon pie made with whole eggs or egg yolks as the thickening agent would be quite different in some of its values from one thickened with flour or cornstarch and containing no eggs. Figures that would be tailored for a better fit to a particular item than the figures in a table could probably be obtained by calculation from ingredients if the cook will divulge the recipe for her specialty.

Tables of food values are prepared for various purposes. In some cases most of the data are to be used with quantities of food that are ready to eat. In other tables, most of the data may apply to foods as they are brought into the kitchen. Values shown may be for raw food although only a cooked form is eaten. Cooking nearly always alters the content of the nutrients, and data for raw and cooked forms of an item would be expected to differ. (Information about conserving food values has been published elsewhere. See the U.S. Department of Agriculture's Home and Garden Bulletin No. 90, *Conserving the Nutritive Value in Foods.*)

In the case of prepared products, manufactured items which are not standardized, and foods in different forms as raw or cooked, the basis of differences in values among tables is obvious. For some other types of foods the differences among published values may be valid but the reasons less obvious. The values may differ for foods that are used as nature produces them. For example, two oranges—even if from the same tree—might differ in content of vitamin C. Two eggs laid in one week by the same hen do not necessarily have an identical amount of nutrients.

Such differences are interesting and important for some research investigations. They need be of no concern for practical dietary planning. They serve to illustrate, however, that the results from an analysis of only a single sample or a limited sampling may not represent the food in general. Sampling can explain some of the differences in published figures.

Values for general use need to be broadly based. Variety, conditions of production, storage, kind and extent of milling, or other form of processing and preparation are among the factors that affect the content of nutrients in our food supplies and in our foods prepared to eat. Those factors of importance known to be related to the content of nutrients in a food are considered in preparing the values published in the food tables issued by the U.S. Department of Agriculture.

Values, once they are derived, may not apply to the foods indefinitely. New strains or varieties may be bred into our basic food stocks. Changes are introduced in storing conditions, processing, preserving, and manufacturing the products we eat. As a result, the values for the nutrients in our foods change. Figures in our tables must be under continual review and revised as needed to keep the data applicable to current food products.

For further reading:

U.S. DEPARTMENT OF AGRICULTURE, *Nutritive Value of Foods*. Home and Garden Bulletin 72, Washington, D.C., 1964.

Evelyn B. Spindler
Margaret C. Browne

Ways and Means of Improving Our Diets—and Half of Us Need to!

We like to think that we in the United States are the best fed people in the world, that everyone has an adequate diet. Recent research, however, indicates this is not necessarily true. There are persons of all ages and all economic levels who need to improve their diets.

To improve diets, it is important to know what people eat and why they eat what they do. Then ways of convincing them to change their food habits, when needed, must be found.

The U.S. Department of Agriculture makes periodic nationwide and smaller special-purpose surveys of the food used by families to learn about American diets. This research is especially important in view of the fast-changing food habits and mobility of today's families. Even though enough food is available so all families could have a "good" diet, the 1965 studies show that only about half the families actually *had* a "good" diet.

To define a "good" diet, we need to refer to some standard. The Food and Nutrition Board of the National Research Council recommends amounts of important nutrients needed by persons of different ages. Measured by the Council's standard, a diet is termed "good" if the nutritive value equals or exceeds the recommended allowances for each of seven nutrients: protein, calcium, iron, vitamin A, thiamine, riboflavin, and ascorbic acid. The Food and Nutrition Board explains, however, that, "If the recommended allowances are used as reference standards for interpreting records of food consumption, it should not be assumed that food practices are necessarily poor or that malnutrition exists because the recommendations are not completely met."

The food consumed by a family obviously does not tell us whether all individuals in the family receive adequate amounts of any given food. If, for example, a family of four buys 2 quarts of milk each day, by taking an average we might assume each member of the family received a pint. In reality one person, such as a teenage son, may drink 1 quart, leaving the remaining quart to be distributed among the other three members of the family. Perhaps the mother drinks no milk and gets less than 1 cup in cooked food.

This example points up the need to know much more about the food habits of individual family members if we are to determine the adequacy of their diets. Such information can help direct educational programs to those who need them most.

As part of the 1965 Nationwide Household Food Consumption Survey, information was obtained on the food intake for 1 day for 14,500 men, women, and children. In general, the diets of females were not as good as those of males. The three groups in need of improved diets were adolescent girls and women ranging from age 9 through 64, older men and women, and infants and children under 3.

Past studies have shown that the

Evelyn B. Spindler is a Nutritionist with the Division of Home Economics, Federal Extension Service.

Margaret C. Browne, the former Director of the Division, is now retired.

percentage of young people with poor diets is likely to increase from childhood to teenage. The teenage girl is likely to be the most poorly fed member of the family. The situation of the girls is more critical than the boys. This is partly because boys consume more food than girls and so have a better chance of getting needed nutrients. A 15-year-old boy needs about 3,000 calories, compared to about 2,400 for a girl the same age. So the boy, in eating one-third extra calories, gets more nutrients.

To better understand why people eat what they do we need to consider some of the factors that influence diets. If we hope to improve diets, we must take a realistic look at the factors relating to poor diets and determine how to combat them.

A number of persons skip meals and particularly breakfast. Many students go to school with no breakfast or a very inadequate one. Many a secretary starts the day with a cup of coffee and a cigarette. If breakfast is omitted, it may not be easy to get all the needed nutrients in the other two meals plus frequent snacks.

A study of 3,500 high school students, carried out in Massachusetts, showed 11 percent of the boys and 19 percent of the girls had no breakfast. An additional 40 percent of the boys and 50 percent of the girls had a poor breakfast.

In a study in North Carolina, 13 percent of the students in the ninth grade missed a meal. This increased to 18 percent in the 10th grade and to 25 percent in the 12th grade.

Why do we make all this fuss about breakfast? In most instances, the body has been without food 8 to 12 hours and needs fuel. Does a good breakfast make a difference? To determine this, experiments were conducted at the University of Iowa. The students tested ate good breakfasts for 5 weeks, then omitted breakfast for 5 weeks. Three scientific measurements were made between 11 a.m. and noon. Reaction time was tested to determine how fast a correct decision could be made. Steadiness or neuromuscular tremor was the second test, and the third, work output, was checked by riding a stationary bicycle.

The researchers found that when breakfast was omitted the students took longer to make decisions, were less steady, and work output was less. We can conclude that when students eat a good breakfast, they are likely to (1) work and play better, (2) be more alert in their thinking and action in the late morning hours, (3) be calmer and steadier, and (4) have more fun and enjoyment.

Fad diets are a common reason for poor food habits. With so much food available to most people and so little physical activity, it is not easy to keep to the balance of calories necessary to maintain normal weight. Many teenage girls and women are looking for an easy way to control their weight. Fad diets seem to have a greater appeal than carefully controlling calories and increasing exercise. Most fad diets do not have the balance of nutrients needed for good health. If the fad diet is followed for a long time or during periods of greater than average need, such as growth for the teenage girl or during pregnancy, the harm can be even greater.

Today many of us consume a significant amount of our calories between meals. The type of food we select as snacks can make a great difference in whether or not we get the nutrients needed each day. Some snack foods are very high in "empty calories" and low in minerals, vitamins, and protein. The greater the percentage of such snack foods in a diet, the more difficult it is to get the recommended amounts of other nutrients.

Generally, the higher a family's income the better the diet. But, income alone does not assure a good diet, as indicated by the 1965 U.S. Department of Agriculture study. It showed that 9 percent of the families with incomes of $10,000 or more had diets designated as poor, but 36 percent of the persons with incomes under $3,000 had poor diets. Certainly the lower the income the more difficult it is to select a diet that contains a recommended amount of all nutrients.

Nutrition education needs to be made available to all segments of the population. Knowledge as to what makes up a good diet is not possessed by everyone in spite of the simplified Daily Food Guide which has been given wide publicity. The U.S. Department of Agriculture receives many letters from students as well as adults asking which foods they need to eat each day in order to have a good diet.

Indifferent attitudes toward the foods they eat accounts for poor food habits of some people. Teenagers tell us they are too busy to eat meals so they grab whatever is most readily available. Older folks may lack the energy or desire to prepare meals for one or two, so they also eat whatever is easiest. Mothers whose children eat lunch at school and whose husbands eat lunch near their work may feel it is not worth while to fix adequate lunches for themselves.

An increasing number of companies have closed their cafeterias and installed vending machines. These dispense sandwiches, candy bars, crackers, cookies, potato chips, and many types of carbonated beverages. In some cases milk, ice cream, and fruit are included. The lunch selected must depend on what is available. By choosing carefully it is possible to get an adequate lunch if the machines provide fruits, milk, salads, and high-protein sandwiches.

We know which segments of the population are likely to have poor diets and many of the contributing factors. The challenge is to convince persons with poor diets to improve their food habits. Many agencies and organizations have programs aimed at improving American diets. These include education, motivation, and food aid. A description of two of the U.S. Department of Agriculture-State programs follows.

The Cooperative Extension Service, since its inception, has devoted many of its resources to nutrition programs for youth and adults. A wide variety of approaches are used to reach its heterogeneous clientele.

Extension home economists work with the 4–H Clubs, Extension homemaker groups, and other women's clubs in the 50 States, the District of Columbia, Puerto Rico, and in the Virgin Islands. More time is devoted to foods and nutrition programs than to any other subject matter area. Thus, over the years, millions of families who participate in educational programs have learned how to select and prepare foods for a good diet.

Much of the teaching is done by volunteer leaders who greatly multiply the number of people to whom nutrition information can be given. They are taught by Extension home economists, and then bring the information to youth and adult groups in their own neighborhoods. The stimulation of group participation and the commitment to try something new generated through group discussion make this an effective method to improve food habits.

Besides its programs for organized groups, Extension has many channels for reaching the general public—radio, TV, and newspapers, to name a few. A series of related articles on nutrition using one or all mass media at about the same time is an effective way to reach a large audience. In some States, this is combined with a group discussion led by a trained volunteer, or followup letters from the Extension home economist. In some areas programs are presented in another language, such as Spanish language broadcasts in the Southwest.

One of Extension's exciting new approaches is the use of program aides. In an attempt to improve the diets of the hard-to-reach poor, nonprofessional aides are trained to go into disadvantaged homes and teach homemakers better ways of feeding their families. Thus the services of the professional home economist are extended to many more of the poor than would otherwise be possible.

An expanded nutrition program was

Nutrition aides in Mississippi prepare foods donated by the USDA to needy families, before holding neighborhood demonstration at home of a recipient.

initiated in November 1968. More than 5,000 poor people are being employed by the Extension Service to be aides. They will work with both rural and urban poor. In the first 6 months of the program, these 5,000 aides helped around 200,000 families to a better diet. If families are to make lasting improvements, the program must be carried on long enough to bring about a change in attitude, to develop new habit patterns and new food skills.

The food problems of a poor family are often related to other problems. Aides are being trained to cope with these broad concerns of the family as well as their specific food and nutrition problems.

To be effective, training is essential for aides. They must be taught how to make working home visits. If the aides come from a middle-class background they must be taught what to expect in a disadvantaged home. The aides must be helped to find ways to begin in a poorly kept home where there are several small hungry children and where a young mother is too tired, harried, and discouraged to try to learn.

If unprepared, an aide might decide that material help was the only solution. Although aides are taught about the services available to families and how to make referrals, they are also trained to provide education and to bring hope and encouragement. Experience indicates that an indigenous aide can communicate well with the poor and quickly establish rapport.

After aides have been instructed in how to make home visits, they are taught food and nutrition subject matter and given an opportunity to practice in role-playing situations. Lessons dealing with food selection and preparation are a good place to start, since feeding the family is almost always a problem with low-income homemakers.

The Extension Service has developed a series of lessons to use in training aides. The first lesson deals with what food means to people. It often comes as a surprise to the aides to find that many people do not sit around a table to eat the conventional three meals a day. In this lesson, aides are made aware of some factors which influence families' food habits, such as the amount of money they can spend for food, their nationality, the part of the country they live in, their religion, the way mothers cook and serve food, and how much they know about nutrition. After this introduction the aide begins making home visits, and by observation and talking with mothers, learns something about the eating habits of families in her area.

Education materials at third- and fourth-grade reading level have been prepared for use with families where appropriate. Publications for aides are written at about eighth-grade level.

Many persons receiving donated foods are puzzled about the use of dry milk, bulgur, and some other unfamiliar foods. Extension agents and trained volunteer leaders have given demonstrations and distributed thousands of leaflets to recipients, teaching them not only how to store and use the food but how it contributes to a well-balanced diet. Some of the literature has been translated into Spanish.

Many families eligible for participation in the U.S. Department of Agriculture food stamp program have been helped to enroll and taught how to use this resource wisely.

Among the special audiences reached by Extension are:

Young Homemakers—The person who most needs information on nutrition for a young family, the young homemaker, does not always know where to go for authentic information. Many Extension home economists hold a series of meetings at a convenient time and place for this audience with much success. The number of programs designed especially for them is increasing. Correspondence and TV courses have been developed for those housebound by very young children.

Teenage Youth—Some of Extension's most successful programs have been a series of meetings for teenagers. In these meetings, nutrition teaching designed to improve the attitudes and

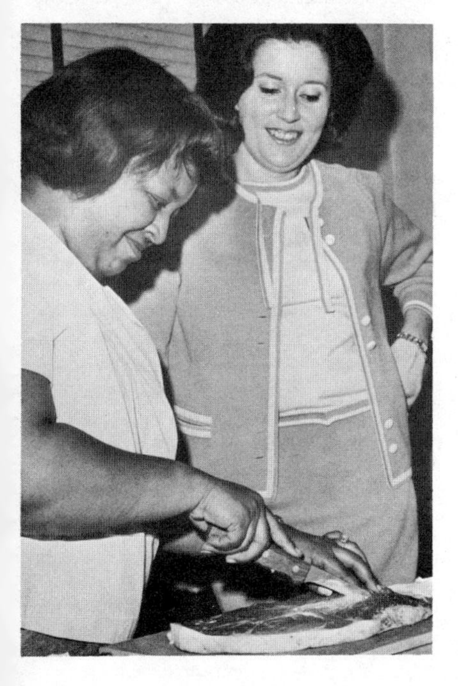

Student in a consumer food economics course shows how to cut meat to get the most use from it, as a USDA meat specialist checks her technique. About 40 attended the eight-week pilot course, with weekly two-hour classes, in the inner city area of Washington, D.C. It was designed to help low-income families improve their food habits and get maximum benefit from the food stamp program.

practices of teenagers has been combined with social activity normal to this age group.

Working Homemakers—Some women may not have time to attend meetings. Specially designed, brief information leaflets are made available at such places as laundromats, beauty parlors, and lunchrooms in places where the women are employed.

Older Folks—Many older folks living on small incomes eat inadequate meals. They can sometimes be reached through organizations such as "golden age" clubs. They welcome the special attention given them at their meetings, and can be helped to improve their eating habits.

Weight Control Groups—Although attaining normal weight is the desired goal, it is more important for group members to improve their diets and develop good food habits for their families as well as for themselves. Because the groups meet for a series of lessons, nutrition can be taught in greater depth.

Professionals of Other Agencies—Extension conducts many nutrition meetings for professionals in related fields who have little or no training in nutrition, such as teachers, nurses, school lunch cooks, the workers with Head Start, and managers of nursing homes.

U.S. Department of Agriculture research on human nutrition (conducted in the Agricultural Research Service and in the State Agricultural Experiment Stations) strives to increase understanding of what foods are needed and in what amounts and combinations they can make the greatest nutritional contribution to normal healthy people. The research is chiefly in three broad areas—nutrition, food science, and food consumption.

If the public is to benefit from this research, USDA must interpret its results in terms of the practical problems of the family food manager, the individual consumer, the teacher or Extension worker, or the Government agency formulating a national or international food program. Examples of the continuing supply of these direct-to-the-consumer practical guides are: "Food for Fitness," "Food and Your Weight," "Food for the Family With Young Children," "Family Fare," and "Vegetables in Family Meals."

Important as these publications are, research must also aid the professional and lay leaders who, through education, welfare service, public health, and related channels, are working with the ultimate consumer—the individual, family, or institution. A widely used aid to leaders is the work on food plans and budgets at different cost levels. These show the amount of different kinds of foods which together meet the nutritional needs of individuals and families.

The plans are revised periodically to keep them in line with new knowledge of nutritional requirements, the nutritive value of foods, changing food habits, and the relative economy of foods. The cost of the food budgets is kept up to date using the retail food prices collected by the Bureau of Labor Statistics.

Judith A. Pheil

Entertaining Can Be Easy, If You Plan It Like This

Most families like to entertain company at meals in their homes—friends, business associates, neighbors, relatives. Good company meals may be simple but should be delicious and nicely served in pleasant surroundings. With a little careful planning, entertaining can be trouble free and enjoyable.

Entertaining will be easier if you know your guests—what they like and what they don't like, and if you know yourself—your capabilities and your facilities and stay within them.

Regardless of the number and kind of guests or the type of service, it pays to plan family or company meals early and carefully. Like planning any other meal, you will include a protein dish containing meat, poultry, fish, eggs, or cheese; a fruit or a salad; vegetables and bread; dessert and beverage. Remember the importance of contrast in flavor—something sweet, something tart, and something bland, something spicy; color—follow a color scheme; texture—something soft, something crisp. Use edible garnishes to make food look attractive, but avoid overdoing it.

Buffet meals usually are limited to a main course, dessert, and beverage. However, a first course of juice or soup and crackers is sometimes served in the living room before inviting guests to the table.

Eliminate as much last-minute preparation as possible. The menu may be as individual and as informal as the service. Substantial, delicious food, easily prepared and attractively served, will make you the "hostess with the mostest."

Foods that can be prepared several hours or days ahead of time are worth considering. Some time-saving suggestions are: Meat loaf, scalloped or casserole dishes, baked ham or turkey, salads and desserts that can be molded or arranged in individual servings and stored for a few hours, fresh vegetables prepared and stored in plastic bags or in the vegetable crisper in the refrigerator.

A well-stocked pantry shelf and home freezer are important to the homemaker as she plans both family and company meals. Many foods available are designed to save the homemaker time and energy. There are frozen foods that provide constant variety in fruits, vegetables, and meats; frozen precooked foods in endless variety; packaged mixes for everything from biscuits, cakes and dessert toppings to meringues, candy, and casserole dishes; quick-cooking cereals; hundreds of canned foods; ready-to-eat bakery products. The job of the busy homemaker is to use these foods to best advantage to save her the most time and energy at home.

Keep the grocery list flexible enough to take advantage of bargains in food your family and friends like, and buy in quantity to save money and shopping time.

Planning meals and spending the food dollar go hand in hand; and again with careful planning, food costs can be kept to a minimum and meals made just as attractive and nutritious. Foods

Judith A. Pheil is Food and Nutrition Specialist, Cooperative Extension Service, the University of Maryland, College Park.

in convenient forms sometimes cost more money but the homemaker will spend much less time in the kitchen.

Here are a few tips to make meals look and taste more extravagant than they actually are:

- Add visual and taste appeal with attractive color, flavor, and texture combinations.
- Serve hot foods hot and cold foods well chilled.
- Take full advantage of herbs and spices and other seasonings and occasionally experiment with new recipes (when you're not expecting guests).
- Watch magazines, newspapers, and television for ideas to "dress up" favorite foods.

Intelligent shopping can save you money, time, and energy. A shopping list is recommended. If you've made meal plans for the week including the company dinner, putting the list together is simple. Look over your menus and write down the items you will need. Check your pantry shelf, refrigerator, and freezer and add any staples that are running low. If you have jotted these down during the week as the supply dwindled, this part of the list will only take a minute. List foods in the order they are stocked on the market shelves. Study the food ads for the day you do your shopping, and make substitutions or additions if you wish. Avoid impulse buying. It doesn't help you stay within your budget.

In spite of all best-laid plans, occasionally a crowd pops in unexpectedly. With no time to prepare ahead, a casserole meal is great when you can rely on ingredients from your pantry shelf and freezer.

Donuts and apple cider as a Halloween treat.

This menu is built around a casserole recipe:

Chicken Tuna Bake
Buttered Green Snap Beans
Cabbage Slaw
Muffins
Peaches with Whipped Topping
Beverage

CHICKEN TUNA BAKE

8 to 10 servings

8-ounce package cut spaghetti or macaroni
1 cup chopped onion
½ cup chopped green pepper
⅓ cup fat
¼ cup flour
2 cups milk
2 cans condensed cream of chicken soup
½ cup chopped pimiento, if desired
2 6½- or 7-ounce cans flaked tuna
Slivered almonds, blanched

Cook pasta as directed on package; drain.

Cook the chopped onion and green pepper in hot fat until tender. Blend flour into fat. Slowly stir in the milk. Cook over low heat until thickened, stirring constantly.

Mix in cream of chicken soup, chopped pimiento, tuna, and pasta. Pour the mixture into a casserole, top with almonds, and bake, uncovered, at 350° F. about 35 minutes.

While the casserole is baking, shred 1 medium head of cabbage (1 pound cabbage makes about 5 cups) and toss it with a dressing made by mixing ½ cup sugar, ¼ cup vinegar, ½ teaspoon salt, and ¾ cup mayonnaise. Chill slaw before serving.

If the beans are frozen, cook them covered in a small amount of water. Canned ones will only need to be heated. Add a small dab of butter or margarine just before serving.

You may want to ask one of the children or a guest to set the table while you open canned peaches and arrange them in dessert dishes and make the coffee. Have someone prepare the muffins from a mix for you so they are ready to pop into the oven when the casserole is done. By the time the other food is on the table, the muffins will be ready to serve piping hot. In an hour or so you can have a delicious meal ready to serve 8 to 10 hungry people, and it will have been easy and great fun.

Don't let weekend guests keep you in the kitchen. Relax and enjoy them by planning wisely. Shop ahead, cook ahead (as much as possible), and use heat-and-serve frozen, canned, and packaged foods.

Here are suggestions for meals for Friday night through Sunday dinner:

FRIDAY NIGHT SUPPER

Oven-Fried Chicken
Creole Rice
Mixed Green Salad
Fruit Compote
Beverage

OVEN-FRIED CHICKEN

8 to 10 servings

½ cup flour
1 teaspoon salt
½ teaspoon pepper, if desired
2 teaspoons paprika
½ cup butter or margarine
2 cut-up, ready-to-cook chickens (2 to 3 pounds each)
or
8 to 10 serving-size chicken pieces

Preheat oven to 400° F.

Mix flour, salt, pepper, and paprika in a bag.

Shake each piece of chicken in the bag to coat well.

Melt fat in a shallow casserole in the oven. Turn pieces of chicken in casserole to coat with fat.

Lay chicken in casserole with skin side down.

Bake for about 30 minutes or until golden brown on underside.

Turn and bake about 20 minutes longer or until tender.

CREOLE BAKED RICE

10 servings

2 cups packaged precooked rice
4 cups canned tomatoes
2 medium onions, chopped
1 medium green pepper, chopped
2 teaspoons salt
2 tablespoons butter or margarine, melted

Mix all of ingredients in a 2½- to 3-quart casserole; cover.

Bake in oven along with chicken at 400° F. for 30 to 45 minutes, or until mixture thickens.

FRUIT COMPOTE

Arrange in your prettiest bowl and chill a combination of two or three fresh or canned fruits— a) melon balls, strawberries, blueberries; b) peach halves, green grapes; c) mandarin oranges, pineapple chunks, dark cherries. Garnish with sprigs of mint.

SATURDAY BREAKFAST

Chilled Juice
Coffee Cake
Individual Cereal Packs
Milk for cereal
Beverage

This is a simple fix-it-yourself breakfast. Set the table the night before. Have the juice ready in the refrigerator. Cover coffee cake, which you've made ahead of time from a mix, to prevent drying. Provide bowls for cereal. Have a pitcher of milk ready in the refrigerator for cereal or beverage. Keep water hot on a candle warmer for making instant coffee.

SATURDAY LUNCH

Clam Chowder
Saltines
Celery and Carrot Sticks
Frozen Cheesecake
Beverage

This menu is just a matter of assembling. Prepare cans of chowder and serve in large bowls. Prepare celery and carrot sticks before lunch and keep in crisper until serving time. Brew a pot of coffee and serve with readymade cheesecake.

SATURDAY NIGHT BUFFET

Hamburger Stroganoff
on
Buttered Noodles
Tossed Tomato, Cucumber, Endive Salad
French Dressing
Baked Custard with Maple Sirup
Beverage

This is an easy menu to serve to any number of guests. You may want to invite several couples.

HAMBURGER STROGANOFF

8 servings

2 pounds ground beef
1 cup chopped onion
4 tablespoons butter or margarine
2 cans condensed cream of mushroom soup
1 teaspoon paprika
1 teaspoon salt
Dash pepper
1 cup dairy sour cream
Cooked noodles, as desired

In frying pan, brown beef and cook onion in fat until tender; stir to separate meat. Add soup and seasonings; simmer 5 minutes. (Stroganoff can be prepared this far a day ahead and stored in refrigerator.)

Just before serving time add the sour cream and heat until the mixture is simmering hot. Do not boil. Serve it over noodles.

SUNDAY DINNER

Broiled Steak
Baked Potatoes
Butter, Margarine, or Sour Cream
Broccoli
Hearts of Lettuce with Italian Dressing
Ice Cream
Beverage

If the weather is nice, the steaks can be grilled outdoors and dinner eaten on the patio. Allow about a half hour for the coals to be hot enough for grilling. Medium-sized potatoes will bake in the oven at 425° F. in 50 to 60 minutes. Wrapped in heavy foil, the potatoes will bake on the outdoor grill in the same length of time. Frozen broccoli requires about 15 minutes on top of the range. Brown-and-serve rolls will heat in oven or on the grill with potatoes during last 10 minutes of baking time.

Your husband will probably want to grill the steaks—this takes 10 to 30 minutes, depending on how well done you like them.

And, of course, the ice cream will be served from the freezer.

When teens give a party, the menu can be simple, but that doesn't mean the food can't be good and plentiful.

How's this for an after-the-game supper—

Baked Ham
Baked Bean Casserole
Relishes
Pumpkin Tarts
Apple Juice

Let the teenagers prepare the food and serve it. They will enjoy their own party.

A canned ham can be baked ahead of time, canned baked beans are used for the bean casserole, and canned pumpkin for the tarts.

BAKED BEAN CASSEROLE

8 servings

6 slices bacon
1 medium onion, chopped
2 1-pound cans pork and beans
1 teaspoon dry mustard
¼ cup brown sugar, packed
½ cup catsup

Fry bacon; remove from frying pan. Brown onion in 1 tablespoon bacon drippings in frying pan. Add beans, mustard, sugar, catsup, and crumbled bacon. Mix well. Pour into casserole. Bake uncovered at 300° F. for 1 hour.

PUMPKIN TARTS

8 tarts

Pastry for one 9-inch double crust pie
3 eggs slightly beaten
2 cups canned pumpkin
¾ cup brown sugar, packed
½ teaspoon salt
1½ teaspoons pumpkin pie spice
1¼ cups milk
1 6-ounce can evaporated milk

Roll pastry into eight 6-inch circles. Fit into large tart pans or muffin tins. In a large bowl mix eggs, pumpkin, sugar, salt, and spice. Stir in milk and evaporated milk. Pour into tart shells, and bake at 400° F. for 40 minutes or until set.

Caramel snowballs may be prepared in advance, and served to young guests with quickly made coffee Mexican style. For four to five medium apples, melt down a pound of caramels in top of double boiler. Impale apples on ice cream sticks, dip in caramel when it has become smooth sauce, and then into flaked coconut. Place apples on wax paper and chill a few minutes in refrigerator until the caramel is firm. Fix the beverage by preparing equal amounts of hot coffee and hot chocolate separately. Pour coffee and chocolate together into mugs.

Charlotte M. Dunn

Picnic Pointers and Frill-Free Ideas for Any Outdoor Meal

There comes a time when the urge for a change of scenery stirs us all. Thoughts of food follow naturally. The lusty aroma of outdoor cooking tempts an appetite at any time. The menu doesn't need a lot of frills. A correctly planned menu is flexible—just switch main courses and you still have a balanced meal to satisfy hearty appetites of fresh air diners.

Planning the outdoor meal comes first. Be it a picnic, a campfire cookout, or a meal on an outdoor grill or a fireplace, the foods must fill the day's nutritional needs with an appealing variety of flavor, texture, and color.

For family and company meals you serve outdoors, consider two important stages in the preparation. The first, vital to the enjoyment of the occasion by host and hostess as well as guests, is the planning and organization of work. Prepare as many foods as possible in your kitchen before carrying to the porch, patio, or backyard. Second, observe the food preparation and the cooking practices necessary for serving quality outdoor meals, both in taste and in nutritive value.

Dewy morning air mixed generously with the unmistakable aroma of food can only mean breakfast in the open. Cook anything from delicious roasted apples filled with orange marmalade and topped with chopped nuts (prepared, wrapped in foil, and stored in the refrigerator the night before) to crisp brown sausages with eggs and a buttery hot bread.

Hot breads offer a variety of choices. Muffins, baked the day before, can be split and warmed in foil. Bread slices are tasty spread with softened butter and poppy seeds, or sugar and cinnamon. Wrap slices in foil, leaving an opening for steam to escape, and heat for 20 minutes on the grill, turning to heat evenly. A home prepared master mix or ready prepared biscuit mix gives you a chance to surprise the family with a kolochy. Add 1 cup milk to 2 cups biscuit mix, stir to a soft dough, and drop biscuits on a lightly buttered pan. Press a hollow in the center of each, fill with tart jelly, and sprinkle with grated cheese. Bake 10 to 15 minutes in a 400° F. oven, a reflector, or a barbecue grill unit.

A barbecue-brunch on a sunny weekend can be a meal to remember. Start with a platter of assorted melon wedges . . . iced honeydew, cantaloup, and watermelon. Then stir up a skillet of superb scrambled eggs. When the eggs are partially cooked, add grated cheese (¾ to 1 cup for 8 eggs). Serve on hot buns or rolls, topped with a touch of bacon or ham. For a flavor change, try slices of smoked pork butt capped with broiled pineapple slices. The smoked pork butt can be cooked and chilled ahead of time, ready to be sliced and broiled at the cookout site.

Hamburgers remain a favorite for outdoor cooking and eating. Tasty, nutritious, low in cost, and easy to fix, this popular choice is a natural for new flavor combinations. Turn the tasty patties into delicious blueburgers. Top the browned hamburgers with a

Charlotte M. Dunn is Extension Specialist in Foods and Nutrition, Cooperative Extension Programs, University Extension, The University of Wisconsin, Madison.

generous spoonful of blue cheese and continue cooking until cheese melts slightly. Or you can fashion double-burgers. Place blue cheese between two uncooked meat patties, press together, and cook. Use your imagination. Other combinations include grated Cheddar cheese, pickle relish, and peanut butter, and grated cheese and grated onion. Mixtures tucked between two patties require a little longer cooking so the ingredients can melt and mingle with the beef. Be sure to use USDA graded lean beef so there will be a minimum of shrinkage.

The old black cast iron skillet is handy for preparing and serving a fresh air lunch on the porch or patio. Try chili and cheese dumplings. Add ¼ cup grated cheese to your basic biscuit mix recipe. Drop spoonsful on top of simmering chili and cook until dumplings are done.

After the successful fisherman comes home with the day's catch, why not try a fish boil? You'll need a large kettle. For a group, a metal washtub or cast iron kettle is suitable. Use at least 1½ gallons of boiling water and ½ cup salt for 8 to 16 medium unpeeled, scrubbed potatoes. Cook at least 45 minutes. When potatoes are nearly tender, add fish. Use large fish, about 4 pounds each, such as lake trout or whitefish. Cut into good sized chunks (4 pieces per fish). Fish pieces can be placed in a basket for easy removal. Cook only until fish is tender—10 to 15 minutes. Serve fish immediately with potatoes left in the jacket, split and topped with plenty of butter. Coleslaw, relishes, and rolls can complete the meal.

Outdoor entertaining is a natural for young people. Let them experience the adventure of planning. The less preparation the better. For an oldtime favorite, use the cast iron skillet to heat chili. Grill frankfurters. Spoon heated chili over buttered-toasted buns, cover with grated Cheddar cheese or slice and top with a frankfurter.

Slash a weiner almost through lengthwise; fill opening with a bit of cheese and grill. Or wrap the cheese-filled weiner with a bacon strip and then grill it.

Doughboys are great fun in camp, at the beach, or right in your own backyard. Prepare a stick about 1 inch in diameter; green wood is preferred. Strip the bark off of 6 inches on one end. Pour several cups of biscuit mix into a plastic bag; turn top of bag down to make cuff. Take the peeled stick and form a well in the center of the biscuit mix. Pour in enough milk or water to form a sticky dough. Stir gently with stick until liquid picks up enough biscuit mix to form soft ball around the stick end. Secure dough ball on stick by pressing gently with hand. Hold over coals, turning slowly to bake ball through and brown evenly (about 7 minutes). Doughboy is done when it slips easily from the stick. Eat piping hot with butter, jam, or jelly—or fill with "wimpy" mixture or roasted weiner.

To make a wimpy filling, melt 1 tablespoon fat, add 1 medium chopped onion, and cook until golden colored. Add 1 pound of ground lean beef and cook until gray in color. Salt and pepper to taste, then add 1 to 1½ cups shredded cheese and stir until melted. Serve mixture in doughboys or buns.

Safety Tips. With warm weather and the exodus outdoors, the potential danger of food poisoning accompanies each outdoor meal—be it a backyard cookout or a family reunion potluck. Precaution and commonsense can prevent a disaster. Germs capable of causing severe gastrointestinal upsets thrive in picnic foods which have not been adequately refrigerated. Food is safest at temperatures above 140° F. and below 45° F. If possible, food should be served immediately after cooking. Careful handling and preparation of food are important.

Foods to be served cold should be kept cold, and hot foods should be kept hot. Food taken on picnics often stays just warm, not cold or hot, for several hours. This moderate temperature is ideal for the rapid reproduction of micro-organisms which produce harmful toxins.

Cooking over a fire (left) in a precast concrete ring, at a Minnesota recreational development. (Right) Barbecuing chicken and other meat.

Bacteria grow best in nonacidic foods like meats, fish, poultry items, eggs, dairy products, and foods made from them. Particularly susceptible are recipes of finely chopped foods such as chicken salad, other meat or egg sandwich fillings, and casseroles. These foods have more surface area where bacteria can grow. Also, in preparation these foods are often handled more. Most sandwich fillings and salads are not reheated after preparation. If this is the case they must be kept cold until serving time.

There are inexpensive ways to keep foods cold—properly packed in an ice chest or in dry ice packs. Empty coffee cans or other containers with tight fitting lids can be filled with water and frozen for use in the ice chest; a plastic bag filled with ice cubes placed in a sturdy container will cool foods and the cubes can be used at campsite. When using ice, food should be placed to touch the container. Cubes, loose or in plastic bags, and ice in cartons should be distributed evenly throughout the cooler.

An easy-to-make cooler-carrier requires two cardboard boxes, with one smaller than the other. Put at least a half inch thickness of newspapers on the bottom of the larger box, and set the smaller one inside. Line newspapers between the sides of the two boxes, put in chilled food and ice, then close the small box lid. Place another layer of newspapers and fasten down the outside box lid. Keep cooler out of direct sunlight.

Picnics. A "picnic" has a special meaning for most people. Sometimes the entire meal is prepared in the kitchen, often some foods are cooked ahead while others are prepared at the cookout site. A fun meal for the entire family, including mother, is one prepared entirely at the picnic area.

Picnic meals prepared partially or completely at the site require some type of cooking apparatus, such as a temporary firebox of bricks or stones piled on each other, or a permanent fireplace, or a portable grill. Menu ideas for this type of meal include cranberry juice, broiled ham, potatoes baked in hot ashes, a combination vegetable salad, whole wheat rolls and milk, or chops or steaks, buns, green salad, sponge cake, and berries.

Food for a plan-ahead picnic can be frozen, then prepared at the cook-out site. Try a barbecued chicken, vegetable bundle, rolls, and no-bake brownies or spiced bananas. Marinate chicken in your favorite sauce, bake for 30 minutes, cool in refrigerator, wrap in foil and freeze. At the picnic, place chicken on slow fire and cook for 30 minutes, basting and turning occasionally, until meat is tender. For the vegetable bundle, break up a 10-ounce package of frozen peas and corn. Mound on a large square of heavy-duty foil. Add tiny pickled onions, drained, or 1 tablespoon instant minced onion, butter, salt, and pepper. Twist foil corners together tightly and freeze until picnic time. Place bundle on hot grill. Cook 25 minutes, remove from grill, and open gently to allow steam to escape. Stir before serving.

Spiced bananas are good cooked on the spot. Allow 1/3 to 1/2 banana per person, peel and place on a square of heavy foil. Brush with lemon juice; sprinkle with or roll in brown sugar, dust with cinnamon and nutmeg, and dot with butter. Put bananas on the grate when you sit down to eat since they must only heat through. Or combine the ingredients, split banana lengthwise, and spread mixture between the halves. Wrap foil securely around bananas, twisting ends. Barbecue on grill 7 to 9 minutes, or on coals 4 to 5 minutes. Turn 2 or 3 times to heat evenly.

Frozen fish fillets and vegetables can be safely transported to picnic grounds. Spread fish with tartar sauce, then wrap in foil ready to cook on the grill. Cook foil-wrapped, seasoned, and cheese-topped broccoli spears at the same time. Pronto picnic salad can be made of canned peas or carrots, hard-cooked eggs, finely cut crisp raw vegetables, broken nut meats, and a savory salad dressing. Toasted frankfurter rolls can be the bread choicc. Fresh fruits eaten out of hand and a beverage complete the meal.

Food-in-foil individual servings or whole meals are easy and convenient. The foil "dishes" are simply tossed into a litter basket. When using foil for outdoor cookery be sure it's the heavy-duty kind.

Hamburgers and vegetables in foil make a quick meal-in-one. Place a hamburger patty, onion slice, 1/2 medium potato, and 1/2 carrot (slice vegetables very thin) on large foil square. Season to taste and place 1/4 slice of bacon on top. Seal with drugstore wrap, and roll ends to make a drip-proof package. Place over hot coals and cook 15 to 20 minutes or until done. Fold back foil to serve.

Another package meal features slices of canned ham spread with marmalade, canned sweet potatoes, and orange slices, arranged on a double thickness of heavy-duty foil. Sprinkle with slivered almonds. Seal package, heat on grill over medium hot coals for about 30 minutes.

Frankfurters, onion slices, canned white potatoes, and a tomato half sprinkled with grated cheese in foil package will only take 15 to 20 minutes to grill.

Potato salad, if made ahead, must be kept well chilled. Try taking cold ingredients in separate containers in the cooler and prepare the salad just before serving.

Salad greens should be prepared at home and stored in plastic wrap, or in a plastic bag ready-to-serve, or in the bowl you plan to serve from. Cover tightly and keep cold. Add tomatoes, cucumbers and other salad items when it's eating time.

Picnic desserts are no problem. Cake, cookies, fresh fruits such as watermelon, peaches, fresh plums, grapes, and pears are alltime favorites. Wash fruits at home and use as a picnic centerpiece until dessert time.

Barbecues. The term "barbecue" originally referred to a whole animal roasted or broiled in its entirety for a feast, or the feast at which such meat is scrved. The origin is obscure, but it probably derives from the French barbe-a-gueue, meaning "from snout to tail." The institution of the barbecue is probably of southern origin.

It is known that the word was used in Virginia before 1700.

In recent years, the outdoor preparation of meals has become increasingly popular, and the principle of the elegant barbecue feast has been simplified to fit the smallest suburban yard. The home barbecue varies from a hooded or open portable charcoal grill to an elaborately constructed fireplace with ovens and flues.

If you are a beginner, it is safe to try hamburgers, frankfurters, or steaks and chops. They are easily prepared on the grill and the cooking technique is the same as indoors. Steaming servings of string beans or sweet corn, together with a bowl of mixed green salad, can complete the menu.

Chicken is easily barbecued. Split a broiler down the back and cook on the grill, broiling the bony side first and then the skin side. Experiment with various basting sauces. If the grill or fireplace has a spit, a whole chicken may be broiled and the sauce swabbed on during cooking.

Shake hands with a whole chicken or turkey to tell when it's done: About 20 minutes before roasting period is up, snip the cord that holds drumsticks to the spit rod so heat can reach all parts of the bird. Grasp end of drumstick with paper towels; when leg moves easily, the bird is done.

Marinating less tender beef cuts such as blade or arm chuck, round or flank steak, will tenderize meat and improve the flavor. A marinade is a mixture of oil, vinegar and/or lemon juice, and seasonings, salt, herbs, garlic, onions, or seasoned salt may be used. Marinate meat in refrigerator for 24 hours or at room temperature for 2 hours before cooking. Cutting narrow grooves or gashes part way through the food's surface (scoring) permits marinade to penetrate meat. Seasoned and nonseasoned commercial tenderizers are available. Follow directions on label. Marinade can also be used to baste meats. Basting, usually done to increase the moisture of foods while cooking, will add a distinctive flavor to meat.

The array of meat available for outdoor cooking goes beyond steaks and chicken to include chops, kabobs, hamburgers, rotisserie roasts, and frankfurters. Meat selection is easier if you look for the U.S. Government inspection stamp for wholesomeness and take advantage of grades for quality guidance.

It is necessary to know meat cuts to guide you in methods of outdoor cookery. When the choice is steak, decide whether you'd like individual ones like club, strip, top loin, T-bone, porterhouse, delmonico, tenderloin (filet mignon), or a steak to serve several, such as a thick sirloin. These come in boneless styles as well as wedge, pin, or flat bone types.

For a lazy way of cooking, choose a cut for your rotisserie. A rack of spareribs "threaded" accordion fashion on the rod, a boneless ham roll, pork rolled Boston shoulder, a rolled pork loin, and boneless rolled lamb shoulder are suggestions.

The delmonico (rib eye) roast is the most elegant beef cut for the rotisserie. Other high quality beef cuts which respond to rotisserie roasting include rolled rump, sirloin tip, or a rolled chuck, often called the English or Boston cut.

Many stores feature rolled, boned lamb roasts. Although lamb supplies are usually low in the summer, ideas for outdoor cooking abound. Experts report there are 30 lamb cuts for backyard banquets.

Kabob your dinner. It's a gay sight to see the colorful food chunks strung on skewers sizzling on the grill. You can skewer anything that you can broil.

For uniform cooking, give each kind of food its own skewer. String cubes of beef or lamb on one. Season and brush with oil, melted butter, or french dressing. Thread scrubbed potatoes on another, whole onions on a third. Leave jackets on vegetables and you won't have to baste them. For quick kabobs simmer a sweet-sour sauce while you thread skewer with chunks of canned luncheon meat, green pepper, and pineapple. Cherry tomatoes can be used to finish off skewer. Brush with sauce, broil or grill just until foods are heated through.

Lamb, canned meat, precooked sausages, beef cubes are all kabob naturals. Combine with olives, pickles, mushroom caps, tomatoes, pineapple chunks, orange segments, green pepper, and onions.

For smoke cookery, use a charcoal fire in barbecue grill with a hood or a lid that closes to make smoke. Soak hickory chips in water or dampen hickory sawdust. Let charcoal fire burn down to low-even heat. Then add damp hickory or fruit woods. Place food on grill or spit. Cover barbecue tightly and finish cooking. This is a slow process. Liquid smoke can be brushed on the meat. Smoked salt can be sprinkled on before cooking or added to the barbecue sauce.

Because steak, hamburgers, chicken, spareribs, the sausage products, and hot dogs are today's most popular headliners for barbecue menus, the outdoor chef strives to make his specialty unique. Palate-teasing flavor combinations in the barbecue sauce or marinade can establish a gourmet reputation. Apply sauce lavishly while the meat is cooking, and prepare extra sauce to serve with the meat.

A tasty sauce for hamburgers is prepared from a package of onion soup mix, 1 cup of russian dressing, ¼ to ½ cup water, and dry mustard to taste. Simmer 10 minutes before using sauce.

Another quick barbecue sauce can be made with 1 can condensed tomato soup, and sweet pickle relish, chopped onion, brown sugar, vinegar, and Worcestershire sauce to taste. Simmer 10 minutes or until onion is cooked. An effective marinade that can also be used to baste meat contains 1 cup of Burgundy wine, 1 small garlic clove (minced), 1 tablespoon apiece of Worcestershire sauce and sugar, 2 tablespoons each of prepared horseradish, minced parsley, prepared mustard, and margarine or butter, ¼ teaspoon each of oregano and pepper, 1 teaspoon salt, 1 small onion (minced). Combine ingredients and heat until table fat melts. Cool. Pour sauce over steak. Chill in refrigerator for at least 8 hours, turning steak several times. Remove steak and strain sauce, keeping solid material as well as liquid. Broil steak on one side, basting occasionally with liquid. Turn, spread top surface with solids from sauce.

Although leaping flames may be picturesque, the secret of successful barbecuing is a solid bed of glowing coals. Whether charcoal, wood, or other fuel is used, light the fire at least 30 minutes ahead of time so it will burn down to ash-gray coals before cooking starts.

With modern grills, you can adjust the cooking rack or grid to control heat. The center of the rack is hotter than the outside, so overbrowning can be avoided by moving food to the grill edges. This is necessary for small pieces like legs, wings, and thighs of chicken.

On nonadjustable grills or with outdoor fires, you can reduce heat by spreading the coals or by occasionally sprinkling them with water. To tame any fat-fed flames, keep a water-filled clothes sprinkler container or clean whiskbroom and water container close at hand.

The amount of charcoal differs with your equipment and the food you plan to barbecue. Large roasts will require more charcoal than broiled foods such as steaks or burgers. A shallow fire is simple to control, fine for broiling.

Often the fireboxes, fireplaces, and grills can be lined with a sheet of foil which will give off more heat and simplifies ash disposal.

There are several ways to keep your grill from burning out. A 1-inch layer of vermiculite can be placed on the foil. This absorbs fat drippings and eliminates flareup. When using a rotisserie, shape an aluminum foil drip catching pan to fit under the meat, or you can use gravel or insulating pellets layered around 1 inch deep on the bottom of the grill to help prevent burning out the firebox. After half a dozen barbecues, clean the gravel in hot water to remove fat drippings, and spread out to dry thoroughly. If your firebox is perforated on the bottom, there will be no need for gravel.

You will add to the life of your grill top if you wait until cooking time to place hood or cover down. Remove it (with asbestos gloves) right after use. For easy cleaning, the grate can be swathed with wet paper towels or newspaper while you eat. Later a few swipes will clean the entire grill; use a scouring pad for stubborn spots. After each use the grate and frame should be cleaned carefully so fat and food particles don't become baked on.

Camping. Well planned meals are essential to a successful camping trip. Itemize foods, equipment, and supplies needed. Avoid planning meals using bulky or heavy foods. Pack with imagination—bulky food in kettles and pans, liquids in small bottles with screw-on caps, plastic bags to carry and store vegetables, baked goods, etc. Don't forget a first aid kit and heavy cotton gloves that will serve as potholders.

Written lists are a camper's best friend. Be sure you have included equipment such as unbreakable plates, cups and bowls, knives, forks, spoons, cooking spoons and cooking knives or forks, tongs, turner, can and bottle opener, pans, kettles, frying pans, containers for dishwashing and scalding, matches in a metal container, pot scrubber, detergent (liquid serves a multipurpose), and a portable grate. This miscellaneous equipment can be kept in a picnic kit. Revise the list to meet your family's needs.

The day has come when campers can "rough it" in nature's backyard, near home, or in a remote mountain area, yet still enjoy the convenience of a variety of foods. No matter where you camp, the food needs to be kept clean and cold.

When refrigeration or cooling facilities are lacking, depend on canned, packaged, and freeze-dried foods. For a long camping trip, plan some meals that come out of the package. Have others that can be cooked over an open fire. Dispose of leftovers if there isn't a way to keep them cold until another meal. The veteran camper stores all fresh or opened food in foil, in a safe place out of temptation from wildlife.

When time permits setting up the camp stove or cooking unit, the menu can be more elaborate.

Campers can be prepared for any activity or change of plans with a variety of foods and menu plans. Serve about four items for most camp meals, whether it's an out-of-hand lunch or a fully cooked meal.

Nonrefrigerated dairy milk products—canned, evaporated milk, condensed milk, nonfat dry milk—can be diluted with cold or warm water for a hot beverage as nutritious as fresh whole milk. Make use of packaged flavorings. These products are satisfactory for "coffee with," over dry cereal, or in a classic white sauce served over canned vegetables and fish. Evaporated milk makes a good base for coating fish fillets to be breaded for frying.

Utensils for camp cooking need not be elaborate or costly. Family members, with imagination and simple materials, can make easy inexpensive equipment and utensils. Heavy-duty aluminum foil should be a staple in the camp kitchen.

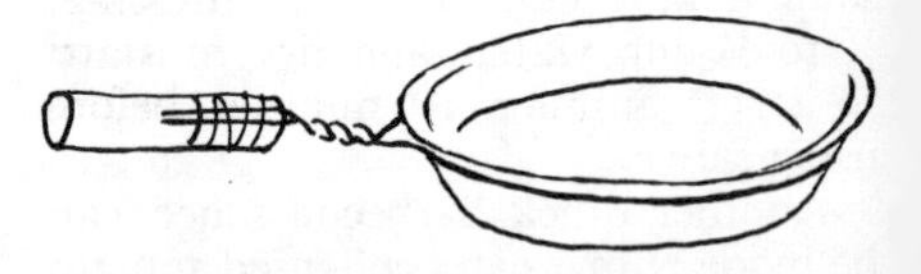

Before leaving for the family camping trip, each member can enjoy concocting outdoor cooking gear. To make a frying pan, straighten a coat hanger; bend in center to form a loop; form around a tin pan. Bring wire ends together; twist several turns; fasten ends to a stick handle or dowel pin with wire or masking tape.

A hanger can be pulled into a square and covered with a double sheet of foil to make a serviceable

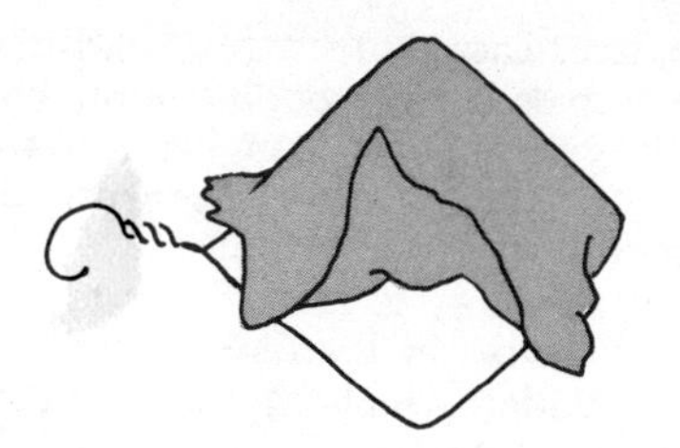

frying pan. Bend the hook downward to provide a handle. When bacon and eggs or other foods are cooked on this pan, the foil depresses slightly to hold fats and juices. These pans can be put to use as individual cook-and-serve plates.

Make skewer for weiners, kabobs, or marshmallows by straightening a coat hanger, and bend one end into a loop to form a handle. Remove the black lacquer from straight end with sandpaper or by burning.

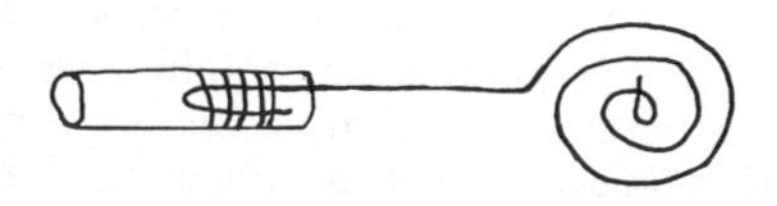

A hamburger broiler is fashioned by curving one half of a coat hanger into a flat coil. Bend up end in coil center to form a prong. For a handle, attach the straight end to a stick or dowel pin with wire or masking tape. Place broiler coil in fire to remove the black lacquer.

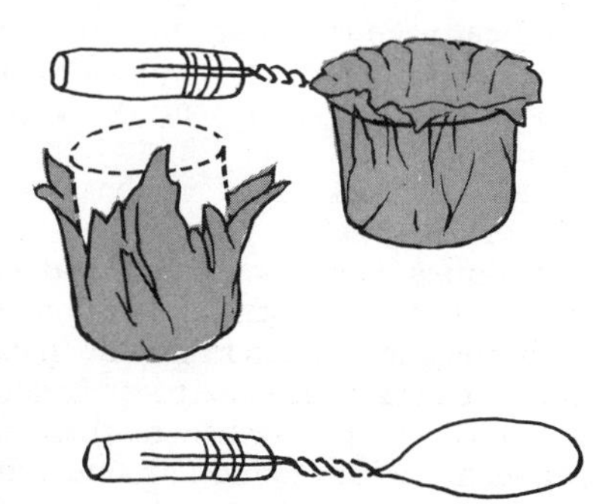

Another handy camp gadget made from a hanger is a frame for a foil cup or individual frying pan. Cut and straighten a wire hanger. Bend the middle part of the long wire around a can of desired size, form a hoop. Twist wire to make hoop secure. Bend remaining wire into a handle. This "hoop rim and handle" is light and easy to carry and store. To use, form a piece of foil around a can of the same size, and insert this foil cup in the wire rim. Roll the foil edges down evenly over the rim to make a very serviceable cup or saucepan.

This same frame can serve as an egg poacher. Lay a small sheet of foil over the cup rim; depress the center only half an inch or so, and fold the foil edges securely underneath the rim. Put a small amount of water in this little pan and when it is boiling, drop an egg into it. When the egg is cooked, pour off remaining water and add a bit of fat, salt, and pepper. Slide egg onto toast, and enjoy poached egg on toast out-of-doors. For a quickie tear a hole in a bread slice, place in lightly buttered frying pan, and break an egg in the hole. Fry until egg solidifies, and then turn.

If you do not have enough cooking utensils, you can easily make an extra kettle. Using a rock and nail or can opener, punch 2 holes on opposite sides of a can at the top. Straighten a hanger; cut to handle length; shape wire into a half circle. Insert wire ends through holes; twist to secure.

Aluminum foil can make a pan do double duty. For less tender cuts of meat and game, cut two double strips of foil and form a crisscross sling in the pan. Let foil ends hang at least 4 inches over outside rim. Place meat or cut-up game in the sling and cover with water. Place lid on the pan and simmer over a bed of coals. Forty to fifty minutes later, test meat with a fork to check for doneness. Remove sling of meat, place vegetables (carrot and onion pieces about the same size) in water; replace sling of meat and finish cooking. To steam fish, cook the vegetables first. During the last 20 minutes place fish in foil sling over boiling water and vegetables; replace lid and cook until tender. Season.

The right kind of fire is essential for successful outdoor cooking. A flaming fire is used only for a few methods, such as planking fish and cooking in a reflector oven. Most outdoor cooking is done over coals. Be patient, it takes about 30 to 45 minutes after lighting a fire to get good cooking coals. If necessary, maintain a fire on the side so you can pull over good coals as needed. Keep the wind at your back.

Be practical in building fires. Large fires waste fuel, are hard to control, and difficult to work over. To build a fire, first scrape ground litter from a 6- to 8-foot circle. Before lighting the fire, assemble everything you need—tinder, kindling and fuel. For tinder, use dry weed tops, pine needles, twigs, or bark from a dead tree. Then add kindling such as pencil-sized branches broken into small pieces, pine cones, fuzz sticks, or trench candles. Dead branches still on the tree are usually drier than those on the ground.

You can quickly whittle "fuzz sticks." Cut pieces of dry, soft wood, pointed at one end. Whittle so that long thin shavings are left attached, cutting toward blunt end. For quick kindling, push pointed ends of "fuzz sticks" into the ground, teepee fashion, over tinder.

The best woods for cooking include dry sugar maple, white oak, hickory, apple, white ash, and ironwood, which provide steady, intense heat and long-lived coals. Birch, poplar, elm, basswood give quick, clean heat, but do not last long. Most evergreens burn quickly, with smoky flames.

An easy way to lay a fire is to prop 2 or 3 pieces of kindling to form air angle under which to place a large handful of tinder. Construct a "teepee" or a "log cabin" about 6 inches around center of tinder, leaving plenty of air space between the sticks. Strike match and place flame under center of the tinder pile. Blow gently at base, if necessary. Feed kindling gradually, until the fire is burning well. Avoid smothering it as you add heavier fuel. Let the fire burn to good coals before beginning to cook.

On your next camping, fishing, or hunting trip, experiment with different types of cooking fires. A trench fire serves a larger group and is relatively safe from burning out of control. Dig the trench running in the same direction with the wind, sloping from ground level at the windward end to a foot deep. Trench may be lined with stones to hold heat. Build several small fires along trench, adding larger sticks gradually and letting them burn down to a continuous bed of red hot coals.

The hunter's or trapper's fire is based on two green logs placed to form a "V" (around 3 inches apart widening to 10 to 15 inches at the windward end). Build fire between the logs, spreading coals the full length. Hottest part will be at the narrow end. The logs confine the fire, shield the cook from its heat, and support utensils.

Whether you serve your outdoor meals in a national campground or with elegance on your private patio, don't get trapped in a rut or become restricted by habit. Be creative. Experiment with menus, foods, and equipment. Plan each meal to be an experience you will relish in solitude or with friends and family. As you savor the special flavors of food in the fresh air, you'll find experience is the best teacher.

Irene H. Wolgamot
Margy Woodburn

Community Meals: Organize, Watch Costs, and Serve Only Safe Food

The community meal, common in an earlier era, survives in today's more sophisticated society, in all parts of the country. Women—and often men, as well—enjoy contributing to their organization through their talents in preparing and serving the meals. They enjoy the sociability of working together. For the guests, the community meal is a pleasant family and neighborhood outing, at a reasonable cost. For many women guests, it provides a holiday from their kitchens. For the sponsoring organization, it promotes fellowship and may increase memberships and funds.

Tiptop organization and management are required to put on a successful community meal. The meal must be good, the tables attractive, and the food service efficient. Costs must be controlled. A friendly and hospitable atmosphere must prevail so that guests have a good time. The sponsoring organization must achieve some or all of its goals for the event.

Dividing responsibility among persons through committees is the usual method of organizing the work. There needs to be a general chairman to whom all committees are responsible.

The general chairman should be a leader who can get cooperation from others. She understands what work has to be done to put on a good community meal. She knows good food and she has high standards of cleanliness and sanitation. She is efficient in managing time, energy, and money.

It's the general chairman who gives guidance to committee chairmen as required on selection of menu, costs, hospitality, tickets, publicity, and the arrangements for preparing and serving the meal. She coordinates their activities and is responsible for their successful functioning. She serves as liaison with officers of the sponsoring organization. She gets information from the health department on the city and State ordinances concerning sanitation for the type of food service offered and plans for meeting the standards.

Committees might include publicity, tickets, hospitality, kitchen, dining room, and cleanup. A financial committee may be needed to coordinate and control costs. For special events in which temporary quarters are used, a committee on facilities will be required to check for adequate wiring, safe water, disposal of liquid and solid waste, restroom facilities for workers, and screening, as well as facilities to prepare and serve food.

The publicity committee's work may consist of one announcement in church or of many announcements through meetings, newsletters, the newspapers, radio, TV, and posters. Sometimes another group in the sponsoring organization handles the publicity for all events. The purpose is clear—to let people know about the community meal and to get them to come.

The tickets might be handled by the publicity committee or by a separate

Irene H. Wolgamot is a Home Economist in the Consumer and Food Economics Research Division, Agricultural Research Service.

Margy Woodburn is Professor and Head, Department of Foods and Nutrition, School of Home Economics, Oregon State University, Corvallis.

group. Arrangements must be made for printing the tickets, selling them, and checking the number sold against the total plates served.

The hospitality committee could arrange for hosts and hostesses who greet guests, help them to meet each other and to get seated at tables.

Hosts may escort honored guests to their places and promote sociability during the entire event. The hospitality committee arranges a place for the guests to put their coats and to assemble before the meal is served.

The kitchen committee plans the menu, purchases the food, prepares the meal, and serves it from the kitchen. A few reserve committee members should be on call if needed to replace those who might be ill. A person should not handle food if she has a boil, an infected cut or burn, respiratory infection, sore throat, or digestive upset.

The dining room committee is responsible for the dining arrangements—tables, chairs, table setting, and food service. It arranges heating and ventilation of the dining room, table decorations, and the recruiting, training, and assignment of waitresses. Reserve waitresses are also needed.

The cleanup committee takes care of kitchen cleanup including dishwashing and disposal of waste. This should not be the responsibility of those who prepared the meal. Cleanup activities have important sanitation and health aspects and should be undertaken by workers who have not already put in hours of work.

The menu should be planned to suit the occasion; the season; type of meal; cost of meal and price to be charged; number and kind of persons to be served; and the equipment, facilities, and workers available. It should be balanced nutritionally and provide both harmony and contrast in flavors, textures, and colors. The usual pattern includes an appetizer, a main protein dish, vegetables, a salad, bread and butter, dessert, and a beverage. Pasteurized milk should be available to adults as well as children.

If refrigerator space is limited, select the less perishable foods; for example, fruit instead of cream pies. Select main dishes and vegetables that do not need refrigeration before preparation and are served directly from the range. If equipment is limited or the workers inexperienced in preparing foods in quantity, avoid foods requiring special care for reasons of safety such as salads and sandwich fillings made with meat, poultry, fish, and eggs; potato salad; cream sauce; cream pies and puffs. Also avoid serving meats cooked ahead to be served cold or rewarmed.

Cost can be controlled and kept as low as possible by (1) estimating the amount of food needed and buying accordingly, (2) buying food in large amounts, (3) buying at lowest cost, perhaps at wholesale prices, (4) standardizing the serving portions, and (5) avoiding food waste.

Check prices and compare before buying. Figure the cost per plate so that cost facts are known. Keep an accurate record of all costs and save for future reference.

Management in preparing the meal determines to a large extent the success of the event, as measured by the pleasure of the guests and the satisfaction of the workers.

Place orders for food a week in advance. One person should be responsible to check all deliveries against orders and handle all bills. Donated foods should be listed and checked as received. Despite a possible saving, perishable foods should be prepared where they will be served so that the committee has control of quality and wholesomeness. In some localities, this is required by law when food is served to the public.

Purchase some emergency canned foods to provide a small number of meals that can be prepared quickly for extra guests. Arrange to return those unopened. Provide jars, waxed paper, aluminum foil, and moisture-proof bags to use for selling any left-over food. Generally, only the less perishable foods should be sold. The purchaser should refrigerate meats and other perishable foods promptly upon returning home.

Assign workers specific kitchen space and foods to prepare (1) appetizers, (2) meat, (3) vegetables, (4) salad and relishes, (5) bread and butter, (6) dessert, and (7) beverages. Provide recipes for the number to be served, with cooking times. Provide information on number of servings to be made from each container.

Types of service include buffet meals and cafeteria service as well as the usual table service. Plates may be served from the kitchen or food may be served on the table, family style.

Cafeteria service requires much less help in the dining room. Tables are set as usual. Guests are served and pay for the dishes they choose at the end of the serving unit.

Management of serving determines how quickly the meal is served, and whether it is served hot. For table service, instruct waitresses on setting the tables and serving. Assign them to specific tables. One waitress can usually serve 10 to 12 persons at long tables; up to 8 at small tables. Times should be established for setting the tables. Water glasses should be filled, and butter, bread, relishes, and cream placed on tables just before the guests are seated.

Plates served from kitchen at church dinner in Hyattsville, Md.

Buffet service requires fewer helpers than table service. Foods for the main course are put on one plate by the guest, who helps himself to some or all of the foods. Keep foods hot with electric grills or other heating units. Use baking dishes that retain heat well. Put small amounts of food out at one time so that frequent replacements keep the table attractive. Consider the most efficient way for the guest to serve himself. Tongs are useful for many items, including rolls and relishes. One or more hot dishes may be served to the guest at the buffet table. Often dessert and beverage are served by waitresses.

Plan serving arrangements in the kitchen so that the serving unit is as near the dining room as possible. Hot dishes should be served hot, cold dishes, cold. When plates are served in the kitchen, assign one person to serve each food and keep the plates moving rapidly. Pass plates from right to left with waitresses receiving plates at end of table nearest to the dining room. Before serving, try different arrangements of food on the plate and select the most attractive one for use on all plates. Have a double serving line to speed service for large groups.

Arrange a space for soiled dishes cleared from the tables. Discard food returned from the tables unless it is in unopened packages.

Records are helpful. If kept in a notebook, simple records can provide useful references for later events. Examples are: Market orders, expense records, menus, and records of committees. A record on each community meal should show: Date, place, type of meal, number of meals served, money taken in, expenses and profit.

Safety for workers should be considered when people work together in a new situation—often in unfamiliar surroundings and with equipment they are not used to. Good organization with a minimum of last minute hurrying goes a long way toward preventing any accidents.

Falls, cuts, and burns are the common types of accidents in kitchens. A check of the kitchen may show hazards that can be corrected. Halls should be well lighted. Stairways should have handrails. There should be no loose steps or boards. During icy weather, ashes or sand should be spread on entrance walks and at doorways.

An annual or semiannual kitchen cleanup provides an opportunity to organize and check equipment for safety. Knife holders, step stools, and portable carts can help workers to work safely. A special cupboard away from the food storage area can provide a safe storage for disinfectants and pesticides.

Keep a first aid kit on hand, and post telephone numbers of doctor and fire department.

Before leaving the kitchen, check all equipment to be sure that all fires are out and all the electrical equipment disconnected.

Instruct all workers on community meals in methods of working to avoid accidents. Important safety precautions are given below.

Avoid falls by: Wearing low heels, wiping up spills, keeping boxes and mops out of the way to prevent tripping, and standing on a step stool or strong box to reach high shelves.

Avoid cuts by: Washing all knives carefully, storing knives in a holder, cutting vegetables on a board, picking up broken glass with a damp paper towel, and using a good can opener.

Avoid burns by: Turning the pan handles away from you, raising kettle lids away from face, and using pot holders.

Avoid fires by: Lighting oven carefully, keeping matches in a covered tin can, and keeping curtains, dish towels, and paper away from range.

Avoid collisions by: Regulating the traffic with IN and OUT doors if needed; walking, not running; and not overloading trays or work space.

Avoid shock by: Handling electrical equipment with dry hands and keeping electric cords in good condition.

Safe food must be planned, not left to chance. Buying is the first step in safety. Be sure that bargain foods are in no way less safe. Purchase all meat and poultry from processors who operate under Federal or State inspection. Buy shellfish from sources approved by the State's shellfish authority. Buy pasteurized dairy products. Use only commercially canned foods in sound, unbulged cans.

Because home processing is done with fewer mechanical controls and safety checks, home canned meats and vegetables should not be used. In some communities, regulations prevent the sale of "homemade" ice cream. If made at home, pasteurized milk or cream and uncracked fresh eggs should be used in the ice cream mix, which should be refrigerated (below 45° F.) until frozen.

All fruits and vegetables should be thoroughly washed to remove any pesticide residues.

Temperature Control is a major step in safety. Bacterial growth is retarded by cold and speeded by warm temperatures (45° to 140° F.). Perishable foods should be kept very cold or hot. If they are held at warm temperatures—above refrigeration temperature and below the serving temperature for hot foods—they may cause food poisoning. Such spoilage may produce no easily detectable signs in the food; the taste, smell, and appearance may all remain quite normal.

The most perishable foods include those with meat, poultry, fish, eggs, or milk as an ingredient. Mixtures or foods that require several steps and handling during preparation are more apt to be contaminated, and so require extra care. However, no matter how carefully food has been prepared, it should be assumed that contamination with harmful bacteria may have occurred and that it must be kept either cold or hot.

Cold Food Cold is a good rule for safety. Food in a refrigerator is not always cold. Temperature on each shelf of the refrigerator should be checked frequently with a thermometer, and operating controls set so that a temperature of 42° F. or below is held to.

It is important not to overcrowd the refrigerator. Food may be refrigerated hot if refrigerator capacity is adequate. Another way to precool food is to immerse the pan of food in cold water for half an hour, stirring occasionally. Cooked food that is to be cooled before storing should be cooled rapidly. The center of the contents of a 5-gallon can or a deep pot will remain warm too long even if in the refrigerator. Use shallow containers so that the layer of food will not be over 2 inches deep. Liquids should be in quantities of a gallon or less to cool. Gravy or broth should be separated from meat for cooling. Refrigerate cream-filled pies or puffs and puddings if held longer than 2 hours before eating.

If frozen food is to be thawed before cooking, defrost it in the refrigerator or in a tightly sealed, moistureproof bag put in cool running water. Most products can be cooked directly from the frozen state.

Hot Food Hot is the matching rule. Often a thermometer is needed to be certain that food is really hot. Food in baked dishes should bubble in the center during cooking, but a temperature of 180° F. or above as shown by a thermometer is a better guide. A meat thermometer is a helpful guide for roasting turkeys. Since the stuffing cooks slowly in the bird, it is safer to bake it separately. Pork should be cooked at least to medium doneness in the most rare part.

Large Quantities of food require a special care in handling. In preparing cooked, boned chicken, it is important to both debone and cool it rapidly. Refrigerate the chicken in shallow layers. If refrigerator space is limited, oven-fried chicken is a better menu choice than creamed chicken or chicken loaf. If ham is sliced or ground, work with small amounts and store it promptly in the refrigerator (below 45° F.). Cover foods lightly for refrigerator storage.

Workers should be healthy, with no infected cuts, burns, or boils. They should have good habits of personal cleanliness, which include handwashing before preparing any food, before leaving restroom, and after using a handkerchief. Hands should be kept away from face and hair. Hairnets or caps are desirable for aesthetic reasons as well as being good sanitary practice. Restroom facilities should be clean and adequate, with ample supplies of soap and either paper towels or air-drying devices.

After handling raw meats or poultry, wash hands well. No smoking in the kitchen or while serving is the rule since a cigarette may carry contamination from mouth to hands. A good cook has to taste the food, so make it easy to use tasting spoons only once.

Waitresses should be in good health and neat. They should pick up cups by the handle and glasses at the base. Plates and bowls should be supported on the bottom.

Equipment should be chosen that is easy to clean. Cutting boards should be of a hard material with no cracks. One board should be labeled for use with raw meats and poultry only, and another reserved for sandwiches and salad ingredients. Clean the boards and other work surfaces, grinders, and knives thoroughly following each use. Check meat slicers and grinders for ease of cleaning before purchasing. Can openers should be easy to clean and should be kept clean. A clean work area is pleasant as well as safe.

Use galvanized containers only for storing dry foods since harmful zinc may be dissolved by beverages and other moist foods. Discard any cracked and chipped dishes.

Dishwashing can be easy or difficult depending largely on the kitchen arrangement and equipment. A dishwashing machine correctly installed is the best equipment. Next best is the three-compartment sink. Lacking one of these, ingenuity in using large containers will be required. Disposable paper or plastic service is a good choice in temporary quarters. Rubber gloves protect workers' hands.

The steps in hand dishwashing are:

Scrape and rinse dinnerware, flatware, and other pieces. A rubber scraper is a good tool to use here.

Wash in the first sink in a hot detergent solution, which is replaced often enough to keep good suds and be reasonably clean. Glass, flatware, dinnerware, and serving pieces are the usual order. Pots and pans should be washed during the preparation period and separately at the end.

Rinse in hot water in the second sink. Dish and flatware baskets are especially useful.

Immerse in the third sink for a minute or longer in very hot water (at least 170° F., as checked frequently with a thermometer) or in a hot solution of chloride (1 ounce of most liquid chlorine-type bleaches per 2 gallons of water) or commercial sanitizer used according to the manufacturer's directions. Disinfectant compounds for use in dishwashing may be purchased at most restaurant supply firms.

Air dry. Knives, forks and spoons should be stacked so that they will be picked up by the handles. Storage space should provide protection from any dust.

For machine dishwashing, the steps are similar. Follow the manufacturer's directions. Keep the machine in good repair so it will run well.

Cloths should not be used for drying dishes. Those used for cleaning tables or serving areas should not be used for other purposes. They should be kept clean and replaced frequently. Paper towels are convenient for many jobs.

Insects and Rodents may carry disease and must be kept out of the area. The annual or semiannual cleanup is a good time to look for evidence of problems. Professional extermination service may be needed. If pesticides are used, read the directions and note any precautions for use in the kitchen. Protect the food and utensils from pesticides.

Quantities of food needed for serving are estimated by multiplying a serving unit of food by the number of persons to be served. Workers should be included as well as guests and it is advisable to allow a small margin above this amount. When the food is served family style, allowance should be made for some second servings.

Some guidelines on purchasing for church suppers and other community meals follow. Other guidance materials given include: Quantities and measures; dinner menus for community meals; directions and timetables for roasting meats and for roasting turkey; and some selected recipes for 25 and 100 portions. For more information, publications on quantity cooking and group feeding should be consulted.

Quantities and Measures

Common measures are:

3 teaspoons = 1 tablespoon
16 tablespoons = 1 cup
2 cups = 1 pint
2 pints = 1 quart
4 quarts = 1 gallon
16 ounces = 1 pound

Large can sizes include:

No. 3 cylinder, 5¾ cups—Fruit and vegetable juices, whole chicken, some vegetables, pork and beans, condensed soups.

No. 10, 12 to 13 cups—Fruits and vegetables.

No. 303, 2 cups—Fruits, vegetables, some meat and poultry products, and ready-to-serve soups.

No. 2, 2½ cups—Juices, ready-to-serve soups, and some fruits.

No. 2½, 3½ cups—Fruits and some vegetables.

Scoop sizes:

The scoop number indicates the number of scoopfuls which equal 1 quart. Sizes commonly used in community meals are: No. 6 (⅔ cup) for serving main dish mixtures and No. 8 (½ cup) for serving vegetables and fruits.

Some common food measures:

1 pound flour, sifted=4 cups
1 pound butter or margarine=2 cups
1 pound hydrogenated fat or lard =2⅓ to 2½ cups

DINNER MENUS FOR COMMUNITY MEALS

Tomato juice
Baked ham
Sweet potatoes
Green beans
Raw vegetable salad
Rolls with butter or margarine
Apple cranberry crunch
Coffee, tea, or milk

Fruit cup
Oven fried chicken
Scalloped potatoes [1]
Cabbage with tart sauce [1]
Celery, carrot sticks
Rolls with jelly, butter, or margarine
Pineapple upside down cake
Coffee, tea, or milk

Fruit juice
Roast turkey, stuffing, gravy
Mashed potatoes
Carrots in sweet sauce
Cranberry sauce
Rolls with butter or margarine
Coleslaw [1]
Ice cream, cookies
Coffee, tea, or milk

Fruit juice
Roast beef
Browned potatoes
Peas and carrots
Celery
Pickles
Applesauce
Rolls with butter or margarine
Cherry cobbler [1]
Coffee, tea, or milk

[1] Recipe given

Directions and Timetable for Roasting Some Selected Meats [2]

Roast meat at 325° F. in uncovered pan, fat side up, allowing space between roasts. Do not add water. Insert thermometer into center of thickest part of meat, away from the bone, fat, or gristle. (See timetable, p. 346.)

Directions and Timetable for Roasting Turkey

Roast the turkey unstuffed, and bake the stuffing separately in shallow pans. (See timetable, p. 346.)

Remove neck and giblets and wash turkey thoroughly. Season turkey cavity with salt as desired. Fold neck skin back and fasten with skewers; fold wings toward back; tie the legs together and fasten to tail.

Place turkey on rack in shallow, uncovered pan, breast up. Brush skin with fat or oil. Do not add water. The turkey may be partially covered with a loose tent of aluminum foil or with cheesecloth dipped in melted fat or oil. When turkey is about half done, unfasten legs to speed cooking. When done, leg joint will move easily and meat will be very soft when drumstick is pressed. The juice will be clear, not pink. If thermometer is used, it should register 185° F. *Do not cook partially on one day and finish cooking the next.*

Scalloped Potatoes

Portion, ⅔ cup

Ingredients	25 portions	100 portions
Butter or margarine	½ cup	2 cups
All-purpose flour	1 cup	1 qt.
Salt	1¾ tsp.	2⅓ tbsp.
Hot milk	2 qt.	2 gal.
Onions, chopped	¼ cup	1 cup
Potatoes, thinly sliced	1 gal.	4 gal.

Melt fat; blend in flour and salt. Stir into milk; cook, stirring constantly, until thickened. Add onions.

Boil or steam potatoes until almost tender and put into 12- x 20- x 2-inch

[2] Roasting directions and timetables and the recipes were provided by Mrs. Mary S. March, Food Technologist, Human Nutrition Research Division, of the Agricultural Research Service.

Guide to Amounts of Some Foods to Buy for 25 and 100 Servings

Food	Approximate size of serving	25 servings	100 servings
APPETIZERS:			
Tomato or fruit juice	½ cup	2 46-oz. cans	8 46-oz. cans
Fruit cocktail	½ cup	1 No. 10 can	4 No. 10 cans
SOUPS:			
Ready-to-serve soups	1 cup	1½ gal.	6 gal.
MEATS:			
Beef round, boneout, for roasting	4 oz.	9 lb.	34 lb.
Ham, bone out, cured, rolled	4 oz.	10 lb.	40 lb.
Ground beef, for meat patties	4 oz.	6 lb.	25 lb.
POULTRY:			
Turkey, ready-to-cook, for roasting	4 oz.	13 lb.	53 lb.
Chicken, ready-to-cook, small fryers.	¼ bird	7 birds	25 birds
SEAFOOD:			
Fish, fillets for baking, frying, or broiling.	4 oz.	10 lb.	40 lb.
VEGETABLES:			
Canned vegetables	½ cup	1¼ No. 10 cans	5 No. 10 cans
Frozen vegetables	½ cup	5–6 lb.	20–24 lb.
Carrots, for cooking	½ cup	7 lb.	25 lb.
Cabbage, for cooking	½ cup	6¼ lb.	25 lb.
Potatoes, for boiling	1 medium	9 lb.	34 lb.
SALADS:			
Cabbage for coleslaw	½ cup	4 lb.	16 lb.
Potatoes for salad	½ cup	4 lb.	16 lb.
DESSERTS:			
Pie	⅙ of pie	5 pies	17 pies
Sheet cake	3″ x 3″	1¼ pans 12″ x 18″	4¼ pans 12″ x 18″
Ice cream, bulk	No. 12 scoop (½ c.)	1 gal.	4 gal.
FRUITS:			
Canned fruits	½ cup	1 No. 10 can	4 No. 10 cans
BEVERAGES:			
Coffee, urn grind	1 cup	⅔ lb.	2½ lb.
Coffee, instant powdered	1 cup	1 2-oz. jar	1 6-oz. jar
Coffee, instant freeze dried	1 cup	¾ cup	3 cups
Tea	1 cup	1½ oz.	6 oz.
Punch	½ cup	1 gal., (scant)	3¼ gal.
OTHER:			
Butter or margarine	1 pat (1 tsp.)	½ lb.	2 lb.
Crackers	2 crackers	½ lb.	2 lb.
Salad Dressing	1 tbsp. (scant)	1½ cups	6 cups

Timetable for Roasting Some Selected Meats

Kind and cut of meat	Weight in pounds	Internal temperature of cooked meat	Cooking time in hours
Roast beef rump, rolled	5	160°–170° F.	3 to 3¼
Roast leg of lamb, rolled	7	180° F.	3½
Fresh pork ham, bone in	10 to 14	185° F.	5½ to 6
Cured ham (mild):			
Cook-before-eating, bone in	12 to 16	160° F.	3½ to 4¼
Fully-cooked, bone in	6	130° F.	1½ to 2
Canned	6 to 10	130° F.	1½ to 2½
Roast leg of veal, bone in	5 to 8	170° F.	2½ to 3½

Timetable for Roasting Turkey

Form of turkey	Weight in pounds	Oven temperature	Cooking time in hours
Whole, ready-to-cook, unstuffed (weight includes neck and giblets).	12 to 16	325° F.	3½ to 4½
	16 to 21		4½ to 6
	21 to 26		6 to 7½

baking pans, one pan for each 25 portions. Add 2 quarts of sauce to potatoes in each pan. Cover and bake 30 minutes at 350° F. Remove cover and bake 15 minutes longer to brown.

For 25 portions, buy 7¼ pounds of potatoes; for 100 portions, 29 pounds.

Cabbage With Tart Sauce

Portion, about ½ cup cabbage and 1 tablespoon sauce

Ingredients	25 portions	100 portions
Cabbage	6¼ lb.	25 lb.
Salt	1⅓ tbsp.	⅓ cup
Sugar	2 tbsp.	½ cup
Paprika	1½ tsp.	2 tbsp.
Lemon juice	½ cup	2 cups
Butter or margarine, melted	1 cup	1 quart
Prepared horseradish	2 tbsp.	½ cup

Remove outer leaves of cabbage and shred or cut into wedges. Boil in 10-pound lots with 2 quarts water and 1⅓ tablespoons of salt for about 15 minutes, or steam in a compartment steamer at 5 to 7 pounds of pressure about 12 minutes or only until cabbage is tender. Drain.

Blend salt, sugar, and paprika. Add lemon juice, fat, and horseradish. Mix well. Pour sauce over hot cabbage.

Coleslaw

Portion, ½ cup

Ingredients	25 portions	100 portions
Vinegar	1¼ cups	1¼ qt.
Sugar	1 cup plus 2 tbsp.	1 qt. plus ½ cup
Celery seed	1½ tsp.	2 tbsp.
Salt	¾ tsp.	1 tbsp.
Pepper	½ tsp.	2 tsp.
Cabbage, shredded	1¼ gal.	5 gal.

Combine all the ingredients except cabbage. Mix well. Stir vinegar mixture into shredded cabbage and let stand at least 10 minutes. Serve cold.

For 25 portions, buy 4 pounds of cabbage; for 100 portions, 16 pounds.

Cherry Cobbler

Portion, ½ cup plus pastry topping

Ingredients	25 portions	100 portions
Filling:		
Sugar	2½ cups	2½ qt.
All-purpose flour	¾ cup	3 cups
Cinnamon, if desired	1½ tsp.	2 tbsp.
Hot cherry liquid	1 qt.	1 gal.
Red food coloring, if desired	2 drops	¼ tsp.
Canned, red, tart, pitted cherries, drained	2½ qt.	2½ gal.
Topping:		
All-purpose flour	3 cups	3 qt.
Salt	1 tsp.	1⅓ tbsp.
Shortening	1¼ cups	1¼ qt.
Cold water	about ½ cup	about 2 cups

For filling, mix dry ingredients; blend gradually into liquid. Cook and stir constantly until thickened.

Pour about 3½ quarts cherry mixture into one 12- x 20- x 2-inch baking pan for each 25 portions.

For pastry topping, blend flour and salt. Cut in fat until the mixture is granular. Add water and mix. Roll out on lightly floured board into 12- x 20-inch rectangles and place on filling in each pan.

Bake at 375° F. for around 45 to 50 minutes or until crust is brown.

For 25 portions, use 7 No. 303 cans or 1 No. 10 can of cherries; for 100 portions, use 4 No. 10 cans.

Ruth M. Leverton

Decisions, Decisions—Now It's All Up to You

This 1969 Yearbook has told the story of food—in terms of products from field to table, nutrients from soil and solar system to human well-being, and economics from producer to consumer. But most especially it has focused on the many ways to choose and to use food for good nutrition and for other satisfactions and enjoyments.

Technological advances in food production, processing, marketing, and preparation for eating have greatly reduced the labor required in the home in order to feed a family. The effort that used to go into home production and preparation is usually directed now toward earning money and then deciding how to spend it—on food and other goods and services we need and want.

Even when there is a comfortable amount of money to spend for food, deciding how to spend it is a responsibility whether you are buying for a family of one or ten. Collectively, you spend billions of dollars a year for food. The decisions you make—about what and how much to buy—directly affect your health and your family's and thus the Nation's health. Your choices influence the kinds and forms of food products put onto the market. When you buy intelligently you help shape the markets for better products.

All these decisions require time and thought. Often they are "hard" to make—not hard in terms of laboring to produce and prepare food, but hard in terms of knowing vital facts about food and nutritional needs on which to make wise choices.

Perhaps these guidelines will be a help to you:

Stop and decide on priorities worthy of your time and attention. Food deserves to be among the top ones. Good food contributes to good living as evidenced by physical, mental, and social well-being. There is a cause and effect relationship between the kind and amount of food you eat and your level of well-being. There is also a cause and effect relationship between your level of well-being and the attainment of the goals in your life. The home may no longer be the chief place where food is produced and prepared. But food is a large and important part of everyone's environment, and much of the training for meaningful living at every age occurs in association with food.

Look for dependable sources of information and aids to guide you in decision-making. This Yearbook was written just for the purpose of helping you choose and use food to give you maximum benefits. Fortunately, many good sources of information are available to you—beginning with your local library and extending to your State university and on to your Federal Government.

Learn what is being done to help you meet your responsibility for feeding yourself and your family well. You are not expected to do the job alone. The chief source of help is your local, State, or Federal Government. It can and does act to keep adulterated, unwholesome, or contaminated products off the market. It can provide for enrichment of salt with iodine, or

Dr. Ruth M. Leverton is an Assistant Deputy Administrator, Agricultural Research Service.

of refined cereals with B vitamins and certain minerals or milk with vitamin D. It can distribute food for dietary improvement among schoolchildren and needy families. It does all this and it can do much more if such services are wanted and supported by the general public.

A relatively small number of public leaders can make decisions and take action in the treatment and control of many diseases through vaccination, immunization, sanitation, a safe water supply, specific drug therapy, and other public health measures. But wise food selection in the market or at the table cannot be accomplished by government action.

No one can compel each person to eat an adequate diet even when the food is available, or even when the food is free. Government cannot decide for people the choices or combinations to make among the many, many foods available to them, or the proportions in which to balance one kind of foodstuff with another, and how to balance total calorie supply against total calorie need. These choices and the resulting level of nutritional well-being lie with the millions of individuals. Right or wrong decisions in the market and at the table will make the difference between good nutrition and malnutrition, between vigor and vulnerability.

Photography

U.S. Department of Agriculture photographers took the bulk of the photographs reproduced in this Yearbook. A new regulation by the Joint Committee on Printing, however, was interpreted as making it no longer possible to give credit to Federal Government photographers for work done as part of their regular duties. Hence the individual credits given below do not include work by USDA staff photographers.

Prints of most of the black and white photos in this book may be obtained from the Photography Division, Office of Information, U.S. Department of Agriculture, Washington, D.C. 20250. These are free to news media; a nominal fee is charged others. News media may borrow duplicate color slides of many of the color photos from the Photography Division. These slides may also be purchased. In ordering prints or slides, please refer to the 1969 Yearbook and give the page number.

The Editor is deeply indebted to the companies and organizations and the State land-grant universities that provided photos for the Yearbook, and which are credited. And he is, of course, as deeply indebted to the many anonymous USDA photographers whose contributions help illustrate the book. A USDA photographer is pictured at the foot of this page.

Please note that the first 32 pages of this Yearbook carry no page numbers. However, Page I is the page on which the first color photo appears. In the photo credits, pages are numbered consecutively with Roman numerals from this point on through the color section. Credits with Arabic numerals indicate black and white photos further back in the book.

Agricultural Extension Service, University of California, photos by William Gelling, cover (bottom), pages 93 (top), 280 (both photos), 283.
American Dairy Association, all 3 photos, pages XVI and XVII.
American Institute of Baking, 291.
Automatic Retailers of America, Inc., XI (top), XI (lower right), 54.
Black Star, photo by Ted Rozumalski, 16 (top).
Campbell Soup Company, XVIII (top).
Chain Store Age, 41 (right), 47, 50.
Cooperative Extension Service, Louisiana State University, photo by Arthur V. Patterson, 298.
Dairy Council of Metropolitan New York, endsheet (top left).
Delmarva Poultry Industry, XXXI (bottom).
Del Monte Corporation, photo by Ernest Braun, VIII.
Dudley-Anderson-Yutzy, XVIII (bottom), XX (top), XXIV (top), XXIX (top), 195.
Evaporated Milk Association, 233.
FMC Corporation, 43.
General Foods Corporation, 30, 59.
General Mills, Inc., XXII, 158, 207, 208, 219, 220, 222 (top), 288.
Giant Food Corporation, XIII (top).
Green Giant Company, XXIX (bottom).
Harshe-Rotman & Druck Inc., 7.
Hot Shoppes, 63, 253 (center).
House Beautiful Magazine, photo by Arthur Beck, XIV.
McCormick & Company, Inc., XIII (bottom), 250 (top, bottom).
National Dairy Council, XXI (top), XXV, 151 (top), 179, 275, 276, 278, 302.
National Live Stock & Meat Board, XII, 277.
National Peanut Council, XXVII (bottom), 200, 201.
National Soft Drink Association, XXX.
National Turkey Federation, 119.
New York State College of Human Ecology, Cornell University, photos by George Lavris, 308, 309.
Pan American Coffee Bureau, 19, 329.
Pickle Packers International, Inc., XXVIII (top), 246.
Poultry and Egg National Board, XV (top), XXVIII (bottom).
Quaker Oats Company, 52.
Safeway Stores, Inc., 26.
Sunkist Growers, Inc., II and III, XIX (top left), XXVI, XXXI (top).
Swift & Company, 256.
Daniel A. Swope, 341.
Wheat Flour Institute, 214 (bottom).

Index

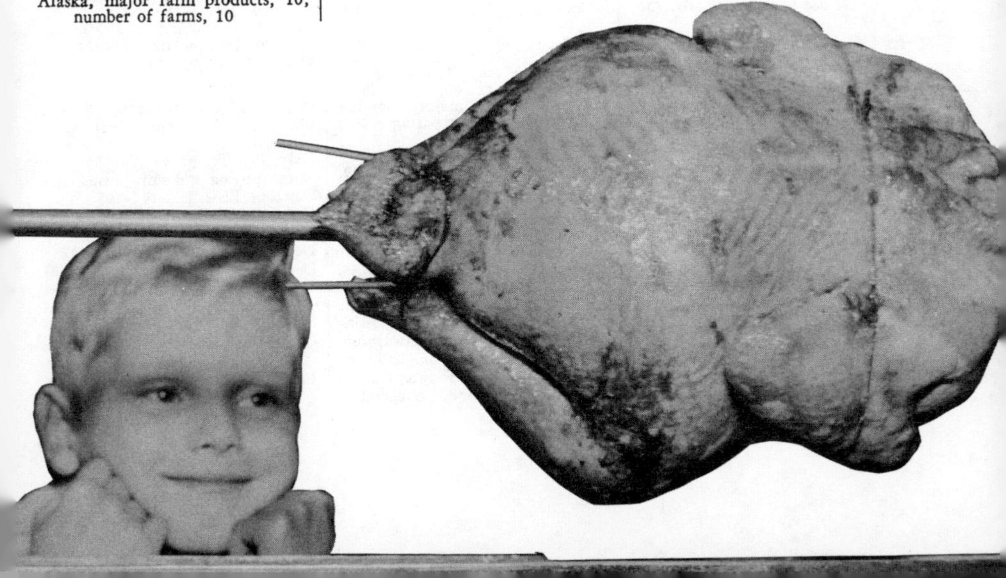

U.S. GOVERNMENT PRINTING OFFICE: 1969 O—326-541